PRECALCULUS

for Christian Schools®

PRECALCULUS

for Christian Schools®

Kathy D. Pilger, Ed.D.
Ron Tagliapietra, Ed.D.

 Bob Jones University Press
Greenville, South Carolina 29614

Note:
The fact that materials produced by other publishers may be referred to in this volume does not constitute an endorsement of the content or theological position of materials produced by such publishers. Any references and ancillary materials are listed as an aid to the student or the teacher and in an attempt to maintain the accepted academic standards of the publishing industry.

PRECALCULUS for Christian Schools®

Kathy D. Pilger, Ed.D
Ron Tagliapietra, Ed.D.

Contributing Authors
Larry L. Hall, M.S.
Kathy Kohler
Phil Larson, M.Ed

Consultants
Garry Conn, MAT
Steve McKisic, M.Ed
Larry Lemon, M.S.

Project Editor
Frank D'Agostino

Compositor/Design
Preface, Inc.

Produced in cooperation with the Bob Jones University Department of Mathematics of the College of Arts and Science, the School of Education, Bob Jones Academy, and Bob Jones LINC.

© 2002 Bob Jones University Press
Greenville, South Carolina 29614

ISBN 1-57924-614-1

15 14 13 12 11 10 9 8 7 6 5 4 3 2

Contents

Introduction

Introduction

This precalculus course is designed to prepare students for calculus and other higher math courses. This includes further study of trigonometry,

Calculus permits calculations of instantaneous speeds rather than average speeds.

logarithms, graphs of rational functions, matrices, and statistics. It also includes an introduction to basic topics in calculus such as sequences, limits, and derivatives.

Practical Use

The topics of precalculus are powerful and practical tools. The course will develop math skills that will help students perform well in standardized tests for colleges or various vocations. The use of statistics is foundational for operations research in business, research and test interpretation in education, and quality assurance in manufacturing. Advanced degrees in business and education require courses in statistics; therefore, a precalculus course is valuable preparation. Since the development of the theory of statistics depends on calculus, an exposure to the concepts of calculus will serve business and education students as well. Furthermore, calculus is foundational for engineers, whether electrical, civil, mechanical, computer, or otherwise. Most engineering schools require not only a year of college calculus but also higher math courses such as differential equations, complex variables, and numerical methods which build on calculus.

Calculus permits determination of areas that are not polygonal.

Mental Discipline

Although we usually associate "practical" with business applications, students will enter other vocations and no two will need to know exactly the same formulas. Furthermore, learning computer keystrokes to run software is very shortsighted because as technology advances, software will change and the keystrokes learned will become obsolete. So what is really practical? Ever since ancient Greece, people have known that the key to education is helping students reach a place where they can answer their own questions. If a student learns to read technical manuals, he will be able to keep up with changing software and will not need a course that teaches the keystrokes every time a new package comes out. Likewise, if a student learns to reason carefully, he will be able to think through the complex problems and issues of business. The most practical skills learned from school, then, involve disciplining one's mind to work through technical manuals and to reason carefully. Precalculus courses provide an important opportunity to develop the kind of mental discipline that will serve the student throughout his entire life.

Christ rose from death and ascended to glory. As Lord, He has the right to delegate His dominion to us. When we humbly serve Him as stewards, we grow more Christlike.

Christian Growth

The most important aspect of education, however, is growing more Christlike. Precalculus provides an opportunity for developing some Christlike attributes, including truth, knowledge, accuracy, precision, and orderliness. Also, it is essential that we test everything against Scripture, even as Christ tested and countered the interpretations of the devil (Matt. 4). Unless we pass every learned idea through biblical tests, we will develop worldly thinking in those areas and will fail to become like Christ. This precalculus text helps students conform their thinking to biblical precepts in three ways. First, the context of Christian truth is evident throughout the book. The book was written by Christians and designed for Christians from the outset; it is not a secular text with Christianity tacked on. Second, the special feature in each chapter helps students test mathematical ideas from Scripture and thereby develop biblical convictions about mathematics. Third, God has delegated to man dominion over the earth, responsibility as a steward of natural resources. The dominion modeling exercises that relate to the data at the opening of each chapter will help students see how their math class can prepare them to fulfill this responsibility before God.

1 Trigonometry

Park rangers warn people never to get within fifteen feet of a live alligator. While alligators might seem clumsy and slow, they can sprint up to thirty miles per hour for short distances. For comparison, a track star can reach only twenty miles per hour for short distances.

The American alligator, *Alligator mississippiensis,* can grow up to a foot a year in the wild. On alligator farms, they can grow up to three feet a year. Biologists study growth patterns as well as behaviors such as speed. Consider the following data for Florida alligators.

Length	Weight	Length	Weight	Length	Weight
94	130	72	38	61	44
74	51	128	366	90	106
147	640	85	84	89	84
58	28	82	80	68	39
86	80	86	83	76	42
94	110	88	70	114	197
63	33	72	61	90	102
86	90	74	54	78	57
69	36				

After this chapter you should be able to

1. label the parts of an angle and place it in standard position.

2. use degrees, minutes, and seconds, as well as radians, to measure an angle.

3. convert radian measure to degree measure and degree measure to radian measure.

4. define and use the six trigonometric ratios.

5. use reference triangles and reference angles to find the trigonometric ratios of angles with measures larger than 90° or less than 0°.

6. solve right triangles.

7. solve triangles using the law of sines and the law of cosines.

8. apply trigonometry to find areas of triangles, slopes of lines, and angles of inclination.

1.1 Angle Measure and Arc Length

In geometry you learned that an angle is the union of two distinct rays with a common endpoint. However, an angle can be viewed as the sweep of a ray moving from an initial position to a final position. The sweep of a clock's hand in a given period of time provides an example of such an angle. The positive *x*-axis is usually the initial position of the ray and is called the *initial ray* of the angle. The final position of the sweeping ray is the *terminal ray* of the angle. The common point that the two rays share is called the *vertex* of the angle.

Definition

Standard position   An angle in standard position has the positive *x*-axis as its initial ray and the origin as its vertex.

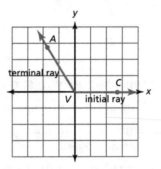

An angle is often named after its vertex, such as ∠*V*. When more than one angle has its vertex at *V*, three letters are used, as in ∠*AVC*. This method of naming avoids confusion since it indicates the rays of the angle as well as the vertex. A third way to name an angle is according to its measure. Lowercase Greek letters such as α (alpha), β (beta), and θ (theta) are often used to label angle measures.

Angles are measured in various ways. If a circle is constructed and divided into **360** equal parts, then each part is 1 *degree*. In today's highly technical world, portions of a degree are important, so each degree is divided into sixty equal parts called *minutes,* and likewise each minute into sixty equal parts called *seconds*. Angle measure is the portion of a circle swept out by a ray moving from an initial to a terminal position. If the ray sweeps counterclockwise, the angle measure is positive; but if the sweep is clockwise, the angle measure is considered negative. Consider the following examples. The arrows in the figures below show that $m\angle ABC = 60°$ and $m\angle EFG = -120°$.

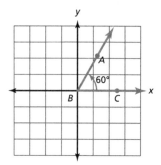 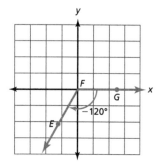

A ray may sweep around a complete circle before taking its terminal position. For example, the angle shown has a measure of **440°**. Notice that $\angle ABC$ with terminal $\overrightarrow{BA}$ has the same position as an **80°** angle. When the terminal rays of two angles are in the same position, the angles are called *coterminal angles.* An infinite number of angles, both positive and negative, are coterminal with any given angle.

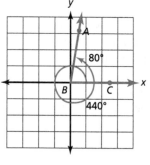

Definition

Coterminal angles   Angles in standard position with the same terminal ray.

The radian, though less familiar than the degree, is a useful unit in trigonometry. Radians correspond to arc lengths measured along a circle's circumference.

Definition

Radian   The measure of an angle formed by two radii of a circle so that the intercepted arc has a length equal to the radius of the circle.

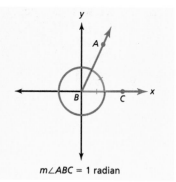

$m\angle ABC = 1$ radian

It is convenient to use a unit circle when measuring radians. The *unit circle* has its center at the origin with a radius of one unit. If ∠ABC is in standard position, its vertex is at the center of the unit circle and its initial ray (on the x-axis) must intersect the unit circle at (1, 0). The terminal ray also intersects the unit circle as shown below, and the measure in *radians* is the length of the intercepted arc.

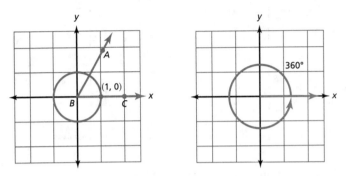

How many radians are in an angle which makes one complete rotation? Since radian measure is the length of an arc, you must determine the circumference of the unit circle to find the radian measure for a complete rotation. Using the formula C = 2πr and the fact that the radius of the unit circle is 1, the circumference of this circle is 2π. Therefore, the radian measure of an angle making one complete rotation is 2π.

At times, you may need to convert angle measures from degrees to radians or from radians to degrees. From the previous paragraph, you can see that 2π radians = 360°. Thus, a semicircle of 180° must have a measure of π radians. You can always convert easily between degrees and radians by setting up a proportion.

$$\frac{n \text{ rad}}{m \text{ deg}} = \frac{\pi}{180}$$

In this proportion, substitute the known measure (either the n radians or the m degrees) and solve for the other measure. Note that the right side of the proportion can also be used as a conversion factor, since it is a form of one (π radians = 180°). When working with angle measures, assume that any angle measure given without a degree symbol is in radians rather than degrees.

EXAMPLE 1   Find the measure of θ in degrees and radians.

Answer

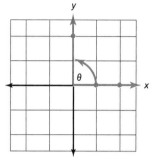

θ sweeps through one quadrant, or $\frac{1}{4}$ of a circle.

$\frac{1}{4}(360°) = 90°$ 1. Use 360° to find θ in degrees.

$\frac{1}{4} \cdot 2\pi = \frac{\pi}{2}$ 2. Use 2π to find θ in radians.

This example shows a special angle called a
quadrantal angle.

Definition

Quadrantal angle   An angle whose terminal ray lies on one of the axes.

Now let's use the unit circle and a circle
concentric with it to examine a relationship of
arc lengths. *Concentric circles* have the same
center but different radii. Consider a central
angle α of the unit circle, having a measure
equal to t radians as shown. A *central angle* is
an angle having its vertex at the center of a circle. On the smaller concentric circle with radius
r, α intersects an arc length of s radians. The
following proportion, proved in geometry, shows
that the ratio of the arc lengths of the two concentric circles is the same as the ratio of their radii:
$\frac{s}{t} = \frac{r}{1}$. Solving for s, we obtain the formula

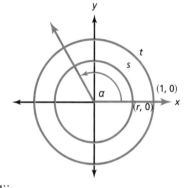

$$s = rt.$$

This formula expresses the length of any arc as the product of its radius and
the radian measure of the central angle formed.

EXAMPLE 2   Find the measure of the angle that cuts off an arc length of
7 in a circle of radius 4.

Answer $s = rt$

$7 = 4t$

$t = \frac{7}{4} = 1.75$ radians

▶ A. Exercises

Sketch each angle in standard position.

1. 45°   3. $\frac{2\pi}{3}$ 5. π

2. 30°   4. $\frac{5\pi}{4}$ 6. 200°

7. Which angles in the figure are positive? negative?

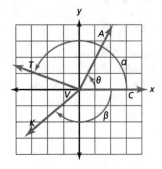

Complete each line of the following table.

	Radians	Degrees
8.	$\frac{\pi}{6}$	
9.		15
10.		120
11.	$\frac{7\pi}{6}$	
12.	$\frac{\pi}{5}$	
13.		270
14.	2π	
15.	$\frac{12\pi}{7}$	
16.	5	
17.		31
18.	2.7	
19.		50

20. Give a positive and a negative angle measure coterminal with 148°.

▶ B. Exercises

Give three angle measures in radians which are coterminal with each of the following. Include at least one positive and one negative angle measure.

21. $\frac{\pi}{4}$ radians

22. $\frac{5\pi}{3}$ radians

23. How many radians are in one degree?

24. How many degrees are in one radian?

Find the missing angle measures, radius measures, and arc lengths in the table below. Give the angle measures in radians.

	Arc Length (s)	Radius Length (r)	Angle Measure (t)
25.		8	$\frac{\pi}{4}$
26.	6π	4	
27.	$\frac{\pi}{2}$		$\frac{\pi}{6}$
28.	3π	6	
29.		5	$\frac{2\pi}{3}$

In *Algebra 1* and *Geometry,* you learned the distance and midpoint formulas. Review them now. If $A(x_1, y_1)$ and $B(x_2, y_2)$ are points in the plane, then the distance between them is $d = \sqrt{(x_2 - x_1)^2 + (y_2 - y_1)^2}$ and the midpoint between them is $M = \left(\frac{x_1 + x_2}{2}, \frac{y_1 + y_2}{2}\right)$.

Determine the distance between each pair of points and also the midpoint of the segment joining them.

30. $(3, -6), (1, 0)$

31. $(5, 1), (-3, 7)$

32. $(3, 7), (-2, 4)$

33. $(-3, -6), (4, 5)$

If M is the midpoint of $\overline{AB}$, find B. Then use distances to justify your answers.

34. $A(5, 1), M(-3, 7)$

35. $A(3, 5), M(9, -2)$

► C. Exercises

C is located such that $\frac{AC}{AB} = k$, a constant. k represents the fraction of the way C is from A to B. In other words if $k = \frac{2}{3}$, C is $\frac{2}{3}$ of the way from A to B.

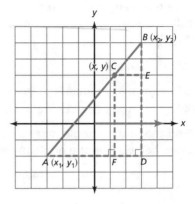

36. Derive a formula to find the coordinates of C using similar triangles ($\triangle AFC \sim \triangle ADB$).

37. Find the point $\frac{2}{5}$ of the distance from $(6, 2)$ to $(8, 4)$.

38. Derive the midpoint formula from the formula derived in exercise 36.

⌁ Dominion Modeling

39. Draw a scatterplot of the alligator data. What patterns do you see in the data?

1.2 Trigonometric Ratios

In the study of trigonometry, six ratios are possible. One way to consider these ratios is in the context of right triangles.

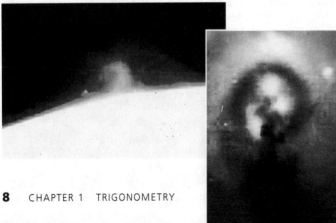

The Galileo spacecraft photographed these two volcanoes on Io, a moon of Jupiter, thus documenting the first active extraterrestrial volcanoes.

In the triangle given, the vertices are A, B, and C. The right angle is at C, and the side opposite is the hypotenuse. The sides $\overline{AC}$ and $\overline{BC}$ are the legs of the right triangle and have lengths b and a respectively. Notice that the length of the leg opposite $\angle A$ is a and the length of the leg opposite $\angle B$ is b. The length of the hypotenuse is c. The Pythagorean theorem relates these lengths.

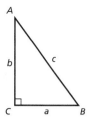

Pythagorean Theorem
In right $\triangle ABC$, the sum of the squares of the lengths of the legs is equal to the square of the length of the hypotenuse.
$$a^2 + b^2 = c^2$$

In right-triangle trigonometry the three basic trigonometric ratios are defined for the acute angles of the triangle as follows:

$$\text{sine of } \angle A \quad = \sin A = \frac{\text{leg opposite } \angle A}{\text{hypotenuse}} = \frac{\text{opp}}{\text{hyp}} = \frac{a}{c}$$

$$\text{cosine of } \angle A \ = \cos A = \frac{\text{leg adjacent } \angle A}{\text{hypotenuse}} = \frac{\text{adj}}{\text{hyp}} = \frac{b}{c}$$

$$\text{tangent of } \angle A = \tan A = \frac{\text{leg opposite } \angle A}{\text{leg adjacent } \angle A} = \frac{\text{opp}}{\text{adj}} = \frac{a}{b}$$

The other three trigonometric ratios, called *reciprocal ratios,* are reciprocals of the three basic ratios.

$$\text{cosecant of } \angle A \ = \csc A = \frac{1}{\sin A} = \frac{\text{hyp}}{\text{opp}} = \frac{c}{a}$$

$$\text{secant of } \angle A \quad = \sec A = \frac{1}{\cos A} = \frac{\text{hyp}}{\text{adj}} = \frac{c}{b}$$

$$\text{cotangent of } \angle A = \cot A = \frac{1}{\tan A} = \frac{\text{adj}}{\text{opp}} = \frac{b}{a}$$

EXAMPLE 1   Find the six trigonometric ratios for $\angle G$ in right $\triangle EFG$.

Answer $g^2 + e^2 = f^2$ 1. Use the Pythagorean
$g^2 + 6^2 = 8^2$ theorem to find g.
$g^2 + 36 = 64$
$g^2 = 28$
$g = \sqrt{28}$
$g = 2\sqrt{7}$

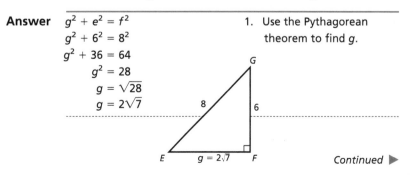

Continued ▶

$$\sin G = \frac{\text{opp}}{\text{hyp}} = \frac{2\sqrt{7}}{8} = \frac{\sqrt{7}}{4}$$

$$\cos G = \frac{\text{adj}}{\text{hyp}} = \frac{6}{8} = \frac{3}{4}$$

$$\tan G = \frac{\text{opp}}{\text{adj}} = \frac{2\sqrt{7}}{6} = \frac{\sqrt{7}}{3}$$

$$\csc G = \frac{1}{\sin G} = \frac{1}{\frac{\sqrt{7}}{4}} = \frac{4}{\sqrt{7}} = \frac{4\sqrt{7}}{7}$$

$$\sec G = \frac{1}{\cos G} = \frac{1}{\frac{3}{4}} = \frac{4}{3}$$

$$\cot G = \frac{1}{\tan G} = \frac{1}{\frac{\sqrt{7}}{3}} = \frac{3}{\sqrt{7}} = \frac{3\sqrt{7}}{7}$$

2. Now that we know g, use the definitions to find the six trigonometric ratios.

There are five angles that are of interest because their exact trig ratios are easily determined. Three of them are contained in the two following special right triangles.

Consider a right triangle whose legs are of equal length, and designate this length as 1 unit as shown below. By the Pythagorean theorem,

$$q^2 = 1^2 + 1^2$$

$$q^2 = 2$$

$$q = \sqrt{2}$$

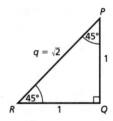

Since angles opposite congruent sides of a triangle are also congruent, and the sum of the angles of a triangle is always 180°, we can conclude that each acute angle has a measure of 45°. From this triangle, all six functions of 45° (or $\frac{\pi}{4}$) can be determined. Notice that $\sin 45° = \frac{1}{\sqrt{2}} = \frac{\sqrt{2}}{2}$.

The second triangle is a 30°-60° right triangle. In equilateral $\triangle ABD$ shown, the altitude $\overline{AC}$ bisects the base and $\angle DAB$. Therefore, if $AB = 2$, then $BC = 1$, and $\angle CAB$ has a measure of 30°. This relationship can best be expressed by the geometry theorem: In a 30°-60° right triangle, the side opposite the 30° angle is one-half the hypotenuse. By the Pythagorean theorem, $AC = \sqrt{3}$, and from this triangle all six of the exact trig ratios of 30° and 60° can be determined.

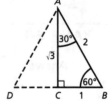

For example, $\tan 30° = \frac{1}{\sqrt{3}} = \frac{\sqrt{3}}{3}$.

Another way to define the trigonometric ratios is by using an angle in the Cartesian plane. Look at angle θ in standard position in the following figure.

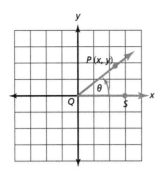
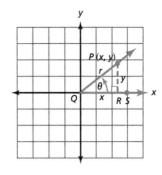

Consider an arbitrary point $P(x, y)$ on the terminal ray of the angle. If a line is drawn perpendicular to the x-axis from P, a right triangle is formed.

The length QR is x, and the length PR is y. If r represents the distance from the origin to P, its value can be obtained using the Pythagorean theorem. Substituting these values into the previous definitions, the trigonometric ratios can be expressed as follows:

$$\sin \theta = \frac{\text{opp}}{\text{hyp}} = \frac{y}{r} \qquad \csc \theta = \frac{\text{hyp}}{\text{opp}} = \frac{r}{y}$$

$$\cos \theta = \frac{\text{adj}}{\text{hyp}} = \frac{x}{r} \qquad \sec \theta = \frac{\text{hyp}}{\text{adj}} = \frac{r}{x}$$

$$\tan \theta = \frac{\text{opp}}{\text{adj}} = \frac{y}{x} \qquad \cot \theta = \frac{\text{adj}}{\text{opp}} = \frac{x}{y}$$

These definitions are often easier to use and are necessary for evaluating trig ratios of quadrantal angles and angles larger than 90°.

EXAMPLE 2 Find the six trigonometric ratios for a 90° angle.

Answer $P = (0, 1)$

1. Choose any point on the terminal ray of the angle.

$x = 0, y = 1, r = 1$

2. Determine the values of x, y, and r. Remember that r represents the distance from the origin to the point on the terminal ray.

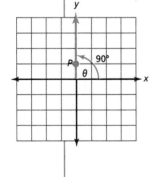

$\cos \theta = \frac{x}{r} = \frac{0}{1} = 0$

$\sin \theta = \frac{y}{r} = \frac{1}{1} = 1$

$\tan \theta = \frac{y}{x} = \frac{1}{0}$ undefined

$\sec \theta = \frac{r}{x} = \frac{1}{0}$ undefined

$\csc \theta = \frac{r}{y} = \frac{1}{1} = 1$

$\cot \theta = \frac{x}{y} = \frac{0}{1} = 0$

3. Use the definitions to state the six trigonometric ratios for θ.

You should memorize the trig ratios for 5 special angles: 0°, 30°, 45°, 60°, 90°. Whenever these angles occur in a triangle, answer with the memorized values, which are exact, instead of rounded values from a calculator.

▶ A. Exercises

Find the six trigonometric ratios for both acute angles in each triangle.

1.

3.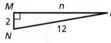

2.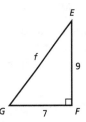

4.

Find the six trigonometric functions for an angle in standard position whose terminal ray passes through the following points.

5. (1, 4)
6. (−3, 2)

7. (−6, −1)
8. (8, −7)

9. (2, 6)
10. (−4, −3)

▶ B. Exercises

Find the six trigonometric ratios for the given angles. Use exact values when possible.

11. $\frac{\pi}{4}$
12. 30°

13. 42°
14. $\frac{\pi}{3}$

Find the six trigonometric ratios for the following quadrantal angles.

15. 180°
16. 270°
17. 0°

Determine the sign of the six trigonometric ratios for the four quadrants in the Cartesian plane.

	Quadrant	sin	cos	tan	csc	sec	cot
18.	I						
19.	II						
20.	III						
21.	IV						

22. List the sines of the five special angles in order of their angle measures. What do you notice? Do the same for their cosines.

Find the exact values for the following.
23. sec 30°
24. csc 45°

▶ C. Exercises
25. Why will the ratios always be the same no matter how large you draw the 30°-60° right triangle or the 45°-45° right triangle?
26. Explain how the exact trig values of a $\frac{13\pi}{6}$ radian angle can be found without using a calculator.

⚏ Dominion Modeling
27. Find a linear model for the alligator data and show it on the scatterplot. Explain when the model *overestimates* the data and when it *underestimates* it. Does it seem to be a good fit? (Do *not* discuss r^2.)
28. What are some inherent limitations with a linear model, and what are the practical meanings of these limitations?
29. What happens when a small child gets on a seesaw with an adult? You may have experienced this yourself: since the adult is bigger, the child goes upward. That is, the adult *influenced* the seesaw more than the child did. Similarly, "influential observations" are data points with excessive "leverage." Consider a linear model of all but the three largest alligators. Draw this new model over the full scatterplot with the original model. How do the two models compare, and how can you tell that the three large alligators are influential observations?

▪ Cumulative Review
30. Give the distance between (2, 7) and (−3, −1).
31. Give the midpoint of the segment joining (2, 7) and (−3, −1).
32. Give the angle θ coterminal with 835° if 0° ≤ θ < 360°.
33. Convert 88° to radians.
34. If sec θ = 7, find cos θ.

1.3 Reference Angles

It is possible to find trig ratios for angles with measures greater than 90° using a first quadrant angle measure. To do so, a *reference angle* must be used.

Reference angle   The angle formed by the terminal ray of the given angle and the *x*-axis.

By drawing a perpendicular segment from any point on the terminal ray to the *x*-axis, you will form a *reference triangle*. The reference angle and triangle can then be used to find the trig values of the original angle.

EXAMPLE 1   Find sin 210°.

Answer

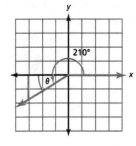

1. Sketch the angle as a third quadrant angle since 180° < 210° < 270°. Label the reference angle θ.

- -

2. Make a reference triangle for the angle by drawing a perpendicular from any point on the terminal ray to the *x*-axis.

- -

$$\theta = 210° - 180° = 30°$$

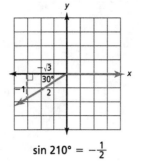

3. Find the measure of the reference angle, θ. Notice that the measure is a special angle, 30°.

- -

4. Label the sides of the reference triangle in your sketch using the 1, 2, $\sqrt{3}$ ratios (Section 1.2). Recall that the *x*- and *y*-coordinates are negative in the third quadrant.

- -

$$\sin 210° = -\frac{1}{2}$$

5. Find sin 210° from the trig ratio $\frac{\text{opp}}{\text{hyp}}$ using the reference triangle.

Since you must give exact values when working with special angles, you should become familiar with the degree measures in each quadrant that have special angles as reference angles. Exercises 16-18 will help you. For all other angles, you may use a calculator.

EXAMPLE 2	Find tan 61°40′.	
Answer	61°40′ ≈ 61.67°	1. Use your calculator to obtain tan 61°40′. The angle may be entered in degrees and minutes or as an equivalent decimal. The decimal is 61.67 because 40′ is $\frac{40}{60}$ of a degree or approximately 0.67 degree. (Consult your calculator manual.)
	tan 61°40′ ≈ 1.855	2. Find the tangent.

Calculators can also easily handle angles greater than 90°.

EXAMPLE 3	Find cos 118°.	
Answer	cos 118° = −0.4695	Use your calculator to find cos 118°.

Since few calculators have keys for cot, sec, or csc, you will need to use the reciprocal ratios to find such values.

EXAMPLE 4	Find csc 63°.	
Answer	csc 63° = $\frac{1}{\sin 63°}$	1. Express the cosecant in terms of its reciprocal, the sine.
	sin 63° ≈ 0.8910	2. Use your calculator to find sin 63°.
	csc 63° ≈ 1.1223	3. Press the reciprocal key 1/x or x^{-1} to obtain csc 63°.

The calculator can also be used to find the angle measure associated with a trig ratio. When solving an equation such as $\sin \theta = \frac{1}{2}$ for θ, the inverse sine key, $\sin^{-1}$, is used with the ratio in decimal form $\left(\frac{1}{2} = 0.5\right)$.

$$\theta = \sin^{-1} 0.5 = 30°$$

Since the sine is also positive in quadrant II, 30° could be the reference angle making $\theta = 180° - 30° = 150°$. Therefore there are two measures for θ, $0° \leq \theta < 360°$, that satisfy the equation. A sine value of $-\frac{1}{2}$ indicates that the angle is a third or fourth quadrant angle, but the reference angle is still **30°**. This would give θ a measure of **210°** or **330°**.

▶ A. Exercises

Give the measure of the reference angle for each and sketch the reference triangle.

1. 75°
2. 160°
3. 320°
4. 238°20′
5. 112°
6. $\frac{2\pi}{3}$
7. $\frac{5\pi}{4}$
8. $\frac{11\pi}{6}$

Use a calculator to find the following ratios.

9. sin 26°20′
10. tan 117°
11. cot 86°50′
12. cos 318°44′
13. csc 12°18′
14. sin $\frac{3\pi}{5}$
15. sec 2.75

▶ B. Exercises

List the angles that have special angles as reference angles in the given quadrant. Include quadrantal angles with any quadrant they bound. Give the positive measures less than 360°.

16. Second quadrant
17. Third quadrant
18. Fourth quadrant

Use special angles to find the ratios. Do not use a calculator for these exercises.

19. csc 315°
20. sec 180°
21. sin 150°
22. cos 225°

23. tan 300°

24. cot 120°

25. sin 210°

26. tan $\frac{5\pi}{6}$

27. cos $\frac{5\pi}{3}$

28. csc $\frac{5\pi}{4}$

Find the angle measures for $0° \leq \theta < 360°$ that are associated with the ratios given here.

29. tan θ = 2.081

30. csc θ = 5.016

31. cot θ = 0.0992

32. cos θ = -0.7916

33. sin θ = -0.5446

▶ C. Exercises

Sketch a reference triangle and identify the reference angle for the following; then find the six trig ratios for each angle given.

34. $\frac{13\pi}{3}$

35. $-\frac{9\pi}{4}$

■ Cumulative Review

36. Convert 27° to radians (use π).

37. Give the radian measure of 27° as a decimal.

The legs of a right triangle are 2 units and 7 units in length, and θ is the smallest angle. Find the following trig ratios.

38. tan θ

39. sin θ

40. cos θ

Approximation Methods

Interpolation

Printed tables sometimes lack the specific value you are looking for. When this happens the simplest estimate is the closest value from the table. A better method, however, is to determine an intermediate value between the values provided in the table. This method is called *interpolation*. Linear interpolation is the simplest type of interpolation and uses proportions to determine the intermediate value. In this course you may take the closest estimate from the table unless you are told to interpolate.

Interpolation is an important skill that is useful with printed tables such as statistical tables. It was especially important with trig tables and log tables, but calculators have rendered these tables obsolete. The example below uses the trig table on page 629 to illustrate interpolation.

EXAMPLE   Find sin 55°14′.

Answer

The closest value in the table is sin 55°10′ = 0.8208. However, you can be more accurate by interpolating. Since the desired angle is between 55°10′ and 55°20′. Use the differences below to set up a proportion.

$$10'\left[4'\begin{bmatrix} \sin 55°10' = 0.8208 \\ \sin 55°14' \\ \sin 55°20' = 0.8225 \end{bmatrix}x \right]0.0017$$

1. Determine sin 55°10′ and sin 55°20′ from the table.

$$\frac{4}{10} = \frac{x}{0.0017}$$
$$0.0068 = 10x$$
$$0.00068 = x$$

2. Determine the ratio of differences; form a proportion by setting the ratios equal to each other; solve for x.

sin 55°14′ = sin 55°10′ + x
sin 55°14′ = 0.8208 + 0.00068
sin 55°14′ = 0.82148

3. Add x (0.00068) to sin 55°10′, or 0.8208, to find sin 55°14′.

sin 55°14′ = 0.8215

4. Round to four decimal places.

▶ Exercises

Interpolate for each of the following.

1. cos 23°57′
2. sin 17°25′
3. tan 62°43′
4. cos 58°38′
5. csc 79°9′

1.4 Right Triangle Trigonometry

In this section you will solve right triangles. This involves finding the measures of all the sides and angles. Study the method for solving a triangle in Example 1.

The descent angle for this Russian Antonov AN-124 to land at Wichita, Kansas, was calculated using trigonometry. Three times the size of a 727, the Condor is even larger than the U.S. Air Force Galaxy, the largest plane made in the United States.

EXAMPLE 1   Solve $\triangle ABC$.

Answer $m\angle A = 90° - 42° = 48°$ 1. Find the measure of $\angle A$.

- -

$\tan 42° = \dfrac{b}{3}$ 2. Find side length b by using
$3 \tan 42° = b$ the tangent ratio.
$2.7 = b$

- -

$\cos 42° = \dfrac{3}{c}$ 3. Find side length c by using
$c = \dfrac{3}{\cos 42°}$ the cosine ratio.
$c = 4.0$

$m\angle A = 48°$	$a = 3$
$m\angle B = 42°$	$b = 2.7$
$m\angle C = 90°$	$c = 4.0$

Solving a right triangle applies to many practical problems. The use of angles in practical problems often involves angles of elevation and depression. The *angle of elevation* is the angle that is formed by a horizontal line and the line of sight as the observer looks at an object that is above the horizontal. The *angle of depression* is the angle formed by a horizontal line and the line of sight as the observer looks at an object that is below the horizontal.

(a)   (b)

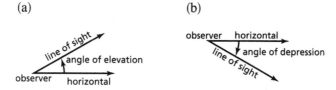

Bearings provide an application from navigation and orienteering that involves triangles. Bearings are often expressed as an angle measure between 0° and 360° and are measured in a clockwise direction from due north. However, bearings may also be expressed by measuring the smallest angle from a north-south line. For instance, the angle that $\overrightarrow{TK}$ forms with the north-south line is described as 27° east of north and symbolized by N 27° E. Think about how you would draw the angle S 48° W.

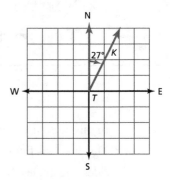

EXAMPLE 2   There are two lifeguard stands located 100 meters apart on a north-south coast. One guard spots an oil derrick at a bearing of S 42°40′ E. If the oil derrick is due east of the other guard, how far is it from the second stand?

Answer

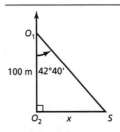

1. Draw a picture of the problem situation. Find the angle in the triangle.

$$\tan 42°40′ = \frac{x}{100}$$
$$100 \tan 42°40′ = x$$
$$x \approx 92.2$$

2. Since you want to find the length of the side opposite the given angle and you know the adjacent side, use the tangent ratio.

The oil derrick is 92.2 meters from the second stand.

▶ A. Exercises

Solve right △ABC, given the following values. Find side lengths to the nearest tenth and angle measures to the nearest minute.

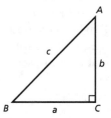

1. $a = 5$, $c = 9$
2. $\angle A = 49°$, $a = 6$
3. $\angle B = 12°40′$, $a = 20$
4. $c = 14$, $b = 8$
5. $\angle A = 64°10′$, $c = 16$

Solve right $\triangle ABC$ (previous figure), given the following values. Find the side lengths to the nearest tenth and angle measures to the nearest tenth of a degree.

6. $a = 7, b = 4$
7. $\angle B = 82°, c = 24$
8. $b = 3, \angle A = 80°$
9. $b = 3, \angle B = 51.5°$
10. $b = 3, a = 7$

▶ B. Exercises

Solve the following word problems. Round measures to the nearest tenth.

11. The angle of depression from the top of a 75-foot lighthouse to a ship out in the ocean is 40′. How far is the ship from the lighthouse?

12. A missile travels at a speed of 900 feet per second and travels at a constant angle of elevation of 73°. After 5 seconds what is its altitude (distance from the ground)?

13. The bottom of a rectangular pool rises at a constant 8° grade from the deeper end of 12 feet to the shallower end of 3 feet. How long is the pool?

14. A guy wire from the top of a 150-foot radio antenna meets the ground 32 feet away from the base of the antenna. What angle is formed by the wire and the ground?

15. A new interstate highway is built so that there is no angle of depression or angle of elevation larger than 5°. If there is a 5° angle of elevation at a certain location, what is the vertical rise that you make if you travel a mile along the road at that angle?

16. A 20-foot ladder is placed against the side of a building. As the base of the ladder approaches the wall, the angle formed by the ladder and the ground increases. If any angle greater than 76° makes it unsafe, what is the highest point the ladder can safely reach? How far from the building should the ladder be placed to reach this height?

17. The captain of a ship sights an anchored ship at a bearing of S 52° E. After the ship travels south for 63 nautical miles, the anchored ship is directly east of the moving ship. At this second sighting, how far apart are the two ships?

▶ C. Exercises

18. A plane takes off from airport A, traveling at a rate of 210 mph. After an hour and a half the plane is directly east of airport B. If airport A is 230.4 miles directly south of airport B, what was the bearing of the airplane as it took off from airport A? (Assume no wind was blowing.)

19. Trent follows a compass bearing of 327° for two miles to avoid a lake. He knows that in his particular location, true north is 8° east of magnetic north. What bearing should he follow in order to reach a point five miles due north (true) of his original position? How far will he have traveled?

▶ Dominion Modeling

20. Draw a quadratic model for the alligator data, and show it on a scatter-plot. Is this a good model? Explain, and give weaknesses and strengths of the model.

21. A quadratic model, you will recall, always has a minimum or a maximum. What is the minimum or maximum, and how is this a strength or a weakness for the model?

Cumulative Review

22. Give the midpoint between (a, b) and $(-a, -b)$.
23. Give $\sin \theta$.
24. Find $\sin 77°$.
25. Find $\cos 500°$.
26. Find $\cot 219°$.

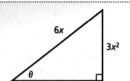

1.5 Law of Sines

You can also solve triangles that are not right triangles. The *law of sines* is one method of solving such a triangle. To apply the law of sines, you must know either the measures of two angles and a side (ASA or SAA) or the measures of two sides and an angle opposite one of the given sides (SSA).

> **Law of Sines**
> In △ABC where *a* is the side length opposite ∠A, *b* is opposite ∠B, and *c* is opposite ∠C, the following proportion exists:
> $$\frac{a}{\sin A} = \frac{b}{\sin B} = \frac{c}{\sin C}.$$

Because the reciprocals of equal ratios are equal, the law of sines can also be written as follows:
$$\frac{\sin A}{a} = \frac{\sin B}{b} = \frac{\sin C}{c}.$$

> *He who loves practice without theory is like the sailor who boards ship without a rudder and compass and never knows where he may cast.*
> —LEONARDO DA VINCI
> (1452-1519)

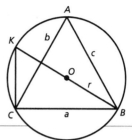

Proof

STATEMENTS	REASONS
1. Let $\triangle ABC$ be inscribed in $\odot O$. Draw a diameter $\overline{BK}$. Let r be the length of the radius of the circle.	**1.** Any triangle can be inscribed in a circle.
2. $KB = 2r$	**2.** The diameter of a circle is twice the radius.
3. $\angle K \cong \angle A$	**3.** Angles inscribed in the same arc are congruent.
4. $\sin K = \sin A$	**4.** Equal angles have equal sine values.
5. $\angle BCK$ is a right angle.	**5.** An angle inscribed in a semicircle is a right angle.
6. $\triangle BCK$ is a right triangle.	**6.** A triangle that contains a right angle is a right triangle.
7. $\sin K = \frac{CB}{KB} = \frac{a}{2r}$	**7.** Definition of sine
8. $\sin A = \frac{a}{2r}$	**8.** Substitution
9. $\frac{a}{\sin A} = 2r$	**9.** Multiplication property of equality

Using the same method with the other angles, you can develop the following equations.

$$\frac{b}{\sin B} = 2r, \frac{c}{\sin C} = 2r$$

The law of sines follows from the transitive property.

$$\frac{a}{\sin A} = \frac{b}{\sin B} = \frac{c}{\sin C}$$

EXAMPLE 1 Solve △ABC if ∠A = 34°, ∠B = 76°, and a = 9. Round measures to the nearest tenth.

Answer

$\frac{a}{\sin A} = \frac{b}{\sin B}$	1. Notice that the given information follows the pattern SAA. Select the portion of the law of sines involving the given sides and angles.
$\frac{9}{\sin 34°} = \frac{b}{\sin 76°}$ $\frac{9 \sin 76°}{\sin 34°} = b$	2. Substitute and solve for b.
$b = 15.6$	3. Use a calculator to find b.
$m∠C = 180° − m∠A − m∠B$ $m∠C = 180° − 34° − 76°$ $m∠C = 70°$ $\frac{a}{\sin A} = \frac{c}{\sin C}$ $\frac{9}{\sin 34°} = \frac{c}{\sin 70°}$ $\frac{9 \sin 70°}{\sin 34°} = c$ $c = 15.1$	4. Likewise determine the length of c. First find ∠C.
$m∠A = 34°$ $a = 9$ $m∠B = 76°$ $b = 15.6$ $m∠C = 70°$ $c = 15.1$	5. Identify the solution of the triangle.

If you are given the length of two sides and the angle measure opposite one of those sides, you can also use the law of sines to solve the triangle. However, this combination of information does not always determine a unique triangle. The three possible cases follow.

1. There may not be a solution.
2. There may be two solutions.
3. There may be a unique solution.

Because SSA does not always determine a unique triangle, it is called the *ambiguous case*. *Ambiguous* means open to multiple interpretations. Some people say that you can interpret the Bible in any way that you want. However, there is no ambiguity in the Bible. "No prophecy of the scripture is of any private interpretation. For the prophecy came not in old time by the will of man: but holy men of God spake as they were moved by the Holy Ghost" (II Pet. 1:20-21). Studying the context and comparing Scripture with Scripture, submitted to the Holy Spirit, enables you to determine God's intended meaning and avoids any private interpretations. That is why you must study and search the Scriptures daily. There is certainly no ambiguity in how to be saved from sin: "Neither is there salvation in any other: for there is none other name under heaven given among men, whereby we must be saved" (Acts 4:12). Faith in Jesus Christ is the only way of salvation.

The diagrams show the three possibilities for the ambiguous case, SSA. In each diagram, sides *a*, *b*, and ∠*B* are given. The altitude of the triangle is *h*.

1. SSA—no solutions

   No triangle exists when $b < h$.
   $$\sin B = \frac{h}{a}$$
   $$a \sin B = h$$
   If $b < a \sin B$, there is no solution to SSA; no triangle is possible.

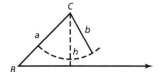

2. SSA—two solutions

   Two triangles exist when
   $$h < b < a$$
   $$a \sin B < b < a$$
   If $a \sin B < b < a$, the solution to SSA can be either of two triangles.

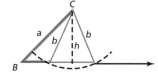

Other than the two situations above, one triangle exists.

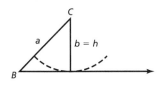
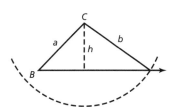

3. SSA—one solution

   One triangle exists when
   $$b = h$$
   $$b = a \sin B$$
   or, one triangle exists when $b \geq a$.
   If $b = a \sin B$ or $b \geq a$, then the solution to SSA is a unique triangle.

EXAMPLE 2 Solve △ABC if a = 5, b = 3, and ∠B = 26°.

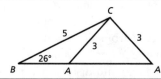

Answer	$a = 5; b = 3$	1. Since this is the ambiguous case (SSA), find the relationship between a, b, and $a \sin B$.
	$a \sin B = 5(\sin 26°) = 2.192$	
	$a \sin B < b < a$	
	Therefore, there are two solutions.	

Case 1

$$\frac{a}{\sin A} = \frac{b}{\sin B}$$

$$\frac{5}{\sin A} = \frac{3}{\sin 26°}$$

$$\frac{5(\sin 26°)}{3} = \sin A$$

$$\angle A = 46.9°$$

2. Apply the law of sines to find ∠A.

$$\angle C = 180° - 26° - 46.9°$$
$$\angle C = 107.1°$$

3. The sum of the angles of a triangle is 180°.

$$\frac{b}{\sin B} = \frac{c}{\sin C}$$

$$\frac{3}{\sin 26°} = \frac{c}{\sin 107.1°}$$

$$c = \frac{3 \sin 107.1°}{\sin 26°} = 6.5$$

4. Solve for side c using the law of sines.

Case 2

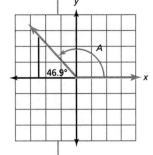

$$\angle A = 180° - 46.9°$$
$$\angle A = 133.1°$$

5. Since the sine of an angle is also positive in the second quadrant, you can find the obtuse angle (second quadrant) that has a reference angle of 46.9°. This gives the measure of ∠A in the second triangle.

$$\angle C = 180° - 26° - 133.1°$$
$$\angle C = 20.9°$$

6. Solve for ∠C in the second triangle.

$$\frac{b}{\sin B} = \frac{c}{\sin C}$$

$$\frac{3}{\sin 26°} = \frac{c}{\sin 20.9°}$$

$$c = \frac{3 \sin 20.9°}{\sin 26°} = 2.4$$

7. Use the law of sines to find c.

8. The two solutions are summarized here.

Case 1	$\angle A = 46.9°$	$\angle B = 26°$	$\angle C = 107.1°$	$a = 5$	$b = 3$	$c = 6.5$
Case 2	$\angle A = 133.1°$	$\angle B = 26°$	$\angle C = 20.9°$	$a = 5$	$b = 3$	$c = 2.4$

Remember from geometry that SSS, SAS, SAA, and ASA all guarantee a unique solution to a triangle. SSA is the only ambiguous case. The pattern AAA represents triangles that are similar and an infinite number of solutions exist.

▶ A. Exercises

Specify the type of pattern and determine the number of triangles that satisfy the given information for △ABC.

1. $a = 5$, $\angle B = 48°$, $\angle A = 68°$
2. $a = 9$, $\angle A = 57°$, $c = 12$
3. $\angle A = 12°$, $\angle B = 106°$, $c = 10$
4. $a = 7$, $c = 2$, $\angle C = 12°$
5. $a = 3$, $b = 7$, $\angle C = 40°$
6. $\angle C = 43°$, $\angle B = 61°$, $b = 9$
7. $b = 18$, $c = 9$, $\angle B = 82°$
8. $a = 2$, $c = 5$, $\angle A = 15°$
9. $a = 3$, $b = 7$, $c = 8$
10. $\angle A = 20°$, $\angle B = 100°$, $\angle C = 60°$

▶ B. Exercises

Solve each triangle. Round sides to the nearest tenth. Give angle measures to the nearest minute or tenth of a degree.

11. $\angle A = 52°$, $\angle B = 49°$, $c = 16$
12. $\angle A = 12°$, $\angle C = 89°$, $a = 9$
13. $\angle B = 82°$, $b = 12$, $c = 6$
14. $\angle B = 33°$, $a = 8$, $b = 4.4$
15. $\angle C = 15°$, $a = 14$, $c = 12$
16. $\angle B = 23°$, $\angle C = 42°40'$, $b = 7$
17. $\angle B = 80°$, $a = 6$, $b = 2$
18. $\angle B = 67°$, $a = 12$, $b = 4$
19. $\angle C = 100°$, $a = 6$, $c = 8$
20. $\angle A = 62°$, $\angle B = 23°$, $b = 9$

▶ C. Exercises

21. A 120-foot tower is atop a cliff next to a river. If the angle of depression from the top of the tower to a point on the opposite side of the river is 29°15′ and the angle of depression from the base of the tower to the same spot is 17°22′, how wide is the river? How high is the cliff?
22. Suppose you are given a triangle classified as SSA to solve. If the given $\angle B$ is obtuse, what can you conclude? Explain.

⬙ Dominion Modeling

23. Consider a cubic polynomial model for the alligator data. Find the model, draw it on a scatterplot, and find r^2. Evaluate this model.
24. Find a quartic polynomial model, draw it on a scatterplot, and find r^2. Does it appear to be superior to a cubic model?

▪ Cumulative Review

25. If one acute angle of a right triangle has a measure of 0.2356 radians, what is the radian measure of the other acute angle?
26. Find two negative angles coterminal with $\frac{5\pi}{6}$.
27. In what quadrants is the cosecant negative, and why?

In right triangle ABC, where $\angle C = 90°$, suppose $a = 3$ and $B = 40°$.
28. Find b.
29. Find $\cos A$.

Pierre de Fermat

Pierre de Fermat was born on August 20, 1601, in a village near Toulouse, France. His father was a leather merchant and his mother came from a family of parliamentary jurists. Although he attended an elementary parochial school in Toulouse, he received most of his subsequent education at home. He matured to be an even-tempered gentleman of integrity and respectability.

In 1631 Fermat graduated from the University of Orléans with a degree in law. Three years later he became a councilor to the parliament in Toulouse, and in 1638 he was assigned to the criminal court. In this position, which he held for the rest of his life, he earned a reputation for being just and fair.

Although Fermat's life-long profession was law, he had strong interests in the classics, foreign languages, ancient science, and mathematics. It was in mathematics, a leisure-time hobby, that he became most famous. He discovered the fundamental principle of analytic geometry in about 1630 and wrote *De Maximis et Minimis* (published after his death) in which he showed methods for finding maxima and minima. Many credit Fermat with the development of the concept of differential calculus nearly twenty years before Leibniz proved the fundamental theorem of calculus. Fermat's correspondence with Pascal laid the foundation of probability.

Fermat was best known for his modern theory of numbers. Two of these theorems bear his name:

(1) Fermat's lesser theorem, which states that if p is prime and if a is any positive integer, then $a^p - a$ is divisible by p, and

(2) Fermat's great theorem, which states that the equation $x^n + y^n = z^n$, where x, y, z, and n are positive integers, has no solution for n greater than 2.

Fermat also thought that numbers of the form $2^{2^n} + 1$, where n is a nonnegative integer, would always be prime. However, about a hundred years later, Euler proved this to be false. He found that for $n = 5$ the resulting value had 641 as a factor. While Fermat was wrong about this, his great theorem, also known as Fermat's last theorem, was correct. Fermat's own proof of this theorem was lost, and the difficulty of its proof challenged mathematicians for several centuries. It remained neither proved nor disproved until 1995.

Because Fermat studied math as a hobby rather than as a profession, and because he was so accomplished in mathematics, he has been called the "Prince of Amateurs." He wrote most of his notes in the margins of books and letters with no intention of ever publishing them. He wrote very few papers, but after his death in 1665 his contributions drew more attention. Five years later his notes were collected and published under the title *Arithmetica*.

Because Fermat studied math as a hobby rather than as a profession . . . he has been called the "Prince of Amateurs."

1.6 Law of Cosines

Did you notice that the law of sines does not apply to solving triangles when the information given is SAS or SSS? When you know the lengths of all three sides or two sides and an included angle, you must use another law, the law of cosines.

> **Law of Cosines**
> **For any triangle ABC, where side lengths opposite angles A, B, and C are a, b, and c, respectively, then $a^2 = b^2 + c^2 - 2bc \cos A$.**

You should recognize that the labeling of the angles and corresponding sides is arbitrary. Therefore $b^2 = a^2 + c^2 - 2ac \cos B$ and $c^2 = a^2 + b^2 - 2ab \cos C$ are alternate forms of the law of cosines.

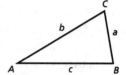

Proof

Let $\overline{CF}$ be the altitude of $\triangle ABC$, so $CF = h$.
Let $x = AF$ and $c - x = FB$. From right $\triangle AFC$,
$\cos A = \frac{x}{b}$. Therefore, $x = b \cos A$ and $b^2 = x^2 + h^2$,
which will be used in the following derivation.

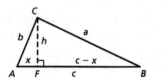

STATEMENTS	REASONS
1. $a^2 = (c - x)^2 + h^2$	1. Apply the Pythagorean theorem to $\triangle BFC$.
2. $a^2 = c^2 - 2cx + x^2 + h^2$ $a^2 = c^2 - 2c(x) + (x^2 + h^2)$	2. Expand the square on the right.
3. $a^2 = c^2 - 2c(b \cos A) + b^2$ $a^2 = b^2 + c^2 - 2bc \cos A$	3. Substitute $b \cos A$ for x and b^2 for $x^2 + h^2$.

The other forms of the law of cosines can be derived in a similar manner using the altitudes from the other two vertices.

EXAMPLE 1   Solve △*FDG* if *f* = 8, *d* = 4, and *g* = 10.

Answer

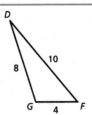

1. Draw a picture to illustrate the problem.

$f^2 = d^2 + g^2 - 2dg \cos F$
$8^2 = 4^2 + 10^2 - 2(4)(10) \cos F$
$64 = 116 - 80 \cos F$
$-52 = -80 \cos F$
$0.6500 = \cos F$
$49°28' = m\angle F$

2. Use the law of cosines because you are given lengths for three sides of the triangle (SSS).

$g^2 = f^2 + d^2 - 2fd \cos G$
$10^2 = 8^2 + 4^2 - 2(8)(4) \cos G$
$100 = 80 - 64 \cos G$
$20 = -64 \cos G$
$-0.3125 = \cos G$
$\angle G = 108°13'$

3. To find another angle, use the law of cosines again. You may question why the law of sines does not apply, since you know the measure of ∠*F*. There are two reasons why the law of cosines is better.

a. If you made an error when calculating the measure of ∠*F* and then use that measure to find another angle measure, it will also be incorrect.

b. If you use the law of sines to find ∠*G* you will get the first quadrant value (71°47′) and will not know whether this is the measure of the angle or the reference angle. Using the law of cosines eliminates this problem since the cosine value will be negative in quadrant II.

$\angle D = 180° - 49°28' - 108°13'$
$\angle D = 22°19'$

4. Find the measure of ∠*D* by subtraction.

Therefore, the solution to △*FDG* is   ∠*F* = 49°28′   *f* = 8
                                        ∠*D* = 22°19′   *d* = 4
                                        ∠*G* = 108°13′   *g* = 10

EXAMPLE 2 Solve △ABC if ∠A = 63°, b = 12, and c = 9.

Answer

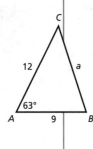

	1. Draw △ABC.
$a^2 = b^2 + c^2 - 2bc \cos A$ $a^2 = 12^2 + 9^2 - 2(12)(9)(\cos 63°)$ $a^2 = 144 + 81 - 216(\cos 63°)$ $a^2 = 126.938$ $a = 11.3$	2. Find a by applying the law of cosines.
$\frac{a}{\sin A} = \frac{c}{\sin C}$ $\frac{11.3}{\sin 63°} = \frac{9}{\sin C}$ $\sin C = \frac{9 \sin 63°}{11.3}$ $\sin C = 0.70965$ $\angle C = 45.2°$	3. Angle C, opposite the shortest side, must be acute. Use the law of sines to find it. If you choose to solve for ∠B first, you may get an incorrect answer. If a triangle contains an obtuse angle, it will be opposite the longest side (side b in this case). We cannot tell if ∠B is obtuse or acute.
$\angle B = 180° - 63° - 45.2°$ $\angle B = 71.8°$	4. Determine the measure of ∠B.

In the exercises you will use the law of sines and the law of cosines to solve triangles in practical situations.

► A. Exercises

Solve △ABC, given the information in each case.
Give measures to the nearest tenth.

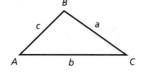

1. $a = 6, b = 5, c = 8$
2. $a = 9, b = 13, \angle C = 28°$
3. $b = 26, c = 18, \angle A = 64°$
4. $a = 52, b = 47, c = 64$
5. $a = 16, c = 25, \angle B = 78°$

State the simplest method of solving the triangle and solve △ABC.

6. $a = 12, b = 7, \angle A = 52°$
7. $\angle A = 19.5°, \angle B = 92°, c = 28$
8. $a = 7, b = 13, c = 9$
9. $\angle A = 60°, \angle B = 90°, b = 10$
10. $\angle A = 20°, b = 13, c = 8$

▶ B. Exercises

Solve the following word problems.

11. A radio antenna is placed on the top of a 200-foot office building. The angle of elevation from a parking lot to the top of the antenna is 21°. The angle of depression looking from the bottom of the antenna to the lot is 10°. What is the height of the antenna?

12. A surveyor knows the measure of one angle of a triangular parcel of land and the lengths of two sides of the land. From the diagram given here, determine the length of the other side.

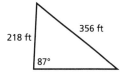

13. How wide is the swamp at the points shown?

14. A tunnel is to be built through a mountain at a particular point. A person stands at one point on one side of the mountain and a second person stands at a point on the other side of the mountain. Each person looks at a surveyor's pole located at the top of the mountain. The pole is 418 feet from the first person and 371 feet from the other person. The lines of sight of the two people form a 69° angle at the pole. How long is the tunnel going to be?

15. A baseball diamond is a square with sides measuring 90 feet. If the distance from home plate to the center field fence is 360 feet, how far is the center field fence from third base?

16. Write a calculator program that takes two sides and the included angle in degrees and determines the third side.

▶ C. Exercises

17. In $\triangle ABC$, $\angle A = 60°$, side $c = \dfrac{1}{\sqrt{6} + \sqrt{2}}$, and side $b = \dfrac{1}{\sqrt{6} - \sqrt{2}}$. Find side a.

18. Write the proof of the law of cosines for a triangle with an obtuse angle.

Dominion Modeling

19. Find the exponential model for the alligator data. Plot the model on a scatterplot and evaluate it. (This might also be called an exponential growth model, although this situation does not include the growth of a particular alligator.)

20. Without finding a sine model, explain why such a model is not useful.

21. Convert 5 radians to degrees.
22. Give the reference angle for −470°.
23. Write 3 reciprocal ratios.
24. In △ABC, find b if $\angle B = 27°$, $a = 8$, and $\angle A = 90°$
25. In △ABC, find b if $\angle B = 27°$, $a = 8$, and $\angle A = 20°$.

1.7 Applications

A line can be described either by its slope (a ratio) or by its inclination (an angle). These terms describe the deviation from the horizontal, but the word *inclination* has a

Heron's formula is the easiest method for calculating areas of triangular lots, such as the one occupied by this building in South Carolina.

nonmathematical meaning also. Without Christ, man is inclined to sin. Thus it reflects our desires and attitudes toward something. There are many things that influence our attitudes about life, but for the Christian, the Bible must be the prime influence on attitudes. Psalm 119:105 says, "Thy word is a lamp unto my feet, and a light unto my path." Proverbs 6:23 states, "For the commandment is a lamp; and the law is light; and reproofs of instruction are the way of life." From these verses you can see that the Word of God should shape our attitudes (inclinations).

The slope is important in describing a line.

Definition

Slope of a line   The ratio of vertical change to horizontal change when moving from one point on the line to another point on the line.

The capital Greek letter delta, Δ, is used in mathematics to represent the words "change in." Since vertical change is associated with the vertical or y-axis, the vertical change is the change in y values, Δy. The horizontal change is the change in x values, Δx. The slope of a line, represented by m, can be denoted in symbols as follows.

$$m = \frac{\Delta y}{\Delta x}$$

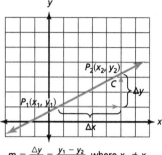

To find Δy, you must subtract the values of the y-coordinates of two points on a line. Likewise, to determine Δx, subtract the values of the x-coordinates of the same two points and in the same order.

$m = \frac{\Delta y}{\Delta x} = \frac{y_1 - y_2}{x_1 - x_2}$, where $x_1 \neq x_2$.

EXAMPLE 1 Find the slope of the line that passes through the points (5, 9), and (−2, 4).

Answer $m = \frac{\Delta y}{\Delta x} = \frac{y_1 - y_2}{x_1 - x_2}$ 1. Write the general formula for slope.

$m = \frac{9 - 4}{5 - (-2)}$ 2. Choose one of the points as (x_1, y_1)
$m = \frac{5}{7}$ and the other point as (x_2, y_2). Let
     $(x_1, y_1) = (5, 9)$; then $(x_2, y_2) = (-2, 4)$.

So the slope of the line passing through (5, 9) and (−2, 4) is $\frac{5}{7}$.

The slope of a line is directly related to the inclination of a line. The *inclination* of a line is the angle that the line makes with a positively directed ray on the x-axis. The angle will be labeled α (alpha).

The slope of the line that passes through P_1 and P_2 is $\frac{y_1 - y_2}{x_1 - x_2}$. How does this slope relate to the angle α? Look at $\triangle P_1 P_2 P_3$. This right triangle has an angle that is equal to the angle of inclination (α) of the line. Since corresponding angles are congruent when parallel lines are intersected by a transversal, $\angle P_1 P_2 P_3 \cong \alpha$.

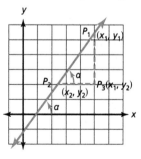

Determine $\tan \alpha$, using $\triangle P_1 P_2 P_3$. Since the tangent ratio is $\frac{\text{opp}}{\text{adj}}$, $\tan \alpha = \frac{P_1 P_3}{P_2 P_3}$.

$P_1 P_3 = y_1 - y_2$ and $P_2 P_3 = x_1 - x_2$.

Therefore, $\tan \alpha = \frac{y_1 - y_2}{x_1 - x_2}$ or $\tan \alpha = m$. Thus, the slope of a line is the tangent of the angle of inclination.

EXAMPLE 2 Find the angle of inclination of the line that passes through (2, 9) and (1, 2).

Answer	$m = \frac{y_1 - y_2}{x_1 - x_2}$	1. Find the slope of the line.
	$m = \frac{9 - 2}{2 - 1}$	
	$m = 7$	
	$\tan \alpha = 7$	2. Use $\tan \alpha = m$ to find angle α. Tan^{-1} is
	$\alpha = 81°52'$	used to find the angle whose tangent is 7.

The angle of inclination of the line that passes through (2, 9) and (1, 2) is 81°52'.

Consider the parallel lines l_1 and l_2. What is true about the slopes of parallel lines?

The x-axis represents a transversal passing through the two parallel lines, l_1 and l_2. Notice that the angles α_1 and α_2 are corresponding angles. Since $l_1 \parallel l_2$, it follows that $\alpha_1 = \alpha_2$ and their tangents are also equal.

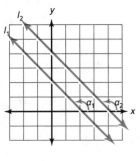

The statement $\tan \alpha_1 = \tan \alpha_2$ implies $m_1 = m_2$. You can then deduce that if two lines are parallel, their slopes are equal. Do you think the converse of this statement is true?

You can also use trigonometry to find the area of a triangle. In the triangle shown, the following trig ratio relates the altitude, h, and the side a. Since $\sin C = \frac{h}{a}$, $h = a \sin C$. By substituting for h in the formula for the area of a triangle ($A = \frac{1}{2}bh$), we obtain the new formula that uses only two sides and the included angle of the given triangle (SAS).

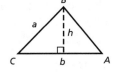

$$A = \frac{1}{2}ab \sin C$$

Any two sides and included angle can be used to find the area. Thus, the other forms of the formula are:

$$A = \frac{1}{2}bc \sin A$$
$$A = \frac{1}{2}ac \sin B$$

EXAMPLE 3　Find the area of △ABC.

Answer

$A = \frac{1}{2}ab \sin C$

$A = \frac{1}{2} \cdot 8 \cdot 12 \sin 82°$

$A = 48 \sin 82°$

1. Since the given information about △ABC involves SAS, use the trig formula for area.

$A = 47.5$ sq. units

2. Include units on the area.

When the given information involves SSA, SAA, or ASA, use the law of sines to find the additional side or angle. Remember that you need two sides and the included angle to use the trig formula for area.

EXAMPLE 4　Find the area of △PQR, assuming that △PQR is acute.

Answer

$\frac{9}{\sin 48°} = \frac{10}{\sin Q}$

$\sin Q = \frac{10 \sin 48°}{9}$

$\angle Q = 55.7°$

$\angle P = 180° - 48° - 55.7°$

$\angle P = 76.3°$

1. Find $\angle P$ using the law of sines (or find QR).

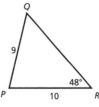

$A = \frac{1}{2}rq \sin P$

$A = \frac{1}{2}(9)(10) \sin 76.3°$

$A = 43.7$ sq. units

2. Apply the area formula.

If all three sides of a triangle are known (SSS), you can use the law of cosines to find an angle, but Heron's formula provides a quick alternative. You may recall this formula from geometry. It uses the semi-perimeter $\left(\frac{a + b + c}{2}\right)$ represented by s.

Heron's Formula
The area of a triangle having sides of length a, b, and c is given by
$A = \sqrt{s(s - a)(s - b)(s - c)}$ where $s = \frac{1}{2}(a + b + c)$.

▶ A. Exercises

Find the slope of the line that passes through the given points.

1. (2, −7), (1, 4)
2. (−5, 3), (2, 9)
3. (−6, −1), (3, 7)
4. (6, 4), (0, 9)
5. (12, 3), (1, −2)
6. (0, 8), (9, 0)

Find the angle of inclination of the line that passes through the given points. Round angle measures to the nearest minute.

7. (−5, 1), (2, 4)
8. (0, 8), (1, −3)
9. (1, 1), (−6, −5)
10. (3, 6), (4, −2)
11. (9, 7), (−3, −7)
12. (5, 4), (2, 6)

▶ B. Exercises

Find the area of △ABC, given the information in each exercise.

13. ∠A = 57°, b = 8, c = 15
14. ∠C = 65°, ∠A = 38°, a = 15
15. a = 2, b = 7, c = 7
16. ∠C = 45°, a = 23, b = 25
17. ∠A = 36°, a = 12, c = 20
18. a = 15, b = 24, c = 32

Find the slope of the line, given the angle of inclination.

19. 30°
20. 45°
21. $\frac{5\pi}{6}$
22. $\frac{3\pi}{4}$
23. 157°
24. 1.82

Graph a line that forms an angle with the x-axis having the following measures.

25. 60°
26. 150°
27. $\frac{\pi}{4}$ radians

▶ C. Exercises

28. Find the area of △ABC if the coordinates of the vertices are A(2, 0), B(8, 6), and C(1, 8).
29. Prove: If the slopes of two lines are equal, the lines are parallel.

⚈ Dominion Modeling

30. For which of the 5 models would extrapolation be most dangerous or even ridiculous?
31. Consider the 5 models you have found for the alligator data. Is there a model for which the three largest alligators are outliers but not influential observations? Is there a model for which they are influential observations but not outliers?

32. Under what conditions may the law of cosines be applied to a triangle?

33. In using the law of sines, which condition is the ambiguous case?

34. When can you solve a triangle given two sides without using the law of sines or the law of cosines?

35. Find the length of an arc of a circle if the radius is **6 ft. 3 in.** and the central angle is **81.7°**.

36. List all angles θ, such that $0° \le \theta < 360°$, that have a reference angle of **30°**.

A solid wooden cube has 6-inch edges. Square holes with 2-inch sides centered in each face are cut through to the opposite face. The edges of the holes are parallel to the edges of the cube. Find the entire surface area in square inches.

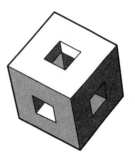

Math *and* Scripture

Human Dominion

God declared the universe He created was good. The nonmaterial things He made, including our ability to reason and patterns in creation, were also created good. Since Adam tended the garden of Eden before the Fall (Gen. 2:15), and since there was no sin before the Fall, Adam's activity was clearly good.

Read Genesis 1:26-28.

1. What role did God give to man with respect to His creation?

Of course, God gave this command before the Fall. Some say that just as creation was good before the Fall, Adam's rule over the earth was good only before the Fall. While it is true that the Fall brought sin into the world and that sin affects everything in creation, one cannot conclude that God has withdrawn the stewardship that He gave man.

Read Genesis 9:1-7.

2. To whom was God speaking? Was it before the Fall?

3. How does it relate to the mandate given to Adam?

Read Psalm 8:4-6.

4. Who was speaking? Was it before the Fall?

5. What does verse six teach?

The mandate shows that physical tools for controlling and managing resources are good. A hammer is not a neutral object; it is a good object, man-made to fulfill one of God's commands.

Of course, God's good can be misused for evil, but the hammer itself is not evil or even neutral. The same is true of God's order in creation. This clearly shows that man is right to build dams and power plants to provide energy. It is also correct to kill animals and plants to provide food for people.

This command, however, does not permit man to control earth's resources in any way that he desires. What restraints did God place on human dominion in the following passages?

6. Gen. 9:5-6

7. Deut. 25:4

8. Prov. 12:10

Man rules the earth, but he is also accountable to God for how he rules. The term that summarizes both aspects is stewardship. A steward manages something for someone else. In the following passages, of what are we to be stewards?

9. 1 Cor. 6:19-20

10. Titus 1:6-7

Developing math skills will help you exercise dominion over the earth, but you must seek to do so in a way that glorifies God and not to use them for your own ends.

> ## Vital Sines
>
> THOU MADEST HIM to have dominion over the works of thy hands: thou hast put all things under his feet. ✒
>
> PSALM 8:6

MAXIMIZING

God commanded Moses to count the people so that Moses could see God's blessing. Moses used this math skill to glorify God. God prohibited David from counting the people because David wanted to glory over the size of his own kingdom. Find these two passages.

Chapter 1 Review

Convert the following radian measures to degree measure.

1. $\frac{3\pi}{4}$
2. 4π
3. $\frac{\pi}{2}$
4. $\frac{7\pi}{9}$

Convert the following degree measures to exact radian measure.

5. 45°
6. 152°
7. 890°
8. 30°
9. Find the length and midpoint of the segment with endpoints $A(3, 7)$ and $B(4, -1)$.

Find the six trigonometric ratios for both acute angles in each triangle.

10.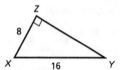

11.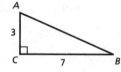

12. Find the six trigonometric functions for an angle in standard position whose terminal ray passes through $(-4, 1)$.
13. Draw a 45°-45° right triangle with right angle C; label all the angle measures and side lengths.
14. Draw a 30°-60° right triangle with right angle C; label all the angle measures and side lengths.

Find the following ratio values.

15. cos 38°40′
16. sin 54°14′
17. tan 120.1°
18. sec 82°15′

Solve right $\triangle ABC$, given the following values. Find side lengths to the nearest tenth and angle measures to the nearest minute.

19. $\angle A = 73°$, $a = 17$

20. $a = 9$, $c = 15$

Solve the following word problems. Round answers to the nearest tenth.

21. A boy who is 5 feet tall stands 40 feet from a flagpole and measures the angle of elevation to the top of the pole to be 62°. How tall is the flagpole?

22. An observer from a pier spots a ship directly east of the pier while looking through his binoculars. The ship is 3 miles out at sea on the first sighting. Some time later the boat is spotted again from the pier at a bearing of S 47° E. How far is the ship from the pier on the second sighting if the ship is going due south?

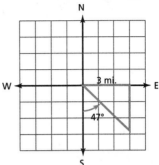

Solve △ABC. Round lengths to the nearest tenth and angles to the nearest degree.

23. $\angle A = 73°$, $\angle B = 52°$, $a = 9$

24. $a = 12$, $b = 8$, $\angle C = 43°$

Find the area of △ABC.

25. $b = 12$, $a = 16$, $\angle C = 37°$

26. $a = 25$, $b = 17$, $c = 12$

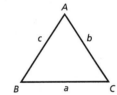

Find the slope for each of the following.

27. Line containing (8, 1), and (−2, 3)

28. Road with an angle of inclination of 12°

Find the angle of inclination for each of the following.

29. Line with a slope of $\frac{10}{3}$

30. Flambeau Falls (Wisconsin), a Class III whitewater rapid that descends 7 feet in a 1200 yard span

31. Give an overall evaluation of these models. Which would you prefer, and why?

32. Explain the mathematical significance of Psalm 8:6.

2 Polynomials

"This car could stop on a dime," they said. But could it? How quickly could one stop and how hard is it to stop at 70 mph compared to 30 mph?

What about the rule stating that for every 10 mph, you should stay one car length behind the vehicle in front of you? Is this enough, or should you keep more distance between vehicles?

Optometry researchers conducted a study to answer some of these questions. At various speeds, researchers studied how long it took drivers to physically respond, as well as how long it actually took for the vehicle to stop. Speed is in miles per hour, and distances are in meters. You will use polynomials to analyze the data.

Speed	Daytime Conditions		Nighttime Conditions	
	Reaction Distance	Stopping Distance	Reaction Distance	Stopping Distance
30	9	22.6	14.3	27.9
40	12	36.4	19.1	43.1
50	15	52.9	23.9	61.8
60	18	72.7	28.7	83.4
70	21	95.4	33.4	107.8

After this chapter you should be able to

1. evaluate functions using function notation.

2. identify relations and functions and give their domains and ranges.

3. identify and graph both linear and quadratic functions.

4. find the vertex of a quadratic function by completing the square.

5. evaluate and perform operations with polynomials.

6. find zeros (and their multiplicities) using the remainder theorem.

7. graph polynomial functions using symmetry, zeros, tails, and relative extrema.

2.1 Relations

Relation   A relation is any set of ordered pairs.

The sets $A = \{(2, 5), (1, 7), (-3, 4), (2, -6), (0, 2)\}$ and $B = \{(a, f), (b, c), (d, g)\}$ are relations since they are both sets of ordered pairs. The members of each pair are related to each other in some way. In mathematics, many relations are described by an equation. For example, if an ordered pair is (x, y) and the relationship between x and y is described by $y = 2x$, you can determine as many ordered pairs as is necessary by choosing arbitrary values for x and determining the related value for y according to the given equation. Because the value of y depends on the value that is chosen for x, y is called the *dependent variable* and x is called the *independent variable*. The set of numbers used for the independent variable, or x, is called the *domain* of the relation. The set of y-values is called the *range* of the relation.

Domain   The set of x-coordinates of the ordered pairs in a relation.

Range   The set of y-coordinates of the ordered pairs in a relation.

If you know the domain and the equation that describes a relation, you can determine the exact set of ordered pairs that make up the relation. If the domain is $D = \{-3, 1, 5, 7\}$ and the defining equation is $y = 2x$, then the relation is

$$\{(-3, -6), (1, 2), (5, 10), (7, 14)\}.$$

You can see that the range is $R = \{-6, 2, 10, 14\}$.

You can graph relations on a Cartesian plane by letting the x-axis correspond to the x-coordinates and the y-axis to the y-coordinates. The relation given in ordered-pair form here can be graphed as follows.

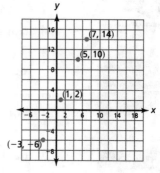

$$\{(-3, -6), (1, 2), (5, 10), (7, 14)\}$$

If the domain is the entire set of real numbers, the graph of the relation is a line that passes through points plotted here. Every ordered pair on that line satisfies the defining equation.

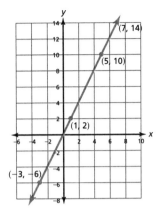

Function A relation in which every first coordinate has one and only one second coordinate associated with it.

The set $\{(2, 5), (3, 9), (2, 7), (1, 6)\}$ is a relation but not a function because the first coordinate 2 is associated with both 5 and 7. However, the set $\{(3, 6), (-2, 1), (4, 5)\}$ is a function because every first coordinate is associated with only one second coordinate. The set $\{5, 7, 2, 8\}$ is neither a relation nor a function because it is not a set of ordered pairs. Is the relation that is graphed in the above figure a function? Can you find two ordered pairs on the line in the figure that have the same first coordinate but different second coordinates? The vertical line test is a quick way to determine whether a graphed relation is a function.

Vertical Line Test

Move an imaginary vertical line across a graph from left to right. If any vertical line touches the graphed relation at more than one point, the graph does not represent a function.

Do you see why the vertical line test works? If two points are on the same vertical line, there will be two y-values (second coordinates) paired with the same x-value (first coordinate).

Relations and functions are also described by circle mappings. One circle represents the domain, while the other circle represents the range. The circle mapping shown represents the relation $\{(3, 7), (4, 1), (4, 4), (2, -1)\}$. It is easily seen that this relation is not a function, since 4 in the domain is paired with both 1 and 4 in the range.

Most functions in math are written using function notation in which a rule is stated together with a domain. The symbols $f(x)$ in the rule $f(x) = 3x - 5$ is read "f of x" or "function of x." The $f(x)$ notation represents the second coordinate that corresponds to the first coordinate x. Since y is also associated with the second coordinate, you can interchange $f(x)$ and y. So the two equations $f(x) = 3x - 5$ and $y = 3x - 5$ represent the same set of ordered pairs.

To evaluate functions, substitute the given domain value for x and simplify. The value or expression in the parentheses specifies the domain value. For instance, $f(5)$ means that you are to determine the value of the function for $x = 5$.

EXAMPLE 1   Evaluate $f(x) = 4x - 7$ and $g(x) = x^2 + 9$ for $x = -3, 0$.

Answer
a. $f(x) = 4x - 7$
     $f(-3) = 4(-3) - 7 = -19$ 1. Substitute the x-values into the function rule and evaluate.

     $f(0) = 4(0) - 7 = -7$
     ordered pairs: $(-3, -19)$, $(0, -7)$

b. $g(x) = x^2 + 9$
     $g(-3) = (-3)^2 + 9 = 18$ 2. Substitute the x-values into the function rule and evaluate.

     $g(0) = 0^2 + 9 = 9$
     ordered pairs: $(-3, 18)$, $(0, 9)$

EXAMPLE 2   If $f(x) = 5x + 3$, find, $f\left(\frac{1}{2}\right)$, $f(2a + 1)$, $f(x^2)$, and $f(x - 3)$.

Answer $f\left(\frac{1}{2}\right) = 5\left(\frac{1}{2}\right) + 3 = \frac{11}{2}$

$f(2a + 1) = 5(2a + 1) + 3 = 10a + 8$

$f(x^2) = 5x^2 + 3$

$f(x - 3) = 5(x - 3) + 3 = 5x - 12$

▶ A. Exercises

1. Give an example of a relation.
2. Give an example of a function.
3. Give an example of a relation that is not a function.

Let $f = \{(7, 2), (-5, 3), (1, 4), (3, 3)\}$ and $g = \{(-6, 3), (1, 4), (6, -3)\}$.
4. Give the domain of function f and of function g.
5. Give the range of function f and of function g.

State the rule that describes the following functions.

6. {(1, 3), (−2, −6), (3, 9)}

7. {(0, 5), (3, 8), (−2, 3), (1, 6), (8, 13)}

8. {(1, 1), (2, 4), (4, 16), (−2, 4)}

9. {(0, −3), (1, −1), (2, 1), (−1, −5)}

10. Verify the equations obtained in exercises 6-9 using a table on the graphing calculator. Each x-value must generate the correct y-value.

Use the vertical line test to determine whether the following relations are functions.

11.

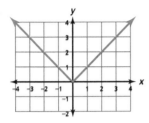

14.

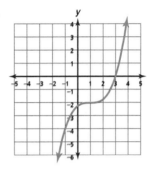

12.

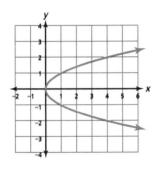

15.

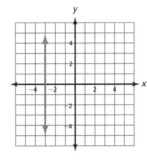

13.

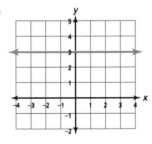

16.

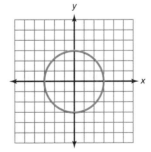

For domain $D = \{-3, 2, 4, 1\}$, evaluate the following.

17. $f(x) = 3x - 5$
18. $g(x) = 2x^2 + 3$
19. $h(x) = -x + 7$
20. $l(x) = x^3 + 2x - 4$

▶ B. Exercises

Refer to the functions in exercises 17-20. Give each as a set of ordered pairs, graph, and circle mapping.

21. $f(x) = 3x - 5$
22. $g(x) = 2x^2 + 3$
23. $h(x) = -x + 7$
24. $l(x) = x^3 + 2x - 4$
25. If $g(x) = \frac{x}{2} + 1$, find
   a) $g\left(\frac{1}{4}\right)$, b) $g(-b)$, c) $g(4x)$, and d) $g(6x - 6)$.

Use a table on the graphing calculator to find the ordered pairs of the given functions with the given domains.

26. $y = 0.25x + 5.9$ $D = \{-3.3, \frac{17}{9}, 154.578\}$
27. $f(x) = \frac{1}{6}x^2 - \sqrt{5}x + 3.7$ $D = \{-5, 0.36, 14.53, 234.1\}$

▶ C. Exercises

28. If $f(x) = x^2 + 2x - 4$, find $\frac{f(x + h) - f(x)}{h}$.
29. Identify which of the following are functions and evaluate each function for the following values of x: $-1, 2, 10$. Show answers as ordered pairs.
   $f(x) = x^4 + 5x^{\frac{3}{2}} - 2x + \frac{1}{2}$; $g(x) = 3x^3 + 4x^2 - \sqrt{5}x + 2$; and
   $h(x) = 5x^3 - \frac{1}{3}x^2 + 8x - 3$

Dominion Modeling

Use the data on braking distance to answer the following questions. Use *speed* and *reaction distance* to answer each question, both for daytime and for nighttime conditions.

30. Draw the scatterplots. What model fits in each case?
31. Give the models and evaluate them using the scatterplots and r^2.
32. Plot the residuals. What do you notice about these plots? How might you have known this from the r^2 and the scatterplots?

33. In what quadrant is the cosine negative? the tangent?
34. In a right triangle, $a = 2$, and $b = 7$. Find A.
35. In a right triangle, $a = 4$ and $A = 20°$. Find c.
36. In what two cases should the cosine law be applied to solve a triangle?
37. In a triangle, $a = 272$ ft, $A = 37°$ and $B = 102°$. Find b and C.

2.2   Linear Functions

Consider the function in Example 1.

EXAMPLE 1   Graph the function $f(x) = 4x + 6$ with domain $D = \{-6, -2, 1, 3\}$.

Answer $f(-6) = 4(-6) + 6 = -18$ $f(1) = 4(1) + 6 = 10$
$f(-2) = 4(-2) + 6 = -2$ $f(3) = 4(3) + 6 = 18$
$f = \{(-6, -18), (-2, -2), (1, 10), (3, 18)\}$

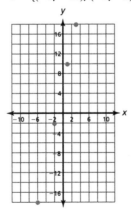

You can see that the range $R = \{-18, -2, 10, 18\}$. Even though the four points lie on a line, the graph consists only of these points. If the domain was not specified, it would be understood that every real number is to be included:

that is, $D = \mathbb{R}$. If that were the case, you would draw a line through the points. Just as you can tell the domain and range from the graph, you can tell that the graph represents a function by using the vertical line test. The rest of this section will review the graphing of lines and the forms of their equations.

According to the definition of slope from Chapter 1, if (x_1, y_1) is a particular point and (x, y) represents any other point on the line, then

$$m = \frac{y - y_1}{x - x_1} \text{ or } y - y_1 = m(x - x_1)$$

This is the *point-slope form* of the line. You can use it to find the equation of the line if you know the slope and a specific point.

EXAMPLE 2   Find the equation of the line passing through $(1, 6)$ and $(3, -1)$.

Answer

$m = \frac{-1 - 6}{3 - 1} = -\frac{7}{2}$ 1. Find the slope.

$y - y_1 = m(x - x_1)$ 2. Apply the point-slope form.

$y - 6 = -\frac{7}{2}(x - 1)$

$y - 6 = -\frac{7}{2}x + \frac{7}{2}$

$y = -\frac{7}{2}x + \frac{19}{2}$

It is convenient to solve for y. The form $y = -\frac{7}{2}x + \frac{19}{2}$ means the same as $f(x) = -\frac{7}{2}x + \frac{19}{2}$.

From the general point-slope form of an equation, you can obtain another form of a linear function. Solve the point-slope equation for y.

$$y - y_1 = m(x - x_1)$$
$$y = m(x - x_1) + y_1$$
$$y = mx - mx_1 + y_1$$
$$f(x) = mx + (y_1 - mx_1)$$

When $x = 0$, notice that $f(0) = m \cdot 0 + (y_1 - mx_1) = y_1 - mx_1$. Thus $(0, y_1 - mx_1)$ is the y-intercept. Then let $b = y_1 - mx_1$, so the y-intercept is $(0, b)$. You can write the equation as $y = mx + b$, which is called the *slope-intercept form* of the line. This form of the line is very useful for graphing.

EXAMPLE 3   Graph $f(x) = 3x - 2$. Give the domain and range. Is it a function?

Answer

$m = 3$ and $b = -2$ 1. Compare $y = 3x - 2$ to $y = mx + b$.

Continued ▶

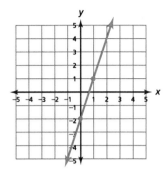

2. Plot the y-intercept $(0, b) = (0, -2)$

3. Move from the intercept to another point on the line, using the slope. Since $m = \frac{\Delta y}{\Delta x} = \frac{3}{1}$, the change in y is positive 3 (up) and the change in x is positive 1 (right). The graph contains the point $(1, 1)$. Draw the line through these two points.

$D = \mathbb{R}$, $R = \mathbb{R}$
The line is a function.

4. The graph shows that all real numbers are included in both the domain and range. Also, the line is a function since it passes the vertical line test.

The form $ax + by = c$ is called the *general linear form* of a line because every line, even vertical lines, can be put into this form. For the function in Example 3, the general linear form is $3x - y = 2$. To obtain general linear form, clear any fractions and make $a > 0$.

Now consider the equation $x = 5$. Since the x-coordinate must always be five, the line passes through $(5, 0)$, $(5, 4)$, and $(5, -3)$. The graph is a vertical line. Since $m = \frac{0 - 4}{5 - 5} = \frac{-4}{0}$, the slope is undefined (vertical lines have no slope); and since you cannot solve the equation for y, it is not possible to write it in function notation. The equation $x = 5$ is a special case of the form $ax + by = c$ in which $a = 1$, $b = 0$, and $c = 5$.

EXAMPLE 4	Write $y = \frac{3}{8}x + 5$ in general linear form.	
Answer	$y = \frac{3}{8}x + 5$	
	$8y = 3x + 40$	1. Clear fractions (multiply by 8).
	$-3x + 8y = 40$	2. Obtain $ax + by = c$ form.
	$3x - 8y = -40$	3. Make $a > 0$ (multiply by -1).

The graph of equations such as $y = 2$ are horizontal lines and are called *constant functions*. In the constant function $y = 2$ or $y = 0x + 2$, the slope is zero. Do not confuse the zero slope of horizontal lines with the undefined slope of vertical lines.

Definition

Constant function   A constant function is a linear function of the form $f(x) = a$, where $a \in \mathbb{R}$.

Remember that parallel lines have the same slope (and the same angle of inclination). What about perpendicular lines? Consider the slopes of the perpendicular lines in the figure, where $l_1 \perp l_2$. Now $l_1 \perp l_2$ can represent any pair of perpendicular lines. Notice that both of these lines go through the origin. Not every pair of perpendicular lines intersect at the origin. But for every pair of perpendicular lines, you can find two perpendicular lines, having the same slopes as the given pair that do intersect at the origin. So the pair shown here are representative of all pairs of perpendicular lines.

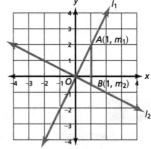

As long as neither line is vertical, the vertical line $x = 1$ will intersect both lines. A has coordinates $(1, m_1)$ and B has coordinates $(1, m_2)$. Notice that $\triangle AOB$ is a right triangle and therefore the Pythagorean theorem applies.

$$(AO)^2 + (OB)^2 = (AB)^2$$

Applying the distance formula, you can determine the actual lengths of the sides of the right triangle and substitute.

$$(AO)^2 + (OB)^2 = (AB)^2$$
$$\left(\sqrt{(1-0)^2 + (m_1 - 0)^2}\right)^2 + \left(\sqrt{(1-0)^2 + (m_2 - 0)^2}\right)^2 = \left(\sqrt{(1-1)^2 + (m_1 - m_2)^2}\right)^2$$
$$1 + m_1^2 + 1 + m_2^2 = (m_1 - m_2)^2$$
$$2 + m_1^2 + m_2^2 = m_1^2 - 2m_1m_2 + m_2^2$$
$$2 = -2m_1m_2$$
$$m_1m_2 = -1$$
$$m_2 = \frac{-1}{m_1} \quad (m_1 \neq 0)$$

This application of algebra that you have learned proves the following theorem:

If two nonvertical lines are perpendicular, their corresponding slopes are negative reciprocals.

EXAMPLE 5 Find the slopes of the lines that are parallel and perpendicular to the line that passes through the points $(5, 4)$ and $(-1, 3)$.

Answer

$$m_1 = \frac{y_1 - y_2}{x_1 - x_2}$$

$$m_1 = \frac{4 - 3}{5 - (-1)}$$

$$m_1 = \frac{1}{6}$$

1. Find the slope of the given line.

Parallel line: $m_2 = \frac{1}{6}$

2. For the parallel line, $m_2 = m_1$.

Perpendicular line: $m_2 = \frac{-1}{\frac{1}{6}}$

$$m_2 = -6$$

3. For the perpendicular line, $m_2 = \frac{-1}{m_1}$.

You can use these slope relationships to help determine equations of lines.

Review the forms of the equation of a line, the slope formula, and slope relationships below before doing the exercises.

Forms of Lines	Name	Most Frequent Use
$y - y_1 = m(x - x_1)$	Point-slope form	Finding equations of lines
$y = mx + b$	Slope-intercept form	Graphing lines
$ax + by = c$	General linear form	Vertical lines and when requested

Slope Formulas	
$m = \frac{y_1 - y_2}{x_1 - x_2}$	definition
$m_2 = m_1$	parallel lines
$m_2 = \frac{-1}{m_1}$	perpendicular lines

▶ A. Exercises

Write the lines in the form indicated.

1. $y - 5 = 4(x - 6)$ in general linear form
2. $y - 2 = \frac{1}{3}(x - 6)$ in slope-intercept form
3. $2x + 4y = 3$ in function form
4. $f(x) = \frac{2}{5}x - 3$ in general linear form

Give the slope and y-intercept of each line.

5. $y = \frac{-2}{3}x + 1$
6. $5x + 2y = 8$

7. $x = 4$

8. $3y - 4 = 11$

Find the slope of a line

9. perpendicular to $y = 4x - 1$.

10. parallel to $3x - 2y = 8$.

▶ B. Exercises

Graph each equation. Give the domain and range of each and tell whether it is a function.

11. $2x + y = 9$

12. $3x - 2y = 8$

13. $x + 4y = -12$

14. $4x - y = 2$

15. $6x + 3y = 9$

16. $x = -1$

17. $3x - 4y = 6$

18. $5x + y = 8$

19. $y = 3$

20. $7x - 3y = -7$

21. $0.2x - 1.3y = 9.75$

22. $4.72x + 3.7y = 21.5$

Give the equation of each line.

23. Slope is $\frac{1}{2}$; y-intercept $(0, 4)$

24. Slope is -3; contains $(2, 4)$

25. Contains $(3, 4)$ and $(-9, -4)$

26. Contains $(2, -3)$ and is parallel to $y = \frac{4}{3}x - 1$

27. Contains $(0, 5)$ and is perpendicular to the line containing $(9, 3)$, and $(-7, -4)$.

Graph the following groups of equations in each exercise, and determine how the numbers in the second and third equations affect the graph as compared to the first equation.

28. $y = 4x$

   $y = 4x - 3$

   $y = 4x + 2$

29. $y = \frac{1}{3}x + 5$

   $y = -3x + 5$

   $y = \frac{1}{3}x$

30. $y = x + 5$
    $y = 2x + 5$
    $y = -2x + 5$
31. What lines are not functions? Why?

▶ C. Exercises

32. Which of the following are linear functions? For those that are, find the ordered pairs corresponding to the domain values: {1, 5, 25} (express coordinates to the nearest hundredth).
    $f(x) = \frac{1}{3}x + 5.\overline{2}$, $g(x) = 5x^{-1} + 3$, $h(x) = \sqrt{3}x - 5$, and $k(x) = 5\sqrt{x} + 7$
33. Transform the general linear equation into an equation of the form $\frac{x}{k_1} + \frac{y}{k_2} = 1$, and tell what k_1 and k_2 represent. Apply the result to the equation $2x + 3y = 7$.

∿ Dominion Modeling

Use the braking data to answer the following questions about speed vs. stopping distance. Give separate answers for both daytime and nighttime conditions.

34. Derive *linear* models. Plot each model with its data, and evaluate them using the scatterplots and r^2.
35. Plot the residuals. How does the shape of the residual plot relate to the corresponding scatterplot with its model? Is there a systematic pattern in the residuals?
36. Why are the linear models above inappropriate even though they have high r^2 values?

■ Cumulative Review

If $f(x) = 3x - 7$ and $g(x) = -3$, find the following.

37. $f(2)$
38. $g(-4)$
39. Give the quadrant and reference angle for 1000°.
40. If the cosine of one acute angle of a right triangle is 0.4462, what are the acute angles of the triangle?
41. The sides of a triangle are in the ratio of 2:3:4. Find the angles to the nearest degree.

2.3 Quadratic Functions

The word *quadratic* comes from the Latin word *quadrus,* which means "square." There is a second degree, or squared, term in a quadratic function. Geometrically, you can see that a quadratic function can represent the area of a square. The four sides of a square suggest another reason for the name *quadratic function.*

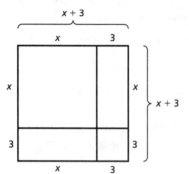

Each cross-section of a radio telescope, such as this one at Owens Valley, California, is a parabola, so all radio waves that come into the dish are reflected to the focus.

Looking at the areas of the individual squares and rectangles in this figure, you can determine the area of the large square by finding their sum.

$$A(x) = (x + 3)(x + 3) = x^2 + 3x + 3x + 9 = x^2 + 6x + 9$$

You can see that the area of this square is a quadratic function. Remember that a function is a set of ordered pairs.

Definition

Quadratic function   A function for the form $f(x) = ax^2 + bx + c$ where a, b, and $c \in \mathbb{R}$ and $a \neq 0$.

EXAMPLE 1   Find the set of ordered pairs described by the quadratic function rule $f(x) = 3x^2 + x - 7$ and the domain $\{-3, -2, 0, 2\}$.

Answer $f(-3) = 3(-3)^2 + (-3) - 7 = 27 - 3 - 7 = 17$
$f(-2) = 3(-2)^2 + (-2) - 7 = 12 - 2 - 7 = 3$
$f(0) = 3(0)^2 + 0 - 7 = 0 + 0 - 7 = -7$
$f(2) = 3(2)^2 + 2 - 7 = 12 + 2 - 7 = 7$
$f = \{(-3, 17), (-2, 3), (0, -7), (2, 7)\}$

Quadratic relations are widely used. The path that a ball follows when it is thrown into the air or the path a bullet takes as it is shot into the air can be modeled by a quadratic function. This shape is called a *parabola*. A three-dimensional shape corresponding to the parabola is the *paraboloid*. A searchlight, the headlights in a car, and television reception disks use paraboloid reflectors.

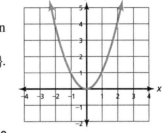

The quadratic function that is used as a base graph for comparison is described by the equation $y = x^2$. Some ordered pairs in this function are $\{(-3, 9), (-2, 4), (-1, 1), (0, 0), (1, 1), (2, 4), (3, 9)\}$. When these ordered pairs are graphed and a smooth curve drawn through them, the result is a parabola.

Since squared quantities cannot be negative, $y = 0$ must be the smallest range value (minimum value of the function), and the corresponding point $(0, 0)$ must be the minimum point on the graph.

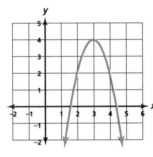

Now consider $y = -2(x - 3)^2 + 4$. The product of -2 and a squared quantity cannot be positive. This means the parabola will be flipped upside down and it will have a highest point (maximum function value). Notice that to obtain 0 in the perfect square, you must substitute 3 for x. This means that the basic parabola $y = x^2$ has been translated 3 units to the right as well as flipped upside down. Finally, adding 4 units to the value of the function causes the graph to be translated 4 units upward.

The form $y = a(x - h)^2 + k$ is the *standard translated form* of the parabola. We will refer to it as the *work form* in this text. The equation could also be written $y - k = a(x - h)^2$, grouping the k value with the y. This form tells you to translate the vertex to (h, k) and that the parabola opens upward if $a > 0$ but downward if $a < 0$.

Since every parabola has a vertex, every quadratic function has a largest range value (maximum) or a smallest range value (minimum). If $a > 0$, the parabola opens upward and has a minimum point. Since every quadratic function can be put into work form by completing the square, you can always find the maximum or minimum point by using work form to find the vertex.

EXAMPLE 2 Graph $y = 3x^2 + 12x + 8$. Give the domain and range.

Answer

$y = 3x^2 + 12x + 8$ $y = 3(x^2 + 4x) + 8$ $y = 3(x^2 + 4x + 4) + 8 - 12$ $y = 3(x + 2)^2 - 4$	1. Complete the square to obtain work form. Factor the 3 out of the variable terms so the coefficient of x^2 will be 1. Take half the coefficient of x, square it, $\left(\frac{4}{2}\right)^2 = 4$, and add the result in the parentheses. Since the parenthesis is multiplied by the 3, compensate by subtracting 12. Simplify.
$a = 3$; since $a > 0$, the graph opens upward (has a minimum value). $x + 2 = x - (-2)$; therefore $h = -2$, the minimum value of the squared factor. $y + 4$ is substituted for y; $k = -4$ is the minimum range value. Translation is left 2 and down 4, moving the vertex to $(-2, -4)$.	2. Determine whether the graph opens upward or downward. The translation of the vertex is determined by identifying the h and k values. The -4 on the right can be thought of as $y + 4$ on the left.
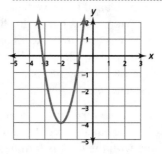	3. Graph the parabola.
	4. From the graph observe that $D = \mathbb{R}$ and $R = \{y \mid y \geq -4\}$.

The *axis (line) of symmetry* cuts the parabola in half. It passes through the vertex (h, k) and mirrors one side of the parabola to the other side of the line. Notice how the parabola is symmetrical with respect to this line. Since the line is vertical, the axis of symmetry has the equation $x = h$.

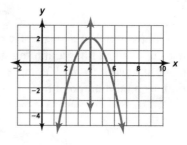

Zero of a polynomial   The number r is a *zero* of $P(x)$ if and only if $P(r) = 0$.

Root of an equation   The number that is a solution of an equation.

Roots and zeros are closely related. The roots of the equation $P(x) = 0$ are the zeros of the polynomial $P(x)$.

The zeros of a polynomial can be real or complex. The real zeros are the points where the graph of its function crosses the x-axis. To find the zeros substitute 0 for $P(x)$ or y and solve for the roots of the resulting equation. Remember when solving a quadratic equation you may find one, two, or no real roots. Therefore, a quadratic function may have one, two, or no real zeros, depending on the function.

EXAMPLE 3   Find the zeros of $y = -x^2 - 6x$ and graph the function.

Answer

$y = -x^2 - 6x$

$0 = -x^2 - 6x$ 1.   Substitute 0 for y to find the roots.

$0 = -x(x + 6)$ 2.   Factor to solve.

$-x = 0$ or $x + 6 = 0$

$x = 0$ $x = -6$

The zeros are 0 and -6.

$y = -x^2 - 6x$ 3.   Now complete the square to change the equation to work form. Factor out a

$y = -(x^2 + 6x)$ negative so the coefficient of x^2 will be 1. Add half the coefficient of x, squared

$y = -(x^2 + 6x + 9) + 9$ inside the parentheses (3^2). Since the 9 is multiplied by -1, -9 was actually added. To maintain equality, 9 must be added outside the parentheses.

$y = -(x + 3)^2 + 9$ 4.   Use work form to identify $a = -1$, $h = -3$, and $k = 9$. The vertex is $(-3, 9)$ and the parabola opens downward.

Continued ▶

5. Graph.

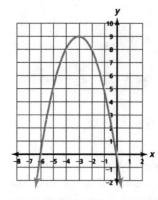

Sometimes you may need the quadratic formula to find the zeros.

EXAMPLE 4   Find the zeros of $f(x) = 5x^2 - x + 2$.

Answer | $5x^2 - x + 2 = 0$ | 1. Set $f(x) = 0$. |
|---|---|
| $x = \dfrac{-b \pm \sqrt{b^2 - 4ac}}{2a}$ | 2. Use the quadratic formula, since $f(x)$ does not factor easily. |
| $x = \dfrac{-(-1) \pm \sqrt{(-1)^2 - 4 \cdot 5 \cdot 2}}{2 \cdot 5}$ | |
| $x = \dfrac{1 \pm \sqrt{-39}}{10}$ | |
| $x = \dfrac{1 \pm \sqrt{39}i}{10}$ | 3. Express the $\sqrt{-39}$ as a complex number. Remember that $\sqrt{-39} = \sqrt{39} \cdot \sqrt{-1}$ and $\sqrt{-1} = i$, so $\sqrt{-39} = \sqrt{39}i$. |
| $x = \dfrac{1}{10} \pm \dfrac{\sqrt{39}}{10}i$ | 4. Write complex numbers in standard form, $a + bi$. |
| $\dfrac{1}{10} + \dfrac{\sqrt{39}}{10}i,\ \dfrac{1}{10} - \dfrac{\sqrt{39}}{10}i$ | 5. List the zeros. |

Since the zeros for the function above are complex numbers, the graph of $f(x)$ does not cross the x-axis. If you want to graph it, you could still find the vertex by completing the square. You also know that it opens upward since $a = 5$ is positive. The y-intercept $f(0) = 2$ will be useful as a guide to the width of the graph when x-intercepts either do not exist or cannot be found easily.

EXAMPLE 5   Find the maximum point in the function described by
$f(x) = -2x^2 + 16x - 2$.

Answer

$f(x) = -2x^2 + 16x - 2$ $= -2(x^2 - 8x) - 2$	1. Complete the square. Factor the leading coefficient from the first two terms.
$= -2(x^2 - 8x + 16) - 2 + 32$	2. Add 16 inside the parentheses (half the coefficient of x, squared). Because of the -2 in front of the parentheses you actually subtracted 32. To compensate for this, you must add 32 outside the parentheses.
$f(x) = -2(x - 4)^2 + 30$	3. Factor to obtain work form.
The maximum point is (4, 30).	4. From this form you can find the vertex $(h, k) = (4, 30)$. This shows that the function is maximized at 30 when $x = 4$. Thirty is the maximum value because no value for x will produce a larger y-value.

▶ A. Exercises

Use $f(x) = x^2 + 4x - 21$.
1. Find $f(-3)$ and $f(2)$.
2. Find all x- and y-intercepts.
3. Which way does the graph open and does it have a maximum or minimum value?
4. Find the maximum or minimum point.
5. Give the domain and range.

Put the following quadratic functions in work form. State the vertex and tell if it is a maximum or minimum point.
6. $g(x) = -2x^2 - 8x + 12$
7. $h(x) = -5x^2 - 30x + 2$
8. $l(x) = 4x^2 + 8x - 1$
9. $h(x) = 3x^2 - 9x - 15$
10. $g(x) = -x^2 - 2x + 7$

▶ B. Exercises

Place the following quadratic functions in work form, then graph.

11. $y = x^2 + 2x - 5$

12. $y = -x^2 + 6x + 4$

13. $y = 2x^2 + 8x - 7$

14. $y = 3x^2 - 12x + 2$

15. $y = x^2 + 3x - 7$

16. $y = -2x^2 - 12x + 4$

17. $y = -x^2 - 5x + 2$

Graph using the graphing calculator.

18. $y = -3.4x^2 + 5.78x + 2.1$

19. $y = \frac{5}{7}x^2 - \frac{15}{43}x + \frac{3}{11}$

Without graphing, find the translation of the parabola, state whether it opens upward or downward, and write the equation of the axis of symmetry.

20. $y = 4x^2 + 8x - 3$

21. $y = x^2 + x - 2$

22. $y = -2x^2 - 4x + 5$

23. $y = -x^2 + x + 7$

Find the zeros of the following functions.

24. $y = x^2 + 5x - 2$

25. $y = -x^2 + x + 20$

26. $y = x^2 + 8x + 16$

27. $y = 3x^2 + 4x - 5$

28. Give the zeros for exercise 27 in decimal form using the zero function on the graphing calculator.

▶ C. Exercises

29. Graph $x = y^2$ and $x = (y - 1)^2 + 3$ on the same graph.

30. Are all parabolas functions? Explain.

Dominion Modeling

Use the data on braking distance to answer the questions on speed versus braking distance. Give separate answers for both daytime and nighttime conditions.

31. Give quadratic models and evaluate them using scatterplots and r^2.

32. Plot the residuals. Is there a pattern in them?

33. An angle in standard position has a terminal ray passing through $(-7, -10)$. Find its exact sine, cosine, tangent, and its angle measure.

34. A function has $D = \{-4, 3, 7\}$ and $R = \{-7, 7, 15\}$. Write the function rule.

35. If $\sin x = \frac{3}{7}$, find $\tan x$.

36. Find the equation of the line joining $(2, 3)$ and $(3, -1)$.

37. Given $(3, -5)$ and $(-2, -7)$, find the length of the segment connecting them and the midpoint.

2.4 Polynomial Functions

Examine the polynomial expression below. The coefficients are real (although sometimes irrational) and the powers of the variables are whole numbers. In a polynomial containing a single variable, the highest power of the variable is the *degree* of the polynomial. The polynomial below has a degree of 5.

$$3x^5 - \sqrt{2}x^4 - x^2 + 6$$

Quadratic and linear functions are special types of polynomials that you studied earlier.

Engineers can use quadratic and cubic polynomials to design roller coasters, such as the Hurler at Carowinds in Charlotte, North Carolina.

	General Rule	Degree
Linear	$f(x) = mx + b$	1
Quadratic	$f(x) = ax^2 + bx + c$	2

Lowercase letters are used to represent the coefficients of these functions. For polynomials of higher degree, it helps to number the coefficients. Notice the numerical subscripts for counting the coefficients on these special polynomials.

	General Rule	Degree
Cubic	$f(x) = a_3x^3 + a_2x^2 + a_1x + a_0$	3
Quartic	$f(x) = a_4x^4 + a_3x^3 + a_2x^2 + a_1x + a_0$	4
Quintic	$f(x) = a_5x^5 + a_4x^4 + a_3x^3 + a_2x^2 + a_1x + a_0$	5

In order to represent an arbitrary (general) polynomial, you must represent the degree by a whole number n. The powers decrease successively by one along with the matching coefficient subscript. Therefore, all polynomial expressions in one variable can be written in the following general form where the coefficients, $a_0, a_1, a_2, \ldots, a_n$, are real numbers and n is a whole number.

$$a_nx^n + a_{n-1}x^{n-1} + a_{n-2}x^{n-2} + \cdots + a_2x^2 + a_1x + a_0$$

Polynomials in one variable are usually written in descending order with the highest power of x appearing first (its coefficient is called the *leading coefficient*) and the a_0 term (called the *constant term*) appearing last. The leading coefficient in the polynomial $3x^5 - \sqrt{2}x^4 - x^2 + 6$ is 3; the constant is 6. The coefficients of the x^4, x^3, and x^2 terms are $-\sqrt{2}$, 0, and -1, respectively.

A *constant polynomial* has no variable terms, but consists only of a constant term. The degree of a constant polynomial is zero. Since $a_0x^0 = a_0(1) = a_0$, the zero power of the variable makes the degree zero. The only exception to this rule is the number 0, called the *zero polynomial,* which has no degree. Since $0 \cdot x^n = 0$ no matter what n is, the power of x cannot be determined.

EXAMPLE 1   Answer the following questions about the polynomial $5x - 7x^2 - 9 + 8x^4$.
a. Write the polynomial in descending order.
b. What is the degree of the polynomial?
c. What is the leading coefficient?
d. What is the constant term?
e. What are the coefficients of the x^3, x^2, and x terms?

Answer   a. $8x^4 - 7x^2 + 5x - 9$
b. The degree is 4.
c. The leading coefficient is 8.
d. The constant is -9 (since a coefficient or constant includes the preceding sign.)
e. The other coefficients are 0, -7, and 5, respectively.

Polynomial function   A function having a polynomial for its rule such as $P(x) = a_n x^n + a_{n-1} x^{n-1} + a_{n-2} x^{n-2} + \cdots + a_2 x^2 + a_1 x + a_0$ where $a_n, a_{n-1}, \ldots, a_0 \in \mathbb{R}$, $a_n \neq 0$, and n is a nonnegative integer.

Therefore, if a function contains a term such as x^{-2}, $\sqrt{x}$, $\frac{2}{x}$, or $\sin x$, that expression is not a polynomial.

EXAMPLE 2   For each of the following, indicate whether it is a polynomial and give the degree.
a. $\frac{1}{3}x^2 + \frac{2}{3}x + 6$
b. 7
c. $x^7 + x^5 + x^3 + x^{-1}$

Answer   a. It is a polynomial of the second degree.
b. It is a zero-degree polynomial since you can think of it as $7x^0$.
c. It is not a polynomial because of x^{-1}. Recall that the definition requires whole numbers for the powers.

To evaluate a polynomial, substitute a given value for the variable.

EXAMPLE 3   Find $P(-1)$, if $P(x) = 6x^5 + 9x^2 - x + 12$.

Answer $P(x) = 6x^5 + 9x^2 - x + 12$
$P(-1) = 6(-1)^5 + 9(-1)^2 - (-1) + 12$
$P(-1) = -6 + 9 + 1 + 12$
$P(-1) = 16$

Polynomials can be added and subtracted (by combining like terms) or multiplied and divided (by applying the laws of exponents). Division of polynomials will become important in solving equations that involve factoring polynomials.

EXAMPLE 4   If $P(x) = 6x^3 + x^2 - 29x + 8$ and $Q(x) = 3x^2 - 7x + 3$, find
a. $P(x) + Q(x)$
b. $P(x) - Q(x)$
c. $P(x) \cdot Q(x)$
d. $P(x) \div Q(x)$

Continued ▶

Answer

a. $P(x) + Q(x) = (6x^3 + x^2 - 29x + 8) + (3x^2 - 7x + 3) = 6x^3 + 4x^2 - 36x + 11$

b. $P(x) - Q(x) = (6x^3 + x^2 - 29x + 8) - (3x^2 - 7x + 3) = 6x^3 - 2x^2 - 22x + 5$

c. $P(x) \cdot Q(x) = (6x^3 + x^2 - 29x + 8)(3x^2 - 7x + 3)$

$$
\begin{aligned}
&= 18x^5 + 3x^4 - 87x^3 + 24x^2 \\
&\qquad\quad - 42x^4 - 7x^3 + 203x^2 - 56x \\
&\qquad\qquad\qquad + 18x^3 + 3x^2 - 87x + 24 \\
\hline
&= 18x^5 - 39x^4 - 76x^3 + 230x^2 - 143x + 24
\end{aligned}
$$

d. $P(x) \div Q(x)$ requires long division.

$$
\begin{array}{r}
2x + 5 \quad \text{R.} \; -7 \\
3x^2 - 7x + 3 \overline{)6x^3 + x^2 - 29x + 8} \\
\underline{6x^3 - 14x^2 + 6x} \\
15x^2 - 35x + 8 \\
\underline{15x^2 - 35x + 15} \\
-7
\end{array}
$$

1. Divide using long division. Be sure all polynomials are in descending order.

$P(x) \div Q(x) = 2x + 5 \;\text{R.} -7$

2. Write the answer.

It is not always easy to identify all of the zeros of a polynomial function. For instance, 1 is obviously a zero of $P(x)$ below, since $P(1) = 0$.

$$P(x) = x^4 - 1$$

But this polynomial actually has four zeros: 1, −1, i, and $-i$. These can be found by solving the equation $x^4 - 1 = 0$.

$$
\begin{aligned}
x^4 - 1 &= 0 \\
(x^2 - 1)(x^2 + 1) &= 0
\end{aligned}
$$

$$
\begin{array}{ll}
x^2 - 1 = 0 \quad \text{or} & x^2 + 1 = 0 \\
x^2 = 1 & x^2 = -1 \\
x = \pm\sqrt{1} & x = \pm\sqrt{-1} \\
x = \pm 1 & x = \pm i
\end{array}
$$

The zeros are −1, 1, $-i$, and i.

You should remember the methods of factoring and the quadratic formula from algebra. These are important tools in finding zeros of polynomials.

EXAMPLE 5 Find any zeros of $P(x) = x^2 + 6x + 24$.

Answer $x^2 + 6x + 24 = 0$

1. Set $P(x) = 0$

$x = \dfrac{-6 \pm \sqrt{36 - 4(24)}}{2}$

2. Because you cannot factor it, use the quadratic formula.

Continued ▶

$$= \frac{-6 \pm \sqrt{-60}}{2}$$

$$= \frac{-6 \pm 2\sqrt{15}i}{2}$$

$$= -3 \pm \sqrt{15}i$$

The two zeros for $P(x)$, $-3 + \sqrt{15}i$ and $-3 - \sqrt{15}i$, are complex conjugates.

EXAMPLE 6   Find the zeros of $P(x)$ if $P(x) = 2x^4 - 13x^2 + 11$.

Answer

$2x^4 - 13x^2 + 11 = 0$	1. Set $P(x) = 0$.
$(2x^2 - 11)(x^2 - 1) = 0$	2. Factor.
$2x^2 - 11 = 0$ or $x^2 - 1 = 0$ $x^2 = \frac{11}{2}$ $x^2 = 1$ $x = \pm\sqrt{\frac{11}{2}}$ $x = \pm\sqrt{1}$ $x = \pm\frac{\sqrt{22}}{2}$ $x = \pm 1$	3. Use the zero product property (if the product is zero at least one factor must be zero) and set each factor equal to zero. Simplify answers.

The four zeros are 1, -1, $\frac{\sqrt{22}}{2}$, $-\frac{\sqrt{22}}{2}$.

It would be nice to have a formula (like the quadratic formula) for any third- or fourth-degree equation, wouldn't it? Actually there are such formulas, but they are too complicated to be of any practical value. The formula for third-degree equations was found by Nicolo of Brescia, and that for fourth-degree equations by Lodovico Ferrari—both Italian mathematicians. However, despite the efforts of many, no one was able to find a formula for fifth-degree equations. About 1820 the Norwegian genius Niels Henrik Abel proved that such a formula does not exist.

It can be very difficult to *prove* that something does not exist, but Abel came up with a mathematical proof that there is no general formula for solutions to a quintic equation. In contrast, atheists often attempt to prove that God does not exist but their reasoning is always faulty. It is true that for the Bible-believer, God's existence is ultimately a matter of faith; the Scripture stresses that we must "believe that he is, and that he is a rewarder of them that diligently seek him" (Heb. 11:6). However, God's existence does not contradict anything in His creation, so those who believe that He does not exist are exercising blind faith.

▶ A. Exercises

Write each polynomial in descending order. State the degree, the leading coefficient, and the constant term.

1. $5x^3 - 6x^4 + 3x - 8$
2. $7x^5 + 3x^3 - 4x$
3. $x^2 + 9$
4. $2x - 6x^4$
5. 28

Indicate whether each of the following is a polynomial; if so, give the degree.

6. $5\sqrt{2}x^3 + 4x^2 - \sqrt[4]{7}$
7. $\pi \sin x - \pi^2 \cos x$
8. $2x^2 - x - \sqrt{x}$
9. 0
10. $17 + 4x + \sqrt{2}$

Evaluate each polynomial function at the indicated value.

11. $P(-1); P(x) = 5x - 9$
12. $Q(\sqrt{3}); Q(x) = x^4 - x^2 + 1$
13. $P(2); P(x) = x^5 - 2x^3 + 14x - 10$
14. $P\left(\frac{1}{2}\right), P(x) = x^2 - 3x - 1$
15. $Q(i); Q(x) = -2x^2 + x$
16. $P(-7.499); P(x) = \frac{77}{69}x^3 - 5.64x^2 + \sqrt{3969}$

If $P(x) = 3x^2 + 4x - 1$ and $Q(x) = x^2 - 2$, find

17. $P(x) + Q(x)$ and $P(x) - Q(x)$
18. $P(x) \cdot Q(x)$ and $P(x) \div Q(x)$

If $P(x) = x^2 - 3x + 5$ and $Q(x) = x - 1$, find

19. $P(x) + Q(x)$ and $P(x) - Q(x)$
20. $P(x) \cdot Q(x)$ and $P(x) \div Q(x)$

▶ B. Exercises

Find the zeros for each of the following.

21. $P(x) = 3x + 81$
22. $P(x) = 4x^2 - 8x + 4$
23. $P(x) = x^2 - 11x + 28$
24. $Q(x) = 9x^2 + 4$
25. $P(x) = x^4 - 16$
26. $Q(x) = -2.22x^3 + 7.413x^2 - 5.8x$

27. Discuss the zeros of the constant function $P(x) = a$.
28. Find a formula for the zeros of the linear function $P(x) = mx + b$.

▶ C. Exercises

29. Find the zeros of $R(x) = x^4 - 4x^2 - 2$.
30. For any degree n, determine the zeros of the binomial function
    $P(x) = x^n - x^{n-1}$.

⚏ Dominion Modeling

Use the data on braking distance to answer the questions on speed versus braking distance. Give separate answers for both daytime and nighttime conditions.

31. Draw a scatterplot. What models appear useful?
32. Would cubic models be useful? Give the models and evaluate them using scatterplots, r^2, and residuals.

■ Cumulative Review

33. Make a circle mapping of $\{(x, y) \mid y = \sin x\}$, where $x \in \left\{0, \frac{\pi}{4}, \frac{\pi}{2}, \frac{3\pi}{4}, \pi\right\}$.
34. Write an absolute value function for $\{(-2, 5), (0,1), (3, 7)\}$.
35. Find the area of a triangle with sides of 215 ft, 385 ft, and 410 ft, then convert to acres (1 acre = 43,560 square feet).

Consider the function $f(x) = 3x^2 - 5x + 2$.

36. Find the zeros of the function.
37. Find the maximum or minimum.

2.5 Factoring Higher-Degree Polynomials

Long division can be time-consuming, but in the rest of this chapter you will often have to divide by a linear polynomial of the form $x - a$. Because you will do this so often, you should learn the shortcut called *synthetic division*. Remember that this method applies only to dividing by polynomials of the form $x - a$.

You will understand the shortcut better if you compare it to the complete long division.

EXAMPLE 1   Divide $2x^5 + 3x^3 - 7x^2 + 3x - 4$ by $x - 2$.

Answer

$$
\begin{array}{r}
2x^4 + 4x^3 + 11x^2 + 15x + 33 \\
x - 2 \overline{)\,2x^5 + 0x^4 + 3x^3 - 7x^2 + 3x - 4} \\
\underline{2x^5 - 4x^4} \\
4x^4 + 3x^3 \\
\underline{4x^4 - 8x^3} \\
11x^3 - 7x^2 \\
\underline{11x^3 - 22x^2} \\
15x^2 + 3x \\
\underline{15x^2 - 30x} \\
33x - 4 \\
\underline{33x - 66} \\
62
\end{array}
$$

1. Write the dividend, expressing all powers of x less than the degree of the dividend. Use zero coefficients as necessary. These act as placeholders to keep your work aligned.

2. Divide, multiply, subtract, and bring down the next term until the degree of the remainder is less than the degree of the divisor.

- -

(Remember how to check a division problem: multiply the quotient by the divisor, add the remainder, and compare the sum to the dividend.)

Synthetic division is a shortened version of the same algorithm that is used to do long division. However, it allows you to leave out repetitive portions of the problem without deleting pertinent information.

This algorithm works only when you divide by a binomial of the form $x - a$, such as Example 1. First, use a (not $-a$) as the "divisor" so that addition can replace subtraction in the synthetic division process. Also, write the coefficients of the dividend on the first line, making sure to represent each power of x. The "0" represents the fact that there is no x^4 term.

$$2 \;|\; 2 \quad 0 \quad 3 \; -7 \quad 3 \; -4$$

To complete the synthetic division problem, bring down the leading coefficient (2), multiply it by the divisor (2), and then write the product (4) under the next coefficient (0). Add the column $\binom{0}{4}$ to get 4 as shown below. Continue this process to the right.

$$
\begin{array}{r|rrrrrr}
2 & 2 & 0 & 3 & -7 & 3 & -4 \\
  & \downarrow & 4 & 8 & 22 & 30 & 66 \\
\hline
  & 2 & 4 & 11 & 15 & 33 & 62
\end{array}
$$

When dividing by a divisor of the form $x - a$, the degree of the quotient will be one less than the degree of the dividend. In the final answer the powers of x must be reinserted: $2x^4 + 4x^3 + 11x^2 + 15x + 33$, remainder 62. If the remainder is zero, the quotient is called the *depressed polynomial*.

EXAMPLE 2   Use synthetic division to find the following quotient:
$$(9x^2 + 6x^5 - x + 12) \div (x + 1)$$

Answer

$(6x^5 + 9x^2 - x + 12) \div (x + 1)$	1. Rewrite the dividend in descending order.
$\begin{array}{r\|rrrrrr} -1 & 6 & 0 & 0 & 9 & -1 & 12 \\ & \downarrow & -6 & 6 & -6 & -3 & 4 \\ \hline & 6 & -6 & 6 & 3 & -4 & 16 \end{array}$	2. Use synthetic division, dividing by -1 since $x + 1 = x - (-1) = x - a$, making $a = -1$.
The quotient is $6x^4 - 6x^3 + 6x^2 + 3x - 4$ R. 16.	3. Write the quotient, inserting the correct powers of x.

Let's examine the value of $P(a)$ for this function.

$$P(-1) = 6(-1)^5 + 9(-1)^2 - (-1) + 12 = -6 + 9 + 1 + 12 = 16.$$

Notice that $P(a)$ and the remainder in the division problem are both equal to 16. The next theorem states that these values will always be equal.

Remainder Theorem
If a number a is substituted for x in $P(x)$, the resulting value $P(a)$ is equal to the remainder obtained when $P(x)$ is divided by $(x - a)$.

Proof

The proof is based on the division algorithm. In divisions such as $23 \div 4 = 5$, R. 3, a relationship exists: $23 = 4 \times 5 + 3$. In other words, if P is the dividend (23), d is the divisor (4), Q is the quotient (5), and R is the remainder (3), then

$$P = d \cdot Q + R.$$

The same relationship applies to polynomials. If the polynomial $P(x)$ is divided by $(x - a)$, resulting in the quotient $Q(x)$ and the remainder $R(x)$, then $P(x) = (x - a) \cdot Q(x) + R(x)$. Since $x - a$ is of the first degree and the remainder always has a lower degree than the divisor, $R(x)$ is of degree 0. Thus $R(x)$ is a number; let it be R. Hence

$$P(x) = (x - a) \cdot Q(x) + R.$$

Now, evaluate $P(a)$ by substituting a for x.

$$P(a) = (a - a) \cdot Q(a) + R$$
$$P(a) = 0 \cdot Q(a) + R$$
$$P(a) = R$$

Thus, the remainder is equal to the value of the polynomial at $x = a$.

EXAMPLE 3 Use the remainder theorem to find $P(3)$ when
$P(x) = x^3 + 2x^2 + 4.$

Answer

$$
\begin{array}{r|rrrr}
3 & 1 & 2 & 0 & 4 \\
& \downarrow & 3 & 15 & 45 \\
\hline
& 1 & 5 & 15 & 49
\end{array}
$$

The remainder theorem states that $P(3)$ is equal to the remainder obtained when $P(x)$ is divided by $(x - 3)$.

Since the remainder is 49, $P(3) = 49$.

$P(3)$ can be found directly by substitution, but this would not require the remainder theorem. Be sure to find $P(3)$ as above when asked to use the remainder theorem. Similarly, when asked to find only the remainder of a division, you could use long or synthetic division, but this would not require the remainder theorem. Be sure to find $P(a)$ when asked to use the remainder theorem to find the remainder from a division by $x - a$.

Factor Theorem

$P(a) = 0$ if and only if $x - a$ is a factor of $P(x)$.

Proof

By the remainder theorem, if $P(a) = 0$, then $P(x) \div (x - a)$ yields the remainder of 0 (meaning that $x - a$ divides $P(x)$ exactly). Thus, $x - a$ is a factor of $P(x)$.

The converse statement can be proved similarly. This theorem, along with the remainder theorem, indicates that to find a zero of $P(x)$, you must find a such that $(x - a)$ is a factor of $P(x)$; or, in other words, a such that $P(x) \div (x - a)$ has a remainder of zero.

EXAMPLE 4   Factor $P(x) = x^3 + 6x^2 - x - 30$ to find the roots of $P(x)$ if $P(2) = 0$.

Answer

$$\begin{array}{r|rrrr}
2 & 1 & 6 & -1 & -30 \\
& \downarrow & 2 & 16 & 30 \\
\hline
& 1 & 8 & 15 & 0
\end{array}$$

1. By the factor theorem, $x - 2$ is a factor. Divide to find the depressed polynomial.

$\therefore P(x) = (x - 2)(x^2 + 8x + 15)$

$P(x) = (x - 2)(x + 3)(x + 5)$ 2. Factor completely.

$x = 2, -3, -5$ 3. Give the roots by applying the zero product property.

The factor theorem also enables you to reconstruct a polynomial from its zeros, although you must be careful. You should clear fractions to obtain a polynomial with integer coefficients. Also, if $P(x)$ has factors with powers, then the power is called the multiplicity of the corresponding zero. For instance, if $P(x) = (x + 7)(x - 5)^3$. Then the zeros are -7 and 5, but 5 has multiplicity 3 since it is the zero of three of the factors.

EXAMPLE 5   Find a polynomial with integer coefficients and the following zeros. Assume single zeros unless multiplicity is given. Zeros of $P(x)$ are $-1, \frac{5}{4}, 3$ (multiplicity 2).

Answer

$x - (-1), x - \frac{5}{4}, x - 3$ are factors.

1. Use the factor theorem to identify factors of $P(x)$.

$x + 1, 4x - 5, (x - 3)^2$

2. Clear fractions and use the definition of multiplicity to obtain all factors of $P(x)$. Note that $(x - 3)$ is a factor twice since it has multiplicity of 2.

Also notice that $4x - 5$ gives the same zero as $x - \frac{5}{4}$.

$$P(x) = (x + 1)(4x - 5)(x - 3)^2$$
$$= (4x^2 - x - 5)(x^2 - 6x + 9)$$
$$= 4x^4 - 25x^3 + 37x^2 + 21x - 45$$

3. Write $P(x)$. Multiply it out, writing terms in descending order.

▶ A. Exercises

Find the quotient, using synthetic division.

1. $(10x^4 + 8x^3 + 6x^2 + 4x + 2) \div (x - 4)$
2. $(x^4 - 5x^2 - 17x + 15) \div (x - 3)$
3. $(4x^2 - 6x^4) \div (x + 2)$
4. $(3x^2 - x^5 + 4x - x^3) \div (x + 1)$
5. $(2x + 3x^2 + 4x^3 + 5x^4) \div (x - 1)$

Without dividing, find the remainder of each quotient by applying the remainder theorem.

6. $(x^3 - 8) \div (x + 2)$
7. $(x^4 - 2x^2 + 4) \div (x - 1)$
8. $(3x^2 + 6x^4 - x^5) \div (x + 1)$
9. $(x^3 + 64) \div (x + 4)$
10. $\left(\sqrt{15}x^4 + 4.6x^3 - 0.75\right) \div (x + \sqrt{3})$
11. Use the formula for factoring the sum of two cubes to factor $x^3 + 64$. How does the answer to exercise 9 relate to these factors?

Without substituting find $P(a)$ by applying the remainder theorem.

12. $P(x) = 8x^2 + 6x - 4, a = 3$
13. $P(x) = 5x^5 - 4x^4 + 3x^3 - 2x^2 + x, a = 2$
14. $P(x) = 10 - 2x + 4x^2, a = -1$
15. $P(x) = x^3 - 5x^2 + x - 1, a = -2$

▶ B. Exercises

Factor each polynomial using the given information.

16. $P(x) = x^3 - 3x^2 - 6x + 8$ if $P(1) = 0$
17. $Q(x) = 2x^3 + 7x^2 + 2x - 3$ if $Q(-3) = 0$
18. $Q(x) = 2x^4 - 5x^3 + x^2 + 5x - 3$ if 1 is a zero of multiplicity 2
19. $P(x) = x^4 + 4x^3 - 13x^2 - 40x + 48$ if 1 and -4 are zeros
20. $Q(x) = x^5 - x^3 + 7x^2 + 12x + 5$ if -1 is a zero of multiplicity 3
21. $P(x) = x^6 + x^4 - x^2 - 1$ if $\pm i$ are both zeros of multiplicity 2

Give a polynomial with integer coefficients having the following zeros. Assume simple zeros (multiplicity 1) unless specified.

22. 1 and 4

23. 2 (multiplicity 3)

24. $\frac{1}{6}$ and $\frac{5}{7}$

25. $\frac{1}{2}$(multiplicity 2) and 5

26. 1, -1, $\frac{1}{3}$, $-\frac{1}{3}$

▶ C. Exercises

27. Find a polynomial with integer coefficients having the following zeros: $3 \pm 2i$, 1 (multiplicity 2), $\pm\sqrt{2}$

28. Factor $3x^7 + 5x^6 - 88x^5 - 208x^4 + 515x^3 + 1341x^2 - 702x - 1890$.

■ Cumulative Review

29. Write $y = \frac{2}{3}x - \frac{5}{6}$ in general form with integer coefficients.

30. Write the general form of the quadratic function $y = 2x^2$ translated 2 units right and 3 units downward from the origin.

31. Find $(3x^5 - 2x^4 + x - 4) - (4x^4 - x^3 + x - 7)$

32. What is the reciprocal ratio for cosecant?

33. Find the area of $\triangle ABC$ given $a = 3.2$ miles, $b = 4.8$ miles and $\angle C = 75°$.

2.6 Zeros of Polynomial Functions

The theorems in this section will help you factor a polynomial and find all its zeros. Think how you factor a polynomial such as $2x^2 - x - 6$. You know that if it factors as $(ax + b)(cx + d)$, $a \cdot c = 2$ and $b \cdot d = -6$. In other words, try $2x$ and x as first terms and try ± 1 and ± 6 or ± 2 and ± 3 as last terms. In each case pick coefficients that are factors of the original leading coefficient and constant term respectively.

Having found the correct factors, $x - 2$ and $2x + 3$, set each equal to zero and solve: $x = 2$ or $x = -\frac{3}{2}$. In each instance the numerator is a factor of the original constant (2 and -3 are factors of the constant -6) and the denominator is the factor of the original leading coefficient (1 and 2 are factors of 2).

EXAMPLE 1   Find the possible rational zeros of $P(x) = 4x^3 - 3x^2 + 7x + 5$.

Answer   Factors of the constant, 5: $c = \pm 1, \pm 5$

Factors of the leading coefficient, 4: $d = \pm 1, \pm 2, \pm 4$.

Possible rational zeros: $\dfrac{c}{d} = \dfrac{\pm 1}{1}, \dfrac{\pm 5}{1}, \dfrac{\pm 1}{2}, \dfrac{\pm 5}{2}, \dfrac{\pm 1}{4}, \dfrac{\pm 5}{4}$

It is possible that none of these are zeros. However, you do not need to consider any other rational numbers as possible zeros. This conclusion comes from the *rational root theorem*. The theorem works only with polynomials whose coefficients are integers.

Rational Root Theorem

If $P(x) = a_n x^n + a_{n-1} x^{n-1} + a_{n-2} x^{n-2} + \cdots + a_2 x^2 + a_1 x + a_0$, where the coefficients are integers, and if $\dfrac{c}{d}$ is a reduced rational root of $P(x) = 0$ (c and d are relatively prime), then c is a factor of a_0, and d is a factor of a_n.

EXAMPLE 2   Find the roots of $6x^3 - 5x^2 - 2x + 1 = 0$.

Answer

c is a factor of 1: ± 1 d is a factor of 6: $\pm 1, \pm 2, \pm 3, \pm 6$. The possible roots are $\pm 1, \pm \frac{1}{2}, \pm \frac{1}{3}, \pm \frac{1}{6}$.	1. Since all the coefficients are integers, use the rational root theorem. Find all the possible rational roots.
$\begin{array}{c|rrrr} 1 & 6 & -5 & -2 & 1 \\ & \downarrow & 6 & 1 & -1 \\ \hline & 6 & 1 & -1 & 0 \end{array}$	2. Try 1 as a possible root. Divide by $x - 1$ using synthetic division.
$\therefore (x - 1)(6x^2 + x - 1) = 0$	3. Use the factor theorem. Since the remainder is zero, $x - 1$ is a factor.
$(x - 1)(3x - 1)(2x + 1) = 0$	4. Factor the resulting depressed polynomial.
Therefore, $x = 1, \frac{1}{3}, \frac{-1}{2}$.	5. Solve for the roots using the zero product property.

It is evident that if the leading coefficient is 1, $d = \pm 1$ and the root must have ± 1 as its denominator. Therefore, all rational roots of such polynomials are integers. Furthermore, any integer roots must therefore be factors of c, the constant term. This corollary is sometimes called the *integral root theorem*. We will simply consider it a special case of the rational root theorem.

EXAMPLE 3 Find the zeros of $P(x) = x^4 + 9x^3 + 15x^2 + 9x + 14$.

Answer

Let $\frac{c}{d}$ be a root of $P(x) = 0$. $c = \pm 1, \pm 2, \pm 7, \pm 14$ $d = \pm 1$. $\frac{c}{d} = \pm 1, \pm 2, \pm 7, \pm 14$	1. Assume that $\frac{c}{d}$ exists.
$\therefore \frac{c}{d} = -1, -2, -7, -14$	2. Possible positive roots can be eliminated since all the coefficients are positive. No positive number will make $P(x) = 0$.
$\begin{array}{r|rrrrr} -2 & 1 & 9 & 15 & 9 & 14 \\ & \downarrow & -2 & -14 & -2 & -14 \\ \hline & 1 & 7 & 1 & 7 & 0 \end{array}$	3. Use synthetic division to test these possible negative roots. Since the remainder is zero when dividing by -2 it is a root and $(x + 2)$ is a factor of $P(x)$.
$P(x) = (x + 2)(x^3 + 7x^2 + x + 7)$ $P(x) = (x + 2)[x^2(x + 7) + (x + 7)]$	4. Factor completely into linear factors. You can factor the cubic by grouping or by further synthetic division, trying any of the possible roots $\frac{c}{d}$ where $c \in \{\pm 1, \pm 7\}$ and $d \in \{\pm 1\}$.
$P(x) = (x + 2)(x + 7)(x^2 + 1) = 0$	5. Set $P(x) = 0$ and solve using the zero product property.
$\therefore$ The zeros are $-2, -7, i,$ and $-i$.	6. Give the zeros.

Sometimes all the possibilities fail. In such a case, you may assume that there is no rational root of that polynomial. For instance, the possible rational roots of $P(x) = x^2 + 3x + 3$ are $\pm 1, \pm 3$. These all fail because the actual roots are not rational. The roots are found using the quadratic formula and are the complex numbers $\frac{-3}{2} \pm \frac{\sqrt{3}}{2} i$.

Though the theorem requires integral coefficients, by the method of Example 4 you can use it even when the coefficients are rational.

EXAMPLE 4   Find the roots of $x^3 - \frac{13}{12}x^2 + \frac{3}{8}x - \frac{1}{24} = 0$.

Answer

Let $P(x) = x^3 - \frac{13}{12}x^2 + \frac{3}{8}x - \frac{1}{24}$.

$24P(x) = 24x^3 - 26x^2 + 9x - 1$

1. Multiply by the common denominator 24 to obtain coefficients that are all integers.

$c = \pm 1$, and

$d = \pm 1, \pm 2, \pm 3, \pm 4, \pm 6, \pm 8, \pm 12, \pm 24$

$\therefore \frac{c}{d} = \pm 1, \frac{\pm 1}{2}, \frac{\pm 1}{3}, \frac{\pm 1}{4}, \frac{\pm 1}{6}, \frac{\pm 1}{8}, \frac{\pm 1}{12}, \frac{\pm 1}{24}$

2. List the possible rational roots.

$24P(x) = \left(x - \frac{1}{2}\right)(24x^2 - 14x + 2)$

$24P(x) = 2\left(x - \frac{1}{2}\right)(12x^2 - 7x + 1)$

$24P(x) = 2\left(x - \frac{1}{2}\right)(3x - 1)(4x - 1)$

3. After trial-and-error using synthetic divisions, you can find the factors.

$P(x) = \frac{1}{12}\left(x - \frac{1}{2}\right)(3x - 1)(4x - 1)$

4. Divide both sides by 24 to solve for $P(x)$.

The roots of $P(x)$ are $x = \frac{1}{2}, \frac{1}{3}$, and $\frac{1}{4}$.

Another useful tool is the *conjugate root theorem*. This theorem shows that complex roots and irrational roots come in pairs for polynomials with appropriate coefficients.

Conjugate Root Theorem

1. **If $P(x)$ is a polynomial with real coefficients and if $z = a + bi$ is a root of $P(x) = 0$, then its conjugate, $\bar{z} = a - bi$, is also a root.**

2. **If $P(x)$ is a polynomial with rational coefficients and if $a + c\sqrt{b}$ is a root of $P(x) = 0$, $a - c\sqrt{b}$ is also a root.**

EXAMPLE 5 $x^4 + x^3 - x^2 + x - 2 = 0$ has $-i$ as one of its roots. Find all the other roots.

Answer

i is also a root of $P(x)$

1. The conjugate root theorem applies since all coefficients are real.

$(x - i)$ and $(x + i)$ are linear factors of $P(x)$.

2. by the factor theorem since $\pm i$ are roots

Continued ▶

$$P(x) = (x + i)(x - i) \cdot Q(x)$$
$$P(x) = (x^2 + 1) \cdot Q(x)$$

3. Write the factors thus far using $Q(x)$ as the unknown factor.

$$
\begin{array}{r}
x^2 + x - 2 \\
x^2 + 1{\overline{\smash{\big)}\,x^4 + x^3 - x^2 + x - 2}} \\
\underline{x^4 + x^2} \\
x^3 - 2x^2 + x \\
\underline{x^3 + x} \\
-2x^2 - 2 \\
\underline{-2x^2 - 2} \\
0
\end{array}
$$

4. Divide to find the factor $Q(x)$. Synthetic division cannot be used since the divisor is second-degree.

$$P(x) = (x + i)(x - i)(x^2 + x - 2)$$
$$0 = (x + i)(x - i)(x + 2)(x - 1)$$

5. Factor completely by factoring the trinomial. Then find the four roots by setting the polynomial equal to 0 and solving.

$P(x) = 0$ when $x = \pm i, -2, 1$.

Discussion now extends to polynomial functions containing complex coefficients. Carl Friedrich Gauss first proved the *fundamental theorem of algebra*. There are many fundamental theorems: fundamental theorems of arithmetic, calculus, and so on. These are so "fundamental" that many other theorems are derived from them. In the Bible, there are also certain fundamentals, without which Christianity would not exist—the deity of Christ, His substitutionary atonement, and the inspiration of the Bible, to name a few. The Christian builds his thoughts and actions on the fundamentals of God's eternal truth.

> *Much of our knowledge is due to a comparatively few great mathematicians such as Newton, Euler, Gauss, or Riemann. They have contributed something to human thought even more lasting than great literature, since it is independent of language.*
>
> –Edward C. Titchmarsh
> (1899-1963)

Fundamental Theorem of Algebra
Every polynomial of degree greater than 0 with complex coefficients has at least one root in the system of complex numbers.

Another theorem based on the fundamental theorem of algebra is the *complete linear factorization theorem*. It tells us how many roots a polynomial equation will have.

Complete Linear Factorization Theorem

Every polynomial of degree n with complex coefficients, where $n > 0$, can be factored into n linear factors.

Proof

Of course, the word linear means that the degree is 1. Thus, we need to show that $P(x) = (x - r_1)(x - r_2)(x - r_3) \ldots (x - r_n)$, where n is the degree of $P(x)$.

By the fundamental theorem of algebra, $P(x)$ has at least one root. Let that root be r_1. Thus, $P(r_1) = 0$. Then $P(x) = (x - r_1)[Q_1(x)]$, where $Q_1(x)$ is another polynomial, according to the factor theorem. Consider $Q_1(x)$, which by the fundamental theorem also has a root; let it be r_2. Therefore, $P(x) = (x - r_1)(x - r_2)[Q_2(x)]$. Repeat this process. The degree of $Q(x)$ decreases by 1 until $Q(x)$ is of degree 0. Then

$$P(x) = (x - r_1)(x - r_2) \ldots (x - r_n)C, \text{ where } C \text{ is a constant.}$$

Hence, $P(x)$ of degree n can be factored into n linear factors. This theorem implies that a polynomial of degree n ($n > 0$) has exactly n roots, namely $r_1, r_2, r_2, \ldots, r_n$. Since the roots need not be distinct, however, this means that there are, at most, n solutions.

EXAMPLE 6   Find the zeros of $P(x) = x^4 - 2x^3 - 3x^2 + 8x - 4$.

Answer

```
1 │  1  −2  −3   8  −4
  │      1  −1  −4   4
  └─────────────────────
     1  −1  −4   4   0
```

$P(x) = (x - 1)(x^3 - x^2 - 4x + 4)$

1. The possible rational zeros are ± 1, ± 2, ± 4. Check 1 using synthetic division.

```
1 │  1  −1  −4   4
  │      1   0  −4
  └─────────────────
     1   0  −4   0
```

$P(x) = (x - 1)^2(x^2 - 4)$

2. Factor the depressed polynomial. Possible rational zeros of this polynomial are still ± 1, ± 2, ± 4. Remember that factors can repeat if a zero has a multiplicity greater than 1. Divide by 1 again, using the depressed polynomial as the dividend.

$P(x) = (x - 1)^2(x + 2)(x - 2)$

3. Factor completely into four linear factors as guaranteed by the complete linear factorization theorem.

The zeros are 1, −2, and 2.

4. Give the zeros.

Is this result consistent with the complete linear factorization theorem? Since $P(x)$ has degree 4, there should be 4 linear factors and four zeros. Notice that there are four factors, but two of them are identical, namely $x - 1$. Since 1 has multiplicity 2, there are also 4 zeros. However, do not list the multiple zero twice.

Finally, these theorems can also help you determine a polynomial if some of its roots are known.

EXAMPLE 7 Suppose that $P(x)$ has integer coefficients and the roots of $P(x) = 0$ are 0, $\frac{2}{3}$, $1 + \sqrt{2}$, and $3 - 2i$. If zero is a root of multiplicity 3, what is the least possible degree of $P(x)$? Write a polynomial that satisfies these conditions.

Answer

$(x - 0)^3 = x^3$	1. Write 3 factors, since 0 has multiplicity 3
$3\left(x - \frac{2}{3}\right) = 3x - 2$	2. Multiply the factor for the root $\frac{2}{3}$ by a constant to clear fractions, since the polynomial has integer coefficients.
$\begin{aligned}&[x - (1 - \sqrt{2})][x - (1 + \sqrt{2})]\\ &= [(x - 1) + \sqrt{2}][(x - 1) - \sqrt{2}]\\ &= [(x - 1)^2 - 2]\\ &= (x^2 - 2x - 1)\end{aligned}$	3. $1 + \sqrt{2}$ guarantees 2 linear factors as irrational conjugate roots. Apply the associative property and multiply using the difference of squares.
$\begin{aligned}&[x - (3 - 2i)][x - (3 + 2i)]\\ &= [(x - 3) + 2i][(x - 3) - 2i]\\ &= (x - 3)^2 - 4i^2)\\ &= x^2 - 6x + 13\end{aligned}$	4. $3 - 2i$ guarantees 2 linear factors as complex conjugate roots. Multiply again using the difference of squares.
The least degree of $P(x)$ is 8.	5. The degree is the total number of linear factors from previous steps.
$\begin{aligned}P(x) &= [x^3(3x - 2)][(x^2 - 2x - 1)(x^2 - 6x + 13)]\\ &= (3x^4 - 2x^3)(x^4 - 8x^3 + 24x^2 - 20x - 13)\\ &= 3x^8 - 26x^7 + 88x^6 - 108x^5 + x^4 + 26x^3\end{aligned}$	6. Multiply the factors to find $P(x)$.

▶ A. Exercises

List all the possible rational zeros for each polynomial.

1. $x^4 - 3x^3 - x^2 + 4$
2. $5x^5 - 4x^3 - 3x^2 + 10x - 7$
3. $x^4 + 16$
4. $2x^3 + 4x^2 + 11x + 3$
5. $2x^3 + 3x^2 - x + 2$

Indicate all zeros and their multiplicities for each polynomial.

6. $(x^2 - 4)(x^2 - 16)$
7. $(x - 6)^4$
8. $x^3 - 6x^2 + 12x - 8$
9. x^{32}
10. $x^4 - 10x^3 + 33x^2 - 40x + 16$

▶ B. Exercises

For each of the polynomials, one of the zeros is given. Find the other zeros.

11. $x^3 + 3x^2 + x + 3$, $x = i$
12. $x^3 + x^2 + 3x - 5$, $x = -1 - 2i$
13. $x^4 + x^3 + 4x^2 + 4x$, $x = 2i$
14. $x^3 - 9x^2 + 22x - 10$, $x = 2 - \sqrt{2}$
15. $2x^3 - 12x^2 - 6x + 36$, $x = \sqrt{3}$

Find the zeros of the following polynomials.

16. $x^3 + 3x^2 - x + 45$
17. $(x + 3)^3$
18. $(x - 1)^2 + 3x - 2x^2$
19. $5x^4 - 16x^3 + 18x^2 - 48x + 9$
20. $x^4 + 4x^2 - 12$
21. $x^4 - \frac{11}{4}x^3 + \frac{9}{4}x^2 - \frac{1}{4}x - \frac{1}{4}$
22. $x^3 - x^2 + 3x - 3$
23. $x^3 + 3\frac{1}{2}x^2 - 14x + 6$
24. $x^4 - 2x^2 + 1$
25. x^2
26. A fifth-degree equation has the roots ± 1 and $\sqrt{3}$. What is the maximum multiplicity that 1 can have? (All coefficients are integers.)

For each set of conditions below, what is the least degree $P(x)$ could have? Write the polynomial, $P(x)$.

27. $P(x)$ has integer coefficients and its zeros are: 1; 5 with multiplicity 2; and -1 with multiplicity 3.

28. $P(x)$ has integer coefficients and its zeros include $-\frac{3}{4}$ and $4 - 3i$.
29. $P(x)$ has real coefficients and its zeros include 5 and $\sqrt{2}$.

▶ C. Exercises

30. Draw the graph of $y = x^2 + 1$. Then find the zeros. Explain your results.
31. Suppose $P_1(x) = x - 1$, $P_2(x) = x^2 - 1$, and $P_3(x) = x^3 - x$. Graph these functions and find their zeros. What is the relationship between the graphs and the roots of the equations? between the number of roots and the polynomial?

Cumulative Review

32. Graph and identify the maximum or minimum point and its value for $f(x) = -x^2 + 4x - 3$.
33. Find the angle of inclination of a line passing through $(2, -3)$ and $(5, 2)$.

Consider $P(x) = 2x^4 - 3x^3 + x^2 - 73x + 5$.
34. Find the remainder when dividing by $x - 4$.
35. Give the degree of the polynomial.
36. Find the sine, cosine, and tangent of $\angle A$ in standard position, whose terminal ray passes through $(-7, 2)$. Give answers to four decimal places.

SCANDINAVIAN MATH

Marius Sophus Lie (1842-1899)
'Photo: AKG London'

> *Niels Henrik Abel . . .*
> *developed many*
> *important mathematical*
> *concepts in his*
> *brief life.*

Scandinavia is the land of the midnight sun, reindeer, fjords, Vikings, and, of course, mathematicians. Denmark's Harald August Bohr (1887-1951) and his brother, Nobel Prize winner Niels Henrik David Bohr (1885-1962), were born of Jewish descent in Copenhagen. Harald was a member of the second place soccer team at the 1908 Olympics in London. He also studied number theory and the Riemann zeta function, and developed the theory of almost periodic functions.

Sweden and Finland also produced famous mathematicians. Niels Fabian Helge von Koch (1870-1924) of Stockholm worked in number theory and determinants but is most famous for the Koch snowflake, an infinitely long continuous curve that fails to have a tangent line at any point! Ernst Leonard Lindelöf (1870-1946) was born in Helsinki when it belonged to Sweden. In addition to work on Fourier series, his work in topology led him to study Lindelöf spaces and to prove a theorem also named for him. Lars Valerian Ahlfors (1907-1996) was also born in Helsinki, but after it had become part of Finland. He received the first Fields Medal, taught at Helsinki, and later at Zurich and Harvard. His important books include *Complex Analysis* (1953), *Riemann Surfaces* (1960), and *Conformal Invariants* (1973).

Norway also produced its share of great mathematicians. Ludwig Sylow (1832-1918) of Oslo contributed to group theory. The three Sylow theorems are basic tools for studying finite groups. Another Norwegian, Marius Sophus Lie (1842-1899), born at Nordfjordeid, is known for Lie groups in abstract algebra. A third, Albert Thoralf Skolem

(1887-1963) of Sandsvaer, refined axiomatic set theory and studied lattices, Diophantine equations, groups, logic, and recursive functions. However, the most famous of all Scandinavian mathematicians is undoubtedly Niels Henrik Abel (1802-1829), who was born in Findöe on the island of Finnoy near Stavanger.

Niels Henrik Abel grew up in poverty and was able to study at Oslo (then Christiania) only with financial assistance from educators who recognized his talent. His father and grandfather were Protestant ministers, but his father died in 1820, leaving Niels to support the family. Such strains hastened Abel's death of tuberculosis at the age of 26. He nevertheless developed many important mathematical concepts in his brief life. He proved theorems on elliptic functions in calculus, extended the binomial theorem to complex numbers and complex exponents, and found a test for the convergence of infinite series. Three mathematical concepts are named after him: Abel's theorem, finding integrals of certain algebraic functions; Abelian functions, which develop from the integrals; and Abelian groups, a synonym for commutative groups.

Abel's most famous contribution, however, proved the impossibility of solving a general polynomial equation of degree five in terms of its coefficients. During his studies at Christiania, Abel thought he had found a quintic formula to parallel the quadratic formula and similar formulas for third and fourth degree equations. However, he soon found his mistake and went on to prove that no such formula is possible. This amazing result ended his own search for the formula as well as the search by other mathematicians, which had gone on for more than 100 years.

Niels Henrik Abel (1802-1829)

Mardalfossen is the most famous waterfall in Norway and would have been familiar to the great Norwegian mathematicians. In fact, Norway boasts half of the world's ten highest waterfalls.

Irrational Solutions

Consider $f(x) = x^4 + 3x^3 + x^2 + 2x + 5$. The
y-intercept is positive, $f(0) = 5$. Since all the
coefficients are positive, all linear factors would
be of the form x plus a constant, and therefore
all zeros negative. The only possible rational
zeros are -1 and -5, but neither turns out to be
a zero, since $f(-1) = 2$ and $f(-5) = 270$. Try
some other values to see if the graph ever drops
below the x-axis. Since $f(-2) = -3$, and the
graph of any polynomial is continuous, and both
ends (tails) of this one approach positive infinity,
there must be two real zeros. The graph must
cross the x-axis to connect $(-2, -3)$ with $(-1, 2)$. Therefore, there is a zero
whose x-coordinate is such that $-2 \leq x \leq -1$. Likewise, there is a zero
between the points $(-5, 270)$ and $(-2, -3)$, so its x-coordinate satisfies
$-5 \leq x \leq -2$. The y-coordinates of the points show that this zero is much
nearer to -2 than -5.

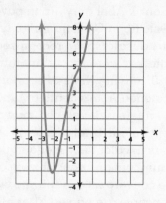

Now that you have found bounds for two of the zeros, you can approximate
them by checking the value of the function at the midpoint of each interval
and comparing it to the ends to determine which half of the interval contains
the zero. If you do this repeatedly until the third decimal place stabilizes, you
will obtain zeros of -1.361 and -2.635. This process is variously called the
bisection method, interval halving, or *binary search.*

The only requirement for a binary search is that you know an *upper bound*
and a *lower bound* for the zero. Often a graph will help you find bounds for
the solution. A quicker method will be discussed using derivatives in calculus,
but this method is so straightforward that you will always have at least one
means of finding a solution.

▶ Exercises

1. Give bounds for the zeros of $f(x)$.

2. Find bounds for the solutions to
$$-1 + x^5 - x^2 = 10x^3 - 16x - x^2.$$

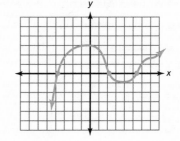

Approximate the least positive solution to each equation.

3. $x^3 - 2x - 5 = 0$

4. $15x^2(x^2 - 2) = 6x^5 - 5(1 + 2x^3)$

5. $e^x = 3x$

2.7 Graphing Polynomial Functions

You have learned many theorems about polynomials. Now you will learn to graph polynomials on the Cartesian plane, and will begin by studying some general patterns for the graphs of polynomials.

None of these graphs represent polynomials.

(a)

(b)

(c)

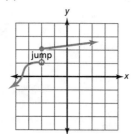 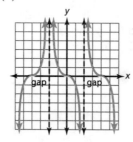 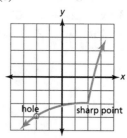

The domain of every polynomial is $\mathbb{R}$ and polynomials are continuous. Therefore the graph of a polynomial will have no jumps (a), gaps (b), or holes (c). Polynomials are *smooth curves*, which means that neither are there sharp points (c). Linear polynomials (degree zero and degree 1) are the only polynomials with linear graphs. No part of the graph of a higher-degree polynomial will be a straight line.

Since every polynomial defines a function, its graph must pass the vertical line test. Thus, a polynomial curve will not look like any of the graphs below.

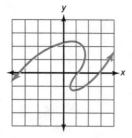 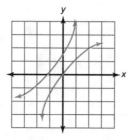 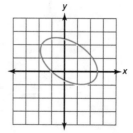

Because of the complete linear factorization theorem, there cannot be more roots than the degree of the polynomial. You have learned that a real root represents an x-intercept. Therefore, an nth-degree polynomial has at most *n* *x*-intercepts. If the polynomial is factorable, you can find the *x*-intercepts, though you may need synthetic division for this. The *y*-intercept of a polynomial $P(x)$ is $P(0)$. Both the *x*- and *y*-intercepts will aid in the graphing of polynomial functions.

Consider the four polynomials graphed below.

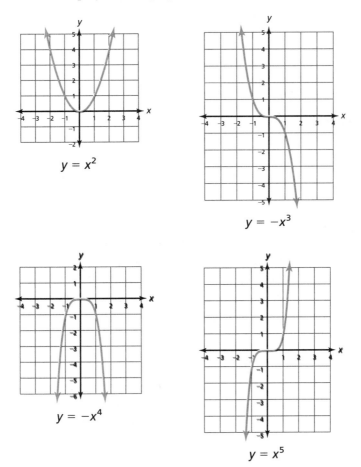

$y = x^2$

$y = -x^3$

$y = -x^4$

$y = x^5$

First, the ends or *tails* of polynomial graphs always approach $+\infty$ or $-\infty$. Even-degree polynomials have both tails pointing in the same direction, while odd-degree polynomials always have one tail up and one tail down. If the leading coefficient is positive, the tails will be up for an even-degree polynomial, and the right tail will be up for an odd-degree polynomial. These patterns reverse if the leading coefficient is negative. Since the tails depend only on degree and determine much of the general shape of the graph, paying attention to the tails is very important. The following chart summarizes the appearance of the tails of polynomial graphs.

		Degree	
		Even	**Odd**
Leading Coefficient	**Positive**	Both tails up	Left tail down, Right tail up
	Negative	Both tails down	Left tail up, Right tail down

EXAMPLE 1 Discuss the tails of a. $P(x) = 2x^5 - 4x^4 - 3x^2 + 1$ and
b. $Q(x) = -3x^4 - 3x^3 + 5$.

Answer   a. For $P(x)$, left tail is down,   The degree of $P(x)$ is odd with
         right tail is up.   positive leading coefficient

        b. For $Q(x)$, both tails are   The degree of $Q(x)$ is even with
        down.   a negative leading coefficient.

Second, in the four graphs shown earlier, there were several types of *symmetry*. Symmetry occurs only when all terms have even degree or if all have odd degree. If all terms have even degree, the graph of the polynomial will be symmetric across the y-axis. If all terms have odd degree (no constant), the graph will display symmetry across the origin (constants are even terms of degree zero).

Third, the even-degree polynomials touched the x-axis without crossing it, but the odd ones crossed. The points of contact are zeros or x-intercepts, and in those graphs the degree was also the multiplicity of the zero. Thus, if the multiplicity of the zero is even, the graph at that point will be tangent to the x-axis without crossing it. If a zero has an odd multiplicity, the graph crosses the axis. For multiplicities greater than 1, the curve is considered tangent to the axis even if it crosses. You will learn more about tangents in future chapters.

Graphing a Polynomial Function

1. Plot the zeros and consider their multiplicities (crosses axis if odd, doesn't if even).
2. Consider the tails based on degree and leading coefficient.
3. Take advantage of symmetry (if any) by considering the degrees of all the terms. (Is the function even, odd, or neither?)
4. Plot the y-intercept $(0, P(0))$, and other strategic points as guides to the height or steepness of the graph.
5. Sketch the curve. Remember to draw it continuous, smooth, and passing the vertical line test.

EXAMPLE 2 Graph $R(x) = x^3 - x^2 - 2x$. Give the domain and range.

Answer

$x^3 - x^2 - 2x = 0$ $x(x - 2)(x + 1) = 0$ $x = 0, x = 2, \text{ or } x = -1$	1. Solve $R(x) = 0$ to find the zeros. All 3 zeros have multiplicity 1, so the graph will cross the x-axis at each.
Left tail down, right tail up	2. $R(x)$ has a positive leading coefficient and its degree is odd.
No symmetry	3. $R(x)$ has both even and odd degree terms.
$R(0) = 0^3 - 0^2 - 2(0) = 0$ $R(1) = 1^3 - 1^2 - 2(1) = 1 - 1 - 2 = -2$ $R\left(-\frac{1}{2}\right) = \left(-\frac{1}{2}\right)^3 - \left(-\frac{1}{2}\right)^2 - 2\left(-\frac{1}{2}\right)$ $\quad = -\frac{1}{8} - \frac{1}{4} + 1 = \frac{5}{8}$ 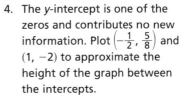	4. The y-intercept is one of the zeros and contributes no new information. Plot $\left(-\frac{1}{2}, \frac{5}{8}\right)$ and $(1, -2)$ to approximate the height of the graph between the intercepts.
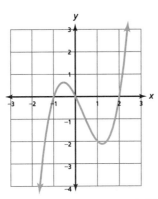	5. Graph the zeros and other points. Connect them with a smooth curve paying attention to multiplicities and tails. From the graph you can see the domain and range.
	$D = \mathbb{R}$ and $R = \mathbb{R}$.

Notice that the graph of $R(x) = x^3 - x^2 - 2x$ has a "mountain" and a "valley." The coordinates of the top of the mountain are $(-0.549, 0.631)$, and the coordinates of the bottom of the valley are $(1.215, -2.113)$. (You can find these points quite easily with the aid of a graphing calculator. See your manual for finding minimum and maximum values.) These points are called *relative extrema*. You can think of a relative extremum as a point where the graph reaches a maximum or minimum compared to other points nearby. The top of the mountain is the *relative maximum*, and the bottom of the valley is the *relative minimum*. Such a polynomial function of degree 3 can have at most 3 roots, and not more than 2 relative extrema. In general, an nth degree polynomial cannot have more than $n - 1$ relative extrema. Since complex roots do not correspond to x-intercepts and are not graphed on the real number line, some polynomials of degree n may have less than $n - 1$ relative extrema.

EXAMPLE 3   Graph $Q(x) = x^4 - 3x^2 - 4$. Give the domain and range.

Answer

$x^4 - 3x^2 - 4 = 0$
$(x^2 - 4)(x^2 + 1) = 0$
$x^2 = 4$ or $x^2 = -1$
$x = \pm 2$ or $x = \pm i$

1. Solve $Q(x) = 0$ to find the zeros. The complex roots do not correspond to x-intercepts. ± 2 have multiplicity 1.

Both tails up

2. The degree of $Q(x)$ is even with a positive leading coefficient.

Symmetry across y-axis

3. All terms of $Q(x)$ have an even degree.

$Q(0) = 0^4 - 3 \cdot 0^2 - 4 = -4$
$Q(1) = 1^4 - 3 \cdot 1^2 - 4 = -6$

4. Find the y-intercept and $Q(1)$.

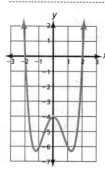

5. Sketch. Plot the intercepts $(\pm 2, 0)$, $(0, -4)$, and the point $(1, -6)$. Take advantage of symmetry to plot $(-1, -6)$. Sketch a smooth curve, noting tails, multiplicities, and that there are 3 relative extrema.

$D = \mathbb{R}, R = \{y \mid y \geq -6\}$

6. You can tell the domain and estimate the range from the graph. The actual minima occur at $x = \pm \frac{\sqrt{6}}{2} \approx \pm 1.225$ and $y = -\frac{25}{4} = -6.25$; thus the actual range is $R = \{y \mid y \geq -6.25\}$, but your sketch provides a good estimate.

EXAMPLE 4   Graph $P(x) = x^3 - 4x^2 - 3x + 12$.

Answer

$$\begin{array}{r|rrrr}
1 & 1 & -4 & -3 & 12 \\
  & \downarrow & 1 & -3 & -6 \\
\hline
  & 1 & -3 & -6 & 6
\end{array}$$

$$\begin{array}{r|rrrr}
4 & 1 & -4 & -3 & 12 \\
  & \downarrow & 4 & 0 & -12 \\
\hline
  & 1 & 0 & -3 & 0
\end{array}$$

$P(x) = (x - 4)(x^2 - 3)$

1. Try synthetic division until you find the zero at $x = 4$, implying that $(4, 0)$ is part of the graph. Then factor completely to identify the other zeros.

Continued ▶

$P(x) = (x - 4)(x + \sqrt{3})(x - \sqrt{3})$.
Therefore, the zeros are 4, $-\sqrt{3}$, $\sqrt{3}$, indicating the x-intercepts are $(4, 0)(-\sqrt{3}, 0), (\sqrt{3}, 0)$.

Left tail down, right tail up	2. The degree is odd with a positive leading coefficient.
No symmetry	3. $P(x)$ has both even and odd degree terms.
$P(0) = 12$ $P(3) = 3^3 - 4 \cdot 3^2 - 3 \cdot 3 + 12 = -6$	4. Find the y-intercept and then $P(3)$ to approximate the relative minimum (x between $\sqrt{3}$ and 4).
	5. Sketch the graph. Notice that $D = \mathbb{R}$ and $R = \mathbb{R}$.

EXAMPLE 5 Graph $P(x) = -x^5 + 2x^3 - x$. Give domain and range.

Answer

$-x^5 + 2x^3 - x = 0$ $-x(x^4 - 2x^2 + 1) = 0$ $-x(x^2 - 1)^2 = 0$ $-x(x - 1)^2(x + 1)^2 = 0$ $x = 0, x = 1, x = -1$	1. Find the zeros. Notice that ± 1 each have even multiplicity, which will make the graph tangent to the x-axis at those zeros. The origin is both an x- and y-intercept.
Left tail up; right tail down	2. $P(x)$ has odd degree with a negative leading coefficient.
Symmetry across the origin	3. All terms have odd degree.
$P\left(\frac{1}{2}\right) = -\left(\frac{1}{2}\right)^5 + 2\left(\frac{1}{2}\right)^3 - \left(\frac{1}{2}\right) = -\frac{9}{32}$	4. Find $P\left(\frac{1}{2}\right)$; use point symmetry to get $P\left(-\frac{1}{2}\right) = \frac{9}{32}$.

Continued ▶

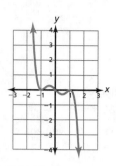

5. Sketch. Remember tails, symmetry, and especially the two tangent points. Observe that $D = \mathbb{R}$, $R = \mathbb{R}$.

▶ A. Exercises

Give the domain and range for each relation. For graphs that could be polynomials, identify the degree as even or odd. For graphs that are not polynomials, explain why they are not.

1.

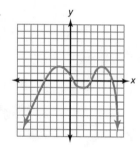

4.

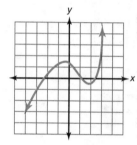

2.

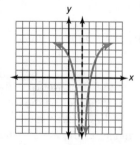

5.

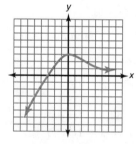

3.

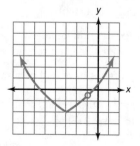

6.

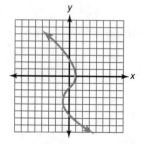

7.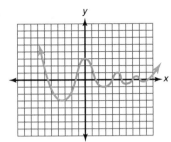

8.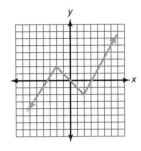

▶ B. Exercises

Discuss the tails of each function. Identify any types of symmetry.

9. $P(x) = x^5 - 3x$

10. $P(x) = -x^2 + 3x - 5$

11. $P(x) = x^4 + 6x^2 - 8$

12. $P(x) = -x^3 - x^2 + 6x - 3$

13. $P(x) = 0$

Refer to the graph at right.
Discuss each aspect of $P(x)$.

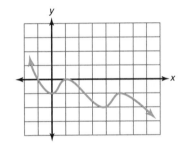

14. Leading coefficient

15. Degree of polynomial

16. Relative extrema

17. Zeros

Let $P(x) = x^3 + 4x^2 + 3x$.

18. Find all the roots

19. Find $P(-4)$, $P(-2)$, $P\left(-\frac{1}{2}\right)$, $P(1)$, and $P(2)$.

20. Sketch the graph.

Continued ▶

Sketch a graph of the following polynomial functions.

21. $y = -x^3 - x^2 + 6x$
22. $y = x^3 - 3x + 2$
23. $f(x) = 2x^3 - 7x^2 - 17x + 10$
24. $g(x) = x^3 - x^2 - x - 2$
25. $y = \frac{1}{2}x^3 - 3x$
26. $y = x^4 + 4x^3 - 2x^2 - 12x + 9$
27. $h(x) = x^4 - 4x^2$
28. $g(x) = -4.3x^5 + 3.71x^3 - 7.9x + 15.68$
29. $p(x) = -5x^8 + 2x^5 - 7x^2 + 8$
30. If $P(x)$ is a polynomial of odd degree, what is its domain and range?

▶ **C. Exercises**

31. Sketch the graph of the function $y = \frac{1}{4}x^4 - \frac{2}{3}x^3 - 4x^2 + 4$.
32. How would the graph of the function $f(x) = x^2 - x - 2$ differ from the graph of $g(x) = \frac{x^3 - 4x^2 + x + 6}{x - 3}$ and why?

Dominion Modeling

33. When following another car, some have said that you should stay one car length apart for every 10 mph. Examine how well this rule corresponds to the data in daytime conditions. Assume that a typical vehicle is 4 m long and that both vehicles are traveling at the same speed. Furthermore, assume that stopping distance includes the reaction distance; so for 50 mph, the stopping distance, 52.9 m, includes 15.0 m to react and another 37.9 m to brake to a stop.

Reaction Distance	Stopping Distance	Braking Distance
15.0 m	52.9 m	$52.9 - 15 = 37.9$ m

If two cars are traveling at 60 mph, one in front of the other, will a car length for each 10 mph protect them from colliding with each other?

34. Since a quadratic model fits the stopping distance data so well, what can you conclude about stopping?

35. A flagpole on level ground casts a 42-foot shadow when the sun is at an inclination of 26°. Find the height of the pole.

36. A segment has endpoints at $A(3, -7)$ and $B(5, 9)$. Find the coordinates of the point one-fourth of the way from A to B.

37. Find the length of an arc of a circle of radius 6 if the arc cuts off a central angle of 60°.

Consider $P(x) = (2x^3 - 3x)(x - 5)$.

38. Write the polynomial in descending order.

39. Give the zeros of the polynomial.

If $f(x) = ax^7 + bx^3 + cx - 5$ (a, b, c are constants) and $f(-7) = 8$, find $f(7)$.

Math *and* Scripture

Bible History

The following table provides a basis for numerous Bible studies and mathematical models, as you will see in future chapters. Complete the table carefully, as you will need it in future projects. Study Genesis 5:3-32, 9:29; 11:10-32, 21:5, 25:7, 25:26, and 35:28. For each patriarch listed, find his age at the birth of his son and his age at death (life span).

1. Adam
2. Seth
3. Enos
4. Cainan
5. Mahalaleel
6. Jared
7. Enoch
8. Methuselah
9. Lamech
10. Noah
11. Shem

12. Arphaxad
13. Salah
14. Eber
15. Peleg
16. Reu
17. Serug
18. Nahor
19. Terah
20. Abraham
21. Isaac

Extend the table to the life spans of the patriarchs below (Gen. 47:28, 50:26).

22. Jacob

23. Joseph

Extend the table above to include Jacob's and Joseph's ages at their sons' birth. Compare these verses in Genesis 41:46-52, 45:6, and 47:9. (For Joseph, you can only provide a range of ages.)

24. What evidence in the context of these passages suggests that God intended to provide us with a full chronology up to Jacob?

25. How does Jude 14 confirm that the first part of the genealogy is complete?

26. What problem do you find when comparing Luke 3:23-38 to the list above?

Because of this problem (which probably results from human transcription), it is wise to consider the dates calculated as approximate.

27. Estimate a margin of error for calculating the age of the earth based on the genealogy problem mentioned in exercise 26.

28. What significant shift do you notice in life spans? Explain.

You will study the decay of life span in future chapters. The fact that life span has decreased is consistent with the scientific law that all things run down and decay. This law is expressed in Scripture in Romans 8:21-22.

Vital Sines

Because the creature itself also shall be delivered from the bondage of corruption into the glorious liberty of the children of God. For we know that the whole creation groaneth and travaileth in pain together until now. ❧

Romans 8:21-22

Chapter 2 Review

Graph each relation. Identify the domain and range and tell if it is a function.

1. $\{(2, 3), (5, 2), (1, 4)\}$

2.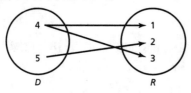

3. $\{(x, y) \mid x = 2\}$

4. $2x + y = 1$

5. $f(x) = -3$

Use $D = \{-2, 0, 1, 4\}$ as the domain. Give the set of ordered pairs described by each function rule and give the degree of each polynomial. Also name the type of function, being as specific as you can.

6. $g(x) = 2x - 9$

7. $h(x) = x^2 + 2x - 1$

8. $f(x) = 7$

9. $k(x) = x^3 - 2x^2 + x - 10$

10. The graph shown is a graph of a polynomial. List three reasons that it is not the graph of $P(x) = 4x^3 - 3x^2 + 5x + 2$.

11. Find the slope and y-intercept of $3x - 5y = 2$.

12. Give the slope of a line perpendicular to $y = 3x - 5$.

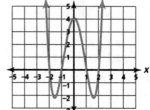

13. Give the equation of the line passing through $(2, 1)$ and $(-1, 4)$.

14. Give the work form of the parabola $y = 3x^2 - 5x + 1$. Find the maximum or minimum value.

15. Give the vertex and axis of symmetry for $y = x^2 - 6x + 7$.

If $P(x) = x^3 - 5x + 1$ and $Q(x) = x + 2$, find

16. $P(x) + Q(x)$ and $P(x) - Q(x)$.

17. $P(x) \cdot Q(x)$ and $P(x) \div Q(x)$.

18. Find $P(4)$ using the remainder theorem.

19. Discuss the tails of $P(x)$.

20. Give the rational roots of $P(x)$.

For $Q(x) = -2(x - 3)^2(2x - 1)(x + 4)^5$,

21. give the zeros and their multiplicities.
22. discuss the tails.

If $R(x)$ has the following zeros, write a polynomial with integer coefficients.

23. $2, 3 - i$
24. $\frac{7}{3}, \sqrt{2}$

Graph each polynomial function. State the domain and range. (Approximate the range for 29 and 30.)

25. $f(x) = -\frac{2}{5}x + 3$
26. $y = x^2 + 4x - 8$
27. $y = -6$
28. $P(x) = x^3 - 2x^2 - 7x - 4$
29. $y = x^4 - 3x^3 - 20x^2 + 6x + 36$
30. $Q(x) = -2x^4 + 20x^2 - 18$
31. Explain how a residual plot can help in the analysis of a model.
32. Explain the mathematical significance of Romans 8:21-22.

3 Functions

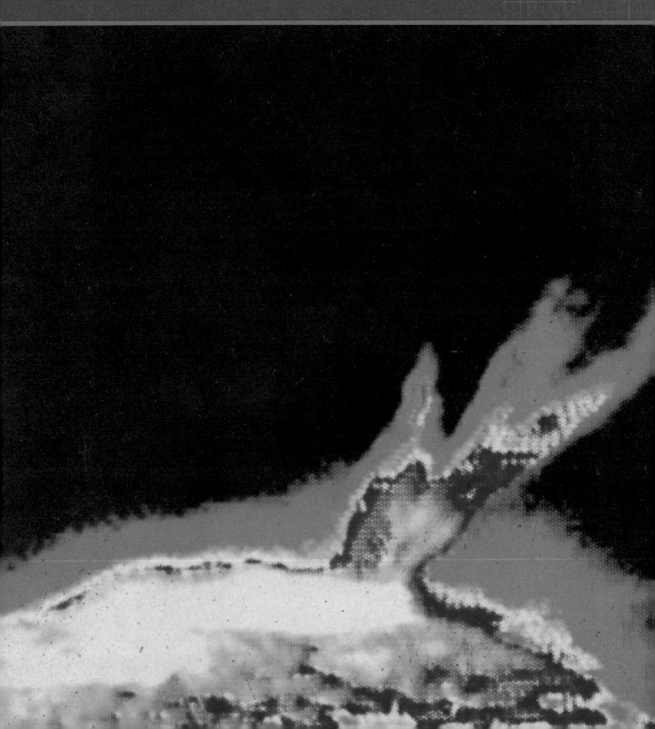

The most dramatic events on the sun's surface are solar flares, huge eruptions often exploding up to millions of degrees Fahrenheit. These explosions can flood the earth with magnetic power, interfering with satellite communications, and possibly influencing our weather.

Solar flares generally detonate near pairs of sunspots, dark spots which are relatively cool at 6300°F. (Normally, the surface of the sun is 10,000°F.) So when we see more sunspots, we expect more solar flares. Since the 1700s, observers have counted sunspots, and records indicate that the number of sunspots fluctuates in a cycle of about eleven years. Recent data follows.

Year	Sunspots	Year	Sunspots
1977	16.7	1989	142
1978	61.3	1990	150.6
1979	123.7	1991	147.6
1980	163.9	1992	123.7
1981	140.3	1993	71.4
1982	137	1994	36.6
1983	92.8	1995	24.2
1984	60.2	1996	10.4
1985	20.5	1997	10.5
1986	13.8	1998	43.7
1987	17.6	1999	82.6
1988	58.2		

After this chapter you should be able to

1. graph power functions and exponential functions.
2. graph piece functions including absolute value functions and greatest integer functions.
3. graph trigonometric functions with various periods and phase shifts.
4. graph functions using tails, symmetry, and relative extrema.
5. find asymptotes and graph rational functions.
6. identify discontinuous functions due to gaps, holes, or jumps.

3.1 Power Functions

Power function   A function of the form $f(x) = Cx^n$ where $C, n \in \mathbb{R}$.

Notice that the definition includes functions in which n is rational or irrational. Our discussion here, however, will be restricted to functions with positive integral exponents. This means they will be polynomial functions and require you to use your knowledge of polynomials.

EXAMPLE 1   For $f(x) = -2x^4$ evaluate $f(-1)$, $f(0)$, $f\left(\frac{1}{2}\right)$, $f(3)$. Find the degree, the domain, the range, and graph the function.

Answer

$f(-1) = -2(-1)^4 = -2 \cdot 1 \quad = -2$
$f(0) \quad = -2 \cdot 0^4 \quad = -2 \cdot 0 \quad = 0$
$f\left(\frac{1}{2}\right) = -2\left(\frac{1}{2}\right)^4 = -2 \cdot \frac{1}{16} = -\frac{1}{8}$
$f(3) \quad = -2 \cdot 3^4 \quad = -2 \cdot 81 = -162$

1. Evaluate as instructed. Remember that -2 is not part of the base. The power is only on the x.

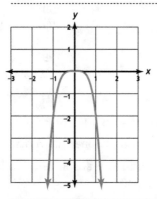

2. Zero is a root of multiplicity 4. The even power indicates symmetry to the y-axis. The only root is $x = 0$. Since the leading coefficient is negative, the tails are down on both the left and right. Therefore, the x-axis is tangent to the graph. Use these facts to sketch the graph.

$D = \mathbb{R}$, $R = \{y \mid y \le 0\}$
The degree is 4.

3. Use the graph for the domain and range. If you think about tails, you can determine the domain and range without graphing. Identify the degree.

EXAMPLE 2   Graph $g(x) = x^3$. Give the domain and range.

Answer

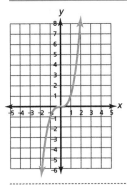

1. Consider the tails (down to the left and up to the right) and symmetry (to the origin). Plot a few key points.
$$g(0) = 0^3 = 0$$
$$g(2) = 2^3 = 8$$
Since $y = x^3$ is not linear, do not connect the points with a straight line.

$D = \mathbb{R}$ and $R = \mathbb{R}$.

2. Give the domain and range.

All equations of the form $f(x) = Cx^n$ are functions (passing the vertical line test) with domain $D = \mathbb{R}$.

Another way to classify functions is as even or odd. A parabola always has a line of symmetry. In the graph of the parabola described by $y = x^2$, the y-axis is the line of symmetry.

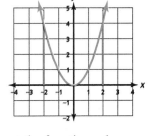

Since symmetry with respect to the y-axis occurs when all the terms are even, such a function is said to be an *even function*. You can determine algebraically whether a function is even by looking at the function rule.

Definition

Even function   A function is even if and only if $f(x) = f(-x)$, $\forall x \in D_f$ (domain of f). ($\forall x$ means "for all x".)

Butterflies, like even functions, display symmetry across a vertical axis.

According to the definition, $y = x^2$ is even, because for any x-value and its opposite, $f(x)$ is the same. For example, $f(2) = 4$ and $f(-2) = 4$. Therefore, $f(2) = f(-2)$ as shown on the previous graph.

One special function is the *identity function,* $y = x$. Note that the x- and y-values are identical for every point on the graph. This is a power function of degree 1.

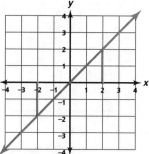

The graph of $y = x$ is not symmetric with respect to the y-axis but instead displays symmetry with respect to the origin. Such a function is called an *odd function.*

Odd function   A function is odd if and only if $f(-x) = -f(x)$, $\forall\, x \in D_f$.

The function $y = x$ is odd because for any x-value and its opposite, the $f(x)$-values are opposites. For example, $f(2) = 2$ and $f(-2) = -2$. Therefore, $f(-2) = -f(2)$ as in the graph above.

Power functions of even degree are even functions and power functions of odd degree are odd functions. Graphs of power functions with negative coefficients look like the mirror image across the x-axis of the power function with a corresponding positive coefficient. For example, $f(x) = x^2$ opens up and $f(x) = -x^2$ opens down.

Functions in general need not be even or odd. A function in which $f(-x) \neq f(x)$ and $f(-x) \neq -f(x)$, is neither even nor odd.

EXAMPLE 3   Determine whether the following functions are even, odd, or neither.
$$f(x) = x^3 \qquad g(x) = x^4 + x^2 \qquad h(x) = x^2 + 2x + 5$$

Answer

$f(x) = x^3$ $f(-x) = (-x)^3 = -x^3 = -f(x)$ $\therefore f$ is an odd function.	1. Determine whether $f(-x)$ is equal to $f(x)$, $-f(x)$, or neither. Since it is odd; its graph is symmetric across the origin. ($\therefore$ means "therefore.")

Continued ▶

$$g(x) = x^4 + x^2$$
$$g(-x) = (-x)^4 + (-x)^2 = x^4 + x^2 = g(x)$$
$\therefore g$ is an even function.

2. Find $g(-x)$. Since it is even, its graph is symmetric across the y-axis.

$$h(x) = x^2 + 2x + 5$$
$$h(-x) = (-x)^2 + 2(-x) + 5 = x^2 - 2x + 5$$
$\therefore h$ is neither even nor odd.

3. $h(-x)$ is not equal to $h(x)$ or to $-h(x)$.

▶ A. Exercises

Graph each power function. Give the domain and range of each and classify as even or odd.

1. $y = x^5$
2. $g(x) = x^6$
3. $y = x^7$
4. $y = -2x^3$
5. $f(x) = -\frac{1}{4}x^4$
6. $f(x) = x^2$

 7. $y = \frac{5}{12}x^{24}$

Using $f(x) = Cx^n$, match.

8. The graph has point symmetry; the left tail points up.
9. The graph has line symmetry; both tails of the graph point down.
10. The graph has line symmetry; both tails of the graph point up.
11. The graph has point symmetry; the left tail of the graph points down.

A. $C > 0$, n is even

B. $C > 0$, n is odd

C. $C < 0$, n is even

D. $C < 0$, n is odd.

▶ B. Exercises

Evaluate.

12. $f(2)$ for $f(x) = 3x^5$
13. $f(-3)$ for $f(x) = -2x^3$
14. $f(\sqrt{7})$ for $f(x) = 2x^4$
 15. $f(-17.95)$ for $f(x) = -2.5x^{16}$

For $f(x) = Cx^n$

16. Find $f(1)$
17. Find $f(\sqrt[n]{3})$
18. Find all zeros.
19. What is the multiplicity of the zero?

20. Give the domain of $f(x)$.
21. Give the range of $f(x)$ if n is odd.
22. If n is even, on what does the range of $f(x)$ depend?
23. Give the range of $f(x)$ if n is even.

▶ C. Exercises

According to the definition, is each function below a power function? If not, state the reason. If so, is it odd or even?

24. $f(x) = 5\sqrt[3]{x}$
25. $f(x) = x^{\sqrt{3}}$

⟋⟍ Dominion Modeling

26. Make a scatterplot of the sunspot data. What pattern do you notice in the data? (*Hint:* Transform the year values by subtracting 1977 from each. Place these values in L_1 and the sunspot values in L_2.)
27. Would linear or quadratic models be appropriate? What degree of polynomial fits the given years? Why is no polynomial appropriate?

Cumulative Review

28. In $\triangle ABC$, find C, given $a = 47$, $b = 63$, and $c = 82$.
29. Is the relation in the graph a function?
30. If $\sin x = 0.3$, find $\csc x$, $\cos (90 - x)$, and $\sec (90 - x)$.
31. Solve $2x^2 - 5x + 7 = x(x + 1)$.
32. Find the slope of the line joining $(2, 7)$ to $(4, -5)$.

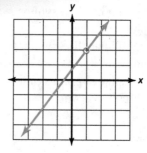

3.2 Exponential Functions

Power functions and exponential functions look similar, but they are distinguished by the location of the

Snails reproduce quickly and their populations can be modeled using exponential growth functions.

variable. If the variable is in the base and the exponent is a constant, then the function is a power function. In contrast, if the variable is in the exponent and the base is a constant, then the function is an *exponential function.*

For example:

$f(x) = x^4$ is a power function, but
$g(x) = 4^x$ is an exponential function.

Definition

Exponential function A function of the form $f(x) = Ca^x$, where $C, a, x \in \mathbb{R}$, and $C > 0$, $a > 0$, and $a \neq 1$.

The degree of a power function is its exponent. In the example above, $f(x)$ has degree 4. Exponential functions do not have degree, but they are classified as growth or decay. *Exponential growth* means that the value of the function increases exponentially as the value of x increases. *Exponential decay* means that the value of the function decreases exponentially as x increases.

Suppose you are working in a laboratory and you know that the number of bacteria in a certain culture doubles each day. You may be interested in knowing how many bacteria will be present in the culture in five days if it begins with 3×10^4 bacteria. The next day the culture has twice as many or $2 \cdot 3 = 6 \times 10^4$ bacteria. After two days there will be $2(2 \cdot 3)$ or $2^2 \cdot 3 = 12 \times 10^4$ bacteria; after three days, $2(2^2 \cdot 3)$ or $2^3 \cdot 3 = 24 \times 10^4$ bacteria, and so forth. The change in population of this bacteria culture over time is called exponential growth and can be described as an *exponential function.* The particular exponential function described in this example is represented as follows.

$f(x) = 3 \cdot 2^x$ (in 10,000s)

Therefore $f(5) = 3 \cdot 2^5 = 3 \cdot 32 = 96$. After 5 days there will be 96×10^4 bacteria. Since y increases as x increases, this is a case of exponential growth. Let's look at the graph of this function.

EXAMPLE 1   Graph $f(x) = 3 \cdot 2^x$. Give the domain and range.

Answer

x	$f(x)$		x	$f(x)$
-4	$\frac{3}{16}$		1	6
-3	$\frac{3}{8}$		2	12
-2	$\frac{3}{4}$		3	24
-1	$\frac{3}{2}$		4	48
0	3		5	96

1. Find ordered pairs that satisfy this function. Remember, $2^{-4} = \frac{1}{2^4} = \frac{1}{16}$

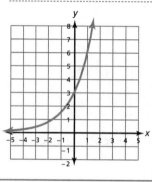

2. Graph some of the ordered pairs on a Cartesian plane.

3. Connect the points with a smooth curve.

4. From the graph you can tell that $D = \mathbb{R}$ and since $f(x) > 0 \; \forall \; x$, $R = \{y \mid y > 0\}$.

In general, the exponential function is defined by $f(x) = Ca^x$, where C is a positive constant, a is the base, $a > 0$, and $a \neq 1$. C represents the initial amount and a represents the rate of growth.

Compare $f(x) = 10^x$, $g(x) = 2^x$, and $h(x) = \left(\frac{3}{2}\right)^x$ on the same graph.

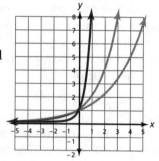

Since $a > 1$, all these functions are increasing as x increases and are exponential growth functions. They intersect at the point $(0, 1)$, since C is 1 in each case and a^0 is always 1.

An exponential function in which $0 < a < 1$ is a reflection in the y-axis of an exponential function where $a > 1$. Since y decreases as x increases for such functions, they are exponential decay functions. Let's look at such a function.

EXAMPLE 2   Graph $y = \left(\frac{1}{2}\right)^x$.

Answer

x	f(x)		x	f(x)
−3	8		1	$\frac{1}{2}$
−2	4		2	$\frac{1}{4}$
−1	2		3	$\frac{1}{8}$
0	1			

1. Find ordered pairs that satisfy this equation.

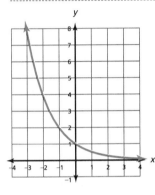

2. Graph these ordered pairs, and connect them with a smooth curve.

Did you notice that exponential functions have no zeros? The graph gets closer and closer to the *x*-axis but never touches it. Since the *x*-axis is horizontal, it is a *horizontal asymptote.*

Now consider an application of exponential functions—compound interest. Suppose you put $200 in the bank at 7% interest compounded annually. During the first year your investment of $200 earns $14 interest.

$$I = Prt = 200(0.07)(1) = 14$$

Therefore your total amount in the bank is $214.

$$A = P + I = 200 + 14 = 214$$

Notice that $A = P + I = P + Prt = P(1 + rt) = P(1 + r)$ when $t = 1$.

You still have 100% of your original deposit of $200, but you have earned 7% more. Your total amount $A = 200(1 + 0.07) = 1.07(200) = \$214$.

If you do not withdraw any money, during the second year you will earn 7% interest on $214. Since you will still have 100% of your $214 with interest added, you will have $(1.07)(\$214) = \$228.98$. How could we have calculated this without calculating the first year's earnings?

Notice that $228.98 = 1.07(214) = 1.07(1.07(200)) = \$200(1.07)^2$.

Likewise, after three years, you will have $228.98(1.07) = \$245.01$

or $[\$200(1.07)^2](1.07) = 200(1.07)^3 = \$245.01$

In other words, $A = \$200(1.07)^t$ after t years. Since 1.07 is a constant, A is an exponential function with the time t as its independent variable. The amount accumulated from compound annual interest after t years is $A(t) = P(1 + r)^t$.

Simple interest is paid only on the original amount. In compound interest, your interest from each year is left in the bank and earns interest in all the following years.

What if the interest is compounded quarterly? Then the process discussed above occurs four times each year. Banks, however, divide the annual interest rate to distribute it over the four quarters. In other words, use $\frac{r}{4}$ instead of r and $4t$ instead of t. Similarly, if interest is compounded n times annually, the accumulated amount after t years is given by $A(t) = P\left(1 + \frac{r}{n}\right)^{nt}$.

Notice that nt represents the number of compounding periods in t years.

EXAMPLE 3   Bank A offers 5% annual interest compounded annually and Bank B offers 4.9% compounded monthly. Which bank will pay more interest on $300 invested for 10 years?

Answer

For Bank A, $A(t) = P(1 + r)^t$
$A(10) = \$300(1 + 0.05)^{10}$
$= \$300(1.05)^{10}$
$= \$488.67$

For Bank B, $A(t) = P\left(1 + \frac{r}{n}\right)^{nt}$ where $n = 12$
$A(10) = \$300\left(1 + \frac{0.049}{12}\right)^{12(10)}$
$= \$300(1.0040833)^{120}$
$= \$489.21$

Bank B will pay $0.54 more. Even with a slightly lower interest rate, the more frequent compounding generates slightly more interest over 10 years.

Another exponential function has the real (but irrational) number e as its base. This number appears often in mathematical applications. The meaning of the number e will be clarified later. For now it is sufficient to know that

$e \approx 2.718281828 \ldots$

This number can be found on your calculator using the e^x key with $x = 1$.

Natural exponential function $f(x) = e^x$, where $x \in \mathbb{R}$.

EXAMPLE 4 Graph $f(x) = e^x$.

Answer

$f(x) = e^x$

x	$f(x)$	x	$f(x)$
−3	0.0498	1	2.7183
−2	0.1353	2	7.3891
−1	0.3679	3	20.0855
0	1.0000		

1. Using a calculator, make a table of ordered pairs. Scientific calculators and graphing calculators should have an e^x key.

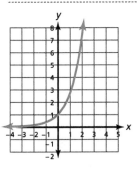

2. Plot the points, and connect them with a smooth curve.

Your work with polynomials and power functions should help you understand translations and opposites of exponential functions.

EXAMPLE 5 For $f(x) = -2^{-x} + 3$, find $f(0)$, $f(1)$, and $f\left(-\frac{1}{2}\right)$. Also graph $f(x)$ and give its domain and range.

Answer

$f(0) = -2^0 + 3 = -1 + 3 = 2$
$f(1) = -2^{-1} + 3 = -\frac{1}{2} + 3 = \frac{5}{2}$
$f\left(-\frac{1}{2}\right) = -2^{-\left(-\frac{1}{2}\right)} + 3 = -2^{\frac{1}{2}} + 3 = -\sqrt{2} + 3$

1. Evaluate as indicated. Notice that (0, 2) is the y-intercept. Recall that negative exponents indicate reciprocals and fractional exponents indicate radicals.

Continued ▶

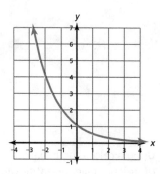

2. Notice that 2^{-x} means the same as $\left(\frac{1}{2}\right)^x$.
$$2^{-x} = (2^{-1})^x = \left(\frac{1}{2}\right)^x$$
This is exponential decay in disguise. The graph of $f(x) = 2^{-x} = \left(\frac{1}{2}\right)^x$ is shown here.

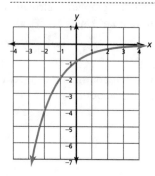

3. Recall that the negative coefficient of a function reflects the decay curve across the x-axis. The graph of $f(x) = -2^{-x}$ is shown here.

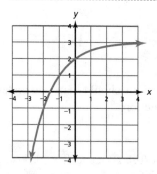

4. Use translation to move the graph up 3 units to obtain $f(x) = -2^{-x} + 3$.

▶ A. Exercises

Graph the following exponential functions by finding at least six ordered pairs. Give the domain and range of each. Classify each as exponential growth or decay.

1. $y = 4^x$
2. $y = \left(\frac{1}{3}\right)^x$
3. $g(x) = 2 \cdot 5^x$
4. $y = -10^x$
5. $y = 3^{-x}$
6. $y = 3^x - 2$

Evaluate each exponential function for $f(-2)$, $f(0)$, $f\left(\frac{1}{2}\right)$, and $f(1)$.

7. $f(x) = 3^x$
8. $g(x) = 4 \cdot 2^{-x}$

▶ B. Exercises

Classify each function as a power function, an exponential function, or as some other function. Identify the degree of power functions and growth/decay of exponential functions.

9. $f(x) = x^7$
10. $q(x) = 7^x$
11. $h(x) = \left(\frac{2}{3}\right)^x$
12. $k(x) = x \cdot \pi^2$
13. $p(x) = 3 \cdot 5^{-x}$
14. $f(x) = 2^3$

From which bank will you earn more money in 8 years if Bank A compounds monthly and Bank B compounds semiannually?

15. Both banks give the same interest rate.
16. Bank A offers 4% and Bank B offers 7%.

Find the value of a bank account in the year 2042, if it is opened with $400 in the year 2000 and pays 6% interest. Assume interest is compounded:

17. annually
18. quarterly
19. monthly
20. weekly
21. daily
22. hourly

To find $y = 2^{1.9}$ graphically, use the graph of $y = 2^x$. Using a graphing calculator, 1.9 can be entered as a value for x in a table to find the corresponding y-value. The ordered pair is (1.9, 3.7321). Give the following y-values.

23. $y = 2^{1.2}$
24. $y = 2^{-0.5}$

To approximate x to the nearest tenth in the equation $2^x = 3$ using a graphing calculator, use a table to find the x-value that corresponds to the y-value closest to 3. Set the table to begin at 0 and increase by 0.1. Scroll down the y column to find the closest value to 3. The corresponding x-value is 1.6. Give the value for x in the following.

25. $5.3 = 2^x$
26. $1.6 = 2^x$

Consider the general exponential function, $f(x) = Ca^x$.

27. Why did the definition of exponential function exclude $a = 1$?
28. Find the domain, range, and intercepts.
29. Graph $y < \dfrac{3^x}{2}$.

Dominion Modeling

30. Using the sunspot data, would an exponential model be appropriate?

Cumulative Review

31. When is a quadratic function a power function?
32. If a power function has degree 1, what is it called?
33. If a polynomial function has degree 0, what is it called?
34. Write the equation of a line through $(-3, 1)$ parallel to $5x - 8y = 10$. Express the answer in general form.
35. Give the smallest positive and negative angle measures coterminal with $-175°$.

If r is the remainder when each of the numbers 438, 1071, and 1493 are divided by d ($d \in \mathbb{N}$ and $d > 1$), find $d - r$.

3.3 Piece Functions

Piece functions are functions that require two or more function rules to define them. Each rule applies to a restricted interval or *piece* of the domain. Since piece functions have more than one function rule, you must select the correct rule based on the x-value.

EXAMPLE 1   Evaluate $f(0)$ and $f(3)$ for $f(x) = \begin{cases} -3x + 2 & \text{if } x < 1 \\ 2^x & \text{if } x \geq 1 \end{cases}$.

Answer

$f(0) = -3(0) + 2 = 2$	Since $0 < 1$, substitute zero into the rule for x-values less than 1: $y = -3x + 2$
$f(3) = 2^3 = 8$	Since $3 > 1$ substitute 3 into the rule for values of $x \geq 1$: $y = 2^x$

Therefore, $f(0) = 2$ and $f(3) = 8$.

EXAMPLE 2   Graph $f(x) = \begin{cases} -3x + 2 & \text{if } x < 1 \\ 2^x & \text{if } x \geq 1 \end{cases}$. Give the domain and range.

Answer

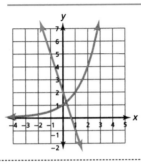

1. You are familiar with both of these types of functions. Graph them on the same coordinate plane. If you consider these graphs together, then $f(x)$ is not a function; it does not pass the vertical line test.

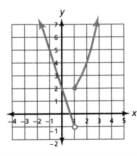

2. To finish graphing, you must determine which graph corresponds to which domain values. For example, the function rule $f(x) = -3x + 2$ applies only for values less than 1, while $f(x) = 2^x$ applies to values greater than or equal to 1. Notice the open dot on the end of the linear function, since 1 is not part of the domain for that piece.

$D = \mathbb{R}$
$R = \{y \mid y > -1\}$

3. The graph of the piece function passes the vertical line test. Find the domain and range from the graph.

The *greatest integer function* has infinitely many pieces. Its domain is the set of real numbers, and its range consists of the set of integers. Each range value is the greatest integer less than or equal to the given domain value. The function is represented using square brackets: $f(x) = [x]$.

EXAMPLE 3 Find the set of ordered pairs described by the greatest integer function $f(x) = [x]$ and the domain $\left\{-5, \frac{-3}{2}, \frac{-3}{4}, 0, \frac{1}{4}, \frac{5}{2}\right\}$.

Answer

$f(-5) = [-5] = -5$	1. The greatest integer less than or equal to -5 is -5.
$f\left(\frac{-3}{2}\right) = \left[\frac{-3}{2}\right] = -2$	2. The greatest integer less than or equal to $-\frac{3}{2}$ or -1.5 is -2.
$f\left(\frac{-3}{4}\right) = \left[\frac{-3}{4}\right] = -1$	3. The greatest integer less than or equal to $-\frac{3}{4}$ is -1.
$f(0) = [0] = 0$	4. The greatest integer less than or equal to 0 is 0.
$f\left(\frac{1}{4}\right) = \left[\frac{1}{4}\right] = 0$	5. The greatest integer less than or equal to $\frac{1}{4}$ is 0.
$f\left(\frac{5}{2}\right) = \left[\frac{5}{2}\right] = 2$	6. The greatest integer less than or equal to $\frac{5}{2}$ or 2.5 is 2.

$$\left\{(-5, -5), \left(\tfrac{-3}{2}, -2\right), \left(\tfrac{-3}{4}, -1\right), (0, 0), \left(\tfrac{1}{4}, 0\right), \left(\tfrac{5}{2}, 2\right)\right\}$$

The rule for the greatest integer function can be written as a piece function.

$$f(x) = [x] = \begin{cases} \vdots \\ -2 & \text{if } -2 \le x < -1 \\ -1 & \text{if } -1 \le x < 0 \\ 0 & \text{if } 0 \le x < 1 \\ 1 & \text{if } 1 \le x < 2 \\ \vdots \end{cases}$$

Since the y-value of each piece is constant, all of the infinitely many pieces are portions of horizontal lines. This function looks like stair steps when graphed. Check that the ordered pairs from Example 3 are on the graph.

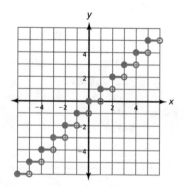

Another important piece function is the absolute value function. Recall the following definition of absolute value.

$$|x| = \begin{cases} x & \text{if } x \ge 0 \\ -x & \text{if } x < 0 \end{cases}$$

If $x \geq 0$, then $|x|$ equals itself. Don't let the other part of this definition confuse you. It says that if $x < 0$, then $|x| =$ the opposite of x. An example will clarify this. First, let $x = 5$; since $x \geq 0$, use the first rule of the definition. Therefore, $|5| = 5$. In contrast, if $x = -5$, then $x < 0$, and the second rule applies. Therefore, $|-5| = -(-5) = 5$. The absolute value will always be nonnegative. It will equal itself if x is positive or zero, and its opposite if x is negative.

EXAMPLE 4   Find the function described by the function rule
$$g(x) = |2x - 3| \text{ for the domain } \{-4, -2, 0, 1, 2, 4\}.$$

Answer

$$\begin{aligned} g(-4) &= |2(-4) - 3| \\ &= |-11| \\ &= 11 \end{aligned} \qquad \begin{aligned} g(1) &= |2(1) - 3| \\ &= |-1| \\ &= 1 \end{aligned}$$

$$\begin{aligned} g(-2) &= |2(-2) - 3| \\ &= |-7| \\ &= 7 \end{aligned} \qquad \begin{aligned} g(2) &= |2(2) - 3| \\ &= |1| \\ &= 1 \end{aligned}$$

$$\begin{aligned} g(0) &= |2(0) - 3| \\ &= |-3| \\ &= 3 \end{aligned} \qquad \begin{aligned} g(4) &= |2(4) - 3| \\ &= |5| \\ &= 5 \end{aligned}$$

$$g = \{(-4, 11), (-2, 7), (0, 3), (1, 1), (2, 1), (4, 5)\}$$

Definition

Absolute value function   The absolute value function is expressed as $\{(x, f(x)) \mid f(x) = |x|\}$.

Because the definition of absolute value consists of two linear rules, $y = x$ and $y = -x$ depending on domain values, the graph of the absolute value function consists of these two linear pieces. Plot the points $(-3, 3)$, $(-2, 2)$, $(0, 0)$, $(1, 1)$, $(3, 3)$ and connect them as shown.

Remember that graphs of functions can be translated on the Cartesian plane. Example 5 shows a translation of the absolute value function.

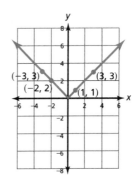

EXAMPLE 5   Graph $f(x) = |x| + 3$. Give the domain and range.

Answer

$f(x) = |x| + 3$

$\{(-4, 7), (-2, 5), (0, 3), (1, 4), (3, 6)\}$

1. Find ordered pairs for this function.

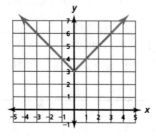

2. Plot these points, and connect them to extend the domain to all real numbers.

3. Domain: $D = \mathbb{R}$

   Range: $R = \{y \mid y \geq 3\}$

In Example 5 the basic absolute value graph was translated up 3 units. Instead of plotting ordered pairs, you could tell from the rule $f(x) = |x| + 3$ to translate $f(x) = |x|$ up three units. What would happen to the graph if $f(x) = |x + 3|$? Graph this function, and check your answer.

You should remember the following general principles of translations from your work with parabolas.

Translating Graphs

1. If x is replaced by $x - a$, where $a \in \mathbb{R}$, the graph translates horizontally. If $a > 0$, the graph moves a units right, and if $a < 0$ (represented as $x + a$), it moves a units left.
2. If y, or $f(x)$, is replaced by $y - b$, where $b \in \mathbb{R}$, the graph translates vertically. If $b > 0$, the graph moves b units up, and if $b < 0$ (represented as $y + b$), it moves b units down.
3. If $g(x) = -f(x)$, then the functions $f(x)$ and $g(x)$ are reflections of one another across the x-axis.

Finally, recall that continuous functions have no gaps, jumps, or holes. You can graph a continuous function without lifting your pencil from the paper. Examples 2 and 3 are not continuous because of jumps. The absolute value functions in Examples 4 and 5 are continuous.

EXAMPLE 6   Graph $g(x) = \begin{cases} 2x + 3 & \text{if } x \leq -2 \\ |x| & \text{if } -1 \leq x < 1. \\ x^3 & \text{if } x > 1 \end{cases}$

Answer

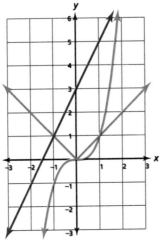

1. Graph the 3 functions.

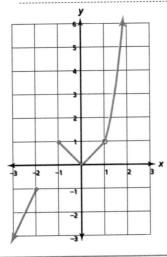

2. Draw the final graph.

3. Write the domain and range. Notice that the values between -2 and -1 are not in the domain. Neither is $x = 1$.
   $D = \{x \mid x \leq -2, -1 \leq x < 1, x > 1\}$
   $R = \{y \mid y \leq -1, y \geq 0\}$

4. $g(x)$ is not continuous due to a gap and a hole.

▶ A. Exercises

Find the function described by the given rule and the domain $\left\{-4, \frac{-1}{2}, 0, \frac{3}{4}, 2\right\}$.

1. $f(x) = |x + 4|$

2. $h(x) = \begin{cases} -6x & \text{if } x < 0 \\ x + 2 & \text{if } x \geq 0 \end{cases}$

3. $h(x) = [x]$

4. $l(x) = 5x - 2$

5. $g(x) = \begin{cases} 4^x & \text{if } x \leq 1 \\ 8x^2 & \text{if } x > 1 \end{cases}$

6. $g(x) = |4x|$

7. $f(x) = \begin{cases} 2x + 5 & \text{if } x < -1 \\ x & \text{if } -1 \leq x \leq 1 \\ x - 1 & \text{if } x > 1 \end{cases}$

8. $g(x) = [3x + 1]$

9. $h(x) = 4$

10. $l(x) = \begin{cases} 4x - 3 & \text{if } x < 0 \\ x + 1 & \text{if } x = 0 \\ -3x & \text{if } x > 0 \end{cases}$

▶ B. Exercises

Without graphing, tell where the graph of the given equation would translate from the standard position for that type of function.

11. $f(x) = |x| - 7$
12. $g(x) = (x + 2)^5$
13. $y = |x + 4|$
14. $y = [x] - 4$
15. $y = [x + 1] + 6$
16. $h(x) = 2^{x-3} + 5$

Give the zeros of each function.

17. $f(x) = [x]$
18. $g(x) = |x|$
19. $h(x) = \begin{cases} x^2 - 4 & \text{if } x \neq 1 \\ 0 & \text{if } x = 1 \end{cases}$

Graph. Give the domain and range of each. Classify each as continuous or discontinuous.

20. $P(x) = \begin{cases} 0 & \text{if } x = 3 \\ 5 & \text{if } x \neq 3 \end{cases}$
21. $f(x) = |x|$
22. $f(x) = 3x - 4$
23. $g(x) = [x]$
24. $y = |x - 6|$

25. $h(x) = \begin{cases} 3 & \text{if } 1 \le x \le 2 \\ 1 & \text{if } x > 3 \\ 0 & \text{otherwise} \end{cases}$

26. $y = |x| - 3$

27. $y = \begin{cases} x & \text{if } x < 1 \\ 2x - 4 & \text{if } 1 \le x \le 4 \\ \frac{1}{3}x & \text{if } x > 4 \end{cases}$

28. $y = [x - 5]$

29. $f(x) = \begin{cases} x^2 & \text{if } -2 < x < 2 \\ 4 & \text{otherwise} \end{cases}$

30. $y = [x] + 6$

31. $f(x) = |x + 3| + 1$

32. $g(x) = \begin{cases} |x| & \text{if } x \le -3 \\ x + 2 & \text{if } -3 < x < 4 \\ 4 & \text{if } x > 4 \end{cases}$

33. $y = \begin{cases} x - 2 & \text{if } x < -2 \\ 3x + 1 & \text{if } x \ge -2 \end{cases}$

34. $h(x) = \begin{cases} x + 3 & \text{if } x < -2 \\ 3^x & \text{if } x > -1 \end{cases}$

▶ C. Exercises

35. Classify the following functions as always, sometimes, or never continuous: a) piece b) absolute value c) greatest integer.

36. Graph $|x - 3| \le y$.

▪ Cumulative Review

37. Give the reference angles for the following angles: 117°, 201°, 295° and −47°.

38. Find the sine, cosine, and tangent of $\frac{2\pi}{3}$.

39. Classify $y = 7(0.85)^x$ as exponential growth or decay.

Consider $f(x) = -x^2 - 4x - 3$.

40. Find $f(-2)$ and $f\left(\frac{-1}{2}\right)$.

41. Find the zeros of the function.

3 Approximation Methods

Population Growth Models

Suppose a mouse population increases by 20% each year. Next year's population is obtained by adding 20% to the present population. In other words, next year's population will be 120% of the current population. Let $r = 1.2$ (the decimal form of 120%).

EXAMPLE 1 Beginning with 10 mice, find the population after 5 years.

Answer

$f(0) = 10$	$= 10$	$= 10$	≈ 10
$f(1) = 1.2(10)$	$= 12$	$= 12$	≈ 12
$f(2) = 1.2(12)$	$= 1.2(1.2)(10) = 1.2^2 \times 10$	$= 14.4$	≈ 14
$f(3) = 1.2(14.4)$	$= 1.2(1.2)(1.2)(10) = 1.2^3 \times 10$	$= 17.28$	≈ 17
$f(4) = 1.2(17.28)$	$= 1.2^4 \times 10$	$= 20.736$	≈ 21
$f(5) = 1.2(20.736)$	$= 1.2^5 \times 10$	$= 24.8832$	≈ 25

In general, $f(t) = A(1.2)^t$ where A is the original population, the growth rate is 20%, and t is the number of years. Thus, in this case, $f(t) = 10(1.2)^t$. An important feature of this model is that it predicts that the mouse population increases continually. Note especially the plot of the exponential model below.

A more realistic model allows for population stability due to disease, predators, and space limitations. The following model is called *logistic growth*.

$$g(t) = 10 + \frac{150}{1 + e^{-0.8(t-10)}}$$

In $g(t)$, $150 + 10 = 160$ represents the maximum possible mouse population, perhaps on a tiny island. The variable t still represents the number of years. Remember e is the irrational number 2.71828 . . . . (For this activity, you may temporarily ignore the meaning of the other values in the logistic function.) This function does not result in a compound growth formula, as you can see in its graph.

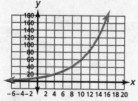

Plot of the exponential model for mice

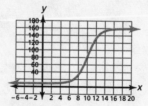

Plot of the logistic model for mice

As you can see in the logistic model, the population grows much more slowly in the beginning, climbs sharply, then levels.

EXAMPLE 2   Repeat Example 1 for 10 mice using the given logistic model.

Answer $g(0) \approx 10.05 \approx 10$
$g(1) \approx 10.11 \approx 10$
$g(2) \approx 10.25 \approx 10$
$g(3) \approx 10.55 \approx 11$
$g(4) \approx 11.22 \approx 11$
$g(5) \approx 12.70 \approx 13$

▶ Exercises

Assume that a fish population in a certain lake grows 40% each year from an initial population of 20. Use the exponential and logistic models as given earlier to aid you.

1. Write the exponential growth model and the logistic model (for the logistic model, assume a maximum population of 400).
2. Calculate the population for the years indicated in the table using each method. Round to the nearest integer.

Year	Exponential	Logistic	Year	Exponential	Logistic
0			12		
2			14		
4			16		
6			18		
8			20		
10					

3. Plot each of the functions found in exercise 1.
4. What limitations do neither model address?

3.4 Periodic Functions

Periodic describes a specific period of time for a cycle. God has made many things periodic. He promised in Genesis 8:22 that the cycle of the four seasons would continue throughout the earth's history. You know that this period is one year. In the same verse, God promises to continue the cycle of day and night (24-hour period). Other cycles include the animal migrations, tides, lunar phases, sunspots, eclipses, meteor showers, comets, ocean currents, and winds.

Since Old Faithful erupts every 80 minutes, a periodic function can approximate its height.

Think about a wheel on a car or bicycle as it rolls forward. Watch the air valve stem as the wheel goes around. Can you graph the path of the valve stem?

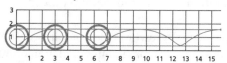

As the tire rolls to the right (figure above), the valve ascends to the top of the wheel and then descends almost to the roadway. The location of the valve for any point on the wheel is given by a periodic function and the graph passes the vertical line test. Notice that the circumference of the wheel (not the tire) determines the period. The graph is a type of a *cycloid* and was first studied by Galileo. Even its name refers to its periodicity.

EXAMPLE 1 Give the graph, period, domain, and range of the function. Then express it in a simpler form.

$$f(x) = \begin{cases} \vdots \\ 0 & \text{if} \ -4 \leq x \leq -1 \\ 1 & \text{if} \ -1 < x < 0 \\ 0 & \text{if} \ 0 \leq x \leq 3 \\ 1 & \text{if} \ 3 < x < 4 \\ 0 & \text{if} \ 4 \leq x \leq 7 \\ 1 & \text{if} \ 7 < x < 8 \\ \vdots \end{cases}$$

Continued ▶

Answer

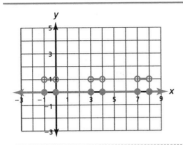

1. Graph the function.

---

period = 4
$D = \mathbb{R}$ and $R = \{0, 1\}$

2. Since the values repeat in 4-unit cycles, the period is 4. Identify the domain and range.

$$f(x) = \begin{cases} 0 & \text{if} \quad 4n - 4 \le x \le 4n - 1 \\ 1 & \text{if} \quad 4n - 1 < x < 4n \end{cases}$$

3. Let n be the number of periods. Express the last two inequalities in terms of n. Since the period is 4, after two periods $4n = 8$. Then $4n - 1 = 7$ and $4n - 4 = 4$.

All the trigonometric functions have specific periods. What is sin 390°?

An angle of **390°** goes all the way around the circle and terminates at the same place as a **30°** angle. Thus, sin **390°** = sin **30°** = $\frac{1}{2}$. The extra 360° (or 2π radians) do not affect the answer. Therefore, adding 2π (or **360°**) to an angle will not change the value of a trigonometric function. You can see that after 2π, the sine values begin to recycle—so the period for the sine function is 2π.

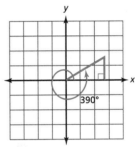

A function is periodic if, for some given constant c, $f(x + c) = f(x) \, \forall \, x$. The smallest such positive value of c is called the period of the function. The discussion above shows that all six trig functions are periodic. However, 2π is not the smallest value of c for two of them. The tangent and cotangent are positive in quadrants I and III. Therefore their trig values repeat every π radians (they have periods of π).

EXAMPLE 2 Write the period relationship for cosine as an identity.

    Answer $\cos(x + 2k\pi) = \cos x \, \forall \, x$, where $k \in \mathbb{Z}$

EXAMPLE 3   Find $\cos \frac{29}{3}\pi$.

Answer

$\cos \frac{29}{3}\pi = \cos\left(\frac{5}{3}\pi + 8\pi\right) = \cos \frac{5}{3}\pi$	1. Find the angle in the interval $[0, 2\pi)$ coterminal with $\frac{29}{3}\pi$ by applying the period relation.
$\cos \frac{5}{3}\pi = \cos \frac{\pi}{3} = \frac{1}{2}$	2. In quadrant IV, $\frac{\pi}{3}$ is the reference angle for $\frac{5}{3}\pi$. Remember the cosine is positive in quadrant IV.

Besides periodic relations, you should also be aware of some other trig relations. Look at the right triangle below.

Since the acute angles of a right triangle are complementary, $m\angle A + m\angle B = \frac{\pi}{2}$ radians, or 90°. Therefore, $m\angle B = \frac{\pi}{2} - m\angle A$. You can use this substitution to prove the cofunction relationship.

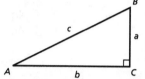

EXAMPLE 4   Prove the cofunction identity $\cos\left(\frac{\pi}{2} - \theta\right) = \sin \theta$.

Answer

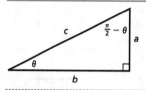

	1. Sketch the right triangle with $m\angle A = \theta$ and $m\angle B = \frac{\pi}{2} - \theta$.
$\cos\left(\frac{\pi}{2} - \theta\right) = \frac{a}{c}$; $\sin \theta = \frac{a}{c}$	2. Observe that $\cos\left(\frac{\pi}{2} - \theta\right)$ and $\sin \theta$ each equal $\frac{a}{c}$.
$\cos\left(\frac{\pi}{2} - \theta\right) = \sin \theta$	3. Substitute.

The *cofunction identities* relate a trig ratio of an angle to the cofunction of its complement. Cofunctions of complementary angles are equal.

Study the table of period and cofunction identities.

Period Identities $k \in \mathbb{Z}$	Cofunction Identities
$\sin(\theta + 2k\pi) = \sin\theta$	$\sin\left(\frac{\pi}{2} - \theta\right) = \cos\theta$
$\cos(\theta + 2k\pi) = \cos\theta$	$\cos\left(\frac{\pi}{2} - \theta\right) = \sin\theta$
$\sec(\theta + 2k\pi) = \sec\theta$	$\sec\left(\frac{\pi}{2} - \theta\right) = \csc\theta$
$\csc(\theta + 2k\pi) = \csc\theta$	$\csc\left(\frac{\pi}{2} - \theta\right) = \sec\theta$
$\tan(\theta + k\pi) = \tan\theta$	$\tan\left(\frac{\pi}{2} - \theta\right) = \cot\theta$
$\cot(\theta + k\pi) = \cot\theta$	$\cot\left(\frac{\pi}{2} - \theta\right) = \tan\theta$

These identities can help you find trig values using the special angles (listed in Section 1.2). You may need some practice recognizing special angles in quadrants II to IV (those with special angles as reference angles).

EXAMPLE 5   List the special angles up to 2π and give the cosine of each.

Answer

QI

θ	$\cos\theta$
0	1
$\frac{\pi}{6}$	$\frac{\sqrt{3}}{2}$
$\frac{\pi}{4}$	$\frac{\sqrt{2}}{2}$
$\frac{\pi}{3}$	$\frac{1}{2}$
$\frac{\pi}{2}$	0

1. First find the cosines for the 30-60 and 45-45 right triangles in quadrant I.

- - - - - - - - - - - - - - - - - - - -

2. Use reference angles to make similar lists for the other quadrants. Remember that the cosine is negative in quadrants II, III.

QII

θ	$\cos\theta$
$\frac{2\pi}{3}$	$-\frac{1}{2}$
$\frac{3\pi}{4}$	$-\frac{\sqrt{2}}{2}$
$\frac{5\pi}{6}$	$-\frac{\sqrt{3}}{2}$
π	-1

QIII

θ	$\cos\theta$
$\frac{7\pi}{6}$	$\frac{-\sqrt{3}}{2}$
$\frac{5\pi}{4}$	$\frac{-\sqrt{2}}{2}$
$\frac{4\pi}{3}$	$-\frac{1}{2}$
$\frac{3\pi}{2}$	0

QIV

θ	$\cos\theta$
$\frac{5\pi}{3}$	$\frac{1}{2}$
$\frac{7\pi}{4}$	$\frac{\sqrt{2}}{2}$
$\frac{11\pi}{6}$	$\frac{\sqrt{3}}{2}$
2π	1

Two other identities can help you with negative angle measures. These identities are called *odd-even identities* for reasons that will become clear in the next section. Look at the quadrant to determine the sign.

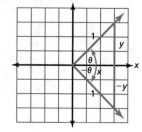

$$\sin(-\theta) = -\sin\theta \text{ and } \cos(-\theta) = \cos\theta$$

Since the triangle in quadrant IV is the same size as that in quadrant I, the following ratios may be found to prove the relations above.

$$\sin(-\theta) = \frac{\text{opp}}{\text{hyp}} = \frac{-y}{1} \qquad \cos(-\theta) = \frac{\text{adj}}{\text{hyp}} = \frac{x}{1}$$

$$\sin\theta = \frac{\text{opp}}{\text{hyp}} = \frac{y}{1} \qquad \cos\theta = \frac{\text{adj}}{\text{hyp}} = \frac{x}{1}$$

▶ A. Exercises

Identify the periods for each of the following.
1. God's cycle of work and rest
2. the phases of the moon

Write period identities for the functions above (in days).
3. Exercise 1
4. Exercise 2
5. List the special angles and give their sines and tangents for quadrants I to IV.

Look at the period identities for the six trig functions.
6. Which four trig functions have a period of 2π?
7. What is the period of the other two trig functions?

▶ B. Exercises

Evaluate. Give exact values when possible.

8. $\sin\frac{55\pi}{4}$
9. $\tan\frac{32\pi}{3}$
10. $\tan\frac{17\pi}{2}$
11. $\cos -84°$

12. $\sin\frac{-16\pi}{3}$
13. $\sin 51°$
14. $\cos\frac{-11\pi}{2}$
15. $\tan 77°$

Prove these cofunction relations using a right triangle diagram.

16. $\sin\left(\frac{\pi}{2} - \theta\right) = \cos\theta$
17. $\tan\left(\frac{\pi}{2} - \theta\right) = \cot\theta$

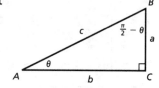

Consider

$$g(x) = \begin{cases} \vdots \\ 0 & \text{if } 0 < x \le 2 \\ 1 & \text{if } 2 < x \le 4 \\ 2 & \text{if } 4 < x \le 5 \\ 0 & \text{if } 5 < x \le 7 \\ 1 & \text{if } 7 < x \le 9 \\ 2 & \text{if } 9 < x \le 10 \\ \vdots \end{cases}$$

18. Graph $g(x)$. Is it periodic?
19. Give the domain, range, and period.
20. Find $g(17)$, $g(\sqrt{899.4})$, and $g(729.58)$.
21. Simplify the function rule for $g(x)$.

Write a period relation for
22. the function of Example 1.
23. the function of exercise 18.

▶ C. Exercises

Write the relationship indicated and then prove it.
24. the relationship of the tangents of negative angle measures to tangents of positive angle measures
25. the period relationship of the cycloid

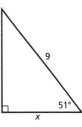 Dominion Modeling

Refer to the sunspot data. Notice that it varies between highs and lows.
26. What is the approximate period based on your scatterplot?
27. Give the range.

■ Cumulative Review

Use synthetic division to answer exercises 28-30.
28. Divide $4x^3 - 3x^2 - 15x - 19$ by $x - 3$.
29. Find $f(5)$ if $f(x) = 4x^3 - 3x^2 - 15x - 19$.
30. Factor and find the zeros of $f(x) = 3x^4 - 16x^3 + 24x^2 - 16$.
31. Graph $f(x)$ as given in exercise 30.
32. Solve for x in the triangle.

3.5 Trigonometric Functions

You can measure angles either in radians or in degrees. For trigonometric functions, radian measure is generally used. The definitions of trigonometric functions relate to the corresponding trigonometric ratios.

Definitions

Sine function $f(x) = \sin x$, where x is an angle measured in radians.

Cosine function $f(x) = \cos x$, where x is an angle measure in radians.

Tangent function $f(x) = \tan x$, where x is an angle measure in radians.

EXAMPLE 1   Find the set of ordered pairs described by $y = \sin x$ when the domain is {0.1745, 0.3840, 1.2392}.

Answer

$y = \sin x$	1. Determine the value of y for
$y = \sin 0.1745 \approx 0.1736$	each value of the domain.
$y = \sin 0.3840 \approx 0.3746$	Remember that the values
$y = \sin 1.2392 \approx 0.9455$	given are angle measures in
	radians.

{(0.1745, 0.1736), (0.3840, 0.3746), (1.2392, 0.9455)}   2. Write the answer as a set.

Having defined the trig functions, consider the domains and ranges of the sine and cosine functions as a step toward making the graphs. (The trig table on page 629 may be used to identify the ranges.) Notice that the sine function increases from 0 to 1 as the angle increases from 0 to $\frac{\pi}{2}$ radians. By contrast, the cosine function begins at 1 and decreases to 0 as the angle goes from 0 to $\frac{\pi}{2}$.

Since the sine values are still positive in the second quadrant, they range from 1 to 0 as the angle increases from $\frac{\pi}{2}$ to π. The cosine, however, is negative in the second quadrant, causing the range of values to go from 0 down to -1. In the third and fourth quadrants the sine is negative, so the values range from 0 to -1

when the angle is in quadrant III and from −1 to 0 in quadrant IV. Cosine values are negative in quadrant III but positive in quadrant IV. These values range from −1 to 0 for third quadrant angles and 0 to 1 for angles in the fourth quadrant.

What about sine and cosine values for angles greater than 2π or less than 0? The trig values for these angles are found using reference angles, so they will also be between −1 and 1. In summary, the trig values for the sine and cosine are as follows:

$$-1 \leq \sin\theta \leq 1, \text{ and } -1 \leq \cos\theta \leq 1.$$

Since these values hold for every angle θ, the range of both the sine and cosine functions is $\{y \mid -1 \leq y \leq 1\}$ or, using absolute value, $\{y \mid |y| \leq 1\}$. Therefore, the graphs of the functions $y = \sin x$ and $y = \cos x$ will never lie outside the lines $y = -1$ and $y = 1$. Let's construct the graphs. To begin, draw a unit circle—a circle with center (0, 0) and radius 1.

To make a graph of the sine function, consider an angle θ whose vertex is on the origin and which intersects the unit circle at a point P. The coordinates of P are $(\cos\theta, \sin\theta)$. To see why a point on the unit circle will have these coordinates, use

$$\cos\theta = \frac{x}{r} = \frac{x}{1} = x \text{ and } \sin\theta = \frac{y}{r} = \frac{y}{1} = y.$$

Thus, $P(x, y) = P(\cos\theta, \sin\theta)$.

You can determine the graph of the sine function, $f(\theta) = \sin\theta$, by considering values of θ between 0 and 2π and their corresponding second coordinates, $\sin\theta$. The height of the unit circle above or below the x-axis for various values of θ corresponds to the value of the sine function; and therefore to the height of the graph above or below the x-axis at those values of θ.

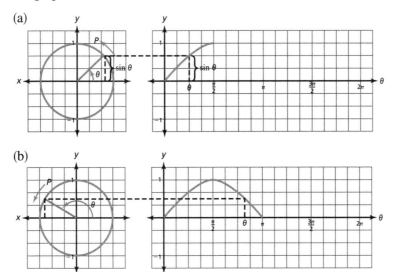

(c)

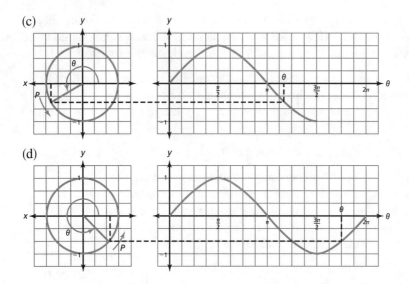

(d)

In Section 3.4 you learned the period identities. The sine function is a periodic function. The graph of the sine function repeats its pattern every time the terminal ray completes a revolution and θ passes a multiple of 2π. The resulting graph is shown below and its period of 2π is obvious.

The graph of the cosine function is similar. However, the range values (the second coordinate of the ordered pairs) of the function $f(\theta) = \cos \theta$ are the first coordinates of points on the unit circle.

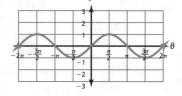

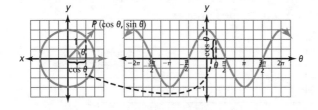

Both the sine and cosine functions are periodic with periods of 2π. You can also see that the domain $D = \mathbb{R}$ for both functions and that $R = \{y \mid -1 \le y \le 1\}$. Both functions are continuous and both have symmetry. Since the sine function is symmetric across the origin, it is an odd function with the property that $\sin (-\theta) = -\sin \theta$. The cosine function is symmetric across the y-axis, so it is an even function with the property that $\cos (-\theta) = \cos \theta$. These identities are called odd-even identities because they reflect whether the function is an odd function or an even function.

Amplitude The amplitude of a function is the absolute value of half the difference between the maximum and minimum values of the function.

$A = \left| \dfrac{m_1 - m_2}{2} \right|$, where m_1 = maximum value and m_2 = minimum value of the function.

Since the range for both $y = \sin \theta$ and $y = \cos \theta$ is $\{y \mid -1 \le y \le 1\}$, the absolute value of half the difference between the maximum and minimum values is $\left| \dfrac{1 - (-1)}{2} \right| = \left| \dfrac{2}{2} \right| = 1$. Therefore, the amplitude of each function is 1.

In general, the amplitude of a sine or cosine function is indicated by the coefficient of the sine or cosine in the function rule. For the functions $f(x) = A \sin \theta$ and $f(x) = A \cos \theta$, the amplitude is $|A|$.

EXAMPLE 2   Graph $y = 2 \sin \theta$.

Answer

$y = 2 \sin \theta$
Amplitude $= |2| = 2$

1. Identify the amplitude of the function.

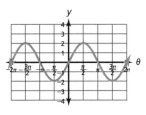

2. Graph the function, using the same general shape as $y = \sin \theta$. However, the amplitude of this function is 2, so the graph increases to 2 and decreases to -2. The period of this function is 2π.

What would happen to the graph if the coefficient were -2? Since $|-2| = 2$, the amplitude is still 2. When $A < 0$, the graph reflects across the x-axis.

Let's examine another quantity that will affect the graph of sine and cosine functions. What do you think would happen to the graph of $y = \cos \theta$ if θ were replaced by $\theta - \pi$? What happened to other functions when x was replaced by $x - h$? If $h > 0$, the graph translates h units right; whereas if $h < 0$, the graph translates h units left. The same type of reasoning applies to these functions. If θ is replaced by $\theta - \pi$ in $y = \cos \theta$, the graph translates π units to the right and if θ is replaced by $\theta + \pi$, the graph translates π units left. A horizontal translation of a trigonometric function is called a *phase shift*.

EXAMPLE 3   Graph $y = \cos(\theta - \pi)$.

Answer

$y = \cos(\theta - \pi)$ phase shift: π units right.	1. Identify the phase shift.
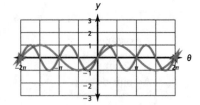	2. Graph using the basic cosine function, $y = \cos\theta$, but shift it π units to the right.

Look at the equation $y = \sin 2\theta$ whose graph is given below. Examine the effect that the coefficient of θ has on the graph of the function by comparing it to the graph of $y = \sin\theta$.

As you can see, the coefficient of 2 changes the period of the function. In fact, the period is π instead of the usual 2π for this sine function. The period of a sine or cosine function will be $\frac{2\pi}{|n|}$ where n is the coefficient of θ in the equation.

The phase shift is also affected by the value of n. The general form of the sine function is $y = A \sin(n\theta - b)$. The phase shift for these trigonometric functions is $\frac{b}{n}$, not b. In order to determine the translation we must think in terms of θ, not $n\theta$. Therefore, the n must be factored out, giving the form $n\left(\theta - \frac{b}{n}\right)$ and yielding a phase shift of $\frac{b}{n}$. In terms of a horizontal translation, the form $y = A \sin n(\theta - h)$ where $h = \frac{b}{n}$ is useful. Some functions may have a modified period and amplitude, and also contain a phase shift.

EXAMPLE 4   Graph $y = -3 \sin\left(\frac{1}{3}\theta - \frac{\pi}{2}\right)$.

Answer

$y = -3 \sin\frac{1}{3}\left(\theta - \frac{3\pi}{2}\right)$	1. Rewrite the function in the form, $y = A \sin n(\theta - h)$.
$|A| = |-3| = 3$	2. Since $A < 0$, the graph reflects across the x-axis with an amplitude of 3. $(-3 \le y \le 3)$

Continued ▶

$$h = \frac{b}{n} = \frac{3\pi}{2}$$

3. Identify the phase shift. Move the graph $\frac{3\pi}{2}$ to the right.

$$\frac{2\pi}{n} = \frac{2\pi}{\frac{1}{3}} = 6\pi$$

One period will begin at $\frac{3\pi}{2}$ and end at $\frac{3\pi}{2} + 6\pi = \frac{15\pi}{2}$. Another begins at $\frac{3\pi}{2} - 6\pi = -\frac{9\pi}{2}$ and ends at $\frac{3\pi}{2}$.

4. Determine the period. From the translated origin $\left(\frac{3\pi}{2}, 0\right)$ find the end of a period in each direction. $\left(\frac{3\pi}{2} \pm 6\pi\right)$

5. Remembering to reflect in the x-axis, sketch a cycle of the graph with the correct amplitude, period, and phase shift. Continue the pattern.

Use a calculator to graph the function $y = \tan x$. Do not expect it to look like the sine and cosine graphs. Since $\tan \frac{\pi}{2}$ is undefined, the graph has no point for that value of x. Such places are marked on the graph with dotted lines called *vertical asymptotes*. These dotted lines are not part of the graph, but are useful guides.

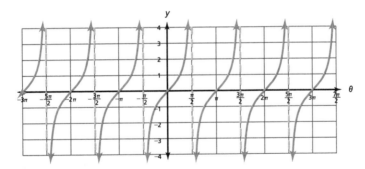

You should see that the period is π, that it is an odd function, and that $D = \{\theta \,|\, \theta \in \mathbb{R} \text{ but } \theta \neq \frac{\pi}{2} + k\pi, k \in \mathbb{Z}\}$ and $R = \mathbb{R}$. Since there is no largest value, there is no amplitude.

Examine the general form of the function, $y = A \tan (n\theta - b)$. The graph of the function becomes steeper as $|A|$ increases (as with parabolas). The value b

causes a phase-shift, as with sine and cosine, translating the previous graph $\frac{b}{n}$ units. The value of n influences the period. The new period is $\frac{\pi}{|n|}$. (Note the difference from sine and cosine graphs.)

▶ A. Exercises

1. Find the set of ordered pairs described by $y = \cos x$ when the domain is {0.1745, 0.3840, 1.239, 0.7854, 1.396}.

2. Find the set of ordered pairs described by $y = \tan x$ when the domain is $\left\{\frac{\pi}{3}, \frac{\pi}{6}, \frac{3\pi}{5}, \frac{-\pi}{4}, 2\pi, \frac{7\pi}{3}\right\}$.

Without graphing, give the amplitude, period, and phase shift for each of the following functions.

3. $y = 3 \cos \theta$

4. $y = \sin\left(\theta - \frac{\pi}{3}\right)$

5. $y = 3 \sin\left(\theta + \frac{\pi}{2}\right)$

6. $y = -4 \cos(\theta + \pi)$

7. $y = 2 \cos 5\theta$

8. $y = \sin\left(3\theta - \frac{\pi}{2}\right)$

9. $y = 2 \cos(2\theta + \pi)$

10. $y = \tan(4\theta - \pi)$

▶ B. Exercises

Write the equation of the sine function with the following characteristics.

11. amplitude = 2
    period = 4π
    phase shift = $\frac{\pi}{2}$
12. amplitude = 1
    period = $\frac{\pi}{2}$
    phase shift = $\frac{\pi}{8}$

Write the equation of the cosine function with the following characteristics.

13. amplitude = 4
    period = 5π
    phase shift = 0
14. amplitude = 1
    period = 6π
    phase shift = $-\frac{\pi}{2}$
15. Give the odd-even identity for tangent. Is this graph continuous?

Give the zeros of each function.

16. $f(x) = \sin x$
17. $g(x) = \cos x$
18. $h(x) = \tan x$

Give the domain and range for the general functions. Assume $A > 0$.

19. $f(x) = A \sin (nx - b)$ and $g(x) = A \cos (nx - b)$
20. $h(x) = A \tan (nx - b)$

Graph.

21. $y = \cos 2\theta$
22. $y = 3 \sin 2\theta$
23. $y = -\sin 2\theta$
24. $y = -\tan \frac{1}{2}\theta$
29. $y = 2 \tan \left(3\theta - \frac{\pi}{2}\right)$

25. $y = -2 \cos \left(\theta - \frac{\pi}{2}\right)$
26. $y = 4 \cos (\theta + \pi)$
27. $y = 3 \sin (2\theta - \pi)$
28. $y = 2 \cos \left(\frac{1}{4}\theta - \pi\right)$
30. $y = -2.74 \sin (4.3\,\theta + 0.562)$

▶ C. Exercises

31. Graph $h(x) = \sin x + 2 \cos x$ by graphing $f(x) = \sin x$ and $g(x) = 2 \cos x$ on the same coordinate system. Estimate and plot the sum of their y-coordinates and draw the curve.
32. Graph $y \geq 2 \sin \frac{2}{3}x$.

Dominion Modeling

33. Find a sinusoidal model and draw it with the data.
34. In the equation $y = a \sin (bx - c) + d$, the d-value determines a horizontal line called the *mid-line* or *axis* of a sinusoidal curve. Find the mid-line of the model.
35. What is the amplitude (distance above or below the mid-line)?

Cumulative Review

36. Write a polynomial function with roots of multiplicity 2 at -3 and at 4.

If $P(x)$ is a quadratic function, and $Q(x)$ is a cubic polynomial function, find the following.

37. The degree of $P(x) + Q(x)$.
38. The degree of $P(x)Q(x)$.
39. The degree of $\frac{Q(x)}{P(x)}$ if the remainder is zero and $P(x) \neq 0$.
40. When is the sum of two quadratic functions not quadratic?

GOTTFRIED WILHELM VON LEIBNIZ

Gottfried Wilhelm von Leibniz was born on July 1, 1646, in the German town of Leipzig and was reared in a Protestant home. His father, who died in 1652, was a professor of moral philosophy. Although he attended the Nicolai School, it was in his father's library that Leibniz taught himself Latin, Greek, the classics, and politics. To prepare for his goal of a career in politics, he began the study of law at the University of Leipzig at the age of 15. He received his bachelor's degree in 1663, and by 1666 he completed the requirement for a doctorate in law. He was denied this degree because certain professors were envious and jealous of him, but to conceal their envy they used Leibniz's age (he was only twenty) as the reason for not awarding him the degree. This injustice prompted him to move to the University of Altdorf, where he received the doctorate in November 1666. Refusing an offer to teach at Altdorf, he pursued politics as a career.

Louis XIV invited Leibniz to Paris to develop a political plan related to resolving a division within the Catholic church. While in Paris, Leibniz came into contact with a Dutch physicist and mathematician, Christian Huygens, who greatly encouraged Leibniz to continue his pursuits in mathematics. Prior to his work in Paris, Leibniz invented a calculating machine capable of addition, subtraction, multiplication, division, and extraction of roots. Leibniz also discovered the following relationship between π and the reciprocals of the odd numbers:

$$\pi = 4(1 - \tfrac{1}{3} + \tfrac{1}{5} - \tfrac{1}{7} + \cdots).$$

In 1684, Leibniz published *A New Method for Maxima and Minima, and also for Tangents*, which is not obstructed

by irrational quantities. This was the first published account of differential calculus. Leibniz followed this work with integral calculus and the fundamental theorem of calculus. His notations dx, dy, and $\int$ are still used today as well as his symbol for congruence and similarity.

The discovery of calculus was subject to much controversy. Isaac Newton, a contemporary of Leibniz, had also made this exact same discovery and accused Leibniz of plagiarism. England believed that Newton was the sole discoverer, and the rest of Europe believed that Leibniz made the original discovery. Today we know that the two great mathematicians independently made the same discovery. Newton discovered the theorem before Leibniz, but did not publish it until 1687, so Leibniz did not copy. Both men deserve credit for the discovery. Such simultaneous discoveries illustrate that math is not solely an invention of the individual mind.

In his later years, Leibniz moved to Hanover, where John Frederick, the duke of Brunswick, employed him as librarian and historian. His duties included genealogical research of the House of Brunswick in order to confirm the Brunswick's claims to half the thrones of Europe. His research required him to travel throughout Germany, Austria, and Italy. While in Rome, the pope urged Leibniz to accept the position of librarian at the Vatican. Leibniz refused the offer because he would not become Catholic to meet a job prerequisite. Shortly thereafter, Leibniz was called to Berlin as a tutor. While in Germany, Leibniz organized the Berlin Academy of Sciences, which remained one of the leading scientific schools in the world until the Nazi take-over prior to World War II.

Leibniz returned to Hanover, where he died on November 14, 1716. In seventy years this philosopher-mathematician accomplished much. His genius touched most of the technologies of the following centuries, laying the basic foundation for the modern computer. His discoveries in mathematics have earned him the awe and respect of all modern mathematicians.

His genius touched most of the technologies of the following centuries

3.6 Reciprocal Functions

Review the definitions of the reciprocal trigonometric ratios:

$$\sec x = \frac{1}{\cos x} \qquad \csc x = \frac{1}{\sin x} \qquad \cot x = \frac{1}{\tan x}$$

These ratios correspond to three trigonometric functions called *reciprocal trigonometric functions:* $y = \sec \theta$, $y = \csc \theta$, and $y = \cot \theta$. Notice that each is the reciprocal of one of the basic trig functions.

These functions are examples of a larger class of *reciprocal functions,* including reciprocals of power, polynomial, and exponential functions. Here are four examples of reciprocal functions.

$$f(x) = \frac{1}{3x^4} \qquad g(x) = \frac{1}{x^2 - 4}$$
$$h(x) = \frac{1}{4^x} \qquad k(x) = \sec x$$

EXAMPLE 1   Find $f(1)$, $g(2)$, $h\left(\frac{1}{2}\right)$, and $k\left(\frac{\pi}{4}\right)$, using the functions above.

Answer $f(x) = \frac{1}{3x^4}$ $\qquad\qquad$ $f(1) = \frac{1}{3(1)^4} = \frac{1}{3}$

$\qquad\qquad$ $g(x) = \frac{1}{x^2 - 4}$ $\qquad\qquad$ $g(2) = \frac{1}{2^2 - 4} = \frac{1}{0}$, which is undefined.

$\qquad\qquad$ $h(x) = \frac{1}{4^x}$ $\qquad\qquad$ $h\left(\frac{1}{2}\right) = \frac{1}{4^{\frac{1}{2}}} = \frac{1}{\sqrt{4}} = \frac{1}{2}$

$\qquad\qquad$ $k(x) = \sec x$ $\qquad\qquad$ $k\left(\frac{\pi}{4}\right) = \sec \frac{\pi}{4} = \frac{1}{\cos \frac{\pi}{4}} = \frac{1}{\frac{\sqrt{2}}{2}} = \frac{2}{\sqrt{2}} = \sqrt{2}$

Since reciprocal functions have denominators, you must be careful about what values are used in the domain. In the example above, $g(2)$ was undefined due to division by zero. This means that 2 is not in the domain of g. The graph will have a vertical asymptote at $x = 2$, much like the graph of $y = \tan x$ has at $x = \frac{\pi}{2}$.

EXAMPLE 2

EXAMPLE 2   Find the domains of $f(x)$, $g(x)$, $h(x)$, and $k(x)$ in the previous functions.

Answer

$f(x)$	$g(x)$	1. Find all values for which the denominator of $f(x)$ and $g(x)$ equals zero.
$3x^4 = 0$	$x^2 - 4 = 0$	
$x^4 = 0$	$x^2 = 4$	
$x = 0$	$x = \pm 2$	

$D = \{x \mid x \in \mathbb{R}, x \neq 0\}$	$D = \{x \mid x \in \mathbb{R}, x \neq \pm 2\}$	2. Exclude those values from the domain.

Since $4^x \neq 0 \; \forall \, x$, the domain of $h(x)$ is $\mathbb{R}$. Since $\cos x = 0$ when $x = \frac{\pi}{2} + k\pi, \, k \in \mathbb{Z}$, the domain of $k(x)$ is $D = \{x \mid x \in \mathbb{R}, x \neq \frac{\pi}{2} + k\pi, \, k \in \mathbb{Z}\}$.

3. Consult the exponential and cosine graphs to verify the domains for $h(x)$ and $k(x)$.

You may recall that reciprocal means the multiplicative inverse. For instance, 5 and $\frac{1}{5}$ are reciprocals because $5 \cdot \frac{1}{5} = 1$. Likewise, $\frac{1}{f(x)}$ is a reciprocal function of $f(x)$ because $f(x) \cdot \frac{1}{f(x)} = 1$. This will help you to recognize reciprocal functions involving negative exponents: $x^n \cdot x^{-n} = x^0 = 1$. Therefore x^n and x^{-n} are reciprocal functions. This makes sense if you remember that $x^{-n} = \frac{1}{x^n}$. In fact, you have already graphed exponential decay functions like $y = 4^{-x}$ which is the reciprocal function for $y = 4^x$.

Look at the numbers 1, 2, 5, 10, 20, 100, and 1000. Think about their reciprocals: $1, \frac{1}{2}, \frac{1}{5}, \frac{1}{10}, \frac{1}{20}, \frac{1}{100}, \frac{1}{1000}$. The larger the number, the closer the reciprocal is to zero and vice-versa. Also, notice that the reciprocal of 1 is itself. Keeping this principle in mind, use the graph of the function $f(x)$ at the right to sketch the graph of its reciprocal function $\frac{1}{f(x)}$ shown below.

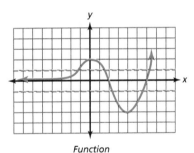

Function

y

Reciprocal function

First, use horizontal lines at $y = 1$ and $y = -1$ to find the points where $f(x) = \pm 1$. Since these points are their own reciprocals, they will be on the reciprocal function graph also. There will be vertical asymptotes for the function $\frac{1}{f(x)}$ whenever $f(x) = 0$. Find the zeros of the function ($x = 2$, $x = 6$) to identify where $f(x) = 0$. Sketch the vertical asymptotes.

Now, apply the principle of reciprocals. The values on the left tail of $f(x)$ are fractions whose values are approaching zero (the denominators are getting larger and larger). The reciprocals of these will get larger and larger, approaching infinity. In contrast, the right tail of $f(x)$ is approaching infinity, yielding reciprocals that will approach zero. This leads us to conclude that $y = 0$ is a *horizontal asymptote*. Likewise, the values near the zeros will become very large (since taking reciprocals does not change signs, keep the graph on the same side of the *x*-axis as $f(x)$).

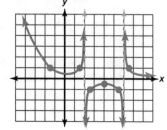

Finally, connect the last parts of the graph by finding the reciprocals. Since $f(0) = 2$, the reciprocal function should have a *y*-intercept at $\left(0, \frac{1}{2}\right)$. You can see that the "hill" is now a "valley." Similarly, the reciprocal at $f(4) = -3$ is $-\frac{1}{3}$. Use the values to finish your sketch.

EXAMPLE 3   Graph $g(x) = \dfrac{1}{x^2 - 4}$. Give the domain and range. Is $g(x)$ continuous? Is $g(x)$ an odd or even function?

Answer

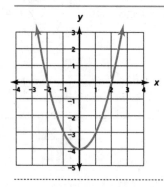

1. Graph $f(x) = x^2 - 4$.

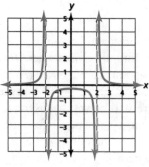

2. Use reciprocal principles to graph $g(x)$.

Continued ▶

$D = \{x \mid x \neq \pm 2\}$
$R = \{y \mid y > 0 \text{ or } y \leq -\frac{1}{4}\}$
$g(x)$ is an even function but is not continuous.

3. Zeros of $f(x)$ correspond to vertical asymptotes of $g(x)$. The range $y \geq -4$ for $f(x)$ becomes $y \leq -\frac{1}{4}$ as part of the range of $g(x)$.

Notice that there are no x-intercepts on the graph of $g(x)$. This means the function is never equal to zero. A fraction equals zero only when the numerator is zero. Since the numerator of $\frac{1}{x^2 - 4}$ is 1, there is no value of x that makes the entire fraction zero. Of course, ± 2 makes the denominator equal to zero, but that causes the fraction to be undefined rather than zero.

EXAMPLE 4   Graph $g(x) = \frac{1}{x^2 - 4}$ again without graphing its reciprocal function first.

Answer

$x^2 - 4 = 0$
$x^2 = 4$
$x = \pm 2$
$D = \{x \mid x \neq \pm 2\}$

1. Find the domain by excluding values where the denominator equals zero.

no x-intercepts

2. Check for x-intercepts. Since the numerator cannot equal zero, the graph cannot touch the x-axis.

x	$g(x)$
-3	$\frac{1}{5}$
0	$-\frac{1}{4}$
3	$\frac{1}{5}$

3. Plot a point in each of the regions determined by the asymptotes (which are at 2 and -2). Since the graph cannot cross the x-axis, points within a region will all be on the same side. Include the y-intercept as one of the points.

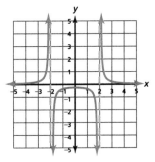

4. Use the asymptotes as guides. Your graph will never quite reach either vertical asymptote or the x-axis.

The method of Example 4 is easier for most rational functions, but the method of Example 3 is convenient for graphing a reciprocal by hand when the function rule is not known. It will also help in graphing the reciprocal trig functions by hand. Since $\csc \theta = \frac{1}{\sin \theta}$, use $y = \sin \theta$ to graph $y = \csc \theta$.

EXAMPLE 5 Graph $y = \csc x$. Give the domain, range, zeros, and period. Is it continuous?

Answer

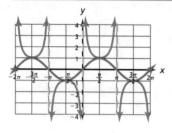

1. Graph sin x.

2. Do reciprocals graphically. Note that the vertical asymptotes will be at $x = 0$ (y-axis) and multiples of π.

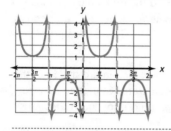

3. Show the final graph.

$D = \{x \mid x \neq k\pi, k \in \mathbb{Z}\}$
$R = \{y \mid y \geq 1 \text{ or } y \leq -1\}$
The function has no zeros; the period is 2π. It is not continuous.

4. Answer the questions from the graph. The range can be more simply expressed by $R = \{y \mid |y| \geq 1\}$.

▶ **A. Exercises**

Graph the reciprocal function of each function graphed below.

1. $f(x)$

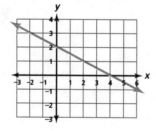

2. $g(x)$

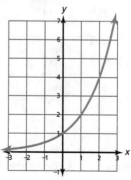

3. $p(x)$

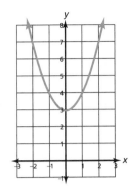

4. $h(x)$

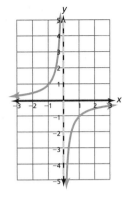

Give the vertical asymptotes of each reciprocal function.

5. $f(x) = \frac{1}{x + 3}$

6. $h(x) = \frac{1}{x^2 + 5x - 14}$

7. $g(x) = \frac{1}{x^2 + 1}$

8. $r(x) = \frac{1}{x^3 - 3x^2 - 13x + 15}$

Evaluate each function as indicated.

9. $f(x) = \frac{1}{x^2 - 25}$ for $x = 2$ and $x = -6$

10. $g(x) = \csc x$ for $x = \frac{\pi}{3}$ and $x = \pi$

▶ B. Exercises

Graph each reciprocal function. Give the domain and range for exercises 11-15.

11. $f(x) = \frac{1}{x + 3}$

12. $h(x) = \frac{1}{x^2 + 5x - 14}$

13. $g(x) = \frac{1}{x^2 + 1}$

14. $h(x) = \frac{1}{x^3 - 3x^2 - 13x + 15}$

15. $g(x) = \frac{1}{x^2}$

16. $f(x) = \frac{1}{3x - 4}$

17. $p(x) = \frac{1}{x^3}$

18. $q(x) = \frac{1}{x^3 + 2x^2}$

19. $y = \frac{1}{x^4 - x^2}$

20. $y = \frac{1}{x^2 - 2x + 1}$

21. $f(x) = \frac{1}{-x^3 + 4.4x - 21}$

Graph the two reciprocal trig functions. Identify the domain, range, zeros, and period. Identify each function as odd, even, or neither, and as continuous or not continuous.

22. $f(x) = \sec x$

23. $g(x) = \cot x$

Give the period for each reciprocal trig function and prove its period identity. (Use the period for its reciprocal function.)

24. $y = \sec \theta$

25. $y = \csc \theta$

26. $y = \cot \theta$

Decide whether each reciprocal function is odd or even and then prove its odd-even identity. (Use the odd-even identity of the reciprocal function.)

27. $y = \sec \theta$

28. $y = \csc \theta$

29. $y = \cot \theta$

Graph the following reciprocal trig functions. Use phase shifts and periods as necessary.

30. $y = -\sec x$

31. $y = \sec\left(x - \frac{\pi}{3}\right)$

32. $y = \cot\left(x - \frac{x}{4}\right)$

⊞ 33. $y = -2.4 \csc (3.1x - 0.685)$

34. If $f(x)$ has domain $\mathbb{R}$ and no zeros, what can you say about the domain and zeros of the reciprocal function $g(x) = \frac{1}{f(x)}$?

▶ C. Exercises

⊞ 35. Graph $y = 3 \csc \left(2x + \frac{\pi}{2}\right)$. Use the graphing calculator to check your graph.

Let $f(x) = \frac{1}{x^n}$ so that $f(x)$ is the reciprocal of a power function ($n \in \mathbb{N}$).

36. Give the domain. Is $f(x)$ continuous? Explain.

37. Give the range. Is $f(x)$ symmetric? Explain.

⊞ Dominion Modeling

Consider again the sunspot data and the sinusoidal model you developed in the previous section. The values predicted by the function may not exactly equal the original data values. For this reason, the symbol $\hat{y}$ ("y-hat") is used to distinguish the predicted value of y for a given x-value from the observed y-value. Using this notation, the predicted points on the curve $(x_i, \hat{y}_i)$ are distinguished from the original data values (x_i, y_i).

38. Use your function to predict the number of sunspots halfway through 1986. Is it close to the actual value of 13.8 sunspots?

39. Add a new column for the predicted $\hat{y}_i$-values.

40. According to the model, when was the first sunspot maximum after 1999? When could we expect the next minimum?

41. Solve $\triangle ABC$ where $A = 58°$, $B = 39°$, and $a = 10.5$.

42. Give the period and amplitude of $y = 5 \sin 3x$.

43. Find $f(4)$ if $f(x) = \begin{cases} x - 8 & \text{if } x < 3 \\ x^2 - 1 & \text{if } 3 \le x \le 9. \\ 7x & \text{if } x > 9. \end{cases}$

44. How many zeros does a cubic polynomial function have? Why?

45. Graph $y = 2^x$ and estimate $2^{0.7}$ from the graph.

3.7 Proper Rational Functions

In mathematics, the word *rational* conveys the idea of a ratio. Just as the rational numbers are ratios of integers, $\left\{ \frac{a}{b} \mid a, b \in \mathbb{Z}, b \ne 0 \right\}$, *rational functions* are ratios of polynomials.

Definition

Rational function   A function $f(x)$ such that $f(x) = \frac{P(x)}{Q(x)}$ where $P(x)$ and $Q(x)$ are polynomials and $Q(x) \ne 0$.

Examples of rational functions are $f(x) = \frac{x^2 - 5}{x + 1}$ and $g(x) = \frac{3x + 2}{x^3 - 6x^2 + 11x - 6}$.

As with reciprocal functions, you can find the domain by excluding values where the denominator is zero. To evaluate rational functions, substitute the given domain value and simplify to find the range.

EXAMPLE 1   Evaluate $f(x)$ and $g(x)$ for $x = 0$ and $x = \frac{1}{2}$. Give the domains.

Answer

$f(x) = \frac{x^2 - 5}{x + 1}$

$f(0) = \frac{0^2 - 5}{0 + 1} = \frac{-5}{1} = -5$

$f\left(\frac{1}{2}\right) = \frac{\left(\frac{1}{2}\right)^2 - 5}{\frac{1}{2} + 1} = \frac{\frac{-19}{4}}{\frac{3}{2}} = \frac{-19}{6}$

$g(x) = \frac{3x + 2}{x^3 - 6x^2 + 11x - 6}$

$g(0) = \frac{3(0) + 2}{0^3 - 6(0)^2 + 11(0) - 6} = \frac{2}{-6} = -\frac{1}{3}$

$g\left(\frac{1}{2}\right) = \frac{3\left(\frac{1}{2}\right) + 2}{\left(\frac{1}{2}\right)^3 - 6\left(\frac{1}{2}\right)^2 + 11\left(\frac{1}{2}\right) - 6} = \frac{\frac{7}{2}}{\frac{-15}{8}} = \frac{-28}{15}$

- -

Let $x + 1 = 0$ to determine when the denominator of $f(x)$ will be 0.

$x + 1 = 0$

$x = -1$

$D = \{x \,|\, x \neq -1\}$

Let $x^3 - 6x^2 + 11x - 6 = 0$ to determine when the denominator of $g(x)$ will be 0.

Possible rational zeros are $\pm 1, \pm 2, \pm 3, \pm 6$.

Use synthetic division to factor the polynomial.

$x^3 - 6x^2 + 11x - 6 = 0$

$(x - 1)(x - 2)(x - 3) = 0$

$x = 1, x = 2, x = 3$

$D = \{x \,|\, x \neq 1, 2, 3\}$

Do you remember the difference between proper and improper fractions? In a proper fraction the numerator is smaller than the denominator:

Proper: $\frac{1}{6}, \frac{2}{4}, \frac{3}{7}$ Improper: $\frac{7}{1}, \frac{9}{6}, \frac{11}{2}, \frac{4}{4}, \frac{5}{3}$

Which of the proper and improper fractions above are not reduced? You can reduce four of them as shown:

$\frac{2}{4} = \frac{1}{2}$ $\frac{7}{1} = 7$ $\frac{9}{6} = \frac{3}{2}$ $\frac{4}{4} = 1$

The same distinctions can be drawn for rational functions by using the degree of the numerator and denominator.

Definition

Proper rational function   A rational function in which the degree of the numerator is less than the degree of the denominator.

A *reduced rational function* is a rational function in which the numerator and denominator have no common factors. In Example 1, $f(x)$ is improper and $g(x)$ is proper.

EXAMPLE 2   Graph $f(x) = \dfrac{1}{x+5}$.

Answer

$x + 5 = 0$ $\qquad x = -5$ $D = \{x \mid x \neq -5\}$	1. Find the domain. There is a vertical asymptote at $x = -5$, since -5 makes the function undefined.
$f(0) = \dfrac{1}{0+5} = \dfrac{1}{5}$; plot $\left(0, \dfrac{1}{5}\right)$ There are no x-intercepts.	2. Find the intercepts. The y-intercept occurs when $x = 0$; x-intercepts occur where $y = 0$ (the numerator is zero).
$f(-6) = \dfrac{1}{-6+5} = \dfrac{1}{-1} = -1$ $f(-4) = \dfrac{1}{-4+5} = 1$	3. Plot more points if necessary. Find one on the other side of the asymptote from the y-intercept.
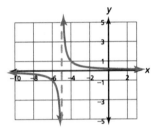	4. Draw the curve, crossing axes only at intercepts. Notice that $R = \{y \mid y \neq 0\}$ and the function is not continuous, since it has a gap.

Take special note of the line $x = -5$ in the graph above. It is a vertical asymptote—a line that the graph approaches but never crosses. Vertical asymptotes occur at any x-value that makes the denominator of a *reduced* rational function equal to zero.

Another type of asymptote is a *horizontal asymptote*. The x-axis ($y = 0$) is a horizontal asymptote in Example 2. The graph of $f(x)$ is said to approach the x-axis *asymptotically*. The x-axis is always a horizontal asymptote for a proper rational function. This is because the denominator, having a higher degree, increases faster than the numerator and makes the fraction approach zero but it is never equal to zero. Horizontal asymptotes tell you what happens to the tails of the graph. The tails are the part of the graph where x is approaching larger numbers in the positive direction and numbers with larger absolute values in the negative direction ($\pm$infinity). A graph can cross a horizontal asymptote, as the next example shows. The horizontal asymptote tells you only about the tails. Both tails will approach this horizontal line.

EXAMPLE 3   Graph $g(x) = \dfrac{x+2}{x^2 - 3x + 2}$.

Answer

$x^2 - 3x + 2 = 0$ $(x-2)(x-1) = 0$ $x = 2$ or $x = 1$	1. Find all vertical asymptotes (where the denominator equals zero).
$g(0) = \dfrac{0+2}{0^2 - 3 \cdot 0 + 2} = \dfrac{2}{2} = 1;\ (0,1)$ $x + 2 = 0$ at $x = -2;\ (-2, 0)$	2. Find all intercepts. The x-intercepts occur when the numerator equals 0.
$g(3) = \dfrac{3+2}{3^2 - 3 \cdot 3 + 2} = \dfrac{5}{2} = 2\frac{1}{2}$ $g\left(\dfrac{3}{2}\right) = \dfrac{\frac{3}{2} + 2}{\left(\frac{3}{2}\right)^2 - 3\left(\frac{3}{2}\right) + 2} = \dfrac{\frac{7}{2}}{\frac{-1}{4}} = -14$	3. Find values in the intervals between and beyond asymptotes.

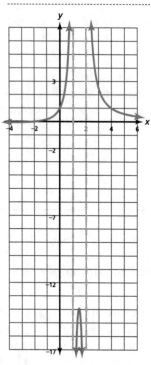

4. Graph. Plot the points and use the asymptotes. Be sure to use the x-axis as an asymptote. Since the only x-intercept is at -2, the graph cannot cross the x-axis anywhere else. The left tail will approach the x-axis from the negative side.

▶ A. Exercises

For each graph below, identify the intercepts, asymptotes, domain, and range.

1.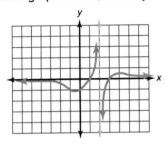

3.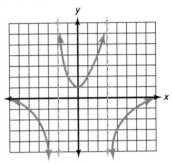

2.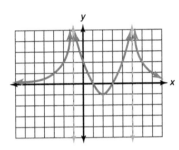

4.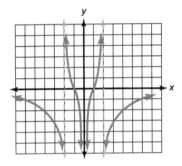

For each function below, give the *y*-intercept, the domain, and any vertical asymptotes.

5. $f(x) = \dfrac{6}{x + 2}$

6. $r(x) = \dfrac{x + 3}{x^2 - 4}$

7. $h(x) = \dfrac{x^2 + 3x - 4}{x^2 + 4x - 12}$

8. $p(x) = \dfrac{x}{x^2 + 3x}$

9. $q(x) = \dfrac{x}{x^2 + 4}$

10. $g(x) = \dfrac{x^2 - 1}{x^3 - 4x^2 - 4x + 16}$

▶ B. Exercises

Decide if each function above is proper and reduced. If it is not, explain why. If it is, give the *x*-intercepts and the horizontal asymptotes. Graph each function and identify any graphs that are continuous, odd, or even.

11. $f(x)$

12. $r(x)$

13. $h(x)$

14. $p(x)$

15. $q(x)$

16. $g(x)$

Graph each rational function below.

17. $f(x) = \dfrac{x + 2}{x^2 + 7x - 3}$

18. $g(x) = \dfrac{x^2}{x^3 - 1}$

19. $r(x) = \dfrac{x}{x^2 + 4x + 4}$

20. $h(x) = \dfrac{x^2 - 1}{x^3}$

21. $l(x) = \dfrac{x^2 - x - 6}{x^3 - 3x^2 - 10x + 24}$

22. $q(x) = \dfrac{x^2 + 2x + 1}{x^4 - 6x^2 + 9}$

23. $k(x) = \dfrac{x^2 + 7.4x - 2.31}{x^3 + 2.3x^2 - 12.48x + 9.18}$

▶ C. Exercises

24. Which of the following are rational functions? If any are not, explain why.

$$f(x) = \frac{3x^2 - 2x + 3\sqrt{2}}{x - \sqrt{5}}, \; g(x) = \frac{(\sqrt{2}x)^2 - \sqrt{3}x - 4}{(x - 3\sqrt{2})^2},$$

$$h(x) = \frac{2x^3 + x^{\sqrt{2}}}{x^2 - \frac{1}{2}}, \; k(x) = \frac{\left(\sin \frac{\pi}{5}\right)x^2}{e^{\sqrt{2}x}}$$

25. Graph $h(x) = \dfrac{1}{x} + \dfrac{1}{x - 2}$ by first graphing $f(x) = \dfrac{1}{x}$, using translation to graph $g(x) = \dfrac{1}{x - 2}$ on the same axes, then estimating and plotting the sum of the two from your curves. Then find the equation algebraically by adding the parts of the function h.

Dominion Modeling

Consider the sunspot data again. In the last section you distinguished predicted values $\hat{y}_i$ from the observed values y_i for the ith value of x. The difference between a predicted and observed value is called a *residual* or an *error*: $e_i = y_i - \hat{y}_i$. The term *error* does not refer to a "mistake"; it means the model does not completely explain all the variation in the data.

26. Find the *residuals* e_i by creating a new column of data from the relationship, $y_i - \hat{y}_i = e_i$. Explain how you get this column on your calculator.

27. Plot the residuals on the *y*-axis for corresponding years on the *x*-axis.

28. A good model should use recognizable patterns in prediction. Thus, if the residual "errors" from the model show any pattern, the model could have been improved. If the residuals appear randomly located, the model is good. Do you see a systematic pattern in the residual plot? Is the model good?

29. When is a residual zero? positive? negative?

Cumulative Review

Consider the following functions.

$$f(x) = x^5 - x^3 \qquad\qquad k(x) = \tan x$$
$$g(x) = 3x^2 + 1 \qquad\qquad p(x) = x^6 - 4x$$
$$h(x) = [x] \qquad\qquad q(x) = \frac{1}{x^2 - 4}$$
$$j(x) = \cos x \qquad\qquad r(x) = |x|$$

30. Which are odd functions?
31. Which are even functions?
32. Which are neither?

Let $f(x) = 3x^5 - 23x^4 + 61x^3 - 61x^2 + 8x + 12$.

33. List all possible integer zeros.
34. Factor $f(x)$.

3.8 Rational Functions

Now that you can graph rational functions that are reduced and proper, you can extend your skills to improper and unreduced rational functions. To graph these you must recognize exceptions to principles regarding x-intercepts and asymptotes. Exceptions and conditions are always important. I Corinthians 15:27-28 shows that God, the Father, is the exception to the rule that everything is under Christ's authority. Likewise, when you quote Romans 10:13, you know that "whosoever" applies to all human beings with the exception of Jesus himself, who is both man and God.

> *Medicine makes people ill, mathematics makes them sad and theology makes them sinful.*
> —MARTIN LUTHER (1483-1546)

The important exception to cancellation rules is that $\frac{0}{0}$ is undefined. Since, $\frac{5}{5} = 1$, you might think that $\frac{0}{0}$ should also be 1. Likewise, since $\frac{0}{3} = 0$, you might think that $\frac{0}{0}$ should also be 0. Since it cannot be both 0 and 1, it is indeterminate and must be left undefined. In fact, since $0 \cdot a = 0 \ \forall \ a$, you could rewrite this as a division $\frac{0}{0} = a \ \forall \ a$, which shows that dividing 0 by itself could result in any real number. Thus, it is impossible to uniquely define this division.

In conclusion, you can cancel only for values where the denominator is not zero.

$$\frac{x-2}{x-2} = 1 \text{ if } x \neq 2$$

It is easy to graph unreduced rational functions if you are careful with values that may not be canceled.

EXAMPLE 1 Graph $h(x) = \dfrac{x-2}{x^2 - 5x + 6}$.

Answer

$h(x) = \dfrac{(x-2)}{(x-2)(x-3)}$ | 1. Factor

$h(x) = \dfrac{1}{x-3}$ if $x \neq 2$ | 2. Reduce the expression, noting the condition required for cancellation.

Continued ▶

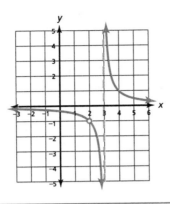

3. Graph the reduced function. Notice the vertical asymptote at $x = 3$. Insert a hole at $x = 2$, the excluded value. Since the original function is undefined at $x = 2$, no point can be graphed for that value.

The domain $D = \{x \mid x \neq 2, 3\}$ can be found by excluding values that make the original denominator equal to zero. However, only one of the two excluded values indicates a vertical asymptote; the other is a hole. This is why vertical asymptotes must be determined from a *reduced* rational function. Zeros of the numerator are usually x-intercepts but only when the rational function is in reduced form.

If a is a zero of both the numerator and denominator of a rational function, then the factor $(x - a)$ cancels if $x \neq a$. Graph the reduced function and place a hole in the graph at $x = a$. In other words, whenever a factor cancels it does not contribute an x-intercept or a vertical asymptote. Instead it identifies a hole in the graph. Be sure to make a note of any cancellation conditions and locate the corresponding holes on your graph.

The function in Example 2 shows a function that is improper (the degree of the numerator equals the degree of the denominator) and unreduced.

EXAMPLE 2 Identify the domain, zeros, asymptotes, and holes of the given function.
$$f(x) = \frac{(x + 2)(x - 1)(x - 3)}{(x - 3)(x + 5)(x - 7)}$$

Answer

$D = \{x \mid x \neq -5, 3, 7\}$	1. Find the domain. The denominator of a rational expression cannot equal zero.
$x - 3$ cancels to reduce the expression. At $x = 3$ there is a hole in the graph.	2. Locate holes on the graph by noticing factors that can cancel.

Continued ▶

Vertical asymptotes occur at $x = -5$ and $x = 7$	3. Use the reduced form to identify vertical asymptotes.
Zeros occur at $x = -2$ and $x = 1$.	4. Identify the zeros using the numerator of the reduced form.

The next examples develop principles for graphing improper rational expressions.

EXAMPLE 3   Draw the graphs of a) $g_1(x) = \frac{1}{x^2}$ and b) $g_2(x) = \frac{3x^2 + 1}{x^2}$.

Answer

a)

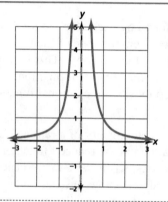

Sketch the graph of g_1, a reciprocal function. Use symmetry across the y-axis, since it is an even function and note that there are no x- or y-intercepts. Also note the vertical asymptote at $x = 0$ ($x^2 = 0$ when $x = 0$) and the horizontal asymptote at $y = 0$ (the rational expression is proper).

b) $g_2(x) = \frac{3x^2 + 1}{x^2} = \frac{3x^2}{x^2} + \frac{1}{x^2} = 3 + \frac{1}{x^2}$ 1. Divide the improper rational expression to obtain a proper one.

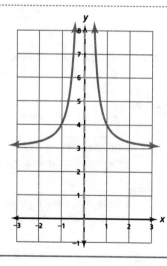

2. Graph $g_2(x)$ by translating $g_1(x)$ up 3 units.

You can easily observe that g_2 is also undefined at $x = 0$, and has the y-axis for its vertical asymptote. But the horizontal asymptote $y = 0$ of g_1 translates to $y = 3$ in g_2. The horizontal asymptote was obtained by division: the quotient of the numerator $P(x)$, divided by the denominator $Q(x)$, is 3 plus a remainder. The remainder $\frac{1}{x^2}$ approaches zero as $|x|$ increases, thus the graph of $g_2(x)$ approaches $y = 3$.

Whenever the degree of $P(x)$ and $Q(x)$ are equal, the quotient (excluding the remainder), and therefore the horizontal asymptote, will be the ratio of the leading coefficients of $P(x)$ and $Q(x)$.

EXAMPLE 4   Find the horizontal asymptote for $r(x) = \dfrac{3x^4 - x^2 + 4}{18x^4 - x^3 + 5x}$.

Answer

Method 1:

$$18x^4 - x^3 + 0x^2 + 5x \overline{)\begin{array}{c} \frac{1}{6} \\ 3x^4 + 0x^3 - x^2 + 0x + 4 \end{array}}$$

$$3x^4 - \tfrac{1}{6}x^3 + 0x^2 + \tfrac{5}{6}x$$

$$\tfrac{1}{6}x^3 - x^2 - \tfrac{5}{6}x + 4$$

$\tfrac{1}{6}$ R. $\tfrac{1}{6}x^3 - x^2 - \tfrac{5}{6}x + 4$

$y = \tfrac{1}{6}$ is the horizontal asymptote.

1. Divide: Since the denominator is not a monomial, use long division.

2. The quotient (not including the remainder) is the asymptote.

Method 2:

$\dfrac{3}{18} = \dfrac{1}{6}$

$y = \tfrac{1}{6}$ is the horizontal asymptote.

Since the degrees of $P(x)$ and $Q(x)$ are equal (both 4), find the ratio of the leading coefficients to obtain the horizontal asymptote.

Can you determine the horizontal asymptote for Example 2? Since the numerator and denominator are both third degree polynomials (imagine multiplying them out), with leading coefficients of 1, the horizontal asymptote is $y = \frac{1}{1} = 1$.

Look at the rational expression: $\frac{0x^2 + 2x + 1}{3x^2 + 5x + 7}$. The horizontal asymptote occurs at the ratios of leading coefficients: $y = \frac{0}{3} = 0$. This should help you see why $f(x) = \frac{2x + 1}{3x^2 + 5x + 7}$ has $y = 0$ as a horizontal asymptote, as does every proper rational function.

We have looked at the cases in which the degree of the denominator is greater than the degree of the numerator and equal to the degree of the numerator.

Let's consider a rational function in which the degree of the denominator is less than the degree of the numerator.

EXAMPLE 5 Graph $f(x) = \frac{x^2 - 4}{x + 2}$.

Answer

$f(x) = \frac{x^2 - 4}{x + 2} = \frac{(x - 2)(x + 2)}{x + 2} = x - 2$ if $x \neq -2$.   1. Factor and reduce.

$f(x)$ is the line $y = x - 2$ with a hole at $x = -2$.   2. Identify the hole. The graph of $f(x)$ looks exactly like that of $y = x - 2$ except that f is not defined at $x = -2$.

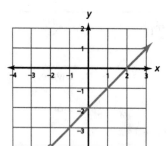

3. Graph the function.

There are no horizontal asymptotes when the degree of the numerator exceeds the degree of the denominator. If you had performed the long division on this function, the remainder would have been zero. If there is a remainder the graph will have a third kind of asymptote. A linear asymptote that is not horizontal or vertical is called an *oblique asymptote*. The example below shows one of these asymptotes.

EXAMPLE 6 Graph $h(x) = \frac{2x^3 - x^2 - 4}{x^2 - 3}$.

Answer

$h(0) = \frac{0 - 0 - 4}{0 - 3} = \frac{4}{3}$ 1. Find the intercepts. The x-intercepts are the zeros of the $2x^3 - x^2 - 4$. There are no rational zeros; the x-intercepts will not be a useful aid to graphing.

The y-intercept is $\left(0, \frac{4}{3}\right)$.

$x^2 - 3 = 0$ 2. Identify the vertical asymptotes.
$x^2 = 3$
$x = \pm\sqrt{3}$ are vertical asymptotes.

Continued ▶

$$\begin{array}{r} 2x - 1 \\ x^2 - 3\overline{)2x^3 - x^2 \qquad\quad - 4} \\ \underline{2x^3 \qquad - 6x} \\ -x^2 + 6x - 4 \\ \underline{-x^2 \qquad + 3} \\ 6x - 7 \end{array}$$

$y = 2x - 1$ is an asymptote.

3. Divide the polynomials to check for an oblique asymptote. By dividing, $h(x) = 2x - 1 + \frac{6x - 7}{x^2 - 3}$. Since the remainder $\frac{6x - 7}{x^2 - 3}$ approaches zero as x approaches infinity, it will not affect the asymptote.

4. Sketch the graph. You may say that h approaches the lateral line $y = 2x - 1$ as $|x|$ increases. Notice on the graph of h that it approaches $y = 2x - 1$.

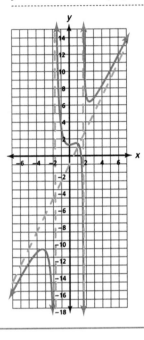

Finally, let's summarize these three types of asymptotes.

Vertical: Vertical asymptotes occur where the denominator of the reduced fraction is 0.

Horizontal: Horizontal asymptotes occur at $y = 0$ if the degree of the denominator is greater than that of the numerator. They occur at $y = r$ if the degrees are equal and the ratio of the leading coefficients is r.

Oblique: Oblique asymptotes occur if the degree of the numerator is one more than the degree of the denominator (and the remainder is not zero).

▶ A. Exercises

Identify the following from the graph.

1. All intercepts
2. The vertical asymptote(s)
3. The oblique asymptote(s)
4. The type of rational function (proper? reduced?)

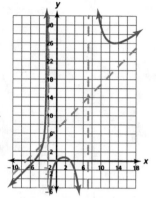

For each rational function below, classify it as proper or improper, reduced or unreduced. Give the domain and identify the asymptotes (type and equation).

5. $f(x) = \dfrac{3x - 1}{x + 5}$

6. $g(x) = \dfrac{8}{x^2 - 4}$

7. $h(x) = \dfrac{3x(x + 2)(x - 5)}{5x(x - 4)(x + 2)}$

8. $p(x) = \dfrac{x^3 - x^2 - 21x - 24}{x^2 + 9}$

9. $q(x) = \dfrac{x^3 - 3x^2 - 10x + 24}{x^3 - 5x^2 - 4x + 20}$

10. $r(x) = \dfrac{x + 2}{2x^3 - 7x^2 - 17x + 10}$

Find the asymptotes and intercepts.

11. $y = \dfrac{x^2 - 4}{x^2 - x - 12}$

12. $y = \dfrac{x^3 - 5x^2 - x + 5}{x - 1}$

13. $y = \dfrac{x^2 - 2x + 1}{x}$

14. $y = \dfrac{4x^2 - 4}{x^4 - 16}$

15. $y = \dfrac{x^2 + x - 2}{2x^2 + 1}$

16. $y = \dfrac{x^2 - 3x + 2}{x^3 - 3x^2 - 4x + 12}$

17. $y = \dfrac{x^2 + 2x}{x^2 - 4x - 5}$

18. $y = \dfrac{x^2 - x - 6}{x - 2}$

19. $y = \dfrac{x^3 - 2x^2 + x - 2}{x^2 - 1}$

20. $y = \dfrac{x^2}{x^2 - 2x + 1}$

► B. Exercises

21-30. Graph the functions from exercises 11-20 above.

31. Graph $f(x) = \frac{x^3}{x + 2}$.

32. Explain why every polynomial is a rational function.

► C. Exercises

33. Reduce the rational function $f(x) = \frac{x^{n+2} + 2x^{n+1} + 4x^n}{x^{n+2} - 8x^{n-1}}$

34. Give all asymptotes and intercepts for the function in exercise 33.

▪ Cumulative Review

35. Find a in $\triangle ABC$ if $A = 47°$, $b = 86$, and $c = 79$.

36. In a 45-45 right triangle, what is the length of the hypotenuse if the legs are a) 5 b) $6\sqrt{2}$ c) $5\sqrt{3}$

37. Explain the steps in finding the angle of inclination of the line $y = -2x + 3$? Find it.

Consider the function $f(x) = \frac{3x + 4}{6x^2 + 5x - 1}$.

38. Find the y-intercept.

39. Find the domain.

Math *and* Scripture

Mathematical Evidence—the Flood

Joseph and his brothers comprise the 13th generation after the Flood. Ruth 4:18-22 and I Chron. 2:1-15 list patriarchs for the 14th through 23rd generations. We do not have life span data for most of these men, but you can include Amminadab and David with the data compiled in Chapter 2.

1. Amminadab (17th generation) was a contemporary of the writer of Psalm 90 (Moses?). What life span does this Psalm identify as *typical?*

2. Find the life span for David (II Sam. 5:4).

3. Plot points for all the patriarchs from Adam to Joseph that you found earlier in Chapter 2 as well as those from exercises 1 and 2 above. What pattern do you notice after the Flood?

It is possible to determine the exponential function for this post-Flood pattern. If you use this method for the generations from Noah to Amminadab, the following function describes post-Flood life span.

$$f(x) = 651.9 \, (1.146)^{-x}$$

4. Graph the exponential function using the points from exercise 3.

Since the model treats the patriarchs' life spans as representative of their generations, the predicted value will not match the actual life span for an individual patriarch.

5. Find predicted life spans for generations 0, 1, 3, 7, 10, 13, and 17, using the exponential decay equation, and compare to the actual life span of each patriarch. Round to the nearest year.

x	y (predicted)	y (actual)	Difference
0			

Use the exponential decay equation and appropriate generation to estimate the following life spans.

6. Pharez   **8.** Adam   **10.** Enoch

7. Hezron   **9.** David   **11.** Ram

Using the formula to estimate life spans within the domain of the model is *interpolation* (though not linear). When predictions are made outside the limits of the model, it is called *extrapolation*. Extrapolations can be useful (as when a manufacturer uses market trends to estimate the quantity of an item to produce), but they are less reliable than interpolations. In this case, extrapolations are completely invalid.

12. Which estimations (exercises 6-11) were interpolations? Are they reasonable?

13. Which were extrapolations? Why are they invalid?

Life span decay provides evidence of a worldwide catastrophe. A flood on the Mississippi River is devastating but cannot shorten the lives of later generations. The decay of life span is one of several evidences of a global catastrophe.

People who think that the Bible is not from God have a hard time explaining the exponential decay. If it were not from God, who could have made up the story of the Flood and had the foresight to provide a chronology of later generations that displays exponential decay of life span as indirect evidence for it? The Bible teaches a global Flood, and even its incidental results provide mathematical verification of it.

MAXIMIZING

Give reasons why God recorded both columns of information that you listed in Chapter 1.

Vital Sines

AND THE WATERS PREVAILED exceedingly upon the earth; and all the high hills, that were under the whole heaven, were covered. ❧

GENESIS 7:19

Chapter 3 Review

Write the set of ordered pairs described by each function rule and the domain $\{-5, -2, 0, 2, 3\}$. Name the type of function that each function rule describes—be specific.

1. $f(x) = 6x^3$
2. $l(x) = x^2 + 2x - 1$
3. $g(x) = 3^x$
4. $r(x) = \frac{1}{x + 3}$
5. $h(x) = x$
6. $q(x) = \frac{x^2 + 4}{x + 6}$
7. $P(x) = x^4 - 3x^3 + 2x^2 - 3x + 4$
8. $g(x) = |x|$
9. $f(x) = \sin\left(\frac{\pi}{6}x\right)$
10. $f(x) = \begin{cases} x + 7 & \text{if } x < -1 \\ x^4 & \text{if } -1 \le x \le 1 \\ x - 4 & \text{if } x > 1 \end{cases}$

Without graphing, give the amplitude, period, and phase shift for the following functions.

11. $y = 2\cos(x + \pi)$
12. $y = -\sin 4x$

Identify all the asymptotes and intercepts of each function. Give the domain.

13. $y = 2^x$
14. $y = \tan x$
15. $h(x) = \frac{x^2 + 4x - 45}{x + 9}$
16. $f(x) = \frac{x^2 - 3x + 7}{x - 1}$
17. $f(x) = \frac{x^3 + 2x^2 - 19x - 20}{x^2 - 3}$
18. $g(x) = \frac{4x^2 - 3}{6x^2 - 24}$
19. Is $y = -3x^2 + |x|$ odd, even, or neither? What kind of symmetry does it have?
20. Find the amount accrued after 5 years from a $250 deposit in a certificate account that earns 8% compounded annually.

Graph. Give the domain and range.

21. $y = |x| - 3$
22. $f(x) = [x + 4]$

23. $y = \begin{cases} |x| & \text{if } x < 0 \\ x + 3 & \text{if } 0 \le x < 3 \\ 2x & \text{if } x \ge 3 \end{cases}$

24. $p(x) = -x^4$

Without graphing, give the amplitude, period, and phase shift for the following functions.

25. $f(x) = \cos\left(2x + \frac{\pi}{2}\right)$

26. $y = 2 \sin 3x$

Graph and give the domain.

27. $h(x) = \frac{3}{x + 2}$

28. $y = \frac{x^3 + 2x^2 - 19x - 20}{x^2 - 3}$

29. $g(x) = 3^x$

30. $y = \csc 2x$

Graph.

31. $y = \frac{1}{2} \cot x$

32. $r(x) = \frac{x^3 - 5x + 1}{x + 2}$

33. $d(x) = \left(\frac{3}{5}\right)^x$

34. $k(x) = 4^3$

35. $q(x) = x^x$ for $x > 0$

36. Evaluate the sinusoidal model for the sunspot data.

37. Explain the mathematical relevance of Gen. 7:19-20.

4 Inverse Functions

After Creation, God told Adam and Eve, "Be fruitful, and multiply, and replenish the earth" (Genesis 1:28). Many years later, Noah heard the same command: "Be fruitful, and multiply, and replenish the earth" (Genesis 9:1).

Some worry about a population explosion resulting in food shortages and famines. Of course, they underestimate changes in agricultural technology among other things.

World population data (including official projections) from 1950 to 2050 appears below. Note especially the reported rates of growth.

Year	Population	% Growth	Year	Population	% Growth
1950	2,555,078,074	1.47	2005	6,460,639,265	1.14
1955	2,779,669,781	1.89	2010	6,823,766,067	1.03
1960	3,039,332,401	1.33	2015	7,175,858,475	0.97
1965	3,345,837,853	2.08	2020	7,518,245,465	0.88
1970	3,707,610,112	2.07	2025	7,840,936,545	0.78
1975	4,088,224,047	1.75	2030	8,140,655,396	0.7
1980	4,456,705,217	1.7	2035	8,417,091,372	0.62
1985	4,854,602,406	1.7	2040	8,668,785,194	0.55
1990	5,283,757,267	1.56	2045	8,897,514,250	0.48
1995	5,690,886,773	1.36	2050	9,104,686,693	
2000	6,080,188,311	1.26			

After this chapter you should be able to

1. identify functions that are one-to-one, increasing, decreasing, nonincreasing, or nondecreasing.

2. perform operations with functions, including composition.

3. find and graph the inverse rule for a given function.

4. graph radical functions and logarithmic functions.

5. apply the definition and laws of logarithms.

6. apply logarithmic functions to problem solving.

4.1 Increasing and Decreasing Functions

To study functions, it is often necessary to describe portions of the graph. Such portions can be indicated by inequalities that describe the *x*-coordinates of the points, but it is faster to specify an interval. A *closed interval* is a segment (interval that includes both endpoints) and is represented with square brackets. An *open interval* is one that does not include its endpoints and is represented with parentheses. The first number line below illustrates the closed interval $[-2, 1]$, while the second number line shows the open interval $(1, 4)$.

The longest bridge-tunnel complex in the world crosses the mouth of Chesapeake Bay, Virginia. A ship passes over the tunnel portion of the complex between man-made islands. Engineers calculate water pressure, an increasing function of depth, for designing the islands, tunnels, bridges, and ships.

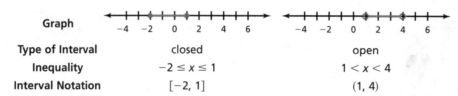

Graph		
Type of Interval	closed	open
Inequality	$-2 \leq x \leq 1$	$1 < x < 4$
Interval Notation	$[-2, 1]$	$(1, 4)$

Some intervals are neither open nor closed. The *x*-values indicated in the interval $0 \leq x < 3$ can be represented $[0, 3)$. This is a half-open (or half-closed) interval because one endpoint is included but the other is not. The number 0 is a lower bound of the interval because no values less than zero are included. Likewise, 3 is an upper bound of the interval, since no number larger than three is included. Notice that a bound may or may not be included in the interval.

Intervals may also be of infinite length. The symbol ∞ means infinity and occurs in intervals with no upper bound. You will use the symbol to represent number line intervals of rays and half-lines that point to the right. Likewise, $-\infty$ is used for rays and half-lines that point to the left. The symbols ∞ and $-\infty$ are not real number bounds, but indicate the lack of a bound. When an interval contains one of these, a parenthesis is used rather than a bracket.

EXAMPLE 1   Write the set shown in interval notation.

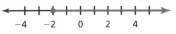

Answer $[-2, \infty)$ -2 is included and the ray has no right endpoint.

Another helpful idea for studying functions is that of a one-to-one correspondence.

Definition

One-to-one correspondence of sets   A pairing of elements of two sets so that any element of either set is paired with exactly one element of the other set.

This definition is more restrictive than the definition of a function. Study the mapping for *f* and notice that although it is a function, it is not one-to-one.

$f = \{(1, 7), (2, 5), (3, 5), (4, 6)\}$

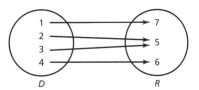

Notice that the domain elements **2** and **3** are both mapped to the same range element, **5**. According to the definition of one-to-one, the range element **5** must be paired with exactly one element of the domain.

Definition

One-to-one function   *f* is one-to-one if and only if $f(a) = f(b)$ implies $a = b$, $\forall\, a, b \in D_f$ (domain of *f*).

Consider the function *g*, represented both graphically and as a circle mapping.

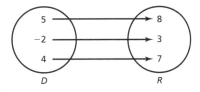

$g = \{(5, 8), (-2, 3), (4, 7)\}$

The function *g* is one-to-one. No horizontal line intersects the graph more than once. Just as the vertical line test identifies functions, the *horizontal line test* indicates that a function is one-to-one if and only if no horizontal line intersects the graph in more than one point.

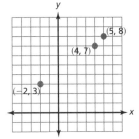

Increasing function   A function is increasing if and only if for any two points x_1 and $x_2 \in \mathbb{R}$, $x_1 < x_2$ implies $f(x_1) < f(x_2)$.

Decreasing function   A function is decreasing if and only if for any two points x_1 and $x_2 \in \mathbb{R}$, $x_1 < x_2$ implies $f(x_1) > f(x_2)$.

Increasing Function

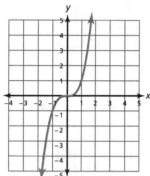

Decreasing Function

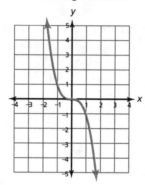

A function that is increasing over its entire domain or one that is decreasing over its entire domain is a *strictly monotonic function*. (The word "strictly" rules out a constant interval.) Some functions are increasing or decreasing over their entire domains, whereas others are strictly monotonic over only an interval of their domains. The first graph below shows a linear function that is decreasing. The second graph shows a quadratic function that is decreasing in the interval $(-\infty, 0]$ and increasing in the interval $[0, \infty)$. Notice that the quadratic function is not strictly monotonic over the entire domain.

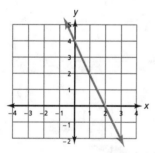

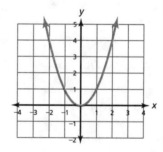

Functions such as the greatest-integer function are monotonic but not strictly monotonic. A *monotonic function* may remain constant over all or part of its domain. It is either nondecreasing or nonincreasing.

Notice that every increasing function is also nondecreasing, that is, it will never decrease as shown in figure (a). A nondecreasing function may, however, remain constant over some interval. The function in figure (b) below is not increasing, but would be nondecreasing.

(a) 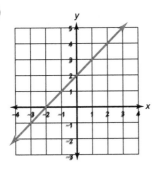   (b)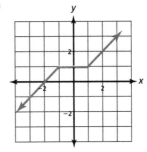

▶ A. Exercises

Give the interval notation for each graph.

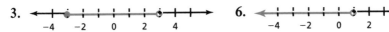

Use proper interval notation to state where the function is increasing, decreasing, or constant. Tell whether the function is one-to-one.

7.

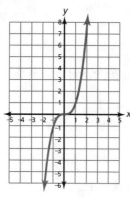

9.

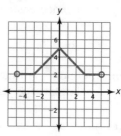

8.

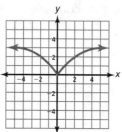

10.

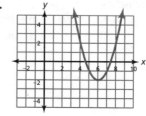

▶ B. Exercises

Graph the following functions. Being as specific as possible, classify each over its entire domain as increasing, decreasing, nonincreasing, nondecreasing, or none. Tell whether the function is one-to-one.

11. $y = x^2$

12. $y = |x|$

13. $y = 2^{-x}$

14. $y = \sin x$

15. $y = x^2 - 3$

16. $y = [x]$

17. $y = 3x + 6$

18. $y = \tan x$

19. $y = \begin{cases} x & \text{if } x \le 1 \\ x + 2 & \text{if } x > 1 \end{cases}$

20. $y = 5$

21. $y = (0.25)^{x+1}$

22. Are monotonic functions always one-to-one? Are strictly monotonic functions?

▶ C. Exercises

23. Prove: If functions f and g are increasing functions, then $f + g$ is also an increasing function.

24. Prove: If function f is strictly monotonic on $[a, b]$, then f is one-to-one on $[a, b]$.

⟨⟩ Dominion Modeling

25. Use the world population data. The populations and years are quite large; in cases like this, statisticians often *transform* the data. Transform the data by subtracting 1950 from all the years to obtain the number of years from the beginning of the study, and then divide the populations by 1,000,000,000.

26. Sketch a scatterplot of the transformed population data.

■ Cumulative Review

Without graphing, classify each type of function and find $f(3)$.

27. $f(x) = \sin \frac{\pi}{2}x$

28. $g(x) = x^2 + 4x + 4$

29. $h(x) = 5 \cdot 2^x$

30. $k(x) = \begin{cases} 2, x < 3 \\ x^2, x \geq 3 \end{cases}$

31. $q(x) = \dfrac{x^2 + x - 1}{x^3 - 2x^2 - x + 5}$

4.2 Operations with Functions

For any function, each value of the range depends on a value from the domain. Most of you depend on your parents for food and shelter. This dependence is part of your relationship with them. A Christian demonstrates a far greater dependence on the finished work of Christ. Colossians 1:14 says of Jesus Christ: "In whom we have redemption through his blood, even the forgiveness of sins." Through the blood of Christ, a Christian has a new relationship with God, looks forward to eternity in heaven, and depends on Him for guidance in every aspect of his daily life.

You can perform any of the four basic operations with functions. This circle mapping shows the addition of the functions $f(x) = 2x$ and $g(x) = 4x - 7$ for the domain $\{1, 2, 5\}$.

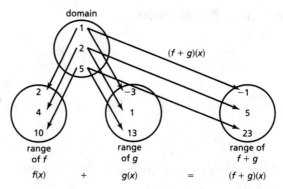

From the ordered pairs of the functions, you can find the sum. Notice that the first coordinate of the sum remains the same as the addends, but the second coordinate for $f + g$ is the sum of the second coordinates of f and g.

$$f = \{(1, 2), (2, 4), (5, 10)\}$$
$$g = \{(1, -3), (2, 1), (5, 13)\}$$
$$f + g = \{(1, -1), (2, 5), (5, 23)\}$$

What is the function rule that describes $f + g$? You can find this rule easily by adding the f and g function rules.

$$(f + g)(x) = f(x) + g(x)$$
$$= (2x) + (4x - 7)$$
$$= 6x - 7$$

Try this rule with the domain $\{1, 2, 5\}$ to see whether you get the same ordered pairs.

The other three basic operations can be found similarly. The following statements summarize the four basic operations with functions.

Operations with Functions
$$(f + g)(x) = f(x) + g(x)$$
$$(f - g)(x) = f(x) - g(x)$$
$$fg(x) = f(x)g(x)$$
$$\frac{f}{g}(x) = \frac{f(x)}{g(x)} \text{ where } g(x) \neq 0.$$

EXAMPLE 1 Let $f(x) = x^2 - 9$ and $g(x) = x + 3$. Find $(f + g)(x)$, $(f - g)(x)$, $fg(x)$, and $\frac{f}{g}(x)$.

Answer

$(f + g)(x) = f(x) + g(x)$ $fg(x) = f(x)g(x)$
$\qquad\qquad = (x^2 - 9) + (x + 3)$ $\qquad = (x^2 - 9)(x + 3)$
$\qquad\qquad = x^2 + x - 6$ $\qquad = x^3 + 3x^2 - 9x - 27$

Continued ▶

$$(f - g)(x) = f(x) - g(x)$$
$$= (x^2 - 9) - (x + 3)$$
$$= x^2 - 9 - x - 3$$
$$= x^2 - x - 12$$

$$\frac{f}{g}(x) = \frac{f(x)}{g(x)}$$
$$= \frac{x^2 - 9}{x + 3}, \text{ if } x \neq -3$$
$$= \frac{(x - 3)(x + 3)}{x + 3}, \text{ if } x \neq -3$$
$$= x - 3, \text{ if } x \neq -3$$

Besides the four basic operations, there is a fifth operation on functions called *composition*. To compose functions, you will need to substitute expressions into them. Example 2 demonstrates some substitutions needed to find compositions of functions.

EXAMPLE 2   Let $f(x) = 5x - 7$ and $g(x) = x^2 + 3x - 2$. Find $f(a + b)$, $f(x^2 - 9)$, $g(4a)$, and $g(3x + 1)$.

Answer

$$f(a + b) = 5(a + b) - 7$$
$$= 5a + 5b - 7$$

$$g(4a) = (4a)^2 + 3(4a) - 2$$
$$= 16a^2 + 12a - 2$$

$$f(x^2 - 9) = 5(x^2 - 9) - 7$$
$$= 5x^2 - 45 - 7$$
$$= 5x^2 - 52$$

$$g(3x + 1) = (3x + 1)^2 + 3(3x + 1) - 2$$
$$= 9x^2 + 6x + 1 + 9x + 3 - 2$$
$$= 9x^2 + 15x + 2$$

Definition

Composition   An operation that substitutes the second function into the first function. In symbols: $g \circ f = g(f(x))$. Read $g \circ f$ as "the composite of g with f," or "g composed with f."

Mapping diagrams provide a useful representation of compositions. Let $f(x) = 3x - 5$ and $g(x) = x^2 - 9$, and let $D_f = \{5, 3, -1, 0\}$.

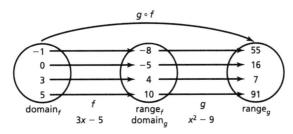

The function $g \circ f$ consists of domain values from function f and range values from function g that correspond to $f(x)$. From the circle diagram you can see that $g \circ f = \{(-1, 55), (0, 16), (3, 7), (5, 91)\}$.

These ordered pairs could be found using the definition of composition of functions as shown for $(g \circ f)(3)$ below. Compare to the third row of the previous mapping diagram.

$$(g \circ f)(3) = g(f(3))$$
$$= g(3 \cdot 3 - 5) \text{ where } f(x) = 3x - 5$$
$$= g(4)$$
$$= 4^2 - 9 \text{ where } g(x) = x^2 - 9$$
$$= 7$$

A function rule for the composition of two functions could also be used to find the ordered pairs. The rule can be found from the rules of the original functions. To find the rule for the composite function, substitute the second function into the first.

EXAMPLE 3   Find $(g \circ f)(x)$ if $f(x) = 3x - 5$ and $g(x) = x^2 - 9$.

Answer

$(g \circ f)(x) = g(f(x))$	1. Use the definition of composition.
$= g(3x - 5)$	2. Substitute for $f(x)$.
$= (3x - 5)^2 - 9$ $= 9x^2 - 30x + 25 - 9$ $= 9x^2 - 30x + 16$	3. Substitute into $g(x)$ and simplify as in Example 2.

Use this rule to check that it obtains the same set of ordered pairs: $\{(-1, 55), (0, 16), (3, 7), (5, 91)\}$. The check for the ordered pair $(3, 7)$ follows.

$$(g \circ f)(3) = 9(3^2) - 30(3) + 16$$
$$= 81 - 90 + 16$$
$$= 7$$

Composition of functions is often used in measurement conversions, such as changing yards to inches. You can multiply the number of yards by 3 to find the number of feet and then multiply the resulting number by 12 to find the number of inches, or you could multiply the number of yards by 36 to find the number of inches in the given number of yards. Multiplying by 36 for this purpose is an example of the composition of functions—it is a single process that combines the work of the two consecutive processes. The function rules that go along with this problem are $f(x) = 3x$ and $g(x) = 12x$. Then

$$(g \circ f)(x) = g[f(x)]$$
$$= g(3x)$$
$$= 12(3x)$$
$$= 36x$$

▶ A. Exercises

Let $f(x) = -2x + 7$, $g(x) = 5x^2$, $h(x) = x - 9$. Evaluate the following.

1. $f(5)$
2. $h(a)$
3. $f(x^2)$
4. $h(x + 4)$
5. $g(3a + b)$
6. $f(x^2 + 4)$
7. $f(a^2 + 4a - 9)$
8. $g(2a)$
9. Find $f(1576)$, $g(1576)$, and $h(1576)$ using a table.

If $f(x) = -2x + 7$, $g(x) = 5x^2$, and $h(x) = x - 9$, perform the following operations.

10. $(f + g)(x)$
11. $fh(x)$
12. $(h - f)(x)$
13. $\frac{f}{g}(x)$
14. $(f - g)(x)$
15. $hg(x)$
16. $(h + f)(x)$
17. $\frac{g}{h}(x)$
18. Graph $\frac{f}{h}(x)$.

▶ B. Exercises

Let $f(x) = \frac{x}{9}$, $g(x) = x - 7$, $h(x) = x^2 + 8$, and $k(x) = 5x - 4$. Find the function rules for the following composition functions.

19. $g \circ h$
20. $f \circ g$
21. $h \circ k$
22. $g \circ f$
23. $k \circ f$

24. $h \circ g$

25. $f \circ k$

26. $g \circ k$

⟨MⓐⓉ⟩ 27. Graph $h \circ f$ without performing the operation algebraically. [*Hint:* Use the form $h(f(x))$].

Use the function rules given above and the domain $\{0, -3, 1, 2\}$. Show a circle mapping and find the composition function rule algebraically.

28. $f \circ h$

29. $k \circ h$

Determine if each operation below is commutative and associative. Explain.

30. addition of functions

31. multiplication of functions

32. composition of functions

⟨MⓐⓉ⟩ 33. Find $(f \circ g)(312)$ if $f(x) = 0.35x + 5.97$ and $g(x) = 2x^2 - 45x + 750$.

▶ C. Exercises

34. The cost of producing microwave ovens for a certain manufacturer is given by the cost function $C(x) = \dfrac{3x^2 - 2400x + 504{,}000}{400}$. This is a function of the number of ovens made, x. The selling price is a function of the cost of producing the ovens and is described by $S(C) = 2.5C$. Find the rule that describes the selling price of the ovens as a function of the number of ovens produced. What is the selling price if 200 ovens are produced? 400 ovens? 700 ovens? How many ovens should the company make to keep the selling price down?

35. There are 1000 meters in a kilometer and 100 centimeters in a meter. Write a function rule to change kilometers to meters and another rule to convert meters to centimeters. Then find the function rule to convert kilometers directly to centimeters by using composition. Use it to find the number of centimeters in 5 kilometers.

▪ Cumulative Review

36. Find the amount in a savings account after five years if $2000 is invested at 5% interest compounded quarterly.

37. Use the exponential growth function $f(x) = C \cdot 2^x$ to find the number of bacteria in a culture after 8 days if there were originally 20 bacteria.

38. Graph the piece function $f(x) = \begin{cases} -1 & \text{if } x < -1 \\ x^3 & \text{if } -1 \le x \le 1. \\ \frac{1}{2}x & \text{if } x > 1 \end{cases}$

39. Find the slope of a line perpendicular to $3x + 5y = 6$.

40. Find $\angle A$ for right triangle ABC with $\angle C = 90°$, $a = 2$, and $b = 3$.

4.3 Finding Inverse Functions

From the preceding sections you are familiar with the concept of a one-to-one function. You know how to use the horizontal line test to determine whether a graphed function is one-to-one. The *inverse of a function,* symbolized f^{-1}, is a relation that results when the first and second coordinates of each ordered pair are interchanged. For example, consider the function and its inverse below.

$$f = \{(3, 5), (2, 9), (-6, 4), (5, 7)\}$$
$$f^{-1} = \{(5, 3), (9, 2), (4, -6), (7, 5)\}$$

The inverse relation is a function when the original function is one-to-one.

From the rule for a particular function, you can find the rule for its corresponding inverse relation by reversing the variables and solving for y.

Finding the Inverse of a Function

1. Interchange the variables (use y instead of $f(x)$).
2. Solve for y and if the inverse is a function, express it using $f^{-1}(x)$.

EXAMPLE 1   Find the inverse function rule for $f(x) = 5x - 7$.

Answer

$f(x) = 5x - 7$ $y = 5x - 7$ $x = 5y - 7$	1. To find the inverse, interchange the independent and dependent variables.
$x + 7 = 5y$ $\frac{x + 7}{5} = y$	2. Solve for y.
$f^{-1}(x) = \frac{1}{5}x + \frac{7}{5}$	3. Since this is a linear function, express it using f^{-1} in slope-intercept form.

Notice that both f and f^{-1} in Example 1 are linear functions and that the graphs of these functions are reflections of each other across the line $f(x) = x$.

The next example investigates $f \circ f^{-1}$ using the function and its inverse from Example 1.

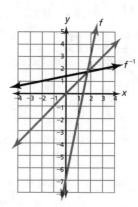

EXAMPLE 2   Find $f \circ f^{-1}$ if $f(x) = 5x - 7$.

Answer

$f^{-1}(x) = \dfrac{x + 7}{5}$ 1. Use $f^{-1}(x)$ from Example 1.

$(f \circ f^{-1})(x) = f(f^{-1}(x))$ 2. Find $(f \circ f^{-1})(x)$ by substituting $f^{-1}(x)$ into $f(x)$.

$\quad = f\left(\dfrac{x + 7}{5}\right)$

$\quad = 5\left(\dfrac{x + 7}{5}\right) - 7$

$\quad = x + 7 - 7$

$\quad = x$

This example illustrates that the composition of a function and its inverse function is always the identity function, $f(x) = x$. This is because the inverse function reverses the process of the original function. You noticed earlier that the identity function $f(x) = x$ also provides the line of reflection that relates the graph of a function and its inverse.

EXAMPLE 3   Graph the inverse of the function shown.

Answer

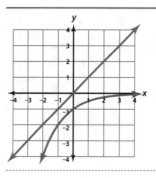

1. Notice that $f(x)$ is one-to-one, so the inverse is a function. Sketch $y = x$ as a guide.

Continued ▶

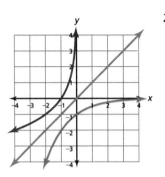

2. Sketch the reflection of $f(x)$ across $y = x$. The y-intercepts become x-intercepts, the x-axis asymptote becomes a y-axis asymptote. This corresponds to interchanging the variables x and y.

▶ A. Exercises

Give the inverse relation for each function below. State whether the inverse is a function.

1. $f = \{(4, 7), (2, -3), (5, 7), (1, 8)\}$
2. $g = \{(-1, 7), (-6, 2), (3, 4)\}$

Determine whether the inverse relation is a function. If it is, write it in function rule notation. If the inverse relation is not a function, show why the original function is not one-to-one.

3. $f(x) = -4x + 6$
4. $y = \frac{x}{2} + 3$
5. $g(x) = |x|$
6. $y = 5x - 4$
7. $y = x^2 - 8x + 16$
8. $f(x) = x^3 + 9$
9. $y = \frac{x + 1}{2x}$
10. $h(x) = \cos x$

▶ B. Exercises

Determine whether the rules given are truly inverse functions.

11. $f(x) = 3x + 9$
    $f^{-1}(x) = \frac{x - 9}{3}$
12. $g(x) = x + 6$
    $g^{-1}(x) = \frac{x}{6}$
13. $h(x) = \frac{7}{x + 2}$
    $h^{-1}(x) = \frac{x + 2}{7}$
14. $f(x) = \frac{x}{x + 1}$
    $f^{-1}(x) = \frac{x}{1 - x}$

15. $f(x) = x^5$

$f^{-1}(x) = \frac{x}{5}$

16. $g(x) = \frac{5}{9}(x - 32)$

$g^{-1}(x) = \frac{1}{5}(9x + 160)$

Find $f^{-1}(x)$ for each function, and draw the graph of both f and f^{-1} on the same Cartesian plane.

17. $f(x) = 2x - 3$

18. $f(x) = x^3$

19. $f(x) = \frac{1}{x + 2}, x \neq -2$

20. Let $f(x) = 5x + 2$. Find a function $g(x)$ such that $(f \circ g)(x) = (g \circ f)(x) = x$.

Graph the function and its inverse on the same graph.

21. $f(x) = -3x - 4$

22. $g(x) = 3x^2 + 2x - 4$

Graph the inverse of each function shown.

23.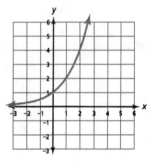

25.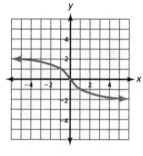

24.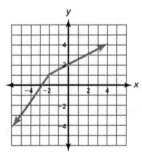

26.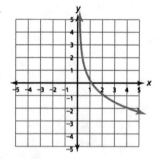

▶ **C. Exercises**

27. Find the inverse of $f(x) = \begin{cases} \frac{1}{4}x & \text{if } x \leq 4 \\ \frac{3x - 4}{x - 1} & \text{if } x > 4 \end{cases}$

28. $ax + by = c$ represents the standard form of a linear function. Find the inverse of this function and compare the slopes of the functions.

⚠️ Dominion Modeling

29. Find a linear model of the transformed data for world population. Sketch this model on the data.

30. Complete the table for the predicted populations and residuals. Use transformed data for both variables, and use the linear model for the predicted values. (Recall the formula for residuals from Chapter 3: $e_i = y_i - \hat{y}_i$, the actual values minus the predicted values.)

L_1 Year'	L_2 Pop'	L_3 Predicted Pop'	L_4 Residuals	L_1 Year'	L_2 Pop'	L_3 Predicted Pop'	L_4 Residuals
0	2.555			55	6.461		
5	2.780			60	6.824		
10	3.039			65	7.176		
15	3.346			70	7.518		
20	3.708			75	7.841		
25	4.088			80	8.141		
30	4.457			85	8.417		
35	4.855			90	8.669		
40	5.284			95	8.898		
45	5.691			100	9.105		
50	6.080						

31. Sketch the residuals plot (with residuals versus transformed years).

32. Using your knowledge of r^2 and residual plots, evaluate the linear model. Be sure to tell whether or not the residuals systematically stray from the model.

▪ Cumulative Review

Use the function $f(x) = -2 \sin\left(3x - \frac{\pi}{2}\right)$ to answer the following questions.

33. What is the period?

34. What is the amplitude?

35. What is the phase shift?

36. What are the zeros?

37. Graph $f(x)$.

4.4 Radical Functions

You have worked with radicals frequently in the past. However, functions may include constants expressed as radicals without being radical functions.

Definition

Radical function   A radical function is a function containing at least one variable in the radicand.

The most common radical function is the *square root function*. All even root functions have both a positive and a negative root, but only the principal (positive) root is used. A square root function, whose simplest form is $f(x) = \sqrt{x}$, indicates only the principal (positive) square root. Plot some points to graph this function.

$\{(0, 0), (1, 1), (2, \sqrt{2}), (3, \sqrt{3}), (4, 2),$
$(9, 3), (16, 4)\}$

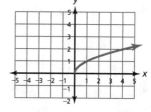

EXAMPLE 1   Find the function described by the rule $h(x) = \sqrt{x + 3}$, where the domain is $\{0, -3, 1, 4, 6\}$.

Answer $h(0) = \sqrt{0 + 3} = \sqrt{3}$ $h(4) = \sqrt{4 + 3} = \sqrt{7}$
$h(-3) = \sqrt{-3 + 3} = 0$ $h(6) = \sqrt{6 + 3} = 3$
$h(1) = \sqrt{1 + 3} = 2$
$h = \{(-3, 0), (0, \sqrt{3}), (1, 2), (4, \sqrt{7}), (6, 3)\}$

For $f(x) = \sqrt{x}$, negative values of x result in complex numbers. To keep the range in the real numbers (for graphing), the domain is $x \geq 0$. Why didn't $x = -3$ result in a complex range value in Example 1? Since $h(x)$ in Example 1 translates $f(x) = \sqrt{x}$ horizontally 3 units to the left, the domain of $h(x)$ is $x \geq -3$.

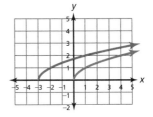

Rational functions require restrictions so the denominator is not zero. Radical functions require the radicand to be nonnegative. Sometimes you may need to consider both in the same function (see Example 2).

EXAMPLE 2   Find the domain for each of the following functions.
a. $g(x) = 3\sqrt{4 - 3x} - 7$, b. $q(x) = \sqrt[3]{5x + 7}$,
c. $r(x) = \dfrac{2x + 4}{(x - 2)\sqrt{x - 1}}$

Answer

---

a. For $g(x)$ $4 - 3x \geq 0$ The radicand is non-
$\qquad\qquad -3x \geq -4$ negative.
$\qquad\qquad x \leq \dfrac{4}{3}$
$\qquad\qquad D_g = \left\{ x \mid x \leq \dfrac{4}{3} \right\}$

- -

b. For $q(x)$ $D_q = \mathbb{R}$ Since the index (3) is odd, no restrictions are needed.

- -

c. For $r(x)$ $x - 1 \geq 0$ $x - 2 \neq 0$ and $\sqrt{x - 1} \neq 0$ Exclude values that
$\qquad\qquad x \geq 1$ $x \neq 2$ and $x \neq 1$ make the radicand
$\qquad\qquad D_r = \{ x \mid x > 1 \text{ and } x \neq 2 \}$ negative or the denominator zero.

Since even functions are not one-to-one, their inverses are not functions. However, with restrictions on the domain, an inverse function can be defined. For $f(x) = x^2$ with $x \geq 0$, $f^{-1}(x) = \sqrt{x}$ is an example of an inverse function. The restricted domain on the original function is indicated on the graph.

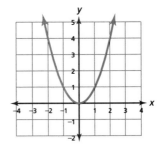

Earlier we mentioned that functions must be one-to-one to have an inverse function. It is possible, however, to find an inverse relation for any function. Example 3 shows how to find a rule for an inverse relation.

EXAMPLE 3   Find the inverse relation of $f(x) = x^2 + 4$. If the inverse is not a function, then restrict the domain so that it becomes one.

Answer

$f(x) = x^2 + 4$

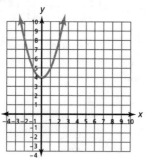

1. Graph $f(x) = x^2 + 4$ to determine whether it is a one-to-one function. The graph does not pass the horizontal-line test; so it is not one-to-one and its inverse is not a function.

$$y = x^2 + 4$$
$$x = y^2 + 4$$
$$y^2 = x - 4$$
$$y = \pm\sqrt{x - 4}$$
$$r^{-1}(x) = \pm\sqrt{x - 4}$$

2. Find the inverse relation and use r^{-1} rather than f^{-1} to designate it.

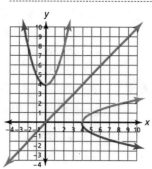

3. Graph the inverse relation.

4. Notice that if the domain of the original function were restricted to $x \geq 0$, (the blue portion of the graph), then $f(x)$ would be one-to-one and would have a function as its inverse.

5. If only the blue portion of f is used ($x \geq 0$), $f^{-1}(x) = \sqrt{x - 4}$, the positive root. The blue portion of the inverse relation is the inverse function.

The value of x in $f^{-1}(x)$ must also be restricted. The domain restriction of $f(x)$, $x \geq 0$, corresponds to the range restriction that $f(x)$ must be 4 or larger. This is the domain restriction of $f^{-1}(x)$ and is found from the graph or by solving $x - 4 \geq 0$. Therefore, the following function rule describes $f^{-1}(x)$:

$$f^{-1}(x) = \sqrt{x - 4}, \text{ where } x \geq 4 \text{ and } x \in \mathbb{R}.$$

Remember, this is an inverse function only on a restricted domain of the original function.

EXAMPLE 4   Find the inverse function for $f(x) = -\sqrt{x} - 4$.

Answer

$f(x) = -\sqrt{x} - 4$	1. The graph of this function is the red portion of the second graph in Example 3.
$y = -\sqrt{x} - 4$ $x = -\sqrt{y} - 4$ $x^2 = (-\sqrt{y} - 4)^2$ $x^2 = y - 4$ $x^2 + 4 = y$ $r^{-1}(x) = x^2 + 4$	2. Find the inverse relation r^{-1}.
$f^{-1}(x) = x^2 + 4,\ x \le 0$	3. Write the inverse relation as an inverse function and restrict the domain so that it is the inverse of the original function. (Refer to the red portions of the graphs for Example 3.)

▶ A. Exercises

Find $f(-3)$ for each function.

1. $f(x) = \sqrt{x + 7}$
2. $f(x) = \sqrt{78 - x}$
3. $f(x) = \sqrt[3]{x - 5}$
4. $f(x) = \sqrt{x + 1}$

Give the domain of each. Also identify the x-intercept and the y-intercept.

5. $f(x) = \sqrt{x - 2}$
6. $g(x) = \sqrt{2x + 5}$
7. $q(x) = \sqrt{x + 1}$
8. $h(x) = \sqrt{9 - x}$
9. $r(x) = \sqrt[3]{x + 2}$
10. $t(x) = \dfrac{5}{x\sqrt{x + 2}}$
11. $f(x) = \sqrt[5]{2x - 4} + 7.75$ (Give intercepts to the nearest hundredth.)

▶ B. Exercises

Graph each radical function. Identify the domain and range.

12. $y = -\sqrt{x}$
13. $g(x) = \sqrt{-x}$
14. $f(x) = \sqrt{x - 1}$

15. $y = \sqrt{x + 4} - 3$

16. $h(x) = \sqrt[3]{x}$

17. $y = \sqrt[3]{x + 3} + 1$

For each graph below, find a one-to-one portion of the graph (restrict the domain), and then sketch the inverse. Write the restricted domains of $f(x)$ and $f^{-1}(x)$ in interval notation.

18.

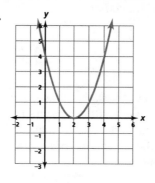

20.

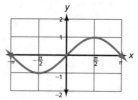

19.

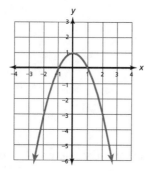

21.

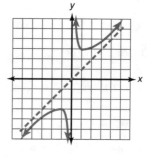

▶ C. Exercises

For each function below, find the inverse relation and restrict the domain of the original function so its inverse is a function.

22. $g(x) = x^2 - 7$

23. $p(x) = x^2 + 8x + 16$

⩗ Dominion Modeling

24. For the world population data, find the r^2 values for the linear, quadratic, cubic, and quartic models.

25. Can you assume that a model with a high r^2 is a great model? Why?

Find the areas of the following triangles.

26. with sides of 29, 36, and 47

27. with $A = 37°$, $b = 12.5$ and $c = 17.0$

28. with a leg of 25 and a hypotenuse of 47

29. Which two trig functions have a period of π?

30. What type of symmetry does an odd function have?

4.5 Inverse Trigonometric Functions

Now you are ready to apply the idea of an inverse function to the trigonometric functions that you studied earlier. First, consider the sine function.

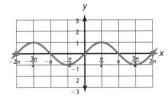

To find a rule for an inverse function, you interchanged the x and y and solved for y. In the case of $y = \sin x$, solving $x = \sin y$ for y requires a symbol for the inverse. Mathematicians use the notation $y = \sin^{-1} x$ or $y = \arcsin x$. This notation means "y is an angle whose sine is x."

Is the sine function one-to-one? As you can see from the graph above, it certainly would not pass the horizontal line test. Since the sine function is periodic, there are infinitely many domain values that have the same sine value. For example, the domain value of 0 corresponds to every integer multiple of π.

The inverse relation can be obtained by interchanging the x and y coordinates and graphing the result. As shown here, the inverse relation is not a function.

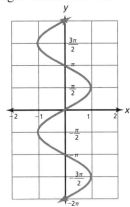

In order for the inverse relation to be a function, the domain of the sine function must be restricted to obtain a one-to-one function. The portion of the domain that is used is the interval $\left[\frac{-\pi}{2}, \frac{\pi}{2}\right]$. Only one angle in this interval will have a given sine value, so the function is one-to-one. Each angle in this range is called the *principal angle*. A capital letter is used, $y = \text{Sin } x$, to indicate the restricted domain of the function. The graph of this part of the sine function is shown below.

The inverse of $y = \text{Sin } x$ is graphed below by reflecting the graph across the identity function, $y = x$. Notice that the inverse Sine is a function with $\left[\frac{-\pi}{2}, \frac{\pi}{2}\right]$ as its range. The inverse sine function, $f(x) = \text{Sin}^{-1} x$, returns the principal angle for a given value of the sine.

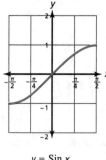

$y = \text{Sin } x$

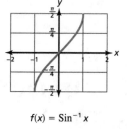

$f(x) = \text{Sin}^{-1} x$

Study the following example to understand this concept better.

EXAMPLE 1 $y = \text{Sin}^{-1} 1$. Find y.

Answer

$y = \text{Sin}^{-1} 1$ 1. Think "what angle from the restricted domain $\left[\frac{-\pi}{2}, \frac{\pi}{2}\right]$ has the value 1 as its sine?"

$y = \frac{\pi}{2}$ 2. You can see from the graph of $f(x) = \text{Sin}^{-1} x$ that when $x = 1$, $y = \frac{\pi}{2}$.

Such calculations are easy on a calculator, but you must remember what the concepts mean in order to understand the answers and to apply them to problems. Understanding concepts—spiritual as well as academic—is essential to your future. Proverbs 4:7 says, "Wisdom is the principal thing; therefore get wisdom: and with all thy getting get understanding."

Since $f(x) = \text{Sin } x$ and $f(x) = \text{Sin}^{-1} x$ are inverse functions, the functions undo each other when their composite is found.

EXAMPLE 2   Find $\sin\left(\operatorname{Sin}^{-1}\frac{1}{2}\right)$.

Answer $\sin\left(\operatorname{Sin}^{-1}\frac{1}{2}\right)$ The result must be $\frac{1}{2}$ because sin and Sin^{-1}
            $= \sin\frac{\pi}{6} = \frac{1}{2}$ are inverses of each other.

The cosine and tangent functions also have inverse functions if the domains of the original functions are restricted. The restriction for the domain of the cosine function is the closed interval $[0, \pi]$. With this restriction, the function is denoted $y = \operatorname{Cos} x$. The restricted domain for the tangent function is $\left(-\frac{\pi}{2}, \frac{\pi}{2}\right)$, the same as that of the sine function, but the endpoints are excluded to form an open rather than closed interval (tan x is undefined at these points).

Many problems that include the inverse trigonometric functions can be solved without the aid of a calculator.

EXAMPLE 3   Find $\sin\left(\operatorname{Cos}^{-1}\frac{3}{4}\right)$.

Answer $\sin\left(\operatorname{Cos}^{-1}\frac{3}{4}\right)$

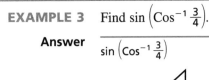

1. Since $\operatorname{Cos}^{-1}\frac{3}{4}$ represents the angle in $[0, \pi]$ having a cosine of $\frac{3}{4}$, it is a first quadrant angle. Its adjacent side is 3 and the hypotenuse is 4. Draw a right triangle and name an acute angle θ.

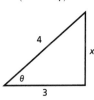

$3^2 + x^2 = 4^2$
$9 + x^2 = 16$
$x^2 = 7$
$x = \sqrt{7}$

2. Use the Pythagorean theorem to find the third side of the triangle. Use the positive root for this distance.

$\therefore \sin\left(\operatorname{Cos}^{-1}\frac{3}{4}\right) = \frac{\sqrt{7}}{4}$ 3. Determine $\sin\theta$ from the diagram.

EXAMPLE 4   Find $\operatorname{Cos}^{-1}\left(-\frac{\sqrt{2}}{2}\right)$.

Answer $\operatorname{Cos}^{-1}\left(-\frac{\sqrt{2}}{2}\right)$ 1. Determine that the angle is a second quadrant angle since the cosine is negative. (Principal range is $[0, \pi]$ for the cosine function.)

$\alpha = \frac{\pi}{4}$ 2. Use the reference angle whose cosine is $\frac{\sqrt{2}}{2}$.

$\theta = \pi - \frac{\pi}{4} = \frac{3\pi}{4}$ 3. Subtract the reference angle from π to determine θ (a second quadrant angle).

Some additional explanation on notation is helpful here. Sin^{-1}, Cos^{-1}, and Tan^{-1} are sometimes represented by the notation Arcsin, Arccos, and Arctan, respectively. *Arc-* is a prefix that indicates an inverse; it stresses that the answer is the measure of an arc (radian measure on a unit circle) or angle. Again, a capital letter is used for the principal value from the restricted domain.

▶ A. Exercises

Graph.

1. $y = \cos x$
2. $y = \text{Cos } x, x \in [0, \pi]$
3. $y = \text{Cos}^{-1} x$
4. $y = \tan x$
5. $y = \text{Tan } x, x \in \left(\frac{-\pi}{2}, \frac{\pi}{2}\right)$
6. $y = \text{Tan}^{-1} x$

Without using a calculator, find the following values.

7. $\text{Sin}^{-1} \frac{\sqrt{3}}{2}$
8. $\text{Cos}^{-1} \frac{1}{2}$
9. $\text{Tan}^{-1} \frac{\sqrt{3}}{3}$
10. $\text{Cos}^{-1} \frac{-1}{2}$
11. $\text{Tan}^{-1} 1$
12. $\sin \left(\text{Cos}^{-1} \frac{\sqrt{2}}{2}\right)$
13. $\tan \left(\text{Sin}^{-1} \frac{1}{2}\right)$
14. $\cos \left(\text{Cos}^{-1} \frac{3}{4}\right)$
15. $\cos \left(\text{Sin}^{-1} \frac{-\sqrt{5}}{3}\right)$
16. $\csc \left(\text{Tan}^{-1} \frac{4}{5}\right)$

Use a calculator to determine the following values.

17. $\text{Sin}^{-1} 0.3420$
18. $\text{Tan}^{-1} 1.732$
19. $\text{Cos}^{-1} 0.7138$

▶ B. Exercises

Graph the given function over its appropriate restricted domain. (State the restricted domain.) Graph its inverse function on the same set of axes.

20. $f(x) = \text{Sec } x$
21. $g(x) = \text{Csc } x$
22. $h(x) = \text{Cot } x$

Use the definitions and a calculator to evaluate the following.

23. $\text{Cot}^{-1} 0.684$
24. $\text{Csc}^{-1} 1.5$
25. $\text{Sec}^{-1} 5.96$
26. $\text{Cos}^{-1} 0.8660$
27. $\text{Sin}^{-1} 0.7854$
28. $\text{Cot}^{-1} -2.819$
29. $\text{Sec}^{-1} 2$

▶ C. Exercises

30. Prove that $\text{Csc}^{-1} x = \text{Sin}^{-1} \frac{1}{x}$.
31. For any relation r, prove that $(r^{-1})^{-1} = r$.

〰 Dominion Modeling

32. What quartic model fits the world population data?
33. Sketch the quartic model with the data.
34. Sketch a residual plot for the quartic model. Do the residuals deviate from the model in a systematic way? Compare with the residual plot in the linear model.

▪ Cumulative Review

35. Give the angle of inclination of the line $3x + 4y = 7$ to the nearest degree.
36. Change $f(x) = \frac{5}{7}x - \frac{1}{4}$ to general form.
37. Give the function rule for the line passing through the points $(-4, 5)$, $(3, 8.5)$, and $(8, 11)$.
38. Find an equivalent expression for $f(x) = \sec\left(\frac{\pi}{2} - x\right)$.
39. Find the inverse of the function $f(x) = \frac{2}{3}x - 5$.

JAPANESE MATH

Japan has contributed to mathematics for centuries. Takakazu Seki Kowa (1642-1708), often called Shinsuke or Seki, was instrumental in the development of Japanese mathematics. Born in Fujioka to a samurai family, he was adopted by nobility. A servant in the noble house recognized nine-year-old Seki's aptitude and introduced him to mathematics. Seki quickly collected and studied all Japanese and Chinese math texts and became an expert. He published *Hatsubi Sampo* in 1674 as a solution to 15 problems which had been posed four years previously. In 1683, he published another work which included a study of integer solutions of $ax - by = 1$ (Diophantine equations) and solutions of systems using determinants. His use of determinants predated that of Leibniz by a decade and is also more general. The Japanese credit him with major concepts in calculus that he passed along to his students. Tradition also holds that he made a pilgrimage to Nara, where he studied and deciphered the Chinese mathematical texts in the temple.

Another important Japanese mathematician, Naonobu Ajima (1732-1798), was born in Tokyo (then called Edo). His book, *Fukyu Sampo*, presented studies of volumes using double integrations and a special system of logarithms for evaluating radicals. He also used advanced

Takakazu Seki (1642-1708)

Japanese mathematicians since the 12th century would know Itsukushima Shrine near Hiroshima, but its now famous gateway, Japan's largest, is more recent, added in 1875.

Japan has contributed to mathematics for centuries.

techniques for finding lengths of circular arcs. The work, however, was not published until after his death.

A modern mathematician, Teiji Takagi (1875-1960), was born in Kazuya near Gifu. He studied math in Tokyo and then went to Germany to study under Hilbert. His papers of 1920 and 1922 generalized Hilbert's class field. He became a professor in Tokyo, proved a conjecture of Kronecker's, and published texts on analysis (1938) and number theory (1948).

The Hall of the Great Buddha at Nara, Japan, is the largest wooden temple in the world. Though it has burned down several times, it has been a national landmark since its dedication in 752.

4.6 Logarithmic Functions

In Section 3.2 you studied the exponential function and looked at its graph and other characteristics. The inverse of the exponential function is the *logarithmic function*. Recall that the graph of the inverse of a function is the reflection of the original function across the line $y = x$. The following graph shows the exponential as well as the logarithmic function.

Chemists, such as these at Los Alamos, New Mexico, use logarithms frequently.

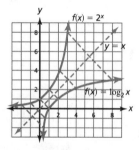

The exponential function graphed here is $f(x) = 2^x$. To find the function rule for the inverse of this function, interchange x and y and then solve. When this is done with $f(x) = 2^x$, a problem occurs. How do you solve $x = 2^y$ for y? Mathematicians devised logarithms to represent the inverse function.

Logarithmic function $f(x) = \log_a x$, where $a > 0$, $a \neq 1$, and $x > 0$. It is the inverse of the exponential function $f(x) = a^x$.

The rule $y = \log_a x$ is equivalent to $a^y = x$; therefore, a is the *base* of the logarithm and y, the *logarithm,* is an exponent.

The logarithmic expression can be written in either of two forms: the usual logarithm form, $y = \log_a x$, or the exponential form, $a^y = x$. It is extremely important that you be able to convert between logarithmic and exponential forms.

$$\text{Log Form} \qquad \text{Exponential Form}$$
$$\log_a x = y \quad \rightarrow \quad a^y = x$$

Notice that the graph of $y = \log_a x$ in the above figure passes through the point (1, 0). Every graph of a logarithmic function passes through (1, 0), since $a^0 = 1$ for any base. The shape of the graph changes only slightly as the value of the base a increases from 1.

EXAMPLE 1 Write $\log_4 64 = y$ in exponential form.

Answer

$\log_4 64 = y$	1. Note that the base of the log is 4 and y is the logarithm.
$4^y = 64$	2. Use the base, 4, as the base of the exponential. Remember that a logarithm is an exponent.

EXAMPLE 2 Write $3^{-5} = \frac{1}{243}$ in logarithmic form.

Answer

$3^{-5} = \frac{1}{243}$	1. Identify 3 as the base and -5 as the exponent.
$\log_3 \frac{1}{243} = -5$	2. Use 3 as the base of the log and -5 as the logarithm.

EXAMPLE 3 Prove $\log_a 1 = 0 \; \forall \, a > 0$ with $a \neq 1$.

Answer

$a^0 = 1$	1. State the zero property of exponents.
$\log_a 1 = 0$	2. Convert to logs.

Because a logarithm is an exponent, the expression $\log_{10} 1000$ asks what exponent on the base 10 yields 1000. The obvious answer is 3 since $10^3 = 1000$. Another way to see this is to recognize that the exponential and the logarithm with the same base are inverse functions and undo one another. Thus, $\log_{10} 10^3 = 3$.

In the previous discussion, the base of the log was 10. A logarithm in base ten is called a *common logarithm*. The base of a common log is not usually written. The statement log 1000 = 3 is understood to be in base 10. Common logs can be found by using the log key on your calculator.

$$\log 4.39 \approx 0.6425$$

> *When I am violently beset with temptations, or cannot rid myself of evil thoughts, [I resolve] to do some Arithmetic, or Geometry, or some other study, which necessarily engages all my thoughts, and unavoidably keeps them from wandering.*
> –Jonathan Edwards
> (1703-1758)

This statement means the same as the exponential form $10^{0.6425} \approx 4.39$.

The second special type of logarithm is the *natural logarithm* whose base is e. Recall that e is an irrational number that is approximately 2.71828. The special notation for a natural logarithm is ln.

$$\log_e 4.72 = \ln 4.72 \approx 1.5518$$

In exponential form this statement is written $e^{1.5518} \approx 4.72$. The value 1.5518 can be found by using the natural logarithm (ln) key on your calculator. Be careful not to mix up natural and common logs.

▶ A. Exercises

Change the following logarithms to exponential form.

1. $\log_2 x = y$
2. $\log_5 25 = 2$
3. $\log_4 \frac{1}{16} = -2$
4. $\log_{12} 144 = 2$
5. $\log 1000 = 3$
6. $\ln 5 = 1.6094$
7. $\ln 1 = 0$
8. $\log 7 = 0.8451$

Explain why the following are true.

9. $\log_a a = 1$
10. $\log_a a^x = x$ and $a^{\log_a x} = x$

Change the following exponential expressions to log form.

11. $5^3 = 125$
12. $2^{-4} = \frac{1}{16}$
13. $8^2 = 64$
14. $\left(\frac{1}{3}\right)^2 = \left(\frac{1}{9}\right)$
15. $7^3 = 343$
16. $5^{-5} = \frac{1}{3125}$

▶ B. Exercises

Graph. Give the domain and range of each.

17. $y = \log_4 x$
18. $y = \log_5 x$
19. $y = \log x$

Evaluate.

20. $\log_2 256$
21. $\log_5 1{,}953{,}125$
22. $\log_4 64$
23. $\log_2 \frac{1}{8}$
24. $\log 10{,}000$
25. $\log_6 \frac{1}{1296}$

26. Verify that a logarithm is the inverse of an exponential by graphing the following equations on the same graph. What will you inspect to determine if they are inverses?

$$y = \log x, \quad y = 10^x$$

▶ C. Exercises

27. Prove that $\log_b 2a \neq 2 \log_b a$ in general. Then algebraically find the value of a for which it is true.

28. Use interval notation to specify the intervals for which the natural logarithm is positive, negative, zero, and undefined. Do the same for the common logarithm.

■ Cumulative Review

Use interval notation to show the intervals of continuity of the following functions.

29. $f(x) = \dfrac{3x^2 - 5}{x}$

30. $g(x) = 3x^2 - 7x + 9$

31. $h(x) = \sqrt{x - 3}$

32. Name three characteristics of a graph that cause a function to be discontinuous. Name an example of each.

33. Certain functions, such as the absolute value function, do not graph as a smooth curve, but have sharp turns in their graphs. Is such a function discontinuous?

MIND OVER MATH

The rule $f(x) = x^2 - 3x + 43$ generates a sequence of prime numbers (41, 41, 43, 47, . . .) when the natural numbers are substituted for x. What value of x will produce the first composite number in the sequence?

4.7 Laws of Logarithms

When you find log $4.35 \approx 0.6385$, you are finding the exponent 0.6385 for the base 10 that equals 4.35. Since logarithms are exponents, the exponent laws apply to them. The laws of logarithms are derived directly from the exponent laws. In the following table, each exponent law is associated with its corresponding law of logarithms.

	Exponent Laws	Laws of Logarithms
Product Law	$x^a \cdot x^b = x^{a+b}$	$\log_b xy = \log_b x + \log_b y$
Quotient Law	$x^a \div x^b = x^{a-b}$	$\log_b \frac{x}{y} = \log_b x - \log_b y$
Power Law	$(x^a)^b = x^{ab}$	$\log_b x^a = a \log_b x$

The laws of logarithms can be used to change expressions to a form involving the operations of addition and subtraction.

EXAMPLE 1   Change $\log \frac{a^2 b}{c^4}$ to a form involving addition and subtraction.

Answer

$\log \frac{a^2 b}{c^4}$

$\log (a^2 b) - \log c^4$ 1. Apply the quotient law.

$\log a^2 + \log b - \log c^4$ 2. Apply the product law.

$2 \log a + \log b - 4 \log c$ 3. Apply the power law.

The three laws of logarithms are the basis for computations that can be done with logarithms. In today's society, with the advent of the many modern calculating devices, logarithms are not used as often as they once were. Before calculators were invented and widely used, however, the logarithm was an extremely useful tool to find the answer to large calculations. The process that was used is illustrated in Example 2.

EXAMPLE 2 Calculate $\dfrac{(3.49)^{12}}{(82)(4.27)}$ using logarithms.

Answer

$x = \dfrac{(3.49)^{12}}{(82)(4.27)}$	1. Set the calculation equal to x.
$\log x = \log\left[\dfrac{(3.49)^{12}}{(82)(4.27)}\right]$ $\log x = \log(3.49)^{12} - \log[(82)(4.27)]$ $\log x = \log(3.49)^{12} - [\log 82 + \log 4.27]$ $\log x = 12\log(3.49) - \log 82 - \log 4.27$	2. Take the log of both sides of the equation. Use the laws of logarithms to expand the right side.
$\log x \approx 3.96966$	3. Evaluate the right side using a calculator.
$x \approx 10^{3.96966}$ $x \approx 9325$	4. Convert from log to exponential form and simplify.

The third and fourth steps in Example 2 were performed on a calculator. Before calculators a common log table would have been used. The use of logarithms changed a complex multiplication/division problem to a simpler addition/subtraction problem. Using the common log table backwards would have done step 4. When the table is used, the inverse process is often called finding the antilog and may be written $x \approx$ antilog **3.96966**. Finding the antilog of a number is the same as using that number as a power of **10**.

Logs and antilogs also offer a method for evaluating roots.

EXAMPLE 3 Find $\sqrt{57}$.

Answer

$x = 57^{\frac{1}{2}}$	1. Express the radical in fractional exponent form.
$\log x = \log 57^{\frac{1}{2}}$ $\log x = \frac{1}{2}\log 57$ $\log x \approx 0.8779$	2. Take the log of both sides, and apply the power law.
$x \approx 10^{0.8779}$ $x \approx 7.55$	3. Use both sides as a power of 10.

Sometimes you will want or need to change bases. For example, if you need to find a logarithm in base 2, tables or calculator keys are not commonly available for that base. The following formula enables you to calculate such logarithms using logarithms in another base (such as common or natural logs). Proof of this is a *C Exercise*.

$$\text{Change of base formula: } \log_b x = \frac{\log_a x}{\log_a b}$$

EXAMPLE 4   Find $\log_2 5.89$.

Answer $\log_2 5.89 = \dfrac{\log 5.89}{\log 2}$ Since you can easily find the common logarithms, use base 10 and the given formula to find the base 2 logarithm.

≈ 2.558

This means that $2^{2.558} \approx 5.89$.

▶ A. Exercises

Change each expression to a form involving addition and subtraction of terms by applying the laws of logarithms.

1. $\log xy$
2. $\log ab^2c$
3. $\log \dfrac{a^4}{b^2}$
4. $\log \dfrac{x^a y^b}{z}$
5. $\log x^3 y^2 z^5$
6. $\log \sqrt[3]{a^2 b^5}$

Find the log of each number in the given base.

7. $\log_3 3.78$
8. $\log_5 28.9$
9. $\log_4 389$
10. $\log_{11} 77$

▶ B. Exercises

Evaluate the following problems using logarithms. Show your work.

11. $(4.97)^2(5.6)$
12. $\dfrac{(871)(4.93)^3}{27.4}$
13. $\sqrt[3]{100}$
14. $\sqrt[10]{5830}$

15. $\sqrt[7]{93}$

16. $\sqrt[15]{89{,}618}$

If $\log_a 5 = P$ and $\log_a 2 = Q$, find the following.

17. $\log_a 10$

18. $\log_a \frac{1}{5}$

19. $\log_a \sqrt{2}$

20. $\log_a \frac{25}{8}$

21. $\log_a 2a^7$

22. $\log_a \frac{\sqrt[3]{5}}{4a}$

▶ C. Exercise

23. Prove the change of base formula.

▪ Cumulative Review

24. Solve $a \tan 3x + b = c$ for x.

25. Write the equations of the natural log function and its inverse, where each of them has been translated left 2 units and down 3 units.

Without graphing, determine whether the following functions are even, odd, or neither.

26. $f(x) = \sin x$

27. $g(x) = x^2 + 4x + 4$

28. $h(x) = |x| + x^2$

Logs and Lines

You may be surprised that there is a relationship between graphs of exponential functions and graphs of lines. Consider the general exponential function

$y = Ca^x$.

By taking the logarithms on both sides,

$\log y = \log Ca^x$
$\log y = \log C + \log a^x$
$\log y = \log C + x \log a$.

If Y is the variable obtained by finding the logarithms of the original y variable ($\log y$), then this is a linear equation in x.

$Y = x \log a + \log C$
or $Y = (\log a)x + (\log C)$

The slope is $m = \log a$ and the y-intercept, $b = \log C$.

This means that you can find equations of exponentials by using the slope-intercept form of a line to obtain the linear log form and then convert back to exponential form.

EXAMPLE   Find the equation of the exponential function through $(1, 4)$ and $(4, 8)$.

Answer

1. $(1, 0.602)$, $(4, 0.903)$ | 1. Convert (x, y) to (x, Y) where $Y = \log y$.

2. $m = \frac{0.903 - 0.602}{4 - 1} = \frac{0.301}{3} \approx 0.1$ | 2. Find the equation of the line through $(1, 0.602)$ and $(4, 0.903)$.
$Y - 0.903 = 0.1(x - 4)$
$Y - 0.903 = 0.1x - 0.4$
$Y = 0.1x + 0.503$

3. $\log y = 0.1x + 0.503$ | 3. Substitute $\log y$ for Y.

4. $y = 10^{0.1x + 0.503}$ | 4. Change to exponential form, $y = Ca^x$.

Continued ▶

---

5. $y = 10^{0.503}\left(10^{0.1}\right)^x$ $y = 3.1842(1.2589)^x$	5. Simplify the right side using the product and power rules for exponents.

▶ Exercises

Follow the steps to find the equation of the exponential function through (3, 5) and (5, 7).

1. Convert (x, y) to (x, Y) where $Y = \log y$.
2. Find the equation of the line through (x_1, Y_1) and (x_2, Y_2).
3. Convert to a power of 10.
4. Convert to exponential form $y = Ca^x$.
5. Use the general form $Y = mx + b$ to give the general form of the corresponding exponential. Identify C and a in $y = Ca^x$.

4.8 Applications of Logarithmic Functions

There are many applications of both exponential and logarithmic functions.

Seismologists use the Richter scale to measure earthquake severity. On this scale, the magnitude of an earthquake is described by the logarithm expression: $M = \log \frac{I}{I_0}$, where I_0 is the standard magnitude of minimum intensity and I is the intensity of the earthquake being measured.

EXAMPLE 1 An earthquake has an intensity reading that is $10^{7.5}$ times that of I_0 (the standard minimum intensity). What is the measurement of this earthquake on the Richter scale?

Answer

$M = \log \frac{I}{I_0}$	1. Write the formula for determining the Richter-scale value.
$M = \log \frac{10^{7.5}\, I_0}{I_0}$	2. In this example $I = 10^{7.5}\, I_0$. Substitute this value for I in the formula.
$M = \log 10^{7.5}$ $= 7.5$	3. Simplify the equation. Note that the common log is the inverse of the exponential with base 10. Alternatively, you can use the power law to get $7.5 \log 10 = 7.5(1) = 7.5$.

The Richter-scale reading for this earthquake is 7.5, which is very serious. Significant damage would probably occur.

An earthquake at Anchorage, Alaska, in 1964 formed these faults and triggered the landslide that destroyed this elementary school. Measured at 251,200,000 times greater than the smallest detectable intensity, it is the worst on record for the Western Hemisphere in the 20th century. What was its magnitude on the Richter scale?

In the field of chemistry, the pH of a substance is defined using logarithms as follows.

$$pH = -\log [H^+],$$

where $[H^+]$ is the concentration of hydrogen ions in a substance in moles per liter. Example 2 shows how to determine the pH of a substance.

EXAMPLE 2 Determine the pH of milk if the hydrogen ion concentration is 4×10^{-7} moles per liter.

Answer

$pH = -\log [H^+]$	1. Write the proper formula for finding pH.
$pH = -\log [4 \times 10^{-7}]$	2. Substitute the known values into the formula.
$pH = -[\log 4 + \log 10^{-7}]$ $= -[\log 4 + (-7)]$ ≈ 6.4	3. Use the laws of logarithms to simplify the right side of the formula.

The pH of milk is 6.4.

Educators and psychologists use "forgetting curves" to study learning and to help people better remember material. The equation for the average test score on previously learned materials is:

$$S(t) = A - B \log (t + 1)$$

where t represents time expressed in months and A and B are constants found by experimentation in a particular course.

EXAMPLE 3 If the average score in a geometry class for a certain exam is given by $S(t) = 73 - 12 \log (t + 1)$, what was the original average score? What will the average score be on the same exam a year later?

Answer

$S(t) = 73 - 12 \log (t + 1)$ $S(t) = 73 - 12 \log (0 + 1)$	1. Write the formula, and substitute the given time (in months) into it.
$= 73 - 12(0)$	2. Evaluate the expression.
$= 73$	3. The original average score was 73.

Continued ▶

$S(t) = 73 - 12 \log (t + 1)$

$= 73 - 12 \log (12 + 1)$

$= 73 - 12 \log 13$

≈ 59.63

4. Find the average score on the same exam a year later.

The average score on the same exam a year later, with an original average score of 73, would be about 59.63.

You may recall that banks offer savings accounts that compound interest in several different ways. Some accounts compound interest yearly or quarterly, while others compound monthly or daily. The amount after t years with n compoundings per year at annual interest rate r is given by the formula:

$$A(t) = P\left(1 + \frac{r}{n}\right)^{nt}.$$

Review exercises 17-22 in Section 3.2. You noticed that interest increases with more frequent compoundings. You can also see that the difference between daily and hourly compounding is small compared to the difference between quarterly and monthly compounding. There is a limit to how much you could earn even if the bank compounded every millisecond, and the limit can be calculated. This calculation involves the number e and is one reason that the number is so important. Obviously, the best type of account (rates being equal) is one that is compounded continuously. The formula for determining the earnings in a continuously compounded account with an initial principal P after t years at rate r is given by the following exponential function.

$$A(t) = Pe^{rt}$$

EXAMPLE 4 $400 is deposited in a savings account with an interest rate of 6% for a period of 42 years. How much will be in the account at the end of 42 years if interest is compounded continuously?

Answer $A(t) = Pe^{rt}$ Write the original formula, and substitute

$A(t) = 400e^{(0.06)(42)}$ the given values into the formula.

$= 400e^{2.52}$

$= \$4971.44$

The amount accumulated after 42 years will be $4971.44

EXAMPLE 5   How long will it take Shannon to save $800 from an initial investment of $430 at $5\frac{1}{2}$% interest with continuous compounding?

Answer

$A(t) = Pe^{rt}$	1. Apply the formula.
$800 = 430e^{0.055t}$	
$\frac{800}{430} = e^{0.055t}$	2. Solve for t.
$\ln \frac{800}{430} = \ln e^{0.055t}$	3. Use logs to undo the exponential
$\ln 1.86 = 0.055t$	since they are inverses. Natural
$\frac{\ln 1.86}{0.055} = t$	logs are appropriate with e.
$t \approx 11.3$	

She must save for about 11.3 years.

▶ A. Exercises

Find the Richter-scale measurement for an earthquake that is the given number of times greater than the standard minimum intensity.

1. 10^6
2. $10^{4.3}$
3. $10^{8.7}$
4. 10^2

The formula for the average score on a particular English exam after t months is $S(t) = 82 - 8 \log (t + 1)$.

5. What is the average score after 5 months?
6. How many months have passed if the average score on the exam is 80? 64? 71?
7. If a group of people lived for 40 years after taking this English exam and took the test again, what would the average score be?
8. According to the results of exercises 5-7, when does most of the forgetting occur after you have studied for an exam?

Find the pH in the substances below according to their given hydrogen ion concentration.

9. Vinegar: $[H^+] = 7.94 \times 10^{-4}$ moles per liter
10. Tomatoes: $[H^+] = 6.3 \times 10^{-5}$ moles per liter

Find the hydrogen ion concentration (in moles per liter) of the following substances, given their pH values.

11. Eggs: pH = 8.8
12. Hominy: pH = 7.3

▶ B. Exercises

Find the maximum amount that a person could hope to accumulate from an initial investment of $1000 at

13. 5% interest for 20 years

14. 6% interest for 8 years

15. 7% interest for 12 years

16. $5\frac{1}{2}$% interest for 3 years

17. How much money is in an account after 15 years if the interest is compounded continuously at a rate of 7% and the original principal was $5000?

18. How much money was originally invested in an account if the account totals $8000 after 4 years and the interest was compounded continuously at a rate of 5%?

19. How much money was originally invested in an account if the account totals $51,539.44 after 25 years and interest was compounded continuously at a rate of 6%?

20. How much money is in an account after 10 years if the interest is compounded continuously at a rate of 6.25% and the original principal was $3700?

21. How much will Jennifer have in her account on her 10th, 16th, 21st, and 30th birthdays if her parents invest $1500 (compounded continuously at a rate of 6%) at the time of her birth?

The atmospheric pressure at a particular height, h, is given by the formula $P = P_0 e^{-kh}$, where P_0 is the pressure at sea level and k is a constant. Use $k = 3.85 \times 10^{-5}$.

22. Find the atmospheric pressure at 3000 feet if the pressure at sea level is 1010 millibars.

23. Find the height if the atmospheric pressure is 827 millibars when the pressure is 1010 millibars at sea level.

▶ C. Exercises

24. Jim invests $1000 at 6% interest compounded continuously. How long will it take for his investment to reach $1350?

25. Jenna invests $468 at 6.25% interest compounded continuously. How long will it take for her investment to reach a value of $1000?

⎍ Dominion Modeling

26. Recall what you have learned about "logs and lines." Transform the "population" data by taking its common logarithm, and find a linear model. Evaluate this model, including a scatterplot of the transformed data, r^2, and a residual plot. To what exponential model is this equivalent?

27. For population growth, an exponential model is often assumed to be appropriate because it assumes a constant rate of growth. Plot the data with an exponential model. Is this model a good fit for the data? Support your answer with the model, r^2, and a residual plot.

28. How could you have known what the residual plots would have been by just looking at the last two scatterplots?

29. Another possible model for the population data is a logistic model, $y = \frac{c}{1 + ae^{-bx}}$. Before regressing the data with a logistic model, sketch the special case of this curve, $y = \frac{1}{1 + e^{-x}}$. Does this curve appear to have any asymptotes? If so, what are they? (*Hint:* Sketch your graph from -5 to 5 on the x-axis and -1 to 2 on the y-axis.)

30. What is the logistic model for the world population data? How good is this model? Support your response with the logistics model, a scatterplot with this model, and a residual plot.

■ Cumulative Review

Find the domain of each function.

31. $p(x) = x^2 - 5$

32. $f(x) = \tan x$

33. $g(x) = \frac{2x + 1}{x - 3}$

34. $h(x) = \ln x$

35. $k(x) = \sqrt{x + 2}$

Math *and* Scripture

Exponential Decay Model

You have seen that the life spans of the patriarchs approximate an exponential decay curve and may wonder how to determine the equation of the curve for yourself. In this activity you will take the first step toward determining this equation, which is to find the logarithms of all the life spans.

Since you know that the decay model applies only to the generations from Noah to Aminadab (and Moses), find the logarithms for these generations.

1. Complete the table below for future reference and carry four decimals in your logarithms.

Generations from Flood	Patriarch	y = Life Span	$Y = \log y$ (logarithm of life span)
0	Noah		
1	Shem		
2	Arphaxad		
3	Salah		
4	Eber		
5	Peleg		
6	Reu		
7	Serug		
8	Nahor		
9	Terah		
10	Abraham		
11	Isaac		
12	Jacob		
13	Joseph		
17	Aminadab		

2. Graph generation (x) against log of life span (Y).

3. What did the transformation do to the shape of the graph?

4. Explain the value of this transformation for finding an equation.

Using information from Chapter 9 or previous Dominion Modeling exercises, you can determine that the slope of the best-fit line is −0.0591 and that the y-intercept is 2.8142.

5. Write the equation of the line.

6. Replace Y with log y and find the exponential function $y = Ca^{-x}$.

7. Graph the line on your answer from question 2.

8. Are all the points close to the line?

In Chapter 3 you discovered mathematical evidence that the story of the Flood is factual. This refutes those who consider it a legend. Other people say that the Flood was restricted to the lands where Noah lived, around Mesopotamia. Read Genesis 7:17-24 again.

9. Explain how verses 19-20 prove that the Flood was global.

10. Explain another aspect of this passage that proves the Flood was global.

MAXIMIZING

In what passage does Christ refer to Noah and the Flood as a factual account of a global Flood?

Vital Sines

FIFTEEN CUBITS UPWARD

did the waters prevail;

and the mountains were

covered. ❧

GENESIS 7:20

Chapter 4 Review

Graph the following functions and determine whether each is increasing, decreasing, nonincreasing, nondecreasing, or none of these. Be as specific as possible. Tell whether the function is one-to-one.

1. $y = -2x + 5$
2. $y = -\sqrt{x + 2}, \ x \geq -2$
3. $y = \cos x$

Without graphing, determine whether the following functions are even, odd, or neither.

4. $y = |3x - 5|$
5. $y = x^2 - 4$
6. $y = 6x$

Write the inverse relation rule for each function. Determine whether the inverse relation is a function.

7. $f(x) = x^3 - 7$
8. $y = 3x - 6$
9. $y = \sqrt{x + 1}$
10. $f(x) = \frac{x}{6} + 2$

Determine whether the rules shown below describe inverse functions.

11. $f(x) = 4x - 8$
    $f^{-1}(x) = \frac{x}{4 + 8}$
12. $g(x) = x^2 + 6x + 9, \ x \geq -3$
    $g^{-1}(x) = \sqrt{x} - 3, \ x \geq 0$

Without using a calculator, find the following values.

13. $\text{Tan}^{-1} \frac{\sqrt{3}}{3}$
14. $\text{Cos}^{-1} \frac{\sqrt{2}}{2}$
15. $\text{Sin}^{-1} \frac{1}{2}$

Use a calculator to determine the following values.

16. $\text{Cos}^{-1} 0.8309$
17. $\text{Tan}^{-1} 0.6432$

Graph the following functions. Give the domain and range.

18. $f(x) = \sqrt{x + 3}$
19. $y = \text{Sin}^{-1} x$
20. $y = \log_6 x$

Find the rule for each compound function. Then evaluate for $x = 2$.
Use $f(x) = 3x + 2$ and $g(x) = x^2 - 1$.

21. $(f + g)(x)$

22. $fg(x)$

23. $\left(\dfrac{f}{g}\right)(x)$

24. $(f \circ g)(x)$

25. $(g \circ f)(x)$

Change the following logarithmic forms to exponential form.

26. $3 = \log_2 8$

27. $\log_{25} 625 = 2$

28. $\log_9 6561 = 4$

Evaluate.

29. $\log_2 \dfrac{1}{32}$

30. $\log_5 15{,}625$

Find.

31. $\cos\left(\mathrm{Tan}^{-1} \dfrac{5}{3}\right)$

32. $\mathrm{Sin}^{-1}\left(\sin \dfrac{4\pi}{3}\right)$

Evaluate using logarithms. Show your work.

33. $\sqrt[4]{95}$

Newton's law of cooling gives the rate at which an object cools. The equation that describes this cooling process is $T = S + Ce^{-kt}$. In this equation T is the temperature of the object after t minutes, and S is the temperature of the surroundings in which the object is cooling. The constants k and C are determined by the type of substance that is cooling. $C = T_0 - S$, where T_0 is the initial temperature, and $k = 0.26$.

34. If cookies are baked at a temperature of 350°F and are placed on a cooling rack to cool in a room with a temperature of 70°F, what will be the temperature of the cookies after 6 minutes?

35. How long will it take the cookies to cool to almost room temperature, 72°F?

36. You have seen that none of the models worked very well for the world population data. However, some worked well on portions of the data. Construct a piece function for the data.

37. Explain the mathematical relevance of Genesis 7:20.

5 Equations

Holstein dairy farming relies on careful management to make a profit. Farmers can strategize heifer growth. If heifers grow too slowly, they will calve too late, resulting in lost income. For instance, a 100-cow herd could lose $9000 to $18,000 by calving at 28 months instead of 24 months.

Data on weight gain is therefore important in herd management.

Age (mo.)	No. Animals	Weight (lbs.)	Height (in.)	Age (mo.)	No. Animals	Weight (lbs.)	Height (in.)
1	47	122.3	31.5	13	32	830.9	49.4
2	25	171.7	33.7	14	23	865.4	49.8
3	27	239.8	35.8	15	23	937.7	50.7
4	26	293.4	37.5	16	35	911.6	50.1
5	33	344.0	39.2	17	31	994.2	51.3
6	30	427.9	41.4	18	34	1052.3	52.2
7	16	479.1	42.7	19	41	1118.4	52.6
8	24	511.3	43.6	20	35	1170.8	52.8
9	39	604.6	45.1	21	28	1162.7	52.1
10	41	662.8	46.4	22	43	1231.6	53.5
11	35	699.1	47.4	23	26	1282.4	53.9
12	25	780.1	49.1	24	19	1358.9	54.2

After this chapter you should be able to

1. find all the solutions to linear and quadratic equations.
2. use the rational root theorem and synthetic division to solve higher-degree polynomial equations.
3. solve rational and radical equations.
4. convert between exponential and log forms of equations.
5. solve logarithmic, exponential, and trigonometric equations.
6. apply trig identities.
7. prove trig identities.

5.1 Polynomial Equations

To solve polynomial equations of the first degree, apply the properties of equality. To solve second-degree equations, you may take square roots, factor, or use the quadratic formula. This section extends techniques for solving equations to polynomials of higher degree.

A polynomial equation is solved by first setting the polynomial equal to zero and then factoring the polynomial. Set each factor equal to zero, and solve the resulting equations to find the roots of the polynomial equation. The factor theorem from Chapter 2 (given below) shows that factors of a polynomial correspond to the zeros of a function. The zeros of the function then correspond to the roots of the equation.

Factor Theorem
If $P(r) = 0$ where $r \in \mathbb{R}$, then $x - r$ is a factor of $P(x)$.

In Section 2.6 you learned from the *complete linear factorization theorem* that every polynomial of degree n factors completely into n linear factors. Therefore, a polynomial equation of degree n has exactly n roots (though some of them may repeat a value or be complex). This provides an upper bound on the number of solutions to a polynomial equation.

Since factors always divide evenly into the polynomial, the remainder theorem (Section 2.5) can be used to check for zeros. Divide synthetically; if the remainder is zero, $x - a$ is a factor and the divisor, a, is a zero of the polynomial.

EXAMPLE 1 Use synthetic division to determine which of the following numbers are roots of the equation $3x^3 - 8x^2 + 5x - 2 = 0.$ {−2, −1, 1, 2}

Answer

$$
\begin{array}{r|rrrr}
1 & 3 & -8 & 5 & -2 \\
  &   & 3 & -5 & 0 \\
\hline
  & 3 & -5 & 0 & -2 \\
\end{array}
\qquad
\begin{array}{r|rrrr}
-1 & 3 & -8 & 5 & -2 \\
   &   & -3 & 11 & -16 \\
\hline
   & 3 & -11 & 16 & -18 \\
\end{array}
$$

$$
\begin{array}{r|rrrr}
2 & 3 & -8 & 5 & -2 \\
  &   & 6 & -4 & 2 \\
\hline
  & 3 & -2 & 1 & 0 \\
\end{array}
\qquad
\begin{array}{r|rrrr}
-2 & 3 & -8 & 5 & -2 \\
   &   & -6 & 28 & -66 \\
\hline
   & 3 & -14 & 33 & -68 \\
\end{array}
$$

The only member of this set that is a root of the equation is 2.

Since $P(2) = 0$, the factor theorem guarantees that $x - 2$ is a factor of the polynomial. Therefore $x = 2$ is a solution of $3x^3 - 8x^2 + 5x - 2 = 0$.

Once you have identified a root of the cubic equation, you can find the other roots using methods for solving quadratic equations. In Example 1, when $3x^3 - 8x^2 + 5x - 2$ was divided by $x - 2$, the quotient was $3x^2 - 2x + 1$ with no remainder. This quotient, when set equal to 0, comprises the *depressed equation*. The zero remainder means the polynomial can be factored as follows:

$$3x^3 - 8x^2 + 5x - 2 = (x - 2)(3x^2 - 2x + 1).$$

Although the quadratic factor is a prime polynomial (will not factor), you can apply the quadratic formula to find the other two roots, which are complex.

EXAMPLE 2 Solve $x^3 + 4x^2 - 2x - 8 = 0$, given that $(x + 4)$ is a factor of the polynomial.

Answer

$x^3 + 4x^2 - 2x - 8 = 0$

$$
\begin{array}{r|rrrr}
-4 & 1 & 4 & -2 & -8 \\
   &   & -4 & 0 & 8 \\
\hline
   & 1 & 0 & -2 & 0 \\
\end{array}
$$

1. If $(x + 4)$ is a factor, -4 is a solution of the equation. Divide the polynomial by $(x + 4)$ using synthetic division.

$(x + 4)(x^2 - 2) = 0$

2. Write the factors.

$x + 4 = 0 \quad$ or $\ x^2 - 2 = 0$

$\quad x = -4 \ $ or $\qquad x^2 = 2$

$\qquad\qquad\qquad\qquad x = \pm\sqrt{2}$

$x = -4, x = \sqrt{2}, \text{ or } x = -\sqrt{2}$

3. Set each factor equal to zero and solve for x.

The rational root theorem is very helpful in identifying possible roots of polynomial equations.

Rational Root Theorem

The only possible rational roots of a polynomial equation

$$a_nx^n + a_{n-1}x^{n-1} + \cdots + a_2x^2 + a_1x + a_0 = 0$$

are of the form $\frac{c}{d}$ where c is a factor of the constant term (a_0) and d is a factor of the leading coefficient (a_n).

EXAMPLE 3   Solve $x^4 + 3x^3 - 21x^2 - 9x + 54 = 0$.

Answer

$x^4 + 3x^3 - 21x^2 - 9x + 54 = 0$ $c = \pm1, \pm2, \pm3, \pm6, \pm9, \pm18, \pm27, \pm54$ $d = \pm1$	1. Determine the factors of the constant term and the factors of the leading coefficient.
$\frac{c}{d} = \pm1, \pm2, \pm3, \pm6, \pm9, \pm18, \pm27, \pm54$	2. Divide each value of c by each value of d. For this equation $\pm\frac{c}{d} = \pm c$, since $d = \pm1$.

$$
\begin{array}{r|rrrrr}
3 & 1 & 3 & -21 & -9 & 54 \\
  & \downarrow & 3 & 18 & -9 & -54 \\
\hline
-6 & 1 & 6 & -3 & -18 & 0 \\
   & \downarrow & -6 & 0 & 18 & \\
\hline
   & 1 & 0 & -3 & 0 &
\end{array}
$$

3. Use synthetic division to find a zero of the polynomial. Since $x = 3$ is a zero, $(x - 3)$ is a factor. The resulting depressed polynomial is $x^3 + 6x^2 - 3x - 18$. Use synthetic division on the depressed polynomial to find a second factor.

$(x - 3)(x + 6)(x^2 - 3) = 0$

4. Since $x + 6$ is a factor and the new depressed polynomial is quadratic, write the equation in factored form.

$x = -6, 3, \pm\sqrt{3}$

5. Use the factors to solve for x.

EXAMPLE 4   Solve $2x^3 + 5x^2 - 2x - 5 = 0$.

Answer

$2x^3 + 5x^2 - 2x - 5 = 0$	
$c = \pm 1, \pm 5$	
$d = \pm 1, \pm 2$	1. Determine the factors of the constant and leading coefficient.

$\frac{c}{d} = \pm 1, \pm 5, \pm \frac{1}{2}, \pm \frac{5}{2}$	2. List the possible rational roots. (Divide each c by each d.)

$\begin{array}{r\|rrrr} 1 & 2 & 5 & -2 & -5 \\ & \downarrow & 2 & 7 & 5 \\ \hline & 2 & 7 & 5 & 0 \end{array}$	3. Use synthetic division to determine the rational roots. You should factor the depressed quadratic polynomial after finding one root.
$(x - 1)(2x^2 + 7x + 5) = 0$	
$(x - 1)(2x + 5)(x + 1) = 0$	

$x = -\frac{5}{2}, -1, 1$	4. Solve using the factorization.

You can now solve any polynomial equation of degree n if it has at least $n - 2$ rational roots, which allow you to depress the equation into a quadratic equation. Some roots are not rational and must be approximated.

▶ A. Exercises

Use synthetic division to determine whether the given number is a root of the equation.

1. $8; x^4 - 55x^2 - 15x - 456 = 0$
2. $-6; x - 2x^2 + 4x^4 - 6x^6 = 0$
3. $14; x^5 - 13x^4 - 14x^3 + x^2 - 28x + 196 = 0$

Use synthetic division to determine whether the binomial is a factor of the polynomial. If it is a factor, write the depressed polynomial.

4. $x + 4; x^3 + 7x^2 + 13x + 4$
5. $x - 10; x^4 - 12x^3 + 26x^2 - 60x$
6. $x + 3; 3x^2 - 4x^3 + 2x^4$

Find all the zeros of the polynomials in

7. exercise 4.
8. exercise 5.
9. exercise 6.
10. Without multiplying the factors, determine whether this polynomial has been factored correctly.
    $x^4 - x^3 - 63x^2 - 99x + 162 = (x + 3)(x - 1)(x + 6)(x - 9)$

▶ B. Exercises

Solve each equation.

11. $x^4 - 3x^2 + 2 = 0$
12. $x^4 - 13x^2 + 36 = 0$
13. $2x^3 + 11x^2 - 7x - 6 = 0$
14. $2x^4 + 6x^3 - 24x^2 - 12x + 40 = 0$
15. $x^4 + 16x + 24 = 2x^3 + 11x^2$
16. $x^3 + x + 6 = 4x^2$
17. $6x^3 - 4x^2 + 3x = 2$
18. $x^4 + 3x^3 - 6x^2 - 28x = 24$
19. $6 - x^2 = 7x - 2x^3$
20. $13x^2 + 20 + x^4 = 24x - 16 + 6x^3$

 Find all real roots of the following polynomial equations using a graphing calculator. Round the solutions to three decimal places.

21. $-4x^3 + 15x - 79 = 0$
22. $-8x^4 - 5.3x^3 + 17x^2 - 4.4x + 16.3 = 0$

▶ C. Exercises

23. Write a possible polynomial equation of degree 4 whose only roots are 2 and −3. How many such equations (in standard form) are possible if the leading coefficient must be 1?

24. Which of the following graphs could possibly represent a cubic function? Explain your choices.

a.

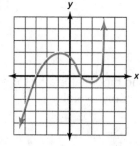

c.

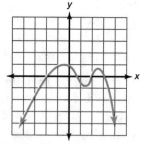

b.

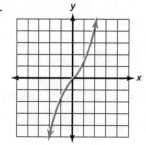

d.

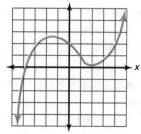

⟨⟩ Dominion Modeling

25. Using the weight and height as independent and dependent variables respectively, draw a scatterplot of the Holstein data.

26. Find a linear model for the Holstein data. Draw the model with the data. What is r^2?

27. Predict the appearance of the residual plot; explain your reasoning. After your prediction, sketch the residuals versus the weight. What conclusion can you draw?

▪ Cumulative Review

28. Use synthetic division to factor $2x^4 - x^3 - 87x^2 + 36x + 540$.

29. Graph the polynomial function $f(x) = 2x^4 - x^3 - 87x^2 + 36x + 540$.

Identify the amplitude, period and phase shift in the following trig functions.

30. $f(x) = \sin 4x$

31. $g(x) = \frac{1}{2} \cos \frac{2}{3} \left(x - \frac{\pi}{4} \right)$

32. $h(x) = 2 \tan \left(\frac{3}{5} x - \frac{\pi}{2} \right)$

> *[checkers or chess] help to develop and improve our powers of thought, and calculation, and judgment. Sometimes, when I am weary with my work, I take down my Euclid, and go over a few propositions; or I work out some of Bland's equations, just by way of amusement. That kind of exercise is as much a recreation to me as running out in the fields would be to a boy at school.*
> —CHARLES HADDON SPURGEON
> (1834-1892)

Linear Splines

A *linear spline* is a continuous piece function with linear pieces. In other words, you can trace the graph of a linear spline without lifting your pencil, unlike most piece functions which have jumps. This property occurs because the range values of consecutive linear pieces match at their common endpoint. Is the piece function $f(x)$ a linear spline?

$$f(x) = \begin{cases} 7x - 5 & \text{if } x < 1 \\ 2x & \text{if } 1 \le x < 2 \\ 4 & \text{if } x \ge 2 \end{cases}$$

First notice that all three rules are linear functions: $7x - 5$, $2x$, and 4. Next you must verify the pieces are consecutive. The first two are consecutive because they each have 1 as an endpoint and the last two are also because each has an endpoint at 2. Finally, check whether the range values match for endpoints of consecutive pieces. The first two rules match at $(1, 2)$ since for $x = 1$, $7x + 5 = 7(1) - 5 = 2$ and $2x = 2(1) = 2$. The last two also match since $2x = 2 \cdot 2 = 4$, which agrees with the constant piece 4. Having verified that the function is continuous (no hole, gap, or jump), graph it.

You can easily graph a linear spline through a given set of points. Put the points in order of their x-coordinates. For each pair of consecutive points, the rule that applies between their x-values is the equation of the line joining the two points.

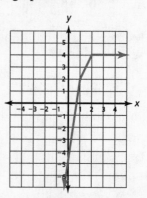

Since $f(x)$ satisfies all three conditions, it is a linear spline. Spline functions are often denoted by $S(x)$, and an individual piece can be referred to with a subscript. For instance, the third piece of the spline function above would be $S_3(x) = 4$.

▶ Exercises

State whether the following are linear splines. If not, give the reason. Include a graph with exercises 1 and 2.

1. $p(x) = \begin{cases} x^2 & \text{if } x \le 0 \\ 3x & \text{if } 0 < x < 2 \\ x + 4 & \text{if } x \ge 2 \end{cases}$

2. $f(x) = \begin{cases} 3x - 1 & \text{if } x < 1 \\ x + 1 & \text{if } 1 \le x \le 4 \\ 2x - 3 & \text{if } x > 4 \end{cases}$

3. $g(x) = \begin{cases} x & \text{if } x \le 0 \\ 5x & \text{if } 0 < x \le 1 \\ 3x + 1 & \text{if } x > 1 \end{cases}$

4. $k(x) = \begin{cases} 2 & \text{if } x \le 3 \\ 4 & \text{if } 3 < x < 4 \\ 6 & \text{if } x = 4 \end{cases}$

5. $q(x) = \begin{cases} 2x & \text{if } x < -2 \\ x - 2 & \text{if } -2 \le x < 3 \\ 3x - 8 & \text{if } 3 \le x < 5 \\ 7 & \text{if } x \ge 5 \end{cases}$

6. Give the linear spline which connects (0, 1), (2, 3), (5, −9), and (8, 0).

5.2 Rational Equations

Architects solve many equations in designing a building like the Millennium Dome in London.

A rational expression is an algebraic expression that is the ratio of two polynomials, $\frac{P(x)}{Q(x)}$, where $Q(x) \neq 0$. A rational equation contains at least one such expression.

Definition

Rational equation An equation that contains at least one rational expression.

Solve rational equations as you would an equation that contains fractions. You must determine the least common multiple of the denominators of the rational expressions in the equation and multiply both sides of the equation by it. This eliminates all the fractions in the equation, reducing it to a polynomial equation. When you multiply the equation by expressions containing variables, you may introduce extraneous roots; therefore, it is necessary to check all roots.

EXAMPLE 1 Solve and check: $\dfrac{3n}{n-5} = \dfrac{3n+1}{n-4}$.

Answer

$$\frac{3n}{n-5} = \frac{3n+1}{n-4}$$

$$(n-5)(n-4)\left(\frac{3n}{n-5}\right) = (n-5)(n-4)\left(\frac{3n+1}{n-4}\right)$$

1. Multiply both sides by the common denominator.

$$3n(n-4) = (n-5)(3n+1)$$
$$3n^2 - 12n = 3n^2 - 14n - 5$$
$$2n = -5$$
$$n = \frac{-5}{2}$$

2. Cancel, simplify, and solve.

$$\frac{3\left(-\frac{5}{2}\right)}{-\frac{5}{2}-5} = \frac{3\left(-\frac{5}{2}\right)+1}{-\frac{5}{2}-4}$$

$$\frac{-\frac{15}{2}}{-\frac{15}{2}} = \frac{-\frac{13}{2}}{-\frac{13}{2}}$$

$$1 = 1$$

3. Check.

This tedious checking process is acceptable but unnecessary for identifying extraneous roots. You need only check that the value is in the domain of all the rational expressions. In other words, if the answer does not create a "0" denominator, it is not extraneous. In Example 1, since $-\frac{5}{2}$ does not make either denominator equal to zero, it is not extraneous. This saves much time, since checking the domains can usually be done mentally.

EXAMPLE 2 Solve and check: $\frac{2x-1}{x+3} + \frac{1}{x^2+x-6} + \frac{x-4}{x-2} = 0.$

Answer

$x + 3$	1. Factor all denominators and determine their LCM to find their lowest common denominator.
$x^2 + x - 6 = (x+3)(x-2)$	
$x - 2$	
The LCM is $(x+3)(x-2)$.	

2. Multiply both sides of the equation by the lowest common denominator.

$$(x+3)(x-2)\left[\frac{2x-1}{x+3} + \frac{1}{(x+3)(x-2)} + \frac{x-4}{(x-2)}\right] = (x+3)(x-2)(0)$$

$(x-2)(2x-1) + 1 + (x+3)(x-4) = 0$ 3. Simplify, and solve for x.
$2x^2 - 5x + 2 + 1 + x^2 - x - 12 = 0$
$3x^2 - 6x - 9 = 0$
$x^2 - 2x - 3 = 0$
$(x+1)(x-3) = 0$
$x = -1, 3$

$D = \{x \mid x \neq -3 \text{ and } x \neq 2\}$;   4. Find the domain of the rational expression to check for extraneous roots. Both solutions are in the domain.
neither root is extraneous.

▶ A. Exercises

Give the least common multiple of the denominators.

1. $\frac{3}{x} + \frac{x}{10} = \frac{11}{2x}$

2. $\frac{x}{x-2} = \frac{x-4}{x-5}$

3. $\frac{2x^2+x+2}{x^2-2x+1} = 2$

4. $\frac{3}{4n^2-7n-2} + \frac{2}{2-n} = \frac{4}{28n+7}$

5. $\frac{2}{r^2+3r-4} = \frac{2}{3r+12} - \frac{r}{r-1}$

6. $8(s+2)^{-1} + 8(s-2)^{-1} = 3$

7. $\dfrac{11 - n^2}{3n^2 - 5n + 2} = \dfrac{2n + 3}{3n - 2} - \dfrac{n - 3}{n - 1}$

8. $\dfrac{1}{t^3 + t^2 - 25t - 25} + \dfrac{2}{t^2 - 25} - \dfrac{3}{t^2 + 6t + 5} = 0$

9. $\dfrac{x + 4}{x^2 - 1} = \dfrac{3x}{x + 1}$

10. $\dfrac{y + 2}{y} - \dfrac{y + 1}{y - 1} = 4$

▶ B. Exercises

11-20. Solve each rational equation above. (Be sure to exclude extraneous roots.)

Solve.

21. What number must be added to both the numerator and denominator of $\frac{2}{17}$ to produce a fraction equivalent to $\frac{2}{5}$?

22. If a flask contains 5 cubic centimeters of a certain medicine and 11 cubic centimeters of water, how much medicine must be added so that the flask is $\frac{2}{3}$ full of medicine?

23. Two planes take off from the Atlanta airport at the same time, going in opposite directions. The speed of both planes in still air would be 600 mph but one is flying 990 miles against the wind (called a head wind) and the other is flying 990 miles with the wind (called a tail wind). If the one with the tail wind lands 20 minutes before the other one, what is the speed of the wind?

Find all real roots of the following rational equations, using a graphing calculator. Round the solutions to three decimal places.

24. $\dfrac{8x^2 + 2x - 5}{3x + 4} = 0$

25. $\dfrac{-2x}{x + 4} = \dfrac{5.5x - 7}{x + 5}$

▶ C. Exercises

26. A swimming pool that usually takes 4 hours to fill took 6 hours to fill because a drainpipe was left open. How long would it take the drainpipe to empty a full pool?

27. Can cross multiplication be used to solve exercise 9? Explain.

⌁ Dominion Modeling

28. Explain why a rational model is inappropriate for the Holstein data.

■ Cumulative Review

29. If an angle θ is in standard position, and $\theta = \tan^{-1} -1.25$, give three points with integral coordinates, through which the terminal ray passes.

30. If the longest leg of a 30-60 right triangle has a length of $5\sqrt{6}$, find the lengths of the other two sides.

31. $\triangle ABC$ is inscribed in a circle of radius 7, and the angles intercept arcs of 60°, 120°, and 180° respectively. Find the angles and sides of the triangle.

32. Discuss the tails of $f(x) = -3x^4 + 5x^3 - 3x^2 + 4x - 7$.

33. Find the simplest polynomial equation with roots of -3 (multiplicity 3) and 1 (multiplicity 2).

5.3 Radical Equations

Radical equation   An equation containing a variable as part of a radicand is called a radical equation.

To solve a radical equation, isolate the radical and raise both sides to the power of the index. If a radical equation contains more than one radical, you may need to repeat the process. You must check the solutions, since extraneous roots can appear when you raise both sides to a power.

EXAMPLE 1   Solve the following equation for x: $\sqrt[3]{x^2} - 1 = 15$.

Answer

$\sqrt[3]{x^2} - 1 = 15$	1. Isolate the radical.
$\sqrt[3]{x^2} = 16$	
$x^2 = 4096$	2. Cube both sides.
$x = \pm 64$	3. Take the square root of each side.
$\sqrt[3]{(\pm 64)^2} - 1 = 15$	4. Check.
$\sqrt[3]{4096} - 1 = 15$	
$16 - 1 = 15$	
$15 = 15$	

EXAMPLE 2   Solve the following equation for x: $\sqrt{x - 5} = x - 7$.

Answer

$\sqrt{x - 5} = x - 7$	1. Square both sides.
$x - 5 = x^2 - 14x + 49$	
$0 = x^2 - 15x + 54$	2. Solve for x.
$0 = (x - 9)(x - 6)$	
$x = 9$ or $x = 6$	

Continued ▶

$$\sqrt{9-5} = 9 - 7 \quad \sqrt{6-5} = 6 - 7$$
$$\sqrt{4} = 2 \qquad\qquad \sqrt{1} = -1$$
$$2 = 2 \qquad\qquad 1 = -1 \text{ is false}$$

3. Check. (Remember that the symbol $\sqrt{}$ denotes only the principal root.) Exclude 6 from the solution since it is extraneous.

Solution: $x = 9$

If there are two radicals, isolate one of them, raise both sides to the appropriate power, isolate the remaining radical, and repeat the process.

EXAMPLE 3 Solve $\sqrt{x^2 + 5x + 3} - \sqrt{x^2 + 3x} = 1$.

Answer

$$\sqrt{x^2 + 5x + 3} - \sqrt{x^2 + 3x} = 1$$
$$\sqrt{x^2 + 5x + 3} = 1 + \sqrt{x^2 + 3x}$$

1. Isolate one of the radicals.

$$x^2 + 5x + 3 = 1 + 2\sqrt{x^2 + 3x} + x^2 + 3x$$

2. Square both sides; use FOIL on the binomial on the right.

$$2x + 2 = 2\sqrt{x^2 + 3x}$$
$$x + 1 = \sqrt{x^2 + 3x}$$

3. Simplify, and isolate the remaining radical.

$$x^2 + 2x + 1 = x^2 + 3x$$

4. Square both sides again.

$$1 = x$$

5. Solve for x.

$$\sqrt{1 + 5 + 3} - \sqrt{1 + 3} = 1$$
$$\sqrt{9} - \sqrt{4} = 1$$
$$3 - 2 = 1$$
$$1 = 1$$

6. Check.

▶ A. Exercises

Solve. Check each solution.

1. $\sqrt{x} = 5$

2. $\sqrt[3]{x} = -4$

3. $\sqrt[5]{x} = 2$

4. $\sqrt[4]{x} + 2 = 5$

5. $\sqrt[4]{\frac{x}{2}} - 5 = -2$

6. $\sqrt{2x + 5} = \sqrt{3}$

7. $\sqrt{3x + 4} = 5$

8. $\sqrt{3x + 4} = x$

9. $\sqrt{x + 4} = x - 2$

10. $\sqrt[3]{n^2 + 2} + 1 = 4$

▶ B. Exercises

Solve. Check each solution.

11. $\sqrt{x^2 + 48} = 2x$

12. $2x = 3 + \sqrt{7x - 3}$

13. $\sqrt{x} + \sqrt{x + 5} = 5$

14. $\sqrt{n + 6} - \sqrt{n} = \sqrt{2}$

15. $\sqrt{r^2 + 3r + 3} + \sqrt{r^2 + r - 1} = 2$

16. $\sqrt{n} + \sqrt{n - 3} = \dfrac{3}{\sqrt{n - 3}}$

17. $\sqrt{p + 1} + \dfrac{2}{\sqrt{p + 1}} = \sqrt{p + 6}$

18. $8 = \sqrt{\dfrac{16}{x}}$

19. $\dfrac{1}{\sqrt{1 - t^2}} = 9$

20. $\sqrt{4x + 5} + 2\sqrt{x - 3} = 17$

21. $\dfrac{1}{2 - \sqrt{x}} = 5$

Find all real roots of the following radical equation, using a graphing calculator. Round the solutions to three decimal places.

22. $\sqrt{x^2 - 3.4x + 17} - \sqrt{4x + 5.6} = 3.3$

Solve.

23. $\dfrac{\sqrt{x+1} + \sqrt{x-1}}{\sqrt{x+1} - \sqrt{x-1}} = \dfrac{4x-1}{2}$

24. $\sqrt[3]{7x+1} = x + 1$

〽 Dominion Modeling

25. For the Holstein data, try a model that bends—a quadratic model. Find the model and r^2, then draw the model with the data.

26. Plot the residuals for the quadratic model. Evaluate the model.

27. Switch your independent and dependent variables to obtain another quadratic model. Evaluate the model. Why is this a useful way to check the value of a radical model?

▌Cumulative Review

28. A triangle has sides of 5, 7, and 9. Find its angles. Are they in the same ratio as the lengths of the sides?

29. In $\triangle ABC$, $\angle A = 36°$, $\angle B = 72°$, and $a = 17.9$. Solve the triangle and classify it by the length of its sides and the measure of its angles.

30. A triangular lot has sides of 450 ft and 570 ft. If the included angle is measured to be 100°, find the third side and the area of the lot in acres. (1 acre = 43,560 square feet).

31. For what value of θ are θ and $-\theta$ coterminal?

32. In a right triangle with legs $a = 2$, $b = 3$, find $\angle A$.

JOSEPH-LOUIS LAGRANGE

Joseph-Louis Lagrange (1736-1813) was born into a French-Italian family as the youngest of 11 children. He was the only one to survive infancy. His wealthy parents spent money extravagantly and left little for Lagrange to inherit. Later in life he realized that this apparent tragedy was a blessing in disguise, because an inheritance would have prevented his pursuit of a career in mathematics, which he began to study at the age of 17. Before reaching his 20th birthday, he was appointed professor of mathematics at the Royal Artillery School in Turin. Soon afterwards, he helped to found the Turin Academy of Sciences.

Lagrange wrote his masterpiece, *Mécanique analytique*, at the age of 23. The work applies calculus both to the physics of forces acting on an object and to probability. In the same year (1759) Lagrange was elected as a foreign member of the Berlin Academy. His *Théorie des fonctions analytiques* dealt with derived functions and presented the first theory of functions of real variables.

In 1764 Lagrange was awarded the grand prize of the French Academy of Sciences for an essay on the libration (very slow oscillation) of the moon. This essay was prompted by a question in his mind: "Why does the moon always present the same face to the earth?" Two years later he received an award for a notable advance in explaining the mechanics of Jupiter's system.

In 1766 Frederick the Great welcomed Lagrange to his Court in Berlin, where he became director of the physico-mathematical division of the Berlin Academy.

Shortly after his arrival, he sent for the woman who became his wife. Lagrange personally cared for her during a lingering illness, from which she finally died. He was deeply grieved upon her death and did not remarry until very late in life. During his remaining years in Berlin, he wrote *On the Solution of Numerical Equations*, which aided in the development of modern algebra. He developed the theory of finite groups, and investigated equations in the second, third, and fourth degree.

After the death of Frederick the Great in 1786, Lagrange accepted Louis XVI's invitation to Paris. His quarters were in the Louvre, and he became a close friend of Marie Antoinette.

At 51 years of age, Lagrange was forced to retire from his work due to nervous exhaustion. For a period of time he was apathetic toward mathematics, but other subjects interested him. Among these subjects were metaphysics, the development of human thought, the history of religions, the general theory of languages, medicine, and botany. Despite the advice of many, Lagrange remained in Paris during the Revolutionary War and afterward regained his love for mathematics. In 1795 he was appointed professor of mathematics at the École Normale. Lagrange's most important work during the Revolutionary period was perfecting the metric system of weights and measures. In his later years he was lonely and depressed. However, he married a girl 40 years his junior, who became a devoted wife and revived her husband's interest in life.

Lagrange, who died in 1813, was highly respected by the French people. Napoleon referred to Lagrange as "the lofty pyramid of the mathematical sciences" and made him a senator, a count of the Empire, and a grand officer of the Legion of Honor. Frederick the Great and the king of the Italian island of Sardinia also honored Lagrange.

Lagrange's most important work . . . was perfecting the metric system of weights and measures.

5.4 Logarithmic and Exponential Equations

Recall from your previous experience that a logarithm is an exponent. Equations can be transformed from log form to exponential form (or vice versa) using the following definition.

The rusty car and old shack in Hackberry, Arizona, testify to the decay of all things as guaranteed by Romans 8:21-22. Exponential functions offer a model for the analysis of decay patterns.

Definition

Logarithm The power to which a base must be raised to yield a given number, denoted $\log_b x$, where b is the base.

A logarithm is the inverse of an exponential; therefore, $\log_b x = y$ is equivalent to $b^y = x$. The fact that a logarithmic function is the inverse of the exponential function is also useful in solving equations. These inverse functions can be performed in either order to undo the function and obtain the original value. Below is a logarithm raised to a power (exponential), then the logarithm taken of an exponential.

$$b^{\log_b x} = x \text{ and } \log_b b^x = x$$

Several laws aid in the solution of equations involving logarithms.

Product law of logs: $\log_b xy = \log_b x + \log_b y$

Quotient law of logs: $\log_b \frac{x}{y} = \log_b x - \log_b y$

Power law of logs: $\log_b x^a = a \log_b x$

Log of 1: $\log_b 1 = 0 \ \forall \ b \in \mathbb{R}, \ b \neq 0$

Here are two suggestions that will help you isolate the variable as you solve logarithmic equations.

1. If you can write the equation so that the log appears on only one side, then use the definition of logarithms to rewrite the equation in exponential form.
2. If both sides of the equation can be written as logs with the same base, then undo the logs on both sides by raising both as powers of the common base.

EXAMPLE 1   Solve $2 \log_5 x = \log_5 9$.

Answer

$2 \log_5 x = \log_5 9$ $\log_5 x^2 = \log_5 9$	1. Write the left side as a single log using the power law.
$5^{\log_5 x^2} = 5^{\log_5 9}$ $x^2 = 9$	2. Perform the inverse function on both sides.
$x = \pm 3$	3. Take the square root of each side.
$x = 3$ is the solution	4. -3 is not a solution, because $\log_5 (-3)$ does not exist. The domain of $y = \log_a x$ is $x > 0$ (Section 4.6). Therefore, only $x = 3$ is an acceptable answer.

EXAMPLE 2   Solve $\log_5 x + \log_5 (2x - 3) = 1$.

Answer

$\log_5 x + \log_5 (2x - 3) = 1$ $\log_5 x(2x - 3) = 1$	1. Write the left side as a single log by applying the product law of logs.
$5^1 = x(2x - 3)$ $5 = 2x^2 - 3x$	2. Convert to exponential form.
$0 = 2x^2 - 3x - 5$ $0 = (2x - 5)(x + 1)$ $x = \frac{5}{2}$ or $x = -1$	3. Solve for x.
$x = \frac{5}{2}$ is the solution.	4. Since -1 is not in the domain of the original log expressions, it is extraneous.

To solve most exponential equations (equations with variables in the exponents) logarithms are needed. However, sometimes you can write all expressions with the same base.

EXAMPLE 3   Solve $3^{2x} = \left(\frac{1}{9}\right)^{x+5}$.

Answer

$3^{2x} = \left(\frac{1}{9}\right)^{x+5}$ $3^{2x} = (3^{-2})^{x+5}$	1. Rewrite $\frac{1}{9}$ as 3^{-2}.
$3^{2x} = 3^{(-2x-10)}$	2. Apply the power law for exponents.
$\log_3 3^{2x} = \log_3 3^{(-2x-10)}$	3. Take the log (inverse operation) of both sides.
$2x = -2x - 10$ $4x = -10$ $x = -\frac{5}{2}$	4. Solve for x.

When the two sides cannot be written with the same base, you must employ an alternate method. If the bases involve 10 or e, convert to log form.

EXAMPLE 4   Solve $10^{x+1} = 4$.

Answer $10^{x+1} = 4$

$x + 1 = \log 4$ $x = \log 4 - 1$	1. Rewrite the equation in log form and solve.
$x \approx -0.3979$	2. Simplify using a calculator.

EXAMPLE 5   Solve $e^{-5x} = 7$.

Answer $e^{-5x} = 7$

$-5x = \ln 7$	1. Rewrite the equation in log form.
$x = \frac{-\ln 7}{5}$	2. Solve for x.
$x \approx -0.3892$	3. Simplify using a calculator.

Most exponential equations do not involve convenient bases. In such cases you may take the log of both sides (using base 10 or e). Study the next example.

EXAMPLE 6   Solve for $5^x = 7$.

Answer

$5^x = 7$	
$\log 5^x = \log 7$	1. Take the common log of each side.
$x \log 5 = \log 7$	2. Apply the power law of logarithms
$x = \dfrac{\log 7}{\log 5}$	and solve for x.
$x \approx 1.209$	3. Find the quotient using a calculator.

In Example 6 you could have converted immediately to log form to obtain $\log_5 7 = x$. While this solution is equivalent, recognizing its decimal equivalent as 1.209 is not so easy. Since calculators do not have a key for base 5 logs, the change of base formula, $\log_b x = \dfrac{\log_a x}{\log_a b}$ (where $a, b \in \mathbb{R}$; $a, b > 0$; $a, b \neq 1$; and $x > 0$), must be used to obtain $\log_5 7 = \dfrac{\log 7}{\log 5}$, an expression appropriate for calculators.

The method shown in Example 6 is superior, since it avoids the need for the conversion formula and also applies to equations having exponentials with unlike bases as in Example 7.

EXAMPLE 7   Solve for x: $3^{2x-1} = 5^x$ (round to hundredths).

Answer

$3^{2x-1} = 5^x$	
$\log 3^{2x-1} = \log 5^x$	1. Take the log of each side.
$(2x - 1) \log 3 = x \log 5$	2. Apply the power law of logarithms.
$2x \log 3 - \log 3 = x \log 5$	3. Solve for x.
$2x \log 3 - x \log 5 = \log 3$	
$x(2 \log 3 - \log 5) = \log 3$	
$x = \dfrac{\log 3}{\log 9 - \log 5}$	4. Apply the power law to express $2 \log 3$ as $\log 9$.
$x \approx 1.87$	5. Use a calculator to approximate the solution.

► A. Exercises

Solve for x.

1. $\log_3 (4x - 7) = 2$
2. $\log_2 x = \frac{5}{2}$
3. $\log_{27} x = \frac{1}{3}$
4. $\log_3 (x + 1) = 2$
5. $\log_{16} x^2 = \frac{-1}{2}$

6. $\log_{125} x = \frac{2}{3}$
7. $2^x = 64$
8. $10^x = 77$
9. $e^{x+1} = 10$
10. $6^x = 12$

Simplify using the laws of logarithms.

11. $\log_5 5\sqrt{5}$
12. $4 \log_2 \frac{1}{8}$

► B. Exercises

Solve.

13. $\log_3 \frac{3}{12} - \log_3 \frac{3}{4} = x$
14. $\log_4 (x^2 - x - 2) - \log_4 (x + 1) = 2$
15. $\log_3 (x + 1) + \log_3 (x + 3) = 1$
16. $\log_2 8^x = -3$
17. $\log_3 x = 2(\log_3 5 + \log_3 4)$
18. $\log (x^2 - 144) - \log (x + 12) = 1$
19. $\frac{1}{2} \log_3 x = 2$
20. $\log_2 (x^2 + 3x + 4) = 1$

Solve for x. Round to the nearest hundredth.

21. $3^{x+1} = 17^{2x}$
22. $5^{x+2} = 15$
23. $e^x = 10^{x+1}$
24. $e^{2x-1} = 10^x$
25. $3^{5x} = 2$
26. $4^{1-x} = 5^x$
27. $12^{x-4} = 3^{x-2}$

Solve.

28. $\log_2 \sqrt{\frac{3x + 4}{x}} = 0$
29. $x^{\log_2 7} = 7$
30. $5^{\log_5 x} = 8$

31. $\log_4 x^8 = \frac{4}{3} \log_4 64$

32. $\left(\frac{1}{625}\right)^{2x-10} = 25^{10x}$

▶ C. Exercises

33. If $x^2 = 3^2$, must $x = 3$? What does this show about the function $f(x) = x^2$?

34. In Example 1, you used the rule that if $a^x = a^b$, then $x = b$. Why is this true?

35. As a contrast, write only the equations needed to solve $\log_5 x = 7$, $\log_5 7 = x$, and $\log_x 5 = 7$.

☲ Dominion Modeling

36. Is a log model or an exponential model more appropriate for the Holstein data? Explain.

▮ Cumulative Review

Classify each of the following identities by name.

37. $\sin x = \cos\left(\frac{\pi}{2} - x\right)$

38. $\sin x = \sin (x + 2\pi)$

39. $\sin (-x) = -\sin x$

40. State the law of cosines.

41. What is the result when the angle in exercise 40 is 90°?

5.5 Identities

The Grand Hotel in Taiwan's capital contrasts sharply with American architecture, but the equations for supporting the structure are the same among engineers in every culture.

The word *identity* means "being the same as something else." The most important identity in history is the identity of Jesus Christ. Jesus claimed identity with the Father when He said "I and the Father are one" (John 10:30). The Jews recognized this as a claim to be God (John 10:31-33). Thomas recognized Christ's deity after His resurrection and worshiped Him, saying "My Lord and my God" (John 20:28).

An identity in mathematics also refers to two things being the same.

> **Definition**
>
> **Identity** An equation that is true for all values in the domain of the variable.

Most equations are not identities because they are true only for certain values of the variable, whereas an identity is true for all values for which the expressions are defined. Since identities are always equal, either side can be substituted for the other at any time. An identity relating two expressions can be very helpful in simplifying. You already know some identities such as $x^0 = 1$ and $(x + 1)^2 = x^2 + 2x + 1$.

An equation that is not an identity is called a *conditional equation*.

Identities have to be proved before they can be accepted as truth. As is true of theorems in geometry, you must begin building a system of trigonometric identities on the foundation of definitions. After an identity is proved, it can be used to prove other identities. The definitions of the trig ratios provide the foundation for this system that will be used later to solve practical problems.

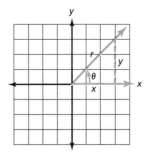

Basic Trigonometric Function	Reciprocal Function
$\sin \theta = \frac{y}{r}$	$\csc \theta = \frac{r}{y}$
$\cos \theta = \frac{x}{r}$	$\sec \theta = \frac{r}{x}$
$\tan \theta = \frac{y}{x}$	$\cot \theta = \frac{x}{y}$

From these definitions you can prove that the reciprocal of each basic trigonometric function is the corresponding reciprocal function. The reciprocal identity relating cosine and secant is proved below.

$$\frac{1}{\cos \theta} = \frac{1}{\frac{x}{r}} = \frac{r}{x} = \sec \theta$$

Because such identities relate the basic trig functions and their reciprocal functions, they are called *reciprocal identities*. The basic reciprocal identities are $\sec \theta = \frac{1}{\cos \theta}$, $\csc \theta = \frac{1}{\sin \theta}$, $\cot \theta = \frac{1}{\tan \theta}$. The other two identities are to be proved similarly in exercises 1 and 2. Any of the three reciprocal identities can also be solved for the basic trig functions. For instance, solving the secant identity above for cosine yields $\cos \theta = \frac{1}{\sec \theta}$.

Other basic trigonometric identities are derived from the Pythagorean theorem and are therefore called *Pythagorean identities*. The Pythagorean theorem states the following relation between the lengths of the legs x and y and the hypotenuse r for any right triangle.

$$x^2 + y^2 = r^2$$

Using this theorem and some algebra, you can see how one Pythagorean identity is derived.

$$x^2 + y^2 = r^2$$
$$\frac{x^2}{r^2} + \frac{y^2}{r^2} = \frac{r^2}{r^2}$$
$$\left(\frac{x}{r}\right)^2 + \left(\frac{y}{r}\right)^2 = 1$$
$$\cos^2 \theta + \sin^2 \theta = 1$$

The remaining Pythagorean identities can be similarly proved.

$$\tan^2 \theta + 1 = \sec^2 \theta$$

$$1 + \cot^2 \theta = \csc^2 \theta$$

Here are several basic pointers to help you begin proving identities.

1. Choose one side of the statement you are to prove. You will usually want to select the more complicated side.

2. Use basic definitions, algebra, and previously proven identities to simplify the chosen expression so that it matches the other side.

3. If you are unable to simplify one side to look like the other side, work on each separately on scratch paper to help determine their relationship. Use your work to help you write the proof in the correct form.
Caution: Do not use properties of equality; to do so would be to assume what you are trying to prove.

4. If you find an identity extremely difficult to prove, then change each member to its basic ratio definition and simplify.

5. If you still cannot prove the identity, try some number values in the equation and see if you can find a counterexample to show that it is false.

EXAMPLE 1   Prove $\dfrac{\sin \theta}{\cos \theta} = \tan \theta$.

Answer

$\dfrac{\sin \theta}{\cos \theta} = \dfrac{\sin \theta}{\cos \theta}$	1. Select the more complicated side. The reflexive property of equality often provides a simple starting point.
$= \dfrac{\frac{y}{r}}{\frac{x}{r}}$	2. Apply the basic definitions to the right side.
$= \dfrac{y}{r} \cdot \dfrac{r}{x}$ $= \dfrac{y}{x}$	3. Simplify the complex rational expression.
$= \tan \theta$	4. Recognize the definition of the tangent ratio.

Therefore, by the transitive property of equality, $\dfrac{\sin \theta}{\cos \theta} = \tan \theta$.

Taking the reciprocal of both sides gives a related identity:

$$\frac{\cos \theta}{\sin \theta} = \frac{1}{\tan \theta} = \cot \theta.$$

Notice that every step in Example 1 had a reason. These reasons involve trig definitions or algebraic properties that are used to simplify.

EXAMPLE 2 Prove $\sin \theta \sec \theta = \tan \theta$.

Answer

$\sin \theta \sec \theta = \sin \theta \, \dfrac{1}{\cos \theta}$	1. Select the expression $\sin \theta \sec \theta$ as the more difficult and write a true statement. This one uses a reciprocal identity. The reflexive property can be used first if you prefer.
$= \dfrac{\sin \theta}{\cos \theta}$ $= \tan \theta$	2. Substitute, using the identity from Example 1 to prove the identity.

Therefore, $\sin \theta \sec \theta = \tan \theta$.

EXAMPLE 3 Prove $\sec^4 \theta - \sec^2 \theta = \dfrac{1}{\cot^4 \theta} + \dfrac{1}{\cot^2 \theta}$.

Answer

$\dfrac{1}{\cot^4 \theta} + \dfrac{1}{\cot^2 \theta} = \dfrac{1}{\cot^4 \theta} + \dfrac{1}{\cot^2 \theta}$	1. Express the right side, using the reflexive property.
$= \tan^4 \theta + \tan^2 \theta$	2. Use the reciprocal identities.
$= \tan^2 \theta \, (\tan^2 \theta + 1)$	3. Factor the right side.
$= (\sec^2 \theta - 1)(\sec^2 \theta)$	4. Use the Pythagorean identity, $\tan^2 \theta + 1 = \sec^2 \theta$.
$= \sec^4 \theta - \sec^2 \theta$	5. Use the distributive property to simplify.

Therefore, $\sec^4 \theta - \sec^2 \theta = \dfrac{1}{\cot^4 \theta} + \dfrac{1}{\cot^2 \theta}$.

▶ A. Exercises

Mimic the proof of the reciprocal identity for secant to prove the other two reciprocal identities.

1. $\csc \theta = \dfrac{1}{\sin \theta}$

2. $\cot \theta = \dfrac{1}{\tan \theta}$

Prove each identity ∀ θ in the domains of the functions.

3. $\tan^2 \theta + 1 = \sec^2 \theta$

4. $1 + \cot^2 \theta = \csc^2 \theta$

5. $\sin \theta + \cos \theta \cot \theta = \csc \theta$

6. $\dfrac{\sin \theta - \cos \theta}{\sin \theta} = 1 - \cot \theta$

7. $\dfrac{\tan \theta \cos \theta}{\sin \theta} = 1$

8. $\dfrac{1 + \tan^2 \theta}{\tan^2 \theta} = \csc^2 \theta$

9. $\sin \theta \sec \theta - \sin \theta \csc \theta = \tan \theta - 1$

10. $\dfrac{\sec \theta}{\cos \theta} - \dfrac{\tan \theta}{\cot \theta} = 1$

▶ B. Exercises

Prove the following identities.

11. $\sec^4 \theta + \sec^2 \theta \tan^2 \theta - 2 \tan^4 \theta = 3 \sec^2 \theta - 2$

12. $\csc \theta - \cot \theta = \dfrac{\sin \theta}{1 + \cos \theta}$

13. $\dfrac{1 + \cos \theta}{\sin \theta} + \dfrac{\sin \theta}{1 + \cos \theta} = 2 \csc \theta$

14. $\dfrac{\tan^2 \theta}{\csc \theta} + \dfrac{\cot^2 \theta}{\sec \theta} = \dfrac{\sin^5 \theta + \cos^5 \theta}{\sin^2 \theta \cos^2 \theta}$

Using the identities from this section and the information given, find each value. Assume θ is a first quadrant angle. Name the identity or identities used.

15. If $\sin \theta = 0.3842$, find $\cos \theta$.

16. If $\tan \theta = 1.3751$, find $\cot \theta$.

17. If $\cos \theta = 0.8764$, find $\tan \theta$.

18. If $\csc \theta = 1.471$, find $\sec \theta$.

19. If $\sec \theta = 1.236$, find $\sin \theta$.

20. If $\cot \theta = 0.8391$, find $\csc \theta$.

▶ C. Exercises

21. Prove $\dfrac{-\sin \theta}{\sec \theta + \cos \theta} + \dfrac{\cos \theta}{\csc \theta - \sin \theta} = \dfrac{\tan \theta}{1 + \cos^2 \theta}$.

22. Prove exercise 13 again but start with the simpler side. Then explain why we usually start with the more complicated side.

Dominion Modeling

23. Now find a cubic model for the Holstein data. What is r^2? Draw the model with the data.

24. Plot the residuals for the cubic model and evaluate.

25. Use your model to estimate the weight of a Holstein that is 50 inches high.

Cumulative Review

26. In $\triangle ABC$, find $\angle A$ if $a = 3$, $b = 7$, and $c = 5$.

27. Solve $\ln 3 = -2 + \ln x$.

28. The remainder of $P(x)$ divided by $x - 7$ is zero and the quotient is $Q(x)$. Draw two conclusions and justify them with theorems.

29. Find the inverse of $f(x) = \frac{x}{x+3}$.

30. Simplify $\dfrac{1}{\sec\left(x + \frac{3\pi}{2}\right)}$.

5.6 Sum and Difference Identities

Recall from Chapter 3 that the cosine function is even (symmetric to the *y*-axis). Therefore $\cos(-\theta) = \cos\theta$. By contrast, the sine function is odd (symmetric to the origin), which allows us to conclude that $\sin(-\theta) = -\sin\theta$. These are two of the odd-even identities.

Other important identities are the sum and difference identities. They can be useful when evaluating trig functions for angles that are not special angles.

Consider the angle $\frac{\pi}{12}$, for instance. How do you determine the value of $\cos\frac{\pi}{12}$? Can you simply rewrite $\frac{\pi}{12}$ as $\frac{4\pi}{12} - \frac{3\pi}{12} = \frac{\pi}{3} - \frac{\pi}{4}$ and then subtract the cosines? Does $\cos\left(\frac{\pi}{3} - \frac{\pi}{4}\right) = \cos\frac{\pi}{3} - \cos\frac{\pi}{4}$? Examine this conjecture using your calculator.

$$\cos\frac{\pi}{12} = 0.9659,\ whereas\ \cos\frac{\pi}{3} - \cos\frac{\pi}{4} \approx 0.5 - 0.7071 = -0.2071$$

Therefore, $\cos(x - y) \neq \cos x - \cos y$. The word cosine is not a factor to be distributed as though it were a real number.

A new identity can be derived to evaluate functions of angles such as $\frac{\pi}{12}$. Study the following diagram.

On the unit circle, two angles in standard position with measures *x* and *y* have been chosen. The letter *x* is the measure of the angle whose terminal side passes through *A*, and *y* that of the angle whose terminal side passes through *B*. You can see that $\angle AOB$ has measure $x - y$. Now, rotate the angle into standard position to get $\angle COD$.

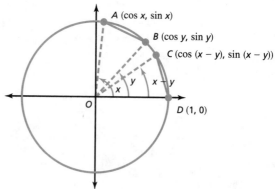

Notice the coordinates where each of the four rays cross the unit circle: $A(\cos x, \sin x)$, $B(\cos y, \sin y)$, $C(\cos(x - y), \sin(x - y))$, $D(1, 0)$.

Because this figure is constructed in the coordinate plane, you can use the distance formula, $d = \sqrt{(x_1 - x_2)^2 + (y_1 - y_2)^2}$, to find the lengths of the two chords, $\overline{AB}$ and $\overline{CD}$. Since the lengths are equal, the following equation results.

$$d_{CD} = d_{AB}$$

$$\sqrt{[\cos (x - y) - 1]^2 + [\sin (x - y) - 0]^2} = \sqrt{(\cos x - \cos y)^2 + (\sin x - \sin y)^2}$$

Square both sides to remove the radicals, then square each binomial.

$$\cos^2 (x - y) - 2 \cos (x - y) + 1 + \sin^2 (x - y)$$
$$= \cos^2 x - 2 \cos x \cos y + \cos^2 y + \sin^2 x - 2 \sin x \sin y + \sin^2 y$$

Rearranging the order of terms,

$$\cos^2 (x - y) + \sin^2 (x - y) - 2 \cos (x - y) + 1$$
$$= \cos^2 x + \sin^2 x - 2 \cos x \cos y + \cos^2 y + \sin^2 y - 2 \sin x \sin y$$

For a given angle, the sum of the squares of the cosine and sine is 1 (by the Pythagorean identity). Apply it once on the left side and twice on the right.

$$-2 \cos (x - y) + 2 = -2 \cos x \cos y - 2 \sin x \sin y + 2$$

Subtract 2 from each side.

$$-2 \cos (x - y) = -2 \cos x \cos y - 2 \sin x \sin y$$

Divide each side by -2.

$$\cos (x - y) = \cos x \cos y + \sin x \sin y$$

This result provides us with a formula for the cosine of the difference of two angles. From this identity, we can derive three other useful identities. The formula for the cosine of the sum of two angles is derived below.

$$\cos (x + y) = \cos [x - (-y)]$$
1. Apply the definition of subtraction.

$$\cos (x + y) = \cos x \cos (-y) + \sin x \sin (-y)$$
2. Apply the identity for cosine of a difference.

$$\cos (x + y) = \cos x \cos y - \sin x \sin y$$
3. Substitute, using $\cos (-\theta) = \cos \theta$ and $\sin (-\theta) = -\sin \theta$.

The proof of the last two identities is left to you in the exercises. All four are listed below for easy reference.

$$\cos (x - y) = \cos x \cos y + \sin x \sin y$$
$$\cos (x + y) = \cos x \cos y - \sin x \sin y$$
$$\sin (x - y) = \sin x \cos y - \cos x \sin y$$
$$\sin (x + y) = \sin x \cos y + \cos x \sin y$$

You now have the tools to use the trig values of $\frac{\pi}{3}$, $\frac{\pi}{4}$, and $\frac{\pi}{6}$ to find the trigonometric values of other angles.

EXAMPLE 1 Find $\cos \frac{\pi}{12}$.

Answer $\cos \frac{\pi}{12} = \cos \left(\frac{\pi}{3} - \frac{\pi}{4} \right)$

$$= \cos \frac{\pi}{3} \cos \frac{\pi}{4} + \sin \frac{\pi}{3} \sin \frac{\pi}{4}$$

$$= \left(\frac{1}{2} \right)\left(\frac{\sqrt{2}}{2} \right) + \left(\frac{\sqrt{3}}{2} \right)\left(\frac{\sqrt{2}}{2} \right)$$

$$= \frac{\sqrt{2} + \sqrt{6}}{4}$$

You can check this fraction and verify that it has the same decimal value as that obtained for $\cos \frac{\pi}{12}$ at the beginning of this section.

$$\frac{\sqrt{2} + \sqrt{6}}{4} \approx \frac{3.8637}{4} = 0.9659 \approx \cos \frac{\pi}{12}.$$

EXAMPLE 2 Find $\sin \frac{5\pi}{12}$.

Answer $\sin \frac{5\pi}{12} = \sin \left(\frac{\pi}{6} + \frac{\pi}{4} \right)$

$$= \sin \frac{\pi}{6} \cos \frac{\pi}{4} + \cos \frac{\pi}{6} \sin \frac{\pi}{4}$$

$$= \left(\frac{1}{2} \right)\left(\frac{\sqrt{2}}{2} \right) + \left(\frac{\sqrt{3}}{2} \right)\left(\frac{\sqrt{2}}{2} \right)$$

$$= \frac{\sqrt{2} + \sqrt{6}}{4}$$

Notice that Example 1 and Example 2 have the same answer. Can you explain why? Remember, cofunctions of complementary angles are equal, or $\cos \left(\frac{\pi}{2} - \theta \right) = \sin \theta$. The angles $\frac{\pi}{12}$ and $\frac{5\pi}{12}$ are complementary, since their sum is $\frac{\pi}{2}$. When rewriting the angle as a sum or difference, you should choose only angles equivalent to multiples of $\frac{\pi}{6}$, $\frac{\pi}{4}$, $\frac{\pi}{3}$, $\frac{\pi}{2}$, or π so that values already known can be substituted. For instance, in Example 1, $\frac{\pi}{12}$ could not have been renamed $\left(\frac{5\pi}{12} - \frac{4\pi}{12} \right)$, because $\cos \frac{5\pi}{12}$ was not known. All values of sine and cosine at $x = \frac{\pi}{12}, \frac{5\pi}{12}, \frac{7\pi}{12}, \frac{11\pi}{12}, \ldots$ (those that will not reduce to known values) will be in the form $\frac{\pm\sqrt{2} \pm \sqrt{6}}{4}$. This is because all have the same reference angle of $\frac{\pi}{12}$. Only the sign(s) will vary depending on the quadrant.

EXAMPLE 3 If $\cos x = \frac{5}{13}$ and $\cos y = \frac{4}{5}$, where x is a first-quadrant angle, and y is in the fourth quadrant, evaluate the following.

a. $\sin x$ c. $\cos (x - y)$

b. $\sin y$ d. $\sin (x - y)$

Continued ▶

Answer

a. $\cos^2 x + \sin^2 x = 1$

$\quad \frac{25}{169} + \sin^2 x = 1$

$\quad\quad \sin^2 x = \frac{144}{169}$

$\quad\quad\; \sin x = \frac{12}{13}$

(Sine is positive in quadrant I.)

c. $\cos (x - y) = \cos x \cos y + \sin x \sin y$

$\quad\quad\quad\quad = \left(\frac{5}{13}\right)\left(\frac{4}{5}\right) + \left(\frac{12}{13}\right)\left(-\frac{3}{5}\right)$

$\quad\quad\quad\quad = \frac{20}{65} - \frac{36}{65}$

$\quad\quad\quad\quad = \frac{-16}{65}$

b. $\cos^2 y + \sin^2 y = 1$

$\quad \frac{16}{25} + \sin^2 y = 1$

$\quad\quad \sin^2 y = \frac{9}{25}$

$\quad\quad\; \sin y = -\frac{3}{5}$

(Sine is negative in quadrant IV.)

d. $\sin (x - y) = \sin x \cos y - \cos x \sin y$

$\quad\quad\quad\quad = \left(\frac{12}{13}\right)\left(\frac{4}{5}\right) - \left(\frac{5}{13}\right)\left(-\frac{3}{5}\right)$

$\quad\quad\quad\quad = \frac{48}{65} + \frac{15}{65}$

$\quad\quad\quad\quad = \frac{63}{65}$

An alternate method can be used just as easily to find sin x and sin y in Example 3. A right triangle can be drawn, the adjacent side and hypotenuse labeled, and the Pythagorean theorem used to find the third side. The sine can then be determined from its defining ratio.

The sum and difference identities are also useful in proving other identities. In Chapter 3 you learned about several trig relationships: cofunctions, period, and odd-even. Each of these relations describes an identity that can be proved using the sum and difference identities.

Here is a summary of these identities. Some of them will help in the next examples.

Odd-Even Identities	Cofunction Identities	Period Identities ($k \in \mathbb{Z}$)
$\sin (-\theta) = -\sin \theta$	$\sin \left(\frac{\pi}{2} - \theta\right) = \cos \theta$	$\sin (\theta + 2k\pi) = \sin \theta$
$\cos (-\theta) = \cos \theta$	$\cos \left(\frac{\pi}{2} - \theta\right) = \sin \theta$	$\cos (\theta + 2k\pi) = \cos \theta$
$\sec (-\theta) = \sec \theta$	$\tan \left(\frac{\pi}{2} - \theta\right) = \cot \theta$	$\tan (\theta + k\pi) = \tan \theta$
$\csc (-\theta) = -\csc \theta$	$\cot \left(\frac{\pi}{2} - \theta\right) = \tan \theta$	$\cot (\theta + k\pi) = \cot \theta$
$\tan (-\theta) = -\tan \theta$	$\sec \left(\frac{\pi}{2} - \theta\right) = \csc \theta$	$\sec (\theta + 2k\pi) = \sec \theta$
$\cot (-\theta) = -\cot \theta$	$\csc \left(\frac{\pi}{2} - \theta\right) = \sec \theta$	$\csc (\theta + 2k\pi) = \csc \theta$

EXAMPLE 4 Prove $\left[\sin\left(\frac{\pi}{2} - x\right)\cos x + \cos\left(\frac{\pi}{2} - x\right)\sin x\right](\cos^2 x - \sin^2 x)$
$$= \cos^4 x - \sin^4 x \; \forall \; x.$$

Answer

$\left[\sin\left(\frac{\pi}{2} - x\right)\cos x + \cos\left(\frac{\pi}{2} - x\right)\sin x\right](\cos^2 x - \sin^2 x)$ $= (\cos x \cos x + \sin x \sin x)(\cos^2 x - \sin^2 x)$	1. Select the left side of the original identity and substitute, using cofunction identities.
$= (\cos^2 x + \sin^2 x)(\cos^2 x - \sin^2 x)$ $= \cos^4 x - \sin^4 x$	2. Simplify and multiply the binomials.

EXAMPLE 5 Prove $\sin^2 x - \cos x \cos (-x) \sin^2 x = \sin^4 x \; \forall \; x.$

Answer

$\sin^2 x - \cos x \cos (-x) \sin^2 x$ $= \sin^2 x - \cos x \cos x \sin^2 x$ $= \sin^2 x - \cos^2 x \sin^2 x$	1. Select the left side; substitute using $\cos x = \cos (-x)$, since cosine is even. Simplify.
$= \sin^2 x \, (1 - \cos^2 x)$	2. Factor $\sin^2 x$ out of both terms.
$= \sin^2 x \, (\sin^2 x)$	3. Because the identity $\sin^2 x + \cos^2 x = 1$ can be rearranged as $\sin^2 x = 1 - \cos^2 x$, you can substitute $\sin^2 x$ for $1 - \cos^2 x$.
$= \sin^4 x$	4. Multiply.

▶ A. Exercises

Find exact values.

1. $\cos \frac{7\pi}{12}$

2. $\cos \frac{-7\pi}{12}$

3. $\sin \frac{11\pi}{12}$

4. $\sin \frac{-11\pi}{12}$

5. $\cos \frac{17\pi}{12}$

6. $\sin \frac{\pi}{12}$

7. $\tan \frac{\pi}{12}$

8. $\cot \frac{\pi}{12}$

9. $\sec \frac{\pi}{12}$

10. $\csc \frac{\pi}{12}$

Given $\sin x = \frac{7}{25}$ and $\sin y = \frac{60}{61}$ such that x is an angle in the first quadrant and y is an angle in the second, evaluate the following.

11. $\cos x$

12. $\cos y$

13. $\tan x$

14. $\sin (y - x)$

15. $\tan (y - x)$

▶ B. Exercises

Prove.

16. $\cos (-x) = \cos x$ (*Hint:* Write $-x$ as $0 - x$.)
17. $\sin (-x) = -\sin x$
18. $\tan (-x) = -\tan x$
19. $\sin \left(\frac{\pi}{2} - x\right) = \cos x$
20. $\cos (x + 2\pi) = \cos x$
21. $\sec \left(\frac{\pi}{2} - x\right) = \csc x$
22. $\cos (\pi - x) = \cos (\pi + x)$
23. $[\cos (x - y)][\cos (x + y)] = \cos^2 x - \sin^2 y$
24. $\sin (x - y) = \sin x \cos y - \cos x \sin y$
25. $\sin (x + y) = \sin x \cos y + \cos x \sin y$
26. $\tan (x + y) = \dfrac{\tan x + \tan y}{1 - \tan x \tan y}$
27. $\tan (x + \pi) = \tan x$
28. $\dfrac{\sin (x - y)}{\sin (x + y)} = \dfrac{\tan x - \tan y}{\tan x + \tan y}$
29. $\dfrac{\cos (x - y)}{\cos (x + y)} = \dfrac{\cot x + \tan y}{\cot x - \tan y}$

▶ C. Exercises

30. Prove that $\dfrac{\cos^2 x + 3 \sin x - 1}{3 + 2 \sin x - \sin^2 x} = \dfrac{1}{1 + \csc x}$.

31. Split $3x$ into separate angles $2x$ and x, then use the appropriate formula from this section to develop a formula for $\sin 3x$.

▮ Cumulative Review

Let $f(x) = 2x + 3$ and $g(x) = 2x^2 + x - 3$.

32. Find $(f + g)(x)$ and $(f - g)(x)$.
33. Find $fg(x)$.
34. Find $\frac{f}{g}(x)$ including the existence condition.
35. Find $(f \circ g)(x)$ and $(g \circ f)(x)$.
36. What algebraic characteristic is true of two functions that are inverses of one another?

5.7 Double-Angle and Half-Angle Identities

There are four more identities that aid in evaluating sine and cosine functions: the double-angle and half-angle identities. These identities will also serve you later as you solve trigonometric equations. The proofs depend on the sum and difference identities.

$\cos 2x = \cos (x + x)$	1. Substitute $(x + x)$ for $2x$.
$= \cos x \cos x - \sin x \sin x$	2. Apply the sum identity for cosine.
$= \cos^2 x - \sin^2 x$	3. Multiply.

You can derive two alternate forms of this identity by applying the Pythagorean identity for sine and cosine to write it in terms of a single trig function:

$$\cos 2x = 2 \cos^2 x - 1$$

$$\cos 2x = 1 - 2 \sin^2 x$$

The following double-angle identity for the sine function can be derived in the same manner as for the cosine.

$$\sin 2x = 2 \sin x \cos x$$

Both half-angle identities are derived from the cosine double-angle identities.

$\cos x = \cos \left[2\left(\frac{x}{2}\right)\right]$	1. Rewrite x as $2\left(\frac{x}{2}\right)$ and apply the double-angle identity for cosine $(\cos 2x = 2 \cos^2 x - 1)$.
$\cos x = 2 \cos^2 \frac{x}{2} - 1$	
$1 + \cos x = 2 \cos^2 \frac{x}{2}$	2. Solve for $\cos \frac{x}{2}$.
$\frac{1}{2}(1 + \cos x) = \cos^2 \frac{x}{2}$	
$\pm\sqrt{\frac{1}{2}(1 + \cos x)} = \cos \frac{x}{2}$	
$\cos \frac{x}{2} = \pm\sqrt{\frac{1}{2}(1 + \cos x)}$	

To derive the half-angle identity for sine, substitute the alternate form of the $\cos 2x$ identity ($\cos 2x = 1 - 2 \sin^2 x$) in step 1. Solve for $\sin \frac{x}{2}$.

$$\sin \frac{x}{2} = \pm\sqrt{\frac{1}{2}(1 - \cos x)}$$

EXAMPLE 1   Find $\sin \frac{\pi}{8}$.

Answer

$\sin \frac{\pi}{8} = \sin \dfrac{\left(\frac{\pi}{4}\right)}{2}$	1. Rewrite $\frac{\pi}{8}$ as half of $\frac{\pi}{4}$.
$= \sqrt{\frac{1}{2}\left(1 - \cos \frac{\pi}{4}\right)}$	2. Apply the half-angle identity for the sine function. The $\pm$ sign is unnecessary since this is a first quadrant angle; the sine is positive.
$= \sqrt{\frac{1}{2}\left(1 - \frac{\sqrt{2}}{2}\right)}$	3. Substitute the value for $\cos \frac{\pi}{4}$.
$= \sqrt{\frac{1}{2} - \frac{\sqrt{2}}{4}}$	4. Distribute.
$= \sqrt{\frac{2 - \sqrt{2}}{4}}$	5. Find a common denominator.
$= \frac{\sqrt{2 - \sqrt{2}}}{2}$	6. Simplify.

EXAMPLE 2   Find $\cos \frac{\pi}{12}$, using a half-angle formula.

Answer

$\cos \frac{\pi}{12} = \cos \dfrac{\left(\frac{\pi}{6}\right)}{2}$	1. Rewrite $\frac{\pi}{12}$ as half of $\frac{\pi}{6}$.
$= \sqrt{\frac{1}{2}\left(1 + \cos \frac{\pi}{6}\right)}$	2. Apply the half-angle identity for cosine. $\cos \frac{\pi}{12}$ is positive because $\frac{\pi}{12}$ is in quadrant I.
$= \sqrt{\frac{1}{2}\left(1 + \frac{\sqrt{3}}{2}\right)}$	3. Substitute the value for $\cos \frac{\pi}{6}$.
$= \sqrt{\frac{1}{2} + \frac{\sqrt{3}}{4}}$	4. Distribute.
$= \sqrt{\frac{2 + \sqrt{3}}{4}}$	5. Find a common denominator and simplify.
$= \frac{\sqrt{2 + \sqrt{3}}}{2}$	

EXAMPLE 3   Prove $\cos 2x = \cos^4 x - \sin^4 x$.

Answer

$\cos^4 x - \sin^4 x = (\cos^2 x - \sin^2 x)(\cos^2 x + \sin^2 x)$	1. Select the right side and factor it.

Continued ▶

$= (\cos^2 x - \sin^2 x)(1)$	2. Apply the Pythagorean identity.
$= \cos^2 x - \sin^2 x$	3. Apply the identity property for multiplication.
$= \cos 2x$	4. Apply the double-angle identity for cosine.

EXAMPLE 4 Prove $\cos 2x = \dfrac{1 - \tan^2 x}{1 + \tan^2 x}$.

Answer

$\dfrac{1 - \tan^2 x}{1 + \tan^2 x} = \dfrac{1 - \tan^2 x}{1 + \tan^2 x}$	1. Select the more complicated side, applying the reflexive property.
$= \dfrac{1 - \frac{\sin^2 x}{\cos^2 x}}{1 + \frac{\sin^2 x}{\cos^2 x}}$	2. Apply identities.
$= \dfrac{\cos^2 x - \sin^2 x}{\cos^2 x + \sin^2 x}$	3. Simplify the complex fraction by multiplying it by 1 in the form of $\frac{\cos^2 x}{\cos^2 x}$.
$= \dfrac{\cos^2 x - \sin^2 x}{1}$	4. Apply the Pythagorean identity.
$= \cos 2x$	5. Apply the double angle identity.

▶ A. Exercises

If x is an angle in the given quadrant, find the possible quadrants for $\frac{x}{2}$ and $2x$.

	Quadrant I	Quadrant II	Quadrant III	Quadrant IV
1. $\frac{x}{2}$	I			
2. $2x$	I or II			

Find the exact values.

3. $\cos \frac{\pi}{8}$

4. $\sin \frac{5\pi}{8}$

5. $\cos \frac{5\pi}{12}$

6. $\sin \frac{\pi}{24}$ (*Hint:* Find $\cos \frac{\pi}{12}$.)

7. $\cos \frac{\pi}{24}$

Prove.

8. $\cos 2x = 2 \cos^2 x - 1$

9. $\cos 2x = 1 - 2 \sin^2 x$

10. $\sin 2x = 2 \sin x \cos x$

Prove.

11. $\sin \frac{x}{2} = \pm\sqrt{\frac{1}{2}(1 - \cos x)}$

12. $\cos^2 \frac{x}{2} = \frac{1 + \sec x}{2 \sec x}$

13. $\csc 2x = \frac{1 + \tan^2 x}{2 \tan x}$

14. $\tan 2x = \frac{2 \tan x}{1 - \tan^2 x}$

15. $\sqrt{\frac{1 - \cos x}{1 + \cos x}} = \frac{\sin x}{1 + \cos x}$

16. $\tan \frac{x}{2} = \sqrt{\frac{1 - \cos x}{1 + \cos x}}$

17. $\frac{2 \sin^2 \frac{x}{2} + \cos x}{\sec x} = \cos x$

18. $\csc^2 \frac{x}{2} = \frac{2 \sec x}{\sec x - 1}$

19. $2 \sin^2 x - 1 = \sin^4 x - \cos^4 x$

20. $\cos^3 x - \sin^3 x = (\cos x - \sin x)\left(1 + \frac{1}{2} \sin 2x\right)$

21. $\sec 2x + \tan 2x = \frac{\cos x + \sin x}{\cos x - \sin x}$

22. $\frac{\sin 2x}{1 + \cos 2x} = \frac{1 - \cos 2x}{\sin 2x}$

23. $\sin 3x + \sin x = 2 \sin 2x \cos x$

► C. Exercises

Prove.

24. $\frac{\sin 3x}{\sin x} - \frac{\cos 3x}{\cos x} = 2$

25. $\cos^4 x = \frac{3}{8} + \frac{\cos 2x}{2} + \frac{\cos 4x}{8}$

26. $\sin^6 x = \frac{5}{16} - \frac{\cos 2x}{2} + \frac{3 \cos 4x}{16} + \frac{\sin^2 2x \cos 2x}{8}$

■ Cumulative Review

27. State two odd-even identities.

28. State the three Pythagorean identities.

29. Write secant and cosecant in terms of sine and cosine. What type of identities are these?

30. Write tangent and cotangent in terms of sine and cosine.

31. Prove $\cot \theta = \frac{\cos \theta}{\sin \theta}$.

5.8 Trigonometric Equations

Trigonometric identities are true for all values of the variable for which the expressions are defined. Trig equations may be true for infinitely many values (unless restricted) but not for all values. Also, identities are proved by simplifying one side until it looks like the other side, but equations are solved by applying properties of equality.

To solve trigonometric equations, you may use identities or any of the techniques you have learned for solving linear, quadratic, and higher-degree equations. First solve for a trig function, then isolate the variable by applying the inverse operation. For instance, when given tan x, solve for x by taking the $\tan^{-1}$ of each side.

EXAMPLE 1   Solve for x: $\tan x - \sqrt{3} = 0$.

Answer

$\tan x - \sqrt{3} = 0$

$\qquad \tan x = \sqrt{3}$ 1. Add $\sqrt{3}$ to both sides.

- -

$\tan^{-1}(\tan x) = \tan^{-1}\sqrt{3}$ 2. Take $\tan^{-1}$ of each side.

- -

$x = \frac{\pi}{3} + k\pi, \ k \in \mathbb{Z}$ 3. The tangent is $\sqrt{3}$ at $\frac{\pi}{3}$. Since the tangent is also positive in quadrant III, adding multiples of π will include all angles where the tangent is $\sqrt{3}$.

Because of the periodic nature of the tangent function, whose period is π, all values of integral multiples of π units from $\frac{\pi}{3}$ $\left(\frac{4\pi}{3}, \frac{7\pi}{3}, \text{etc.}\right)$ are also solutions, as reflected in the answer to Example 1. If the equation had involved the sine or cosine function, to include all answers you would have added $2k\pi$ to the solutions, since the period of these functions is 2π.

Rather than finding all roots, it is customary to restrict roots of trig equations to the *primary solutions* (those in the interval $0 \le x < 2\pi$).

EXAMPLE 2 Solve $2 \cos^2 x + 3 \cos x + 1 = 0$ for $x \in [0, 2\pi)$.

Answer

$2 \cos^2 x + 3 \cos x + 1 = 0$ $(2 \cos x + 1)(\cos x + 1) = 0$	1. Factor. You can think of the equation as $2u^2 + 3u + 1 = 0$ with $u = \cos x$.
$\cos x = \dfrac{-1}{2}$ or $\cos x = -1$	2. Solve for $\cos x$ using the zero product property.
$x = \cos^{-1} \dfrac{-1}{2}$ or $x = \cos^{-1} -1$	3. Take $\cos^{-1}$ of each side.
$x = \dfrac{2\pi}{3}, \dfrac{4\pi}{3}, \pi$	4. Cosine is -1 at π. Cosine is $\frac{1}{2}$ at $\frac{\pi}{3}$. Use this as a reference angle to find second and third quadrant angles where the cosine is negative. $\left(\pi - \frac{\pi}{3}\right) = \frac{2\pi}{3}$ (second quadrant) and $\left(\pi + \frac{\pi}{3}\right) = \frac{4\pi}{3}$ (third quadrant)

If more than one function appears in an equation, try to express all of them in terms of one function or to separate them by factoring.

EXAMPLE 3 Solve $\sin 2x = \cos x$ over the interval $0 \le x < 2\pi$.

Answer

$\sin 2x = \cos x$	
$2 \sin x \cos x = \cos x$	1. Apply the trigonometric identity $\sin 2x = 2 \sin x \cos x$.
$2 \sin x \cos x - \cos x = 0$ $\cos x(2 \sin x - 1) = 0$ $\cos x = 0$ or $2 \sin x - 1 = 0$ $\cos x = 0$ or $\sin x = \dfrac{1}{2}$	2. Subtract $\cos x$ from each side, factor, and solve. (Note that factoring separates sine and cosine.)
$x = \dfrac{\pi}{2}, \dfrac{3\pi}{2}, \dfrac{\pi}{6}, \dfrac{5\pi}{6}$	3. The value of zero for the cosine yields two quadrantal angles. Sine is positive in the first and second quadrants. In quadrant I, $x = \frac{\pi}{6}$, and $\pi - \frac{\pi}{6} = \frac{5\pi}{6}$ in the second.

EXAMPLE 4 Solve $3 \csc x - \sin x = 2$ over the interval $0 \le x < 2\pi$.

Answer

$3 \csc x - \sin x = 2$	
$\dfrac{3}{\sin x} - \sin x = 2$	1. Apply the reciprocal identity for cosecant.
$3 - \sin^2 x = 2 \sin x$ $\sin^2 x + 2 \sin x - 3 = 0$ $(\sin x - 1)(\sin x + 3) = 0$ $\sin x - 1 = 0$ or $\sin x + 3 = 0$ $\sin x = 1$ or $\sin x = -3$	2. Multiply the equation by $\sin x$ to clear the fractions. Solve for x.
$x = \dfrac{\pi}{2}$	3. Since $\sin x$ ranges from -1 to 1, it can never equal -3. Only $\sin x = 1$ contributes a solution.

It is wise to check solutions to trigonometric equations because you can introduce extraneous roots when multiplying an equation by a trigonometric function or when squaring both sides of an equation.

EXAMPLE 5 Solve $\cos x + \sin x = 1$ for $x \in [0, 2\pi)$.

Answer

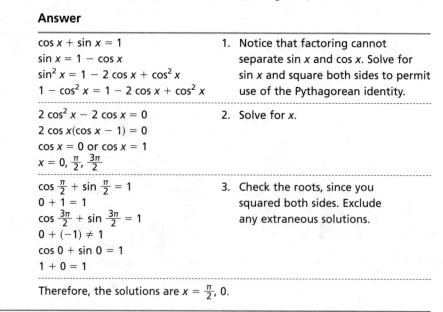

$\cos x + \sin x = 1$ $\sin x = 1 - \cos x$ $\sin^2 x = 1 - 2 \cos x + \cos^2 x$ $1 - \cos^2 x = 1 - 2 \cos x + \cos^2 x$	1. Notice that factoring cannot separate $\sin x$ and $\cos x$. Solve for $\sin x$ and square both sides to permit use of the Pythagorean identity.
$2 \cos^2 x - 2 \cos x = 0$ $2 \cos x(\cos x - 1) = 0$ $\cos x = 0$ or $\cos x = 1$ $x = 0, \dfrac{\pi}{2}, \dfrac{3\pi}{2}$	2. Solve for x.
$\cos \dfrac{\pi}{2} + \sin \dfrac{\pi}{2} = 1$ $0 + 1 = 1$ $\cos \dfrac{3\pi}{2} + \sin \dfrac{3\pi}{2} = 1$ $0 + (-1) \ne 1$ $\cos 0 + \sin 0 = 1$ $1 + 0 = 1$	3. Check the roots, since you squared both sides. Exclude any extraneous solutions.

Therefore, the solutions are $x = \dfrac{\pi}{2}, 0$.

EXAMPLE 6 Solve for the primary roots to the nearest ten-thousandth: $\sec^2 x = 3 \tan x - 1$.

Answer

$\sec^2 x = 3 \tan x - 1$	
$1 + \tan^2 x = 3 \tan x - 1$	1. Apply the Pythagorean identity $\sec^2 x = 1 + \tan^2 x$.
$\tan^2 x - 3 \tan x + 2 = 0$ $(\tan x - 1)(\tan x - 2) = 0$ $\tan x = 1$ or $\tan x = 2$	2. Solve for $\tan x$.
$x = \frac{\pi}{4}, \frac{5\pi}{4}$, 1.1071, 4.2487.	3. Tangent is positive in the first and third quadrants; both equations have two solutions. Use a calculator to find $\tan^{-1} 2$. Be sure to use radian mode.

In Example 6 there are four solutions in the interval $0 \le x < 2\pi$ because the values of the tangent function are positive in quadrants I and III and there are two angles. To find the values of x in quadrant III, you had to add π to the first-quadrant values. Similar uses of reference angles were made in Examples 2 and 3 for the sine and cosine. Remember that if the equation is of the form $\tan^2 x = 1$, then $\tan x = \pm 1$ and x has four solutions, one in each quadrant. The following chart summarizes this information.

Trigonometric Function	Sign	Quadrant	Other Angle Measure with Reference Angle x
sine	+	I, II	$x, \pi - x$
	−	III, IV	$\pi + x, 2\pi - x$
cosine	+	I, IV	$x, 2\pi - x$
	−	II, III	$\pi - x, \pi + x$
tangent	+	I, III	$x, \pi + x$
	−	II, IV	$\pi - x, 2\pi - x$

▶ A. Exercises

Find the primary solutions of each equation.

1. $\sin x + 1 = 0$
2. $\cot x + 1 = 0$
3. $2 \cos x = \sqrt{3}$
4. $4 \cos^2 x - 3 = 0$

5. $4 \sin^2 x - 3 = 0$

6. $2 \sin x - 1 = 0$

7. $2 \sin^2 x - 1 = 0$

8. $2 \cos^2 x - \sqrt{2} \cos x = 0$

9. $\cot^2 x - \sqrt{3} \cot x = 0$

10. $\tan x - \tan^2 x = 0$

▶ B. Exercises

Find the primary solutions of each equation.

11. $\sec x - 2 \cos x = 1$

12. $\cos^2 x - 3 \sin x = 3$

13. $\sin 2x = \sin x$

14. $\sin 2x + \cos x = 0$

15. $\tan x - 3 \cot x = 0$

16. $\cos 2x + \cos x + 1 = 0$

17. $\tan^2 x - \sin^2 x = \tan^2 x \sin^2 x$

18. $2 \cos x + 2 \sec x = 5$

19. $\sin \left(x + \frac{\pi}{4} \right) = 1$

20. $2 \cos \left(x - \frac{\pi}{3} \right) = \sqrt{2}$

21. $\dfrac{\sin x}{1 - \cos x} = \dfrac{\cos x}{1 + \sin x}$

22. $8 \sin^4 x - 2 \sin^2 x - 3 = 0$

23. $\sin^2 3x = 0$

24. $\cos^2 \frac{x}{2} = \frac{1}{4}$

25. $\cos^2 4x + \cos 4x = 0$

Find the primary solutions of each equation. Round to the nearest ten-thousandth.

26. $\dfrac{3}{1 + 5 \sin x} = 2$

27. $5 \cos x + 3 \cos 2x = 3$

28. $3 \sin^2 x = 2 \cos x \sin x$

29. $2 \csc^2 x - \cot x - 5 = 0$

▶ C. Exercises

Find the primary solutions of each equation.

30. $\cos 3x + \cos x = \cos 2x$

31. $\tan^3 x + \tan^2 x - 3 \tan x - 3 = 0$

Dominion Modeling

32. Explain why there is no need to consider a trigonometric model for the Holstein data.

Cumulative Review

Solve the following equations.

33. $e^{-2x} = 3$

34. $2x^2 - 5x + 1 = 0$

35. $2x^{-5} = \frac{1}{16}$

36. $\sqrt{x - 5} + 3 = 7$

37. $3 = \frac{x}{x + 1} + \frac{5}{x}$

MIND OVER MATH

State a double-angle identity for each of the six trig functions. Each identity may involve two different trig functions, but one of them must appear on both sides of the equal sign.

Math *and* Scripture

Linear Spline Model

Using your basic chronology of the patriarchs from Chapter 2, investigate the long life spans in more detail. First, make a graph with the horizontal axis representing the generations from the Flood. So for Noah $x = 0$, for Shem $x = 1$ (1 generation after the Flood), and for Methuselah $x = -2$ (2 generations before the Flood). Use the vertical axis for life span.

1. Refer to your graph in Chapter 3. Which of the points seems out of place? Explain.

2. Connect the points on your graph with lines (except the one that's abnormal). What kind of function is it?

3. Give the rule for the function in exercise 2. (Find the equation of the line between each pair of points).

Linear interpolations such as those in Chapter 1 use a line to estimate intermediate values. This shows how often you use linear splines. Use your spline (substitute the correct generation value for x) to estimate the life spans of each man below.

4. Ram

5. Salmon

Consider the supernatural departure of Enoch. Estimate his natural life span if God had not taken him supernaturally. Use the following three methods.

6. Use the spline to estimate how old Enoch would have lived to be if God had not taken him.

7. Use the average life span of the patriarchs from Adam through Noah.

8. Use the average life span of the patriarchs through Noah but excluding Enoch.

9. Which of the three is invalid? Why?

MAXIMIZING

Find all the references to Enoch in the Bible.

The linear spline is a continuous model developed from data points representing life spans for generations, which are represented by integers. Connecting the points with a model suggests that the intermediate values have meaning.

10. What would $x = -6.5$ mean?

11. Approximate the life span if $x = -6.5$.

12. Use the exponential decay equation to estimate the life span for $x = 3.7$.

13. What would $x = 3.7$ mean?

14. Are the use of such generations justified?

Splines are useful on data that is viewed as exact rather than representative. Since we are really more interested in average life span for each generation (viewing each patriarch as *representative* of his generation), other methods are superior and you will learn one of these methods later in this book. If you look at the overall pattern of the graph, you can see why lines are not the best models for the data.

15. Do the representative points look like they lie roughly on a line?

Vital Sines

AND ENOCH WALKED WITH God: and he was not; for God took him. ❧

GENESIS 5:24

Chapter 5 Review

Solve for x.

1. $3x^2 + 6x - 9 = 0$

2. $x(2x + 1) = 28$

3. $2x^2 + 9x + 3 = 0$

4. $\sqrt{-x + 6} = x - 4$

5. $x^3 + 5x^2 - 8x - 12 = 0$

6. $x^3 + 5x^2 - 2x - 10 = 0$

7. $\dfrac{4x + 4}{x + 1} = \dfrac{9x + 3}{x + 7}$

8. $\dfrac{4}{x^2 - x - 6} + \dfrac{3}{x^2 - 2x - 3} = \dfrac{8}{x^2 + 3x + 2}$

9. $\log_5 8 = \log_5 x$

Solve for x. Give exact values.

10. $4^{3x-1} = 8^{x+1}$

11. $\sqrt[3]{x^2 + 2} + 9 = 12$

12. $\log_7 (2x - 7) = 2$

13. $\log (x + 1) - \log x = 1$

14. $2 \sin x = \cos^2 x + 2$

15. $3\sqrt[5]{x} - 2 = 7$

16. $3 \log_2 (x - 1) + \log_2 4 = 5$

17. $\sin 2x + \cos 2x = 1$

18. $\sqrt{x^2 + 2x + 1} + \sqrt{x^2 - 2x + 1} = 4$

19. $x^4 + x^3 - 19x^2 - 49x - 30 = 0$

20. $41^{2x-1} = 3^x$

21. $e^x = 5^{2x+1}$

22. $2 \cos x + \sec x = 3$

Prove these period and cofunction identities.

23. $\sin (x + 2\pi) = \sin x$

24. $\cos \left(\dfrac{\pi}{2} - x \right) = \sin x$

25. $\tan \left(\dfrac{\pi}{2} - \theta \right) = \cot \theta$

26. $\csc \left(\dfrac{\pi}{2} - \theta \right) = \sec \theta$

Prove.

27. $1 - \sin x \cos x \tan x = \cos^2 x$

28. $\sec x - \cos x = \sin x \tan x$

If $\cos \theta = 0.6235$ and $\sin \theta = 0.7818$, find the following.

29. $\tan \theta$

30. $\cos 2\theta$

31. $\sin \frac{1}{2}\theta$

32. $\sin \left(\theta - \frac{\pi}{3}\right)$

33. Compare the linear, quadratic, and cubic models for the Holstein data. Which is most appropriate? Defend your view with a discussion of (1) the nature of the model and (2) the residual plots.

34. Explain the mathematical relevance of Genesis 5:24.

Many people assume microphones will pick up every sound nearby, but each microphone is designed for a specific purpose. For instance, a microphone designed for interviewing picks up two speakers in opposite directions but not extraneous sounds from other directions. Such a microphone has a bidirectional *reception pattern* called a "figure eight."

The table shows sample data for several microphone reception patterns, giving decibel ratings for a 1 MHz tone.

Angle	Omni-directional	Cardioid	Sub-cardioid	Figure Eight	Hyper-cardioid	Short Shotgun	Shotgun
0	25.0000	25.0000	25.0000	25.0000	24.0000	24.0000	8.0000
30	25.0000	23.3253	24.4641	21.6506	21.8564	22.2583	0.0000
60	25.0000	18.7500	23.0000	12.5000	16.0000	17.5000	16.0000
90	25.0000	12.5000	21.0000	0.0000	8.0000	11.0000	24.0000
120	25.0000	6.2500	19.0000	12.5000	0.0000	4.5000	16.0000
150	25.0000	1.6747	17.5359	21.6506	5.8564	4.2583	0.0000
180	25.0000	0.0000	17.0000	25.0000	8.0000	6.0000	8.0000
210	25.0000	1.6747	17.5359	21.6506	5.8564	4.2583	0.0000
240	25.0000	6.2500	19.0000	12.5000	0.0000	4.5000	16.0000
270	25.0000	12.5000	21.0000	0.0000	8.0000	11.0000	24.0000
300	25.0000	18.7500	23.0000	12.5000	16.0000	17.5000	16.0000
330	25.0000	23.3253	24.4641	21.6506	21.8564	22.2583	0.0000
360	25.0000	25.0000	25.0000	25.0000	24.0000	24.0000	8.0000

After this chapter you should be able to

1. sketch planes intersecting right conical surfaces to form conic sections.

2. state the locus-point definition of each nondegenerate conic section and derive their equations.

3. graph equations of circles, ellipses, parabolas, and hyperbolas.

4. write equations of conics given various information.

5. explain *eccentricity* and relate it to conic sections.

6. relate the conic sections to forms of the general equation $Ax^2 + Bxy + Cy^2 + Dx + Ey + F = 0$.

7. graph polar equations, using polar coordinates, and convert between polar and rectangular coordinates.

"**A**nd he is before all things, and by him all things consist" (Colossians 1:17). To this verse A. T. Robertson wrote, "Christ is the controlling and unifying force in nature" (*Word Pictures, Online Bible*). We may therefore expect to find wonderful order in His handiwork, nature.

Rainbows are portions of conic sections.

Mathematics provides analogies for us to model Christ's creative order. Along with its analytical beauty, conic sections have been one of the most fruitful areas for developing mathematical models of creation.

Definition

Conical surface   The union of all lines that connect a point that is not in a given plane to the points of a simple curve in the given plane.

If the curve in the given plane, called a *generating curve*, is a circle, then the conical surface is called a *circular cone*.

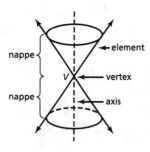

The given point *V* is the *vertex*, and the lines passing through it are the *elements* of the conical surface. The line connecting the vertex to the center of the generating curve is the *axis*; the vertex divides the cone into upper and lower parts called *nappes*.

When a plane cuts across a surface or solid, the result is a *section*. In a *cross section*, the plane cuts across the surface at right angles to the axis. A *conic section* is the intersection of a plane and a right circular cone.

A plane can intersect a cone in any of seven ways. The first four are the most important: circle, parabola, ellipse, and hyperbola. The other three possibilities occur only if the plane passes through the vertex of the cone, and are called *degenerate conics*. They form a point, a line, or two intersecting lines, all of which you have previously studied and graphed.

Now examine the various ways to section a cone. When a plane slices a right circular conical surface, the intersection is one of the following curves. Which one depends on the angle of the slice?

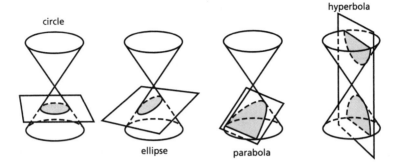

Definitions

Circle   The intersection of a right circular conical surface and a plane that is perpendicular to the axis of the conical surface (except at the vertex).

Ellipse   The intersection of a right circular conical surface and a plane that is not parallel to an element of the surface, is not perpendicular to the axis of the surface, and intersects only one nappe of the surface.

Parabola   The intersection of a right circular conical surface and a plane that is parallel to an element of the conical surface.

Hyperbola   The intersection of a right circular conical surface and a plane* that intersects both nappes of the conical surface (except at the vertex).

*Note that the plane does not have to be parallel to the axis.

These terms describe models of the universe that God ordered. God put the stars in their courses and made the Sun and Moon to rule the day and night as well as to establish the seasons and times (Gen. 1:14). He simply spoke to give their orbits shape and to regulate their rates to cause eclipses and equinoxes. The planets travel in elliptical orbits. Some meteors follow parabolic orbits; others move in a hyperbolic path.

Some other mathematical models of God's creation include the fact that gravity holds a satellite in orbit around the earth in an elliptical path (path *A* in the following figure). However, if the satellite accelerates sufficiently, it will break away from its orbit in a hyperbolic path (path *B*). As the satellite accelerates more, the path of the hyperbola widens (path *C*).

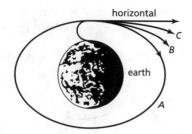

In addition to defining each conic section as a section of a cone, the conics can also be defined as a set of points that satisfy a certain condition, or a *locus* of points. Each conic section is a locus of points in the coordinate plane satisfying a quadratic relation of the form

$$Ax^2 + Bxy + Cy^2 + Dx + Ey + F = 0.$$

Each term of this equation affects the graph in some way. Notice that if $A = B = C = 0$, the quadratic degenerates into a linear relation forming one of the degenerate conic sections, a line. Further, if B is not equal to zero, the equation represents a rotation of one of the nondegenerate conic sections. Rotated graphs can be quite complicated and will be reserved for college math courses. In this book, conic sections have $B = 0$. The values of D, E, and F translate the curve. Completing the square will enable you to identify the amount of the translation, which will be invaluable for graphing.

Identifying the Type of Nondegenerate Conic Section

1. *Circle* if A and C are non-zero and equal.
2. *Ellipse* if A and C are non-zero, not equal, and have the same sign.
3. *Parabola* if A or C equals zero, but not both.
4. *Hyperbola* if A and C are non-zero, and exactly one of them is negative.

In this chapter, we will also define each conic section as a locus of points and derive general equations for them. Let's begin with the circle.

Definition

Circle   The locus of points in a plane at a fixed distance (*radius*) from a fixed point (*center*) in the plane.

The locus definition can be used to derive a general equation for the curve. Let the center of a circle be C with coordinates (h, k) and let the radius be r. Let P be any point on the circle with coordinates (x, y).

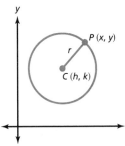

Every point on the curve lies at a distance r from C; therefore, applying the distance formula, we get

$$\sqrt{(x - h)^2 + (y - k)^2} = r$$

Squaring both sides yields the translated form that we will use as the *work form* of a circle:

$$(x - h)^2 + (y - k)^2 = r^2.$$

Remember that (h, k) is the center of the circle and r is its radius. These are the two essential pieces of information needed to write the equation of a specific circle.

EXAMPLE 1 Write the equation of a circle with radius 4 and center at $(2, -1)$ in work form.

Answer $(x - h)^2 + (y - k)^2 = r^2$
$(x - 2)^2 + [y - (-1)]^2 = 4^2$
$(x - 2)^2 + (y + 1)^2 = 16$

EXAMPLE 2 Graph the circle in Example 1. Does the graph represent a function? Give the domain and range.

Answer The vertical line test shows that this circle is not a function. A circle would never be a function.

$D = \{x \mid -2 \le x \le 6\}$
$R = \{y \mid -5 \le y \le 3\}$

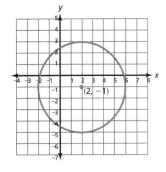

EXAMPLE 3 Graph the function $f(x) = \sqrt{9 - (x - 3)^2} - 1$.

Answer

$y = \sqrt{9 - (x - 3)^2} - 1$
$y + 1 = \sqrt{9 - (x - 3)^2}$
$(y + 1)^2 = 9 - (x - 3)^2$
$(x - 3)^2 + (y + 1)^2 = 9$

1. You could simplify the radicand to define the domain and substitute values for x to produce ordered pairs. However, the quickest way to graph this function is to note

Continued ▶

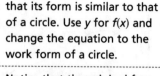

that its form is similar to that of a circle. Use y for $f(x)$ and change the equation to the work form of a circle.

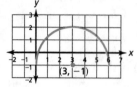

2. Notice that the original function called only for the positive root. Therefore, $y + 1 \geq 0$, and $y \geq -1$. This function is a portion of the circle with radius 3 and center $(3, -1)$ and represents the top half of the circle, so the range is $-1 \leq f(x) \leq 2$. The resulting semicircle is a function.

The equations of circles are not always written in work form. They often take the standard form previously given: $Ax^2 + Bxy + Cy^2 + Dx + Ey + F = 0$. Recall that this quadratic equation represents a circle only when A and C are equal (in sign as well as in absolute value). When a circle is given in this form, it must be rewritten in work form to reveal the center and radius for graphing. Accomplish this by completing the square on each variable.

The following four steps summarize the process of completing the square on x. Follow the same process to complete the square on y.

Completing the Square

1. Group the x-terms, group the y-terms, and place the constant term on the opposite side of the equation.
2. Factor the coefficient of x^2 from the terms that contain x.
3. Take the numerical coefficient of the x-term and divide it by 2; then square the resulting quotient. Add this number inside the parentheses to get a perfect square.
4. Compensate for this addition on the other side of the equation. Remember the coefficient in front of the parentheses!
5. Repeat steps 2-4 for the y-terms.
6. Factor the perfect squares and simplify the other side of the equation.

EXAMPLE 4   Graph $x^2 + y^2 + 4x - 6y = 12$.

Answer

$$x^2 + y^2 + 4x - 6y = 12$$
$$(x^2 + 4x +) + (y^2 - 6y +) = 12$$

1. Rearrange the terms, grouping the x-terms and the y-terms. The coefficients of x^2 and y^2 are both 1.

$$(x^2 + 4x + 4) + (y^2 - 6y + 9) = 12 + 4 + 9$$

2. Complete the square on each variable. Remember to add to *both* sides of the equation.

For x: $\frac{1}{2} \cdot 4 = 2$. $(2)^2 = 4$

For y: $\frac{1}{2} \cdot -6 = -3$. $(-3)^2 = 9$

$$(x + 2)^2 + (y - 3)^2 = 25$$

3. Factor and simplify.

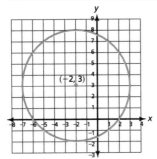

4. Graph. The center is at $(-2, 3)$ and the radius is 5.

The fact that $A = C = 1$ in the original equation guarantees that the graph will be a circle. Since the linear terms $4x$ and $-6y$ are present, the center of the circle is translated both horizontally and vertically.

EXAMPLE 5   Find the center and radius of the circle
$5x^2 + 5y^2 - 10x + 30y = -5$. Give the domain and range.

Answer

$$5x^2 - 10x + 5y^2 + 30y = -5$$

1. Rearrange terms by variable.

$$5(x^2 - 2x) + 5(y^2 + 6y) = -5$$

2. Factor out the coefficient of each squared term.

Continued ▶

$5(x^2 - 2x + 1) + 5(y^2 + 6y + 9) = -5 + 5 + 45$	3. Complete the square. Be sure to consider the factors of 5. Add 5 and 45 to the right side.
$5(x - 1)^2 + 5(y + 3)^2 = 45$	4. Factor and simplify.
$(x - 1)^2 + (y + 3)^2 = 9$ center $(1, -3)$ radius 3	5. Divide both sides by 5 to obtain work form for the circle.

$D = \{x \mid -2 \le x \le 4\}$ and $R = \{y \mid -6 \le y \le 0\}$.

Another relation to consider is a circular inequality. To graph a circular inequality of the form $(x - h)^2 + (y - k)^2 \le r^2$, include all points on all the circles in the plane with center (h, k) but with radii less than or equal to r. The graph would include the circle with radius r and its shaded interior. In contrast, for the inequality $(x - h)^2 + (y - k)^2 \ge r^2$, the circle and its exterior would be shaded.

EXAMPLE 6   Graph the following system, and shade the solution set.
$$x^2 + (y - 2)^2 \le 16$$
$$(x - 1)^2 + (y - 3)^2 \le 16$$

Answer

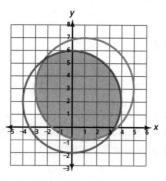

Graph each circle and consider the interiors, since the inequality is $\le$. The solution to a system of equations or inequalities is the intersection of the graphs. Shade the intersecting region.

▶ A. Exercises

Find the center and radius of each circle. Give the domain and range.

1. $(x - 3)^2 + y^2 = 49$
2. $x^2 + y^2 = 1$
3. $(x - 5)^2 + (y + 1)^2 = 8$
4. $x^2 + y^2 + 8x = 0$
5. $x^2 + y^2 + 6x + 4y + 4 = 0$

6. $8x^2 + 8y^2 - 16x + 80y = -200$
7. $6x^2 + 6y^2 + 12x = 24$
8. $7x^2 + 7y^2 + 42x - 28y = -84$

Graph.
9. $x^2 + y^2 \leq 4$
10. $x^2 + y^2 < 1$
11. $(x + 3)^2 + y^2 \geq 4$
12. $(x - 1)^2 + (y - 1)^2 > 1$

Write the work form of the equation of the circle
13. with radius 2 and center $(0, -4)$.
14. with radius 9 and center $(2, 2)$.

▶ B. Exercises

Graph.
15. $9 \leq x^2 + y^2 \leq 25$
16. $f(x) = \sqrt{9 - (x + 1)^2} + 2$

Write the work form of the equation of the circle
17. containing the point $(8, 9)$ with center $(3, -3)$.
18. containing the point $(5, 4)$ with center $(0, 3)$.
19. with $(-3, -2)$ and $(-9, -8)$ at the endpoints of a diameter.
20. with $(2, -1)$ and $(-2, 5)$ at the endpoints of a diameter.
21. tangent to the y-axis at $(0, 1)$ and to the x-axis at $(1, 0)$.
22. tangent to the y-axis at $(0, 1)$ and to the x-axis at $(-1, 0)$.
23. with center $(2, 5)$ and area 121π.
24. with center $(5, -3)$ and circumference 8π.

Write the equation of each line in standard form.
25. The line tangent to a circle with center $(-1, 2)$ at the point $(2, 3)$
26. The line perpendicular to the tangent in exercise 25 at the same point

⎍ Graph the following using a graphing calculator.
27. $x^2 + y^2 = 3.3$
28. $(x - 4.2)^2 + (y + 1.6)^2 = 5.75$

▶ C. Exercises

Write the equation of the circle
29. with center on the line $x + y = 6$ and tangent to the x-axis at $(2, 0)$.
30. containing the points $(0, -9)$, $(-5, -10)$, and $(7, -2)$.

31. From the top of a 210-foot cliff, the angle of depression of a ship at sea is 4°. Find the distance from the foot of the cliff to the ship.

32. Classify each as exponential growth or decay: radiocarbon dating, post-Flood life span, population.

33. How do earthquakes measured at 7 and 5 respectively on the Richter scale compare in intensity?

Shawna makes an initial investment of $5000.

34. How much does she have after 10 years if the interest is 4.5% compounded continuously?

35. How much would she have if it were compounded annually?

6.2 Ellipses

Statuary Hall in the Capitol building in Washington, D.C. If you stand and whisper at one focus in this elliptical "whispering gallery," a person at the other focus can clearly hear you, even though no one between the foci can.

Consider the following definition of an ellipse as a locus of points.

Definition

Ellipse   The locus of points in a plane such that the sum of the distances from two fixed points (*foci*) is a constant.

The segment containing the foci (F_1 and F_2) is called the *major axis*. The *center* $C(h, k)$ is the midpoint of the segment joining the foci and c represents the distance from the center point to each focus. For an ellipse that is elongated horizontally, the major axis is horizontal, while an ellipse elongated vertically has a vertical major axis. The *minor axis* is the segment perpendicular to the major axis through the center. Each of the four points where a major or minor axis intersects an ellipse is called a *vertex*. The value a (called the *semimajor axis*) represents the distance from the center to a vertex on the major axis, while b (called the *semiminor* axis) represents the distance from the center to a vertex on the minor axis.

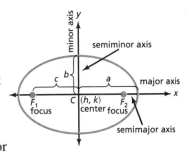

To form an ellipse, think of a string with slack in it attached to the two foci. If the string is kept taut, moving a pencil along the string will draw an ellipse. The pencil point represents a point of the ellipse, while the string on each side of the pencil shows the distance to each focus. You can see that the length of the string remains constant as stated in the definition. This length is easy to determine by placing the pencil at vertex V_1 on the major axis. Notice that the portion F_1V_1 that overlaps the longer piece of string is the same length as F_2V_2.

The distance from V_1 to F_1 is $a - c$, and its distance from F_2 is $a + c$. The sum of these distances is $a - c + a + c = 2a$. Therefore, the constant sum in the definition is always the length of the major axis.

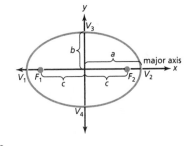

Now place the pencil at vertex V_3 on the minor axis. Notice that the pencil divides the string into equal halves. Since the string is of length $2a$, each half has length a. Applying the Pythagorean theorem to right $\triangle CF_1V_3$ shows that $b^2 + c^2 = a^2$. Solving for c^2, we obtain the equation relating the key parameters of an ellipse $a^2 - b^2 = c^2$.

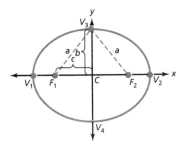

The equation of an ellipse centered anywhere in the plane can be derived using these relationships and the definition. If the center point is (h, k) and the major axis is horizontal, the foci are c units to either side of the center and therefore have the coordinates $(h - c, k)$ and $(h + c, k)$.

Choose any point $P(x, y)$ on the ellipse and find the distances from P to foci F_1 and F_2, using the distance formula. Applying the definition of an ellipse, $d_{PF_1} + d_{PF_2} = 2a$.

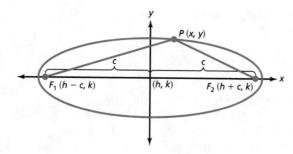

$$d_{PF_1} + d_{PF_2} = 2a$$

$$\sqrt{[x - (h - c)]^2 + (y - k)^2} + \sqrt{[x - (h + c)]^2 + (y - k)^2} = 2a$$

Regroup terms by the associative property.

$$\sqrt{[(x - h) + c]^2 + (y - k)^2} + \sqrt{[(x - h) - c]^2 + (y - k)^2} = 2a$$

To eliminate the radicals, solve for either radical expression and square both sides. Note that $(x - h)$ and $(y - k)$ are left intact throughout the derivation.

$$\sqrt{[(x - h) + c]^2 + (y - k)^2} = 2a - \sqrt{[(x - h) - c]^2 + (y - k)^2}$$

$$[(x - h) + c]^2 + (y - k)^2 = 4a^2 - 4a\sqrt{[(x - h) - c]^2 + (y - k)^2} + [(x - h) - c]^2 + (y - k)^2$$

Subtract $(y - k)^2$ from both sides and square the terms remaining outside the radical, using FOIL.

$$(x - h)^2 + 2c(x - h) + c^2 = 4a^2 - 4a\sqrt{[(x - h) - c]^2 + (y - k)^2} + (x - h)^2 - 2c(x - h) + c^2$$

Subtract the $(x - h)^2$ and c^2 terms from both sides. Isolate the remaining radical and square both sides.

$$2c(x - h) = 4a^2 - 4a\sqrt{[(x - h) - c]^2 + (y - k)^2} - 2c(x - h)$$

$$4c(x - h) - 4a^2 = -4a\sqrt{[(x - h) - c]^2 + (y - k)^2}$$

$$c(x - h) - a^2 = -a\sqrt{[(x - h) - c]^2 + (y - k)^2}$$

$$c^2(x - h)^2 - 2a^2c(x - h) + a^4 = a^2\{[(x - h) - c]^2 + (y - k)^2\}$$

Square the binomial $[(x - h) - c]^2$ and distribute the a^2.

$$c^2(x - h)^2 - 2a^2c(x - h) + a^4 = a^2[(x - h)^2 - 2c(x - h) + c^2 + (y - k)^2]$$

$$c^2(x - h)^2 - 2a^2c(x - h) + a^4 = a^2(x - h)^2 - 2a^2c(x - h) + a^2c^2 + a^2(y - k)^2$$

Add $2a^2c(x - h)$ to both sides; then subtract a^2c^2 and $c^2(x - h)^2$ from each side. All variable terms will then be on the right and all constant terms on the left.

$$c^2(x - h)^2 + a^4 = a^2(x - h)^2 + a^2c^2 + a^2(y - k)^2$$

$$a^4 - a^2c^2 = a^2(x - h)^2 - c^2(x - h)^2 + a^2(y - k)^2$$

Factor out an a^2 from the left side. Then factor $(x - h)^2$ out of the first two terms of the right side.

$$a^2(a^2 - c^2) = (a^2 - c^2)(x - h)^2 + a^2(y - k)^2$$

Recall that $a^2 - b^2 = c^2$, which implies $a^2 - c^2 = b^2$. Substituting,

$$a^2b^2 = b^2(x - h)^2 + a^2(y - k)^2$$

Divide both sides by a^2b^2, reduce, and apply the symmetric property.

$$\frac{a^2b^2}{a^2b^2} = \frac{b^2(x - h)^2}{a^2b^2} + \frac{a^2(y - k)^2}{a^2b^2}$$

$$\frac{(x - h)^2}{a^2} + \frac{(y - k)^2}{b^2} = 1$$

With an ellipse in this work form, you can plot the center, (h, k), and move $\pm a$ horizontally and $\pm b$ vertically to find the vertices on the major and minor axes. If the major axis is vertical, the semimajor and semiminor axis lengths will reverse. Note the switch in position of a and b in the formula.

$$\frac{(x - h)^2}{b^2} + \frac{(y - k)^2}{a^2} = 1$$

The center is still (h, k), but you move $\pm a$ vertically and $\pm b$ horizontally. We can summarize the two types of ellipses as follows:

Equation	Center	Foci	Major/Minor Axes	Graph
$\dfrac{(x - h)^2}{a^2} + \dfrac{(y - k)^2}{b^2} = 1$	(h, k)	$(h - c, k)$ $(h + c, k)$	Major: on the line $y = k$ Minor: on the line $x = h$	
$\dfrac{(x - h)^2}{b^2} + \dfrac{(y - k)^2}{a^2} = 1$	(h, k)	$(h, k - c)$ $(h, k + c)$	Major: on the line $x = h$ Minor: on the line $y = k$	

EXAMPLE 1   Graph $\dfrac{(x+3)^2}{9} + \dfrac{(y-1)^2}{4} = 1$.

Answer

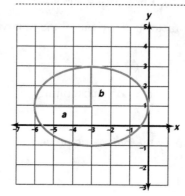

1. The center, (h, k), is $(-3, 1)$.

2. $a^2 = 9$, so the semimajor axis $a = 3$; $b^2 = 4$, so the semiminor axis $b = 2$. Locate the vertices and sketch the ellipse.

EXAMPLE 2   Graph $49(x-2)^2 + 4(y-1)^2 = 196$.

Answer

$$49(x-2)^2 + 4(y-1)^2 = 196$$

1. Put the equation in work form by dividing both sides by 196.

$$\dfrac{49(x-2)^2}{196} + \dfrac{4(y-1)^2}{196} = 1$$

$$\dfrac{(x-2)^2}{4} + \dfrac{(y-1)^2}{49} = 1$$

2. Reduce.

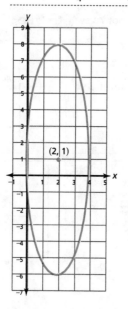

3. $(2, 1)$ is the center, $a = 7$, and $b = 2$. The major axis of this ellipse is vertical, since $49 > 4$ and 49 is under the y^2-term.

The equation of an ellipse can be written if the center and lengths of the semi-major axis and semiminor axis are known.

EXAMPLE 3   Write the equation of the vertically elongated ellipse with center (2, 0), semimajor axis 5, and semiminor axis 2.

Answer

$\dfrac{(x-h)^2}{b^2} + \dfrac{(y-k)^2}{a^2} = 1$

$\dfrac{(x-2)^2}{2^2} + \dfrac{(y-0)^2}{5^2} = 1$

1. Substitute the given values into the work form of an ellipse: $(h, k) = (2, 0)$, $a = 5$, and $b = 2$. Since the major axis is vertical, a^2 goes under the y^2-term.

$\dfrac{(x-2)^2}{4} + \dfrac{y^2}{25} = 1$

2. Simplify.

EXAMPLE 4   Find c in Example 3, then find the coordinates of the foci.

Answer

$c^2 = a^2 - b^2$
$c^2 = 25 - 4$
$c^2 = 21$
$c = \pm\sqrt{21}$

1. From Example 3 you know that $a = 5$ and $b = 2$. Solve for c.

$(2, \sqrt{21})$ and $(2, -\sqrt{21})$

2. Find the foci. The ellipse is vertically elongated with foci on the vertical axis $x = 2$ and center (2, 0).

EXAMPLE 5   Rewrite the ellipse in Example 3 in standard form: $Ax^2 + Bxy + Cy^2 + Dx + Ey + F = 0$.

Answer

$100\left[\dfrac{(x-2)^2}{4} + \dfrac{y^2}{25}\right] = 100 \ (1)$

$25(x-2)^2 + 4y^2 = 100$

1. Multiply both sides by 100 to clear fractions. (100 is the LCM of 4 and 25.)

$25(x^2 - 4x + 4) + 4y^2 = 100$

2. Square the binomial.

$25x^2 - 100x + 100 + 4y^2 = 100$

3. Distribute.

$25x^2 + 4y^2 - 100x = 0$

4. Simplify.

From the standard form, you can tell the following about this ellipse:

1. $A \neq C$ (but A and C are both positive); this is the correct form for an ellipse.
2. $B = 0$; the ellipse is not oblique (rotated about a point).
3. $E = 0$; the ellipse is not translated vertically.

When an ellipse is written in standard form, it must be algebraically transformed into work form to reveal the center, semimajor axis, and semiminor axis. Grouping, completing the square, factoring, and dividing by the constant are necessary tools for this derivation.

EXAMPLE 6   Write the equation $4x^2 + 16y^2 - 8x + 64y + 4 = 0$ in work form.

Answer

$4x^2 + 16y^2 - 8x + 64y + 4 = 0$ $4x^2 - 8x + 16y^2 + 64y = -4$	1. Rearrange the terms by variables.
$4(x^2 - 2x) + 16(y^2 + 4y) = -4$	2. Factor out the coefficient of each squared term.
$4(x^2 - 2x + 1) + 16(y^2 + 4y + 4) = -4 + 4 + 64$	3. Complete the square on both variables.
$4(x - 1)^2 + 16(y + 2)^2 = 64$	4. Factor the completed squares.
$\dfrac{(x - 1)^2}{16} + \dfrac{(y + 2)^2}{4} = 1$	5. Divide by 64.

A person is eccentric if his behavior deviates from normal. Jesus Christ expects His disciples to be eccentric, since living a Christlike life is not normal in this world (Titus 2:14). Likewise, in mathematics, conic sections are eccentric if they deviate from a circle. *Eccentricity* is a measure of this deviation. The eccentricity of an ellipse is the ratio of focal distance (from the center to a foci) to the length of the semimajor axis: $e = \frac{c}{a}$. Since c and a are distances and $c < a$, the eccentricity of any ellipse is $0 < e < 1$.

EXAMPLE 7   Find the eccentricity of the two ellipses shown.

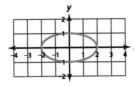 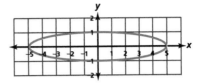

Answer

First Ellipse	Second Ellipse
$a = 2, b = 1$	$a = 5, b = 1$
$a^2 - b^2 = c^2$	$a^2 - b^2 = c^2$
$2^2 - 1^2 = c^2$	$5^2 - 1^2 = c^2$
$c^2 = 3$	$c^2 = 24$
$c = \sqrt{3}$	$c = 2\sqrt{6}$
$e = \frac{c}{a} = \frac{\sqrt{3}}{2} \approx 0.866$	$e = \frac{c}{a} = \frac{2\sqrt{6}}{5} \approx 0.980$

Notice that the eccentricity increases as the ellipse deviates more and more from a circle (gets more elongated). As the foci get closer together (left figure), the ellipse becomes less elongated and the focal distance gets shorter. For a circle, the focal distance would be zero (foci merge into the center) and the semimajor axis would be the radius. In the case of a circle, $e = \frac{0}{r} = 0$, which is consistent with the idea of eccentricity, since a circle does not deviate from a circle.

▶ A. Exercises

Graph. Give the domain and range of each.

1. $\frac{(x + 1)^2}{9} + \frac{(y - 5)^2}{4} = 1$
2. $16(x + 4)^2 + 25(y + 3)^2 = 400$
3. $x^2 + 4y^2 = 16$
4. $9(x - 2)^2 + 36(y - 2)^2 = 144$
5. $25x^2 + 9y^2 - 54y = 144$
6. $9x^2 + 81y^2 - 108x + 324y = 81$
7. $\frac{x^2}{9} + \frac{y^2}{4} \leq 1$
8. $\frac{(x - 2)^2}{9} + \frac{(y - 2)^2}{4} \leq 1$
9. $4x^2 + y^2 \leq 100$
10. $16x^2 + 4y^2 \geq 64$

▶ B. Exercises

Graph.

11. $f(x) = \dfrac{2\sqrt{9 - x^2}}{3}$

12. $f(x) = \dfrac{3\sqrt{25 - (x + 1)^2}}{5}$

13. $f(x) = 3\sqrt{1 - x^2}$

Graph the system of inequalities, shading the solution set.

14. $x^2 + y^2 - 6x - 2y \leq -1$
    $25x^2 + 4y^2 - 150x - 8y \leq -129$

15. $25x^2 + 49y^2 \leq 1225$
    $49x^2 + 25y^2 \leq 1225$

16. $16x^2 + 36y^2 + 256x - 504y \leq -2212$
    $x^2 + y^2 + 16x - 10y \geq -88$

🔲 Use a graphing calculator to graph each of the following.

17. $2x^2 + 3x + 5y^2 = 0$

18. $\dfrac{(x + 1)^2}{4} + \dfrac{(y - 2)^2}{9} = 1$

Write the general equation of the ellipse if

19. $a = 5$, $b = 2$, the center is (2, 3), and the foci lie on the line $y = 3$.
20. $a = 6$, $b = 4$, the center is (0, 1), and the foci lie on the line $x = 0$.
21. $a = 17$, $c = 8$, the center is at the origin, and the foci lie on the line $y = 0$.
22. $b = 9$, $c = 12$, the center is (2, −5), and the foci lie on the line $x = 2$.
23. the foci are at (0, 4) and (0, −4), and the semimajor axis is 5.
24. the foci are at (6, 0) and (−6, 0), and the semimajor axis is 9.
25. the eccentricity is 0.6, the center is at the origin, the semimajor axis is 5, and the foci lie on the x-axis.
26. the eccentricity is 0.28, the center is (4, 1), the semimajor axis is 25, and the foci lie on the line $y = 1$.
27. Many architects have taken advantage of the elliptical phenomenon known as the whispering chamber. If a room has an elliptical ceiling, a person standing at one focus can whisper and be heard clearly by someone standing at the other focus, while those between the two foci hear nothing. The sound waves bounce off the elliptical ceiling directly to the other focus. For the following ellipse, find the two strategic locations in the coordinate plane where you could whisper and be heard.

    $49x^2 + 4y^2 + 294x + 8y = -249$

▶ C. Exercises

28. The earth travels around the Sun in an elliptical path with the Sun at one focus. The semimajor axis of the ellipse is about 1.49×10^8 km. If the eccentricity of the ellipse is 0.017, find the *perihelion* (the closest distance the earth gets to the Sun) and the *aphelion* (the farthest distance the earth gets from the Sun).

29. The formula for the area of an ellipse is $A = \pi ab$. Find the area of an ellipse with semimajor axis of 12 units and eccentricity of 0.75.

■ Cumulative Review

30. A 52° central angle of a circle intercepts an arc whose length is 358 feet. Find the radius of the circle.

31. How many degrees are there in 1.5 radians?

32. Express the measures of the angles of a 30-60 right triangle in decimal radians.

33. Give the exact value of tan 60°.

34. Find two angles to the nearest degree such that $\cos x = 0.39$ where $0 \le x < 360°$.

6.3 Parabolas

Although you have graphed parabolas before, you may not have analyzed one as a locus of points.

Definition

Parabola   The locus of points in a plane that are equidistant from a fixed point (*focus*) and a fixed line (*directrix*) in the plane.

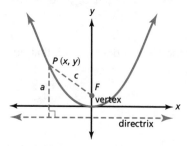

The vertex of the parabola is the point closest to the directrix. If you drop a perpendicular from the focus to the directrix, the vertex is the midpoint of the segment joining them. If $P(x, y)$ is a point on the parabola, the distance c from the point to the focus and the distance a from the point to the directrix are equal. The value p represents the distance from the vertex to the focus or directrix. If the vertex of the parabola is translated to the point (h, k) and represents a minimum point, then the focus is the point $(h, k + p)$ and the directrix is the line $y = k - p$.

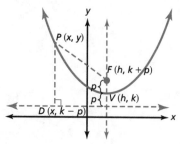

Use the definition above to derive the equation of a parabola. Find the distances from the focus to a point on the curve and from that point to the directrix. Since the point P is on the parabola, the definition requires that these distances be equal.

$$d_{PF} = d_{PD}$$

$$\sqrt{(x - h)^2 + [y - (k + p)]^2} = \sqrt{(x - x)^2 + [y - (k - p)]^2}$$

Apply the associative property to group y and k instead of k and p.

$$\sqrt{(x - h)^2 + [(y - k) - p]^2} = \sqrt{[(y - k) + p]^2}$$

Square both sides. Keep $(x - h)^2$ and $(y - k)$ intact throughout the derivation.

$$(x - h)^2 + [(y - k) - p]^2 = [(y - k) + p]^2$$

Square the binomials involving y.

$$(x - h)^2 + (y - k)^2 - 2p(y - k) + p^2 = (y - k)^2 + 2p(y - k) + p^2$$

Subtract $(y - k)^2$ and p^2 from each side, and solve for y.

$$(x - h)^2 - 2p(y - k) = 2p(y - k)$$

$$(x - h)^2 = 4p(y - k)$$

$$\tfrac{1}{4p}(x - h)^2 = y - k$$

$$y = \tfrac{1}{4p}(x - h)^2 + k$$

The quadratic function above is usually represented as $y = ax^2 + bx + c$, or in work form as $y = a(x - h)^2 + k$, where a represents the leading coefficient. Notice that p is a distance and is therefore always positive, whereas a can be either positive or negative. Thus, $|a| = \tfrac{1}{4p}$. You may recall that this coefficient a determines whether the parabola opens up (has a minimum point, $a > 0$) or down (has a maximum point, $a < 0$); it also affects the shape (width) of the curve. Solving the equation for p, it is easy to find the distance from the vertex to the focus (and to the directrix): $p = \tfrac{1}{4|a|}$.

EXAMPLE 1   Find the distance p and the vertex of the parabola
$y = 2(x - 3)^2 + 6$.

Answer

$$p = \tfrac{1}{4|a|}$$

$$p = \tfrac{1}{4|2|}$$

$$p = \tfrac{1}{8}$$

1. Find the distance from the focus to the vertex and from the vertex to the directrix using $p = \tfrac{1}{4|a|}$.

vertex $= (3, 6)$

2. From the equation, the vertex is (h, k).

Conversely, the equation of a parabola can be determined from the vertex and the distance p.

EXAMPLE 2   Write the equation of the parabola with vertex $(2, -1)$ and $p = \frac{1}{4}$.

Answer

$\|a\| = \frac{1}{4p}$ $\|a\| = 1$	1. Find a.
$y = (x - 2)^2 - 1$ or $y = -(x - 2)^2 - 1$	2. Write the equation in work form. There are two such parabolas, one opening up and one down.

The general form of the first, $y = (x - 2)^2 - 1$, is obtained by squaring and simplifying: $y = x^2 - 4x + 4 - 1$ or $y = x^2 - 4x + 3$.

EXAMPLE 3   Write the equation of the parabola with focus $(5, -6)$ and directrix $y = 2$.

Answer

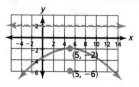	1. Plot the focus and draw the directrix. Plot the vertex halfway between the focus and the directrix, and find its coordinates $(5, -2)$. Sketch the parabola; remember that it curves around the focus.
$p = 4$	2. Determine p. From the vertex $(5, -2)$ to the focus $(5, -6)$ is 4 units.
$\|a\| = \frac{1}{4p}$ $\|a\| = \frac{1}{4(4)}$ $\|a\| = \frac{1}{16}$	3. Using p, find a. Since p is a distance, this will always yield a positive value and the sign must be considered separately.
$a = -\frac{1}{16}$	4. Since the parabola has a maximum point and opens down, a is negative.
$y = -\frac{1}{16}(x - 5)^2 - 2$	5. Write the equation.

Is a parabola a function? Look at the examples discussed so far in this section, and use the vertical line test. All parabolas of the form $Ax^2 + Dx + Ey + F = 0$ are functions with work form $y = a(x - h)^2 + k$. Notice that there are no xy- or y^2-terms ($B = 0$ and $C = 0$, respectively) in the standard form. Parabolas with this trait are functions because they open upward ($a > 0$) or downward ($a < 0$).

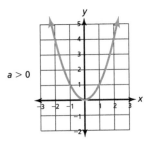

$a > 0$

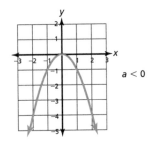

$a < 0$

Now examine the case where $A = 0$ and $B = 0$, in the standard equation: $0x^2 + 0xy + Cy^2 + Dx + Ey + F = 0$. When you complete the square on an equation of this form and transform the equation into work form, since there is no x^2-term, solve for x rather than y:

$$x = a(y - k)^2 + h.$$

Notice the positions of h and k here compared to the other form. This parabola still has (h, k) as its vertex, and a still determines the width of the curve and the direction it opens (left or right). However, two values of y can generate the same x-value, as shown in Example 4.

EXAMPLE 4   In the relation $x = 3(y - 2)^2 + 1$, find x when $y = 0$ and when $y = 4$.

Answer
$x = 3(y - 2)^2 + 1$ $x = 3(y - 2)^2 + 1$
$x = 3(0 - 2)^2 + 1$ $x = 3(4 - 2)^2 + 1$
$x = 3(-2)^2 + 1$ $x = 3(2)^2 + 1$
$x = 3(4) + 1$ $x = 3(4) + 1$
$x = 13$ $x = 13$

Both $(13, 0)$ and $(13, 4)$ lie on this parabola, which is therefore not a function. In fact, no parabola of this form is a function; it opens to the right ($a > 0$) or the left ($a < 0$) instead of upward or downward. Also, the directrix is a vertical line.

EXAMPLE 5   Graph $x \geq \frac{1}{2}(y - 3)^2 + 2$.

Answer

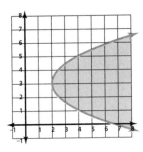

Because $\frac{1}{2} > 0$, the parabola will open to the right. The vertex is $(2, 3)$. Plot points for y-values near $y = 3$. Since the inequality is $\geq$, shade inside the parabola (to the right).

EXAMPLE 6   Graph the parabola $2x^2 + 4x - y - 1 = 0$. Find the focus and directrix and place them on the graph.

Answer

$2x^2 + 4x - y - 1 = 0$	1. This quadratic is in general form with $C = 0$ (no y^2-term).
$y = 2x^2 + 4x - 1$	2. Solve for y.
$y = 2(x^2 + 2x) - 1$ $y = 2(x^2 + 2x + 1) - 1 - 2$	3. Complete the square. Adding and subtracting 2 on the right side is equivalent to adding 2 to both sides.
$y = 2(x + 1)^2 - 3$	4. Factor.
$p = \dfrac{1}{4\lvert a \rvert} = \dfrac{1}{4\lvert 2 \rvert} = \dfrac{1}{8}$	5. Find p.
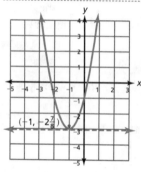	6. Graph the parabola with vertex $(-1, -3)$, opening upward ($a > 0$). Plot points around $x = -1$.
	7. Draw the directrix $\frac{1}{8}$ unit below the vertex: $y = -3\frac{1}{8}$.
	8. Plot the focus $\frac{1}{8}$ unit above the vertex: $\left(-1, -2\frac{7}{8}\right)$.

$\left(-1, -2\frac{7}{8}\right)$

A parabola deviates from the path of a circle even more than an ellipse does. The ellipse never gets wider than its axes, whereas the parabola widens as the focus and directrix get farther apart. The width of a parabola approaches infinity as the distance p between the vertex and the focus approaches infinity. An alternate definition for conic sections involves sets of points having a constant ratio of distances to a fixed point (focus) and a fixed line (directrix). The ratio in this case is the eccentricity and for parabolas the ratio is always 1, since these two distances are equal.

From this alternate definition it is clear that other types of conic sections also have directrices, although they have not been used in the definitions given. In an ellipse, as shown in the figure, $e = \dfrac{PF}{PD} < 1$.

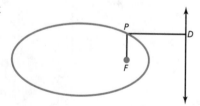

► A. Exercises

Graph each parabola, its focus, and its directrix.

1. $y = x^2 + 5$
2. $y = (x + 1)^2$
3. $y = (x - 2)^2 + 4$
4. $y = -(x + 2)^2 + 4$
5. $y = \frac{-1}{2}(x - 1)^2 + 6$
6. $y = 3x^2 - 9$
7. $x = y^2 - 5$
8. $x = (y + 3)^2 - 1$
9. $x = -(y - 4)^2$
10. $x = 2(y - 4)^2$
11. $\frac{1}{4}x^2 + 4x - y + 17 = 0$
12. $y^2 - x - 8y + 18 = 0$
13. $y = 3.15x^2 + 5.9$

Find the eccentricity of each parabola.

14. Exercise 1
15. Exercise 6

► B. Exercises

Graph each. Give the domain and range.

16. $y \geq \frac{1}{2}(x - 5)^2$
17. $y < (x + 1)^2$
18. $y = 3 - x^2$
19. $x > \frac{1}{4}(y - 2)^2 + 5$

Graph each system. Shade the solution set.

20. $y \leq -(x - 5)^2 + 5$
    $y \geq (x - 5)^2 - 3$
21. $4x^2 + 9y^2 + 48x + 90y \leq -333$
    $y^2 - x + 10y + 19 \geq 0$
    $-y^2 - x - 10y - 31 \leq 0$
22. $y < 3.5x^2 - 6.9$
    $4x \leq 3.76y^2 - 1.7$

Refer to the following parabolas for exercises 23-25.

$y = \frac{1}{4}x^2, y = \frac{1}{2}x^2, y = x^2, y = 4x^2$

23. Graph them on the same coordinate plane.
24. What happens to the shape of the parabolas as $|a|$ (the coefficient of x^2) gets larger?

25. What happens to the shape of the parabola as $|a|$ approaches 0?

26. As the parabola opens wider, what happens to the focus and directrix? Explain how this is a logical occurrence, using the relationship between a and p.

27. Graph the functions $f(x) = \sqrt{4 - x}$. (*Hint:* Let $y = f(x)$, and square both sides. Remember to graph only the principal roots of the equation.)

28. Make a sketch of a parabola with vertex (h, k) and opening to the right. Label the focus and the directrix in terms of h, k, and p. Choose a point on the curve, $P(x, y)$, and drop a perpendicular from the point to the directrix. Label the point of intersection, using y, h, and p. Using these general points and the locus-point definition, derive the work form of the parabola: $x = \frac{1}{4p}(y - k)^2 + h$.

29. Graph the parabola $y = \frac{1}{4}(x - 12)^2 + 1$. Locate the focus and directrix. Draw the segment through the focus parallel to the directrix. (This is called the focal chord.) Compare the length of this segment to p. Do you think it would be in the same ratio to p in every parabola? Explain your answer. (*Hint:* Drop the perpendiculars from the endpoints of the segment down to the directrix.)

▶ C. Exercises

Consider the following system.

$y = \frac{1}{4}(x - 3)^2 + 4$

$(x + 1)^2 + (y - 8)^2 = 25$

$(x - 5)^2 + (y - 5)^2 = 4$

30. Graph the system.

31. Each circle has its center on the parabola and passes through the focus. How is the directrix related to each circle?

32. Would any circle that has its center on a parabola and passes through the focus be related to the directrix in this way? Explain.

▌Cumulative Review

33. Use interval notation for the range of each of the six trig functions.

34. Give 3 ways of finding $\cos x$ if $\sin x$ is known.

Solve each equation.

35. $\ln \cos x = -2$

36. $8 - 5x^2 + 3x^3 = 11x + x^3 + 12$

37. $2^{\sqrt{1 + \csc x}} = 5$

6.4 Hyperbolas

As pointed out earlier, every general quadratic equation corresponds to the graph of a circle, an ellipse, a parabola, or a hyperbola unless it is degenerate. The hyperbola is the last of these conic sections.

Definition

Hyperbola   The locus of points in a plane such that the difference of the distances from two fixed points *(foci)* to a point of the locus is a constant.

The *center* of the hyperbola is the midpoint of the segment joining the foci. Since the line containing the foci cuts across the hyperbola, it is called the *transverse axis* and each of the two points where it intersects the hyperbola is a *vertex*. The line perpendicular to the transverse axis at the center is called the *conjugate axis*. Notice that it does not intersect the hyperbola.

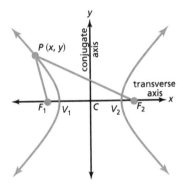

In a hyperbola, the *difference* of the distances from a point on the curve to the foci yields a constant value. In contrast, recall that for an ellipse the *sum* of the distances to the foci is constant; while in a parabola the distances to the focus and directrix are *equal*. To determine the value of the constant difference, examine the following hyperbola.

Let V_1 and V_2 be the vertices of the hyperbola; then the distances to the foci are

$$d_{V_1F_1} = c - a$$

$$d_{V_1F_2} = c + a$$

and

$$d_{V_1F_2} - d_{V_1F_1} = (c + a) - (c - a) = 2a$$

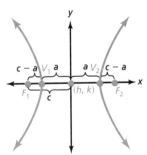

Since the difference is constant, the difference of these distances must be the same as the difference of the distances at any other point. When a hyperbola with a horizontal transverse axis is translated so that its center is (h, k), the coordinates of its foci are $(h - c, k)$ and $(h + c, k)$.

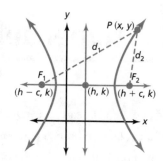

As in the case of the ellipse, you can now derive the equation for a hyperbola.

Subtract the distances from a point P to each of the foci and set the difference equal to $2a$. Apply the distance formula.

$$d_{PF_1} - d_{PF_2} = 2a$$

$$\sqrt{[x - (h - c)]^2 + (y - k)^2} - \sqrt{[x - (h + c)]^2 + (y - k)^2} = 2a$$

Add the second radical to both sides, and apply the associative property to group x and h rather than h and c. Remember to keep $(x - h)$ and $(y - k)$ intact. Then square both sides.

$$\sqrt{[(x - h) + c]^2 + (y - k)^2} = 2a + \sqrt{[(x - h) - c]^2 + (y - k)^2}$$

$$[(x - h) + c]^2 + (y - k)^2 = 4a^2 + 4a\sqrt{[(x - h) - c]^2 + (y - k)^2} + [(x - h) - c]^2 + (y - k)^2$$

Subtract $(y - k)^2$ from each side; then square the binomials.

$$[(x - h) + c]^2 = 4a^2 + 4a\sqrt{[(x - h) - c]^2 + (y - k)^2} + [(x - h) - c]^2$$

$$(x - h)^2 + 2c\,(x - h) + c^2 = 4a^2 + 4a\sqrt{[(x - h) - c]^2 + (y - k)^2} + (x - h)^2 - 2c(x - h) + c^2$$

Subtract $(x - h)^2$ and c^2 from each side. Add $2c(x - h)$ to each side.

$$2c(x - h) = 4a^2 + 4a\sqrt{[(x - h) - c]^2 + (y - k)^2} - 2c(x - h)$$

$$4c(x - h) = 4a^2 + 4a\sqrt{[(x - h) - c]^2 + (y - k)^2}$$

Divide each side by 4, subtract a^2 from each side, then square both sides.

$$c(x - h) = a^2 + a\sqrt{[(x - h) - c]^2 + (y - k)^2}$$

$$c(x - h) - a^2 = a\sqrt{[(x - h) - c]^2 + (y - k)^2}$$

$$c^2(x - h)^2 - 2a^2c(x - h) + a^4 = a^2\{[(x - h) - c]^2 + (y - k)^2\}$$

Square the quantity in brackets and distribute a^2 on the right side.

$$c^2(x - h)^2 - 2a^2c(x - h) + a^4 = a^2\{(x - h)^2 - 2c(x - h) + c^2 + (y - k)^2\}$$

$$c^2(x - h)^2 - 2a^2c(x - h) + a^4 = a^2(x - h)^2 - 2a^2c(x - h) + a^2c^2 + a^2(y - k)^2$$

Add $2a^2c(x - h)$ to both sides, then place constants on the left and terms with variables (x and y) on the right.

$$c^2(x - h) + a^4 = a^2(x - h)^2 + a^2c^2 + a^2(y - k)^2$$
$$a^4 - a^2c^2 = a^2(x - h)^2 - c^2(x - h)^2 + a^2(y - k)^2$$

Now factor as you did when deriving the equation of the ellipse. (Factor the a^2 from the left and $(x - h)^2$ from the first two terms on the right.)

$$a^2(a^2 - c^2) = (a^2 - c^2)(x - h)^2 + a^2(y - k)^2$$

Notice that you again get $(a^2 - c^2)$, but this time it is a negative number since $c > a$ (see the graph). For this reason, it is more useful to factor out -1 to obtain $(c^2 - a^2)$. We will name this difference b^2.

$$-a^2(c^2 - a^2) = -(c^2 - a^2)(x - h)^2 + a^2(y - k)^2$$
$$-a^2b^2 = -b^2(x - h)^2 + a^2(y - k)^2$$

Now divide by $-a^2b^2$, and apply the symmetric property.

$$1 = \frac{-b^2 \, (x - h)^2}{-a^2b^2} + \frac{a^2(y - k)^2}{-a^2b^2}$$
$$\frac{(x - h)^2}{a^2} - \frac{(y - k)^2}{b^2} = 1$$

Since $b^2 = c^2 - a^2$, you can also express this relationship as $a^2 + b^2 = c^2$. As pointed out earlier, the values of a and c on the graph of a hyperbola are similar to those distances on the graph of an ellipse. The value of b is somewhat more complicated because there are no vertices on the conjugate axis.

The values a and b are respectively $\frac{1}{2}$ of the horizontal length and the vertical width of the *fundamental rectangle*. The diagonals of this rectangle form the *asymptotes* of the hyperbola. The asymptotes are lines that the curve approaches but never intersects. For a simple example, consider the hyperbola with center $(0, 0)$ and horizontal transverse axis. Its general equation follows.

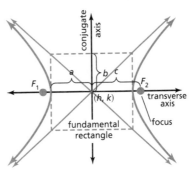

$$\frac{x^2}{a^2} - \frac{y^2}{b^2} = 1$$

Solve the general equation of the hyperbola for y.

$$\frac{y^2}{b^2} = \frac{x^2}{a^2} - 1$$
$$\frac{y^2}{b^2} = \frac{x^2 - a^2}{a^2}$$
$$y^2 = \frac{b^2(x^2 - a^2)}{a^2}$$
$$y = \pm\frac{b}{a}\sqrt{x^2 - a^2}$$

As x gets larger, the subtraction of the constant a^2 becomes less and less significant. For this reason, the larger x becomes, the closer $\sqrt{x^2 - a^2}$ gets to $\sqrt{x^2}$, or x. Of course, no matter how large x is, subtracting a^2 from x^2 makes *some* difference, so the radical only approaches x and never precisely reaches it. Since the radical approaches x, the hyperbola $y = \pm\frac{b}{a}\sqrt{x^2 - a^2}$ asymptotically approaches $y = \pm\frac{b}{a}x$, which are lines with slopes $\frac{b}{a}$ and $\frac{-b}{a}$ and y-intercept $(0, 0)$ at the center of the hyperbola. So as x gets larger and larger, the hyperbola gets closer and closer to the lines, or asymptotes. Because the lines are slanted rather than vertical or horizontal, they are called *oblique asymptotes*. When a hyperbola is translated the asymptotes are translated with it. The equations of the asymptotes of a hyperbola with center (h, k) are

$$y = \pm\frac{b}{a}(x - h) + k.$$

If a hyperbola opens vertically, then the transverse and conjugate axes interchange, which affects the foci and the equations of the asymptotes. Note the differences.

	Hyperbola Opens Horizontally	Hyperbola Opens Vertically
General Form	$Ax^2 - Cy^2 + Dx + Ey + F = 0$	$Cy^2 - Ax^2 + Dx + Ey + F = 0$
Work Form	$\dfrac{(x - h)^2}{a^2} - \dfrac{(y - k)^2}{b^2} = 1$	$\dfrac{(y - k)^2}{a^2} - \dfrac{(x - h)^2}{b^2} = 1$
Equations of the Asymptotes	$y = \pm\dfrac{b}{a}(x - h) + k$	$y = \pm\dfrac{a}{b}(x - h) + k$
Foci	$F_1(h - c, k)$ $F_2(h + c, k)$	$F_1(h, k - c)$ $F_2(h, k + c)$
Transverse Axis	$y = k$	$x = h$
Graph		

EXAMPLE 1   Graph $\dfrac{x^2}{9} - \dfrac{(y-3)^2}{9} = 1$.

Answer

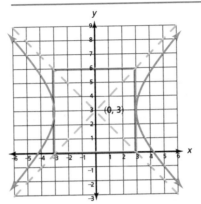

1. Locate the center of the hyperbola at (0, 3).

2. Sketch the fundamental rectangle, using $a = 3$ and $b = 3$. (Note that a can be equal to, less than, or greater than b.)

3. Use the rectangle to draw the asymptotes.

4. Sketch the hyperbola with vertices at (3, 3) and (−3, 3).

EXAMPLE 2   For the hyperbola $9x^2 - 4y^2 + 18x + 8y = 31$, find a and b, the center, the foci, the equation of the transverse axis, and the equations of the asymptotes.

Answer

$9x^2 - 4y^2 + 18x + 8y = 31$

$9x^2 + 18x - 4y^2 + 8y = 31$
$9(x^2 + 2x) - 4(y^2 - 2y) = 31$
$9(x^2 + 2x + 1) - 4(y^2 - 2y + 1) = 31 + 9 - 4$
$9(x + 1)^2 - 4(y - 1)^2 = 36$
$\dfrac{(x + 1)^2}{4} - \dfrac{(y - 1)^2}{9} = 1$

1. Obtain work form by completing the square. Divide by 36 to obtain 1 on the right. Observe that the resulting form determines a hyperbola that opens horizontally.

$a^2 = 4$, so $a = 2$; $b^2 = 9$, so $b = 3$.
(−1, 1) is the center;
$y = 1$ is the transverse axis.

2. Read a, b, and the center from the equation. The transverse axis is the horizontal line through the center.

$c^2 = a^2 + b^2$
$c^2 = 4 + 9$
$c^2 = 13$
$c = \sqrt{13}$
foci $(-1 - \sqrt{13}, 1)$, $(-1 + \sqrt{13}, 1)$

3. Determine the foci by calculating c; the coordinates of the foci are at about (−4.6, 1), (2.6, 1).

$y = \dfrac{3}{2}(x + 1) + 1$

$y = \dfrac{3}{2}x + \dfrac{5}{2}$

and

$y = -\dfrac{3}{2}(x + 1) + 1$

$y = -\dfrac{3}{2}x - \dfrac{1}{2}$

4. Find the asymptotes.

Notice the standard form of the hyperbola in Example 2. The A and C values of the general conic have opposite signs. Since A is positive, the hyperbola opens right and left. When C is positive and A is negative, the hyperbola opens up and down.

The hyperbola, like the ellipse, has an eccentricity given by $e = \frac{c}{a}$. Since $c > a$, the eccentricity is always greater than 1. Thus, hyperbolas have the greatest eccentricity of any conic section and deviate the most from a circle. This isn't surprising if you consider the sections of cones. Let S represent the angle that the section makes with the plane of the generating curve of the cone and let P represent the angle that an element of the cone makes with the plane of its generating curve.

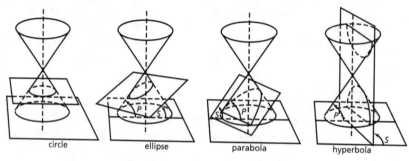

| circle | ellipse | parabola | hyperbola |

	Eccentricity	Conic Section
Circle	0	$m\angle S = 0$ (horizontal cross section)
Ellipse	$0 < e < 1$	$0 < m\angle S < m\angle P$
Parabola	1	$m\angle S = m\angle P$
Hyperbola	$e > 1$	$m\angle S > m\angle P$

To obtain the equation of a hyperbola, you must know or be able to determine the center and the distances a and b. Remember that for a hyperbola, $c^2 = a^2 + b^2$.

EXAMPLE 3   Write an equation of a hyperbola with the center $(2, 3)$, the transverse axis $x = 2$, and eccentricity $\frac{3}{2}$.

Answer

$\dfrac{(y - 3)^2}{a^2} - \dfrac{(x - 2)^2}{b^2} = 1$

1. The hyperbola opens vertically, since the transverse axis is a vertical line.

Let $c = 3$ and $a = 2$; then, $b = \sqrt{3^2 - 2^2} = \sqrt{5}$.

$\dfrac{(y - 3)^2}{4} - \dfrac{(x - 2)^2}{5} = 1$

2. In simplest form $e = \frac{3}{2} = \frac{c}{a}$. Thus $c = 3$ and $a = 2$. Note, however, that $c = 6$ and $a = 4$ is also possible as well as any other values with a ratio of $\frac{3}{2}$. Solve for b.

▶ A. Exercises

Graph the hyperbola. Find (a) its center, (b) the equation of its transverse axis, (c) the coordinates of its foci, and (d) the equations of the asymptotes.

1. $\dfrac{x^2}{9} - \dfrac{y^2}{16} = 1$

2. $\dfrac{(y-1)^2}{4} - \dfrac{(x+3)^2}{25} = 1$

3. $\dfrac{(x-2)^2}{36} - \dfrac{y^2}{16} = 1$

4. $\dfrac{(y+3)^2}{9} - \dfrac{(x+1)^2}{9} = 1$

5. $25(x+1)^2 - 9y^2 = 225$

6. $4x^2 - 16y^2 = 64$

7. $y^2 - 9x^2 + 4y - 18x = 14$

8. $16x^2 - 25y^2 - 150y = 625$

9. $4x^2 - y^2 - 40x + 4y = -92$

10. $4y^2 - 49x^2 + 24y - 294x = 601$

▶ B. Exercises

Find the domain and range of each hyperbola or inequality. (Graph if necessary.)

11. $\dfrac{x^2}{9} - \dfrac{y^2}{4} = 1$

12. $\dfrac{(x-2)^2}{40} - \dfrac{(y+1)^2}{9} = 1$

13. $\dfrac{(y+1)^2}{4} - \dfrac{x^2}{16} = 1$

14. $\dfrac{x^2}{9} - \dfrac{(y-1)^2}{4} \geq 1$

15. $\dfrac{x^2}{25} - \dfrac{y^2}{100} \leq 1$

Write the simplest equation of the hyperbola with the following traits; it may be helpful to graph the data.

16. Center at the origin, x-intercepts (±3, 0), one asymptote with equation $y = 4x$

17. Center at the origin, y-intercepts (0, ±8), one asymptote with equation $y = -2x$

18. Foci at (5, 0) and (−5, 0), $e = \dfrac{5}{3}$

19. Foci at (0, 17) and (0, −17), $e = \dfrac{17}{15}$

20. The difference of the distances from any point on the curve to (0, 10) and (0, −10) is 12.

21. The difference of the distances from any point on the curve to (28, 3) and (3, 3) is 48

22. Center at (2, 4), vertex at (6, 4), one asymptote with the equation $y = x + 2$

23. Center at (−3, −3), one focus at (−3, 2), and vertex at (−3, 1)

Restrict the range to assure that these curves will be functions; then write the equations in functional notation.

24. $\frac{x^2}{9} - \frac{y^2}{16} = 1$

25. $\frac{(y + 1)^2}{4} - \frac{(x + 3)^2}{9} = 1$

26. If a line is parallel to an asymptote of a hyperbola, will the line intersect the hyperbola? If so, in how many points will it intersect?

▶ C. Exercises

27. What relationship exists between the asymptotes of the following hyperbola: $\frac{(x + 2)^2}{4} - \frac{(y - 1)^2}{4} = 1$? What condition will guarantee this relationship?

28. Justify your conclusion.

■ Cumulative Review

Give a function that satisfies the following conditions.

29. Monotonically increasing with a range such that $f(x) > 1$

30. A cube root function translated two units to the right and four units up

31. A sine function with an amplitude of 3, period of π, and phase shift of π

If $f(2) = 5$, $g(2) = 8$, $f(8) = 7$, $g(5) = 6$, find the following.

32. $(f + g)(2)$ and $(fg)(2)$

33. $(f \circ g)(2)$

 MIND OVER MATH

If Diane drove 60 mph from the New York state line to a point exactly halfway home and then drove 50 mph for the remainder of the trip, what was her average speed for the entire trip?

6.5 Variation

You have already seen that ellipses are practical for calculating orbits of planets and satellites and that parabolas are useful for calculating trajectories of baseballs and bullets. However, you may not realize how important other conics are in variation problems. Here's a quick review of the three types of variation.

The work done in raising an elevator varies directly with the number of floors it ascends. The glass elevator at the SI Center in Stuttgart, Germany, incorporates modern technology but simulates an antique.

Equation	Type of Variation	Translated into Words
$y = kx$	direct	y varies directly as x.
$y = \dfrac{k}{x}$	inverse	y varies inversely as x.
$y = kxz$	joint	y varies jointly as x and z.

The k in each case is a constant called the *constant of variation* ($k > 0$). Another term for variation is proportionality. Direct variation can also be read as "y is directly proportional to x." Thus, k is also called the *constant of proportionality*.

EXAMPLE 1   The distance a freight train travels varies directly as the time traveled. If it travels **50** miles in **2** hours, how far will it travel in **7** hours at the same rate?

Answer

$y = kx$	1. Select direct variation.
$50 = k(2)$ $25 = k$	2. Find the constant of variation.
$y = kx$ $y = 25x$	3. Substitute for k.
$y = 25(7)$ $y = 175$ miles	4. Find the distance.

EXAMPLE 2 *Q* varies inversely with *n*. If *Q* = 18 when *n* = 8, find *n* if *Q* = 20.

Answer

$Q = \dfrac{k}{n}$	1. Select inverse variation
$18 = \dfrac{k}{8}$ $144 = k$	2. Find *k*.
$Q = \dfrac{144}{n}$	3. Substitute for *k* to find the specific variation.
$20 = \dfrac{144}{n}$ $20n = 144$ $n = 7.2$	4. Use the given value of *Q* to find *n*.

Recall that lines are degenerate conic sections, and notice that direct variation is a linear relationship. Comparing $y = kx$ to $y = mx + b$, we see $b = 0$, so the line always passes through the origin. Also, the slope of the line is the constant of variation. Since $k > 0$ for direct variation, the line has a positive slope.

If lines describe direct variation, what is inverse variation? Answering this question requires some background.

Inverse comes from the idea that as *x* increases, *y* must decrease. Conversely, as *y* increases, *x* must decrease. Rewrite $y = \frac{k}{x}$ by clearing the fractions to obtain $xy = k$ ($k > 0$). Notice that this fits the general form

$$Ax^2 + Bxy + Cy^2 + Dx + Ey + F = 0$$

if $B = 1$, $F = -k$, and $A = C = D = E = 0$. To determine which conic section it represents, consider the following example.

The equation $xy = 16$ would contain the points (1, 16), (2, 8), (4, 4), (8, 2), and (16, 1). As *x* increases in value, *y* decreases. Other solutions to the equation include (−1, −16), (−2, − 8), (−4, −4), and (−8, −2). Plot the points to discover that the graph is a familiar conic section.

The equation $xy = 16$ represents a hyperbola lying in quadrants I and III. Notice that it has been rotated so that the asymptotes are the axes. The center is at the origin, and the transverse axis is $y = x$. The foci are derived below.

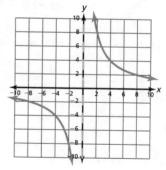

EXAMPLE 3 Find the coordinates of the foci for the hyperbola $xy = 16$.

Answer

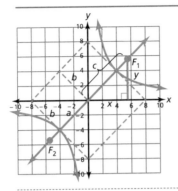

$\sqrt{(-4)^2 + (-4)^2} = \sqrt{32} = 4\sqrt{2}$	2. Use the distance formula to find a, which is the distance from $(0, 0)$ to $(-4, -4)$.
$a = b = 4\sqrt{2}$	3. Notice in the graph that a is one leg of a 45-45 right triangle, and therefore $a = b$.
$c^2 = a^2 + b^2$ $c^2 = 32 + 32$ $c^2 = 64$ $c = 8$	4. Compute c using the known formula relating a, b, and c in hyperbolas.
$x^2 + y^2 = 8^2$ $x^2 + x^2 = 64$ $2x^2 = 64$ $x^2 = 32$ $x \approx \pm 5.7$	5. To determine the coordinates of a point 8 units from the origin on the line $y = x$, use the Pythagorean theorem.

The foci are at $(-5.7, -5.7)$ and $(5.7, 5.7)$.

In summary, direct variations are linear, and all inverse variations are rotated hyperbolas. As for joint variation, since there are three or more variables, it cannot be graphed in the plane.

▶ A. Exercises

Find the constant of variation if
1. B varies directly with F, and $B = 20$ when $F = 4$.
2. R varies inversely with P, and $R = 15$ when $P = 3$.
3. M varies jointly with s and t, and $M = 120$ when $s = 4$ and $t = 5$.

4. q varies directly with r, and $q = 3$ when $r = 12$.
5. d varies inversely with a, and $d = 8$ when $a = 0.5$.

Write the general equation and graph each variation.
6. P varies directly with Q where the constant of variation is $\frac{2}{3}$.
7. A varies inversely with B where the constant of variation is 6.
8. m varies directly with n where $m = 1$ when $n = 4$.
9. y varies directly with x where $y = 9.8$ when $x = 5$.
10. y varies inversely with x where $y = 2$ when $x = 5$.
11. y varies directly with x where $y = 2.444$ when $x = 0.74$.

Answer each question.
12. If p varies directly with q, and $p = 12$ when $q = 6$, find p when $q = 8$.
13. If v varies inversely with w, and $v = 16$ when $w = 6$, find v when $w = 4$.
14. If y varies jointly with x and z, and $y = 200$ when $x = 8$ and $z = 5$, find y when $x = 10$ and $z = 10$.
15. If s varies directly with t, and $s = 21$ when $t = 7$, find t when $s = 12$.
16. If b varies inversely with d, and $b = 6$ when $d = 30$, find b when $d = 16$.

▶ B. Exercises

17. For a given resistance, Ohm's law states that voltage (V) in an electric circuit varies directly with the current (I). If there are 10 volts when the current is 3 amps, what is the voltage when there are 5 amps of current?
18. Sales tax varies directly with the cost of the item. In a certain state, the tax on a $24 item is $1.32. Find the tax on a $57 item.
19. Annual interest in a certain bank account varies directly with the amount invested. If $150 would earn $8 annually, how much must be invested to earn $18?
20. A city population varies inversely with the square root of the unemployment rate. If the population is 137,800 with 5% unemployment, how large will it be when unemployment rises to 6%?
21. Grade point average varies inversely with time spent watching TV. Bill has a 2.8 average when he watches TV 18 hours per week. He wants to get his grades up to a 3.5 average and is willing to study in place of TV. How much TV can he still watch?
22. $C = 2\pi r$ is a familiar formula. Write in words using variation. Identify the constant of variation.

▶ C. Exercises

Kepler's third law of planetary motion states that the squares of the sidereal periods (of revolution) of the planets are directly proportional to the cubes of their mean distance from the sun.

23. Using T as the orbital period and R as the mean distance from the sun, express the relation as a variation.

24. If an orbiting body has a period of 420 days and a mean distance of 2.3×10^6 miles from the sun, find k.

⊞ Dominion Modeling

25. Add a column to the microphone table to convert degrees to radians.

▪ Cumulative Review

Write an equation for each of the following conic sections.

26. Circle of radius 4 with center at (1, 3)
27. Ellipse centered at (2, 1) and vertically elongated with 4 and 6 as minor and major axes
28. Parabola with maximum at (1, 5) and focus at (1, 3)
29. Hyperbola with a vertical transverse axis of 6 units and a conjugate axis of 8 units with center at (−1, 3)
30. Graph the ellipse in exercise 27.

INDIAN MATH

Srinivasa Ramanujan (1827-1920)

> *The history of math dates as far back in India as it does in Western civilization.*

The history of math dates as far back in India as it does in Western civilization. However, the earliest individual mathematician from India whose writings still remain is Aryabhata (476-550), who was born at the city now called Patna. He summarized mathematics as it was known to the Hindu world in his day. His two main works were *Aryabhatiya* and *Siddhanta*. The first, published in 499, covers arithmetic and continued fractions; algebra, including quadratic equations; and trigonometry. He gave 3.1416 as an approximation for π, constructed a table of sines, and developed the power series for the sine function. This first work also covered geometry and included correct formulas for the areas of circles and triangles, but incorrect formulas for the volumes of spheres and pyramids. The second book set forth correct results in astronomy, including the idea that the apparent rotation of the heavens is actually due to the earth's rotation on its axis, the length of the year correct to the nearest hour, and the correct explanation of eclipses. The most amazing aspect of this book, however, is that he correctly explained that the orbits of the planets are ellipses!

Indian mathematics continued to develop throughout the Middle Ages. The two most important mathematicians of this period were Brahmagupta (598-679) and Bhaskara (1114-1185). Brahmagupta developed notation in algebra and found formulas for the area and diagonal of a cyclic quadrilateral. He also worked on arithmetic sequences and quadratic equations. Bhaskara showed knowledge of zero and negative numbers. For instance, he knew that $x^2 = 9$ has two solutions. His works, the most famous of which is *Lilivati* (meaning "The Beautiful"), is considered the most advanced math known to the world in the 12th century.

Madhava, in the 1500s, found infinite series for the sine, cosine, and arctangent functions. Until recently, it was thought that Newton and Gregory first derived them a century and a half later. This shows that mathematics continued in India into the modern age. The two most important modern mathematicians of India, however, are Ramanujan and Rajagopal.

The Ganges River, the heart and lifeblood of India, has been well-known to every mathematician in India's long history.

Srinivasa Ramanujan (1887-1920), whose poverty and self-taught genius make an interesting story, eventually came to the attention of mathematicians at Cambridge. In spite of the lack of formal education, his dissertation on highly composite numbers was accepted at Trinity College, Cambridge. In 1918 he became a fellow of the college as well as the first Indian member of the Royal Society of London. Other original results included partial sums and products of hypergeometric series and the theory of prime numbers. His early death from tuberculosis was the culmination of lifelong health problems.

Another recent mathematician, Cadambathur Rajagopal (1903-1978), was born in Madras, taught math at Madras Christian College, and eventually died in Madras at the age of 75. Besides his studies of Indian math history that recognized the contributions of Madhava, he contributed results on sequences, series, and functions of a complex variable.

The Meenakshi Temple at Madurai, India, is in the state of Tamil Nadu. The capital of this state is Madras, where Ramanujan and Rajagopal did much of their mathematics.

6 Approximation Methods

Quadratic Splines

The disadvantage of linear splines is that they take abrupt turns at the nodes (or knots) of the piece function. By piecing together quadratic functions, a smooth curve is obtained. The spline function, $S(x)$, is given below. The points (x_i, y_i) are the nodes through which the model is to pass. The value of $z_1 = 0$, and the rest of the z_i-values are computed using the formula below.

$$S(x) = \begin{cases} \dfrac{z_2 - z_1}{2(x_2 - x_1)}(x - x_1)^2 + z_1(x - x_1) + y_1 & \text{if} \quad x_1 \leq x \leq x_2 \\[2mm] \dfrac{z_3 - z_2}{2(x_3 - x_2)}(x - x_2)^2 + z_2(x - x_2) + y_2 & \text{if} \quad x_2 \leq x \leq x_3 \\[2mm] \dfrac{z_4 - z_3}{2(x_4 - x_3)}(x - x_3)^2 + z_3(x - x_3) + y_3 & \text{if} \quad x_3 \leq x \leq x_4 \\[2mm] \quad\quad\quad\vdots & \quad\quad\vdots \\[2mm] \dfrac{z_n - z_{n-1}}{2(x_n - x_{n-1})}(x - x_{n-1})^2 + z_{n-1}(x - x_{n-1}) + y_{n-1} & \\[2mm] & \text{if} \quad x_{n-1} \leq x \leq x_n \end{cases}$$

where $z_{i+1} = \dfrac{2(y_{i+1} - y_i)}{x_{i+1} - x_i} - z_i$ for $0 \leq i \leq n - 1$.

EXAMPLE 1 Find a quadratic spline that passes through the following five points. $(0, 2)$, $(2, 6)$, $(3, 5)$, $(5, 1)$, $(8, 7)$

Answer

$z_1 = 0$

$z_2 = \dfrac{2(y_2 - y_1)}{x_2 - x_1} - z_1 = \dfrac{2(6 - 2)}{2 - 0} - 0 = 4$

$z_3 = \dfrac{2(y_3 - y_2)}{x_3 - x_2} - z_2 = \dfrac{2(5 - 6)}{3 - 2} - 4 = -6$

$z_4 = \dfrac{2(y_4 - y_3)}{x_4 - x_3} - z_3 = \dfrac{2(1 - 5)}{5 - 3} - (-6) = 2$

$z_5 = \dfrac{2(y_5 - y_4)}{x_5 - x_4} - z_4 = \dfrac{2(7 - 1)}{8 - 5} - 2 = 2$

1. First find the z_i-values.

$$S(x) = \begin{cases} \dfrac{4 - 0}{2(2 - 0)}(x - 0)^2 + 0(x - 0) + 2 = x^2 + 2 \\[2mm] \dfrac{-6 - 4}{2(3 - 2)}(x - 2)^2 + 4(x - 2) + 6 = -5(x - 2)^2 + 4x - 2 \\[2mm] \dfrac{2 - (-6)}{2(5 - 3)}(x - 3)^2 - 6(x - 3) + 5 = 2(x - 3)^2 - 6x + 23 \\[2mm] \dfrac{2 - 2}{2(8 - 5)}(x - 5)^2 + 2(x - 5) + 1 = 2x - 9 \end{cases}$$

2. Now substitute the x-, y-, and z-values into the spline formula.

Continued ▶

$$S(x) = \begin{cases} x^2 + 2 & \text{if } 0 \le x \le 2 \\ -5x^2 + 24x - 22 & \text{if } 2 \le x \le 3 \\ 2x^2 - 18x + 41 & \text{if } 3 \le x \le 5 \\ 2x - 9 & \text{if } 5 \le x \le 8 \end{cases}$$

3. Write each quadratic in standard form.

Recall that the spline is a piece function, and the individual functions are often subscripted $S_1(x)$, $S_2(x)$, . . . In particular, for the example above, $S_2(x) = -5x^2 + 24x - 22$.

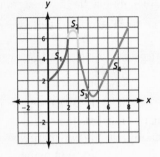

EXAMPLE 2 Using Example 1, estimate y-values for $x = 1$ and $x = 6$.

Answer

$S(1) = (1)^2 + 2 = 3$	1. Use $x^2 + 2$, since 1 is in the first interval.
$S(6) = 2(6) - 9 = 3$	2. Use $2x - 9$ since 6 is in the last interval.

▶ Exercises

Use Example 1 to determine the following.
1. Evaluate the spline at $x = 4$.
2. At a given node x_i, two rules apply. Show that both rules give the same value for the function at each node.

Fit a quadratic spline to each set of data points, then find $S(6)$.
3. (2, 3), (4, 5), (7, 2), (9, 5)
4. (1, 9), (2, 3), (4, 7), (6, 11), (9, 3)
5. Prove that $S(x_i) = y_i$ for $1 \le i \le n$. ($S(x_i)$ is the ith term of the spline.)

6.6 Polar Coordinates

Since *Algebra 1*, you have been graphing in the rectangular coordinate system called the Cartesian plane. You will now learn an alternative system of graphing that has advantages for certain kinds of curves. The new system uses *polar coordinates*.

A dart board's design illustrates polar coordinates. The rings are at various radii from the center, and the sectors at various angles are distinctively colored.

The *pole*, labeled *O*, serves as the central reference point for polar coordinates, much as the origin serves for Cartesian coordinates. However, polar coordinates differ sharply from Cartesian coordinates in other ways. First, while the Cartesian plane has two perpendicular axes as reference lines (the *x*- and *y*-axes), polar coordinates have only a single reference ray called the *polar axis*, which corresponds to the positive *x*-axis in the Cartesian system. Second, the Cartesian plane uses a grid of horizontal and vertical distances from the reference lines; in polar coordinates the grid involves concentric circles and angles much like a dartboard.

Polar coordinates consist of an ordered pair, but the coordinates refer to the circular grid rather than to the rectangular grid. The first coordinate *r* represents the radial distance from the pole. The second coordinate represents the measure of the angle θ from the polar axis to the terminal ray containing the point. Thus, any point *P* is designated by an ordered pair (r, θ).

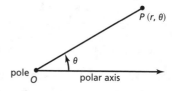

Examine the point (**3, 60°**) in the polar system:

Recall that $\theta + 2\pi$ (for $k \in \mathbb{Z}$) provides infinitely many alternative angles for the same terminal ray as θ. This means there are infinitely many ways to name the same point.

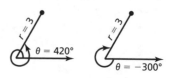

In fact, you can even employ negative values of the radius r if you use an angle that deviates from θ by 180°.

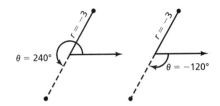

EXAMPLE 1 Locate the point (4, 90°) and write the coordinates in four other ways.

Answer

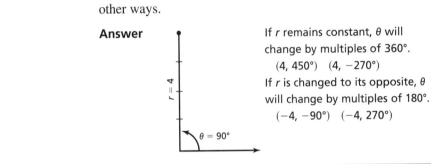

If r remains constant, θ will change by multiples of 360°.

(4, 450°) (4, −270°)

If r is changed to its opposite, θ will change by multiples of 180°.

(−4, −90°) (−4, 270°)

To see the relationship between the polar and rectangular systems, superimpose them so that the pole and origin coincide and so that the polar axis lies on the positive x-axis. Drop a perpendicular from point $P(r, \theta)$ to the polar axis (x-axis).

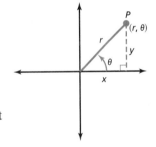

Notice that r represents the hypotenuse of a right triangle with legs x and y. By the Pythagorean theorem, $x^2 + y^2 = r^2$. So r can be expressed as

$$r = \sqrt{x^2 + y^2}$$

To relate the angle to the rectangular coordinates, consider which trig function involves both the adjacent and opposite legs. Since $\tan \theta = \frac{y}{x}$, the angle itself can be expressed using the inverse tangent function.

$$\theta = \tan^{-1} \frac{y}{x}$$

To find the formulas for x and y in terms of r and θ, trig functions will again prove useful. Since by definition $\cos \theta = \frac{x}{r}$ and $\sin \theta = \frac{y}{r}$, solve for the rectangular coordinates.

$$x = r \cos \theta$$
$$y = r \sin \theta$$

These four relationships allow points, lines, and curves to be converted from one system to the other.

EXAMPLE 2   Express the rectangular coordinates (5, −12) in polar form.

Answer

$r = \sqrt{x^2 + y^2}$ 1. Substitute the known rectangu-

$r = \sqrt{5^2 + (-12)^2}$ lar values to find r.

$r = \sqrt{25 + 144}$

$r = \sqrt{169}$

$r = 13$

$\theta = \text{Tan}^{-1} \dfrac{-12}{5}$ 2. Find θ, using your calculator.

$\theta \approx -67.4°$

(13, −67.4°) or equivalently, (13, 292.6°)   3. Express (5, −12) in polar form.

It is good to mentally check the graphs to assure the points are in the same quadrant. Such a check will enable you to catch a sign or computational error.

EXAMPLE 3   Write the equation of the line $x = 2$ in polar form.

Answer $x = 2$

$r \cos \theta = 2$ Substitute for x, using its polar equivalent $x = r \cos \theta$.

The equation of a vertical line obviously is much different in polar coordinates than in rectangular coordinates.

EXAMPLE 4   Write the equation $r = 3$ in rectangular form and describe its locus.

Answer

$r = 3$

$\sqrt{x^2 + y^2} = 3$ 1. Replace r with its rectangular equivalent.

$x^2 + y^2 = 9$ 2. Square both sides.

The rectangular form is a circle of radius 3.

EXAMPLE 5 Write the equation $\theta = 30°$ in rectangular form and describe its locus.

Answer

$\theta = 30°$	
$\tan \theta = \dfrac{\sqrt{3}}{3}$	1. Find the tangent of both sides.
$\dfrac{y}{x} = \dfrac{\sqrt{3}}{3}$	2. Substitute. $\left(\tan \theta = \dfrac{y}{x}\right)$
$y = \dfrac{\sqrt{3}}{3} x$	3. Solve for y.

From the rectangular form, you can see that the equation represents a line through the origin with slope $\dfrac{\sqrt{3}}{3}$. This corresponds to a line inclined at 30° with the horizontal. Since r can be positive or negative, the polar equation represents the entire line.

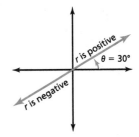

EXAMPLE 6 Write $r = 4 \sin \theta$ in rectangular form, and describe the locus.

Answer

$r = 4 \sin \theta$	1. Multiply both sides by r to obtain recogniz-
$r^2 = 4r \sin \theta$	able forms.
$x^2 + y^2 = 4y$	2. Substitute using $r^2 = x^2 + y^2$ and $y = r \sin \theta$.
$x^2 + y^2 - 4y = 0$	3. Subtract $4y$ from each side; then complete
$x^2 + (y^2 - 4y + 4) = 4$	the square.
$x^2 + (y - 2)^2 = 4$	

You should recognize the final equation as a circle of radius 2 that has been translated up two units. In polar coordinates, its center would be $\left(2, \dfrac{\pi}{2}\right)$.

What do you think the graph of $r = 4 \cos \theta$ would look like? Exercise 23 contains a similar problem.

▶ A. Exercises

Write each point, using rectangular coordinates; round to the nearest tenth. Check the points mentally.

1. $(2, 30°)$
2. $(5, 45°)$

3. $(-1, 180°)$

4. $\left(-2, \frac{-3\pi}{2}\right)$

5. $\left(3, \frac{2\pi}{3}\right)$

6. $\left(-1, \frac{11\pi}{6}\right)$

Write each point, using polar coordinates; round to the nearest degree. Check the points mentally.

7. $(2, 2)$

8. $(-3, -4)$

9. $(15, 8)$

10. $(0, 1)$

▶ B. Exercises

Transform the equation into polar form and describe the locus.

11. $x = 6$

12. $y = 7$

13. $x + y = 3$

14. $2x - y = 4$

15. $x^2 + y^2 = 25$

16. $x^2 + 4y^2 = 16$

Transform the equation into rectangular form and describe the locus.

17. $r \cos \theta = 5$

18. $r \sin \theta = -1$

19. $r = -5$

20. $\theta = \frac{5\pi}{6}$

21. $r = 6 \sin \theta$

22. $r = 8 \cos \theta$

Match each description to the equation that generates it.

23. $r = 2 \cos \theta$ A. circle at the origin

24. $r \sin \theta = 5$ B. circle translated on the polar axis

25. $r = 8$ C. circle translated on $\theta = \frac{\pi}{2}$

26. $r \cos \theta + r \sin \theta = 2$ D. ellipse

27. $r^2 \cos^2 \theta - r^2 \sin^2 \theta = 9$ E. horizontal line

28. $r \cos \theta = -7$ F. hyperbola

29. $r = 8 \sin \theta$ G. oblique line

30. $r = 0$ H. parabola

31. $r \sin \theta = r^2 \cos^2 \theta$ I. point

32. $9r^2 \cos^2 \theta + 4r^2 \sin^2 \theta = 36$ J. vertical line

▶ C. Exercises

33. Given the point (3, 32°), express all possible ordered pair representations for this point.

Dominion Modeling

Consider the microphone reception data.

34. Give a sinusoidal model for the omnidirectional microphone. Plot it first on a rectangular graph, and then on a polar graph.

35. Find a model for the figure eight microphone reception pattern. Give its graph in rectangular coordinates. Be sure that your sketch is rotated just like the one given. (*Hint*: consider absolute values with cosine.)

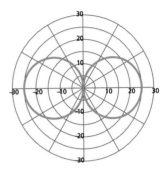

36. How would your figure eight model differ if you had used sine instead of cosine? Give a sketch.

Cumulative Review

37. Starting with $\sin^2 x + \cos^2 x = 1$, prove the other two Pythagorean identities without resorting to using x, y, and r.

38. Find the perimeter of a triangle whose vertices are (8, 9), (2, −7), and (−1, 10).

39. Find the smallest angle in the triangle of exercise 38.

40. Write a function for a direct variation through (3, 4).

41. Find the function for an inverse variation if $x = 4$ when $y = 1$.

6.7 Polar Coordinates and Graphs

By now you should be able to recognize some basic lines and circles in polar form. However, other polar equations can also be graphed by plotting points. Make a table of values where r is dependent on θ. Plot points at intervals of $\frac{\pi}{6}$ or less.

EXAMPLE 1   Graph $r = \theta$ in the polar system.

Answer

θ	$\frac{\pi}{6}$	$\frac{\pi}{4}$	$\frac{\pi}{3}$	$\frac{\pi}{2}$	$\frac{2\pi}{3}$	$\frac{3\pi}{4}$	$\frac{5\pi}{6}$
r	0.5	0.8	1.0	1.6	2.1	2.4	2.6

θ	π	$\frac{7\pi}{6}$	$\frac{5\pi}{4}$	$\frac{4\pi}{3}$	$\frac{3\pi}{2}$	$\frac{5\pi}{3}$	$\frac{7\pi}{4}$	$\frac{11\pi}{6}$	2π
r	3.1	3.7	3.9	4.2	4.7	5.2	5.5	5.8	6.3

1. In order to plot r (a real number), you will need to express θ in radians rather than degrees

   Express r in decimal form, and round to the nearest tenth.

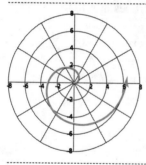

2. Plot the points to determine the polar graph (a spiral).

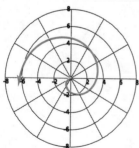

3. Since θ is measured in radians, it is easily seen that negative values of θ result in opposite values of r. You can use symmetry to sketch the spiral resulting from negative values of θ. It will spiral in the opposite direction.

Consider the equation $r = k$ where k is constant. Since the radius is constant, the graph is a circle of radius k centered at the origin. The graphs of equations of the form $r = k \sin \theta$ and $r = k \cos \theta$ are also circles. Recall that the range of $\sin \theta$ and $\cos \theta$ spans the interval $[-1, 1]$. Since they never exceed 1, the equations $r = k \sin \theta$ and $r = k \cos \theta$ must have a range of $-k \leq r \leq k$. In Section 6.6, Example 6, you discovered that the equation $r = 4 \sin \theta$ was a circle of radius 2 with center $\left(2, \frac{\pi}{2}\right)$. The radius in each case would be $\frac{k}{2}$ with centers at $\left(\frac{k}{2}, \pm\frac{\pi}{2}\right)$ for $r = k \sin \theta$ and $\left(\frac{k}{2}, 0\right)$ or $\left(\frac{k}{2}, \pi\right)$ for $r = k \cos \theta$. Therefore, their graphs are contained inside the circle $r = k$. They will intersect $r = k$ only when $\sin \theta = \pm 1$ $\left(\text{at } \theta = \pm\frac{\pi}{2}\right)$ or $\cos \theta = \pm 1$ (at $\theta = 0$ or π), respectively.

Though $r = k \sin n\theta$ and $r = k \cos n\theta$ are not circles, they have extreme radius values on the circle $r = k$ since $\sin n\theta \leq 1$.

EXAMPLE 2   Graph $r = 5 \cos 3\theta$.

Answer

$\cos 3\theta = \pm 1$

$3\theta = k\pi, k \in \mathbb{Z}$

$\theta = 0, \pm\frac{\pi}{3}, \pm\frac{2\pi}{3}, \pm\pi, \pm\frac{4\pi}{3}, \pm\frac{5\pi}{3}, \ldots$

1. Find angles for which the radius is the maximum of 5.

---

2. Make a table

θ	0	$\frac{\pi}{6}$	$\frac{\pi}{4}$	$\frac{\pi}{3}$	$\frac{\pi}{2}$	$\frac{2\pi}{3}$	$\frac{3\pi}{4}$	$\frac{5\pi}{6}$	π	$\frac{7\pi}{6}$	$\frac{5\pi}{4}$	$\frac{4\pi}{3}$	$\frac{3\pi}{2}$	$\frac{5\pi}{3}$	$\frac{7\pi}{4}$	$\frac{11\pi}{6}$	2π
r	5	0	$\frac{-5\sqrt{2}}{2}$	-5	0	5	$\frac{5\sqrt{2}}{2}$	0	-5	0	$\frac{5\sqrt{2}}{2}$	5	0	-5	$\frac{-5\sqrt{2}}{2}$	0	5

3. Graph.

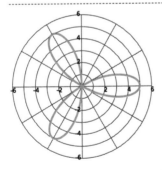

You can see that the graph is symmetric across the polar axis ($\theta = 0$). For $r = 5 \sin 3\theta$, where $n = 3$, the graph is symmetric across $\theta = \frac{\pi}{2}$. Also, for $0 \le \theta < 2\pi$, the values trace out the 3 loops twice. This repetition occurs for odd values of n only. The value of n determines the number of loops. If n is odd there are n loops; if n is even there are $2n$ loops. These loops are called petals because the graphs are called *roses*.

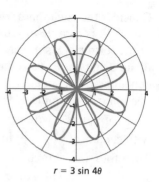

$r = 3 \sin 4\theta$

EXAMPLE 3   Graph $r = 3 + 2 \sin \theta$.

Answer

$0 \le \theta < 2\pi$ $r = 3 + 2 \sin \theta$ $r = 3 + 2(1) = 5$ $r = 3 + 2(-1) = 1$	1. Determine the domain (possible values of θ) and range (possible values for r). Think in terms of angles and radial distances. The entire curve lies between the concentric circles $r = 1$ and $r = 5$.

θ	0	$\frac{\pi}{6}$	$\frac{\pi}{3}$	$\frac{\pi}{2}$	$\frac{2\pi}{3}$	$\frac{5\pi}{6}$
r	3	4	4.7	5	4.7	4

2. Make an appropriate table.

θ	π	$\frac{7\pi}{6}$	$\frac{4\pi}{3}$	$\frac{3\pi}{2}$	$\frac{5\pi}{3}$	$\frac{11\pi}{6}$	2π
r	3	2	1.3	1	1.3	2	3

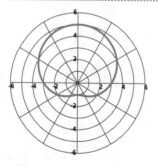

3. Graph the points and connect them in order of the table. Expect symmetry across the vertical line $\theta = \frac{\pi}{2}$ since the trig function is $\sin \theta$. This shape is called a *limaçon* (lee-mah-sohn).

► A. Exercises

Graph each relation.

1. $r = 2$
2. $\theta = \frac{\pi}{3}$
3. $\theta = \frac{\pi}{4}$
4. $r = -3$
5. $r = 5.57$
6. Describe the graph of the equation $\theta = k$ where k is constant.

Graph.

7. $r = 16 \cos \theta$
8. $r = 3 \sin \theta$
9. $r = - \cos \theta$
10. $r = -4.4 \cos \theta$

Describe the shape and placement of each polar curve.

11. $r = k \cos \theta$ where k is constant
12. $r = k \sin \theta$ where k is constant

► B. Exercises

How many petals does each polar rose below have? Give the maximum value of r.

13. $r = 7 \sin 9\theta$
14. $r = 2 \cos 6\theta$
15. $r = 5 \sin 8\theta$
16. $r = -6 \cos 7\theta$

Sketch each polar rose.

17. $r = 2 \cos 4\theta$
18. $r = \sin 5\theta$
19. $r = 4 \sin 2\theta$
20. $r = -4 \cos 2\theta$

Plot points, and graph the curve.

21. $r = 2\theta$
22. $r = \frac{1}{2}\theta$
23. $r = 4(1 - \sin \theta)$
24. $r^2 = 25 \sin 2\theta$
25. $r = 3.2 + 2.3 \sin \theta$

▶ C. Exercises

Change each equation to rectangular coordinates, express it in general form, and classify the curve.

26. $r = \dfrac{2}{1 - \cos \theta}$

27. $r = 2\sqrt{\sec 2\theta}$

〰 Dominion Modeling

28. From the microphone data, give a sinusoidal model for the cardioid reception pattern. Plot it first on a rectangular graph, then on a polar graph.

29. From the microphone data, give a sinusoidal model for the subcardioid reception pattern. Plot it on both rectangular and polar graphs.

■ Cumulative Review

30. Given $A(3, -9)$ and $B(-2, 7)$ as the endpoints of a segment, find the points that are one-quarter, one-half, and three-quarters of the way from A to B.

31. Give the inverse relation of $2x^2 + 3y^2 = 16$ in $f(x)$ notation. Restrict the domain of the original relation to make the inverse a function.

32. Find $\log_3 127$.

33. In what quadrants are the sine, cosine, and tangent negative?

34. Which conic sections are never functions? Which are sometimes functions? Which are always functions?

6.8 Graphing Polar Equations

Although you can always graph polar equations by plotting points, it is faster if you recognize the form of the equation. In the last section you should have learned to recognize circles, roses, and spirals. The chart below summarizes polar equations in cosine. Look closely at the ones that have not been discussed. Also, be sure you can picture what changes will occur by using sine instead of cosine in each equation.

Type		General Form	Graph	Symmetry
Circle	Center at pole	$r = a$	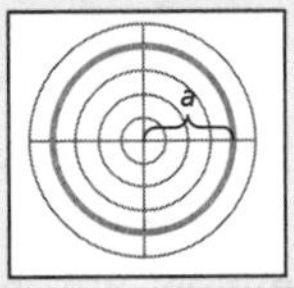	pole, any line through pole
	Center on polar axis	$r = a \cos \theta$	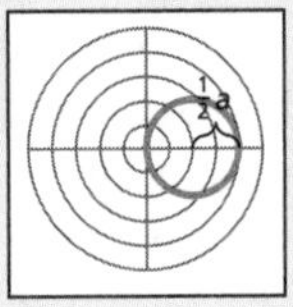	polar axis
Lemniscate		$r^2 = a^2 \cos 2\theta$	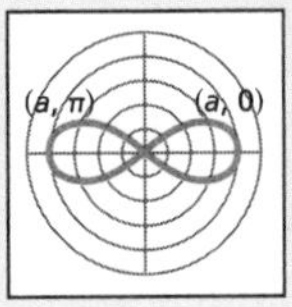	pole, polar axis, $\theta = \frac{\pi}{2}$
Limaçon	Cardioid $|a| = |b|$	$r = a + b \cos \theta$ or $r = a(1 + \cos \theta)$	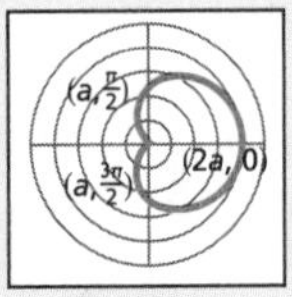	polar axis
	Without loop $|a| > |b|$	$r = a + b \cos \theta$	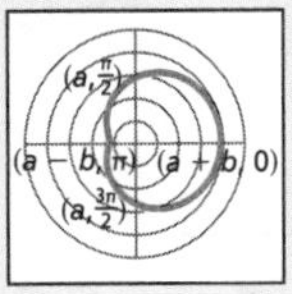	polar axis
	With loop $|a| < |b|$	$r = a + b \cos \theta$	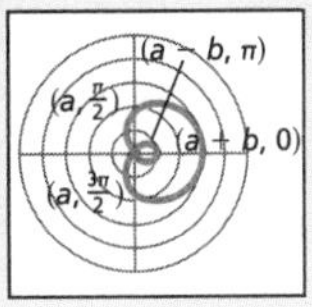	polar axis

Type		General Form	Graph	Symmetry
Spiral	Archimedes'	$r = a\theta$ for $\theta \geq 0$	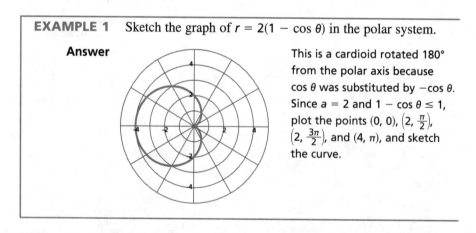	none
Rose	n is even (2n petals)	$r = a \cos n\theta$		polar axis
	n is odd (n petals)	$r = a \cos n\theta$		polar axis

A polar curve is symmetric with respect to the polar axis if it contains $\pm\cos\theta$, since $\cos(-\theta) = \cos\theta$. If $\cos\theta$ is replaced by $-\cos\theta$, in each case the graph will look the same but will be rotated 180° around the pole. This rotation occurs because $-\cos\theta = \cos(\pi - \theta)$. The appearance of some graphs would not be affected by such a rotation, such as the four-petal rose shown in the table above. If a polar curve contains $\pm\sin\theta$, it is also rotated 180° about the pole and is symmetric to the line $\theta = \frac{\pi}{2}$. This is because $\sin(\pi - \theta) = -\sin\theta$.

EXAMPLE 1 Sketch the graph of $r = 2(1 - \cos\theta)$ in the polar system.

Answer

This is a cardioid rotated 180° from the polar axis because $\cos\theta$ was substituted by $-\cos\theta$. Since $a = 2$ and $1 - \cos\theta \leq 1$, plot the points $(0, 0)$, $\left(2, \frac{\pi}{2}\right)$, $\left(2, \frac{3\pi}{2}\right)$, and $(4, \pi)$, and sketch the curve.

If $\cos\theta$ is replaced by $\sin\theta$, the curve retains the same shape but rotates 90° counterclockwise from the positions shown in the table above. This happens because $\cos\left(\frac{\pi}{2} - \theta\right) = \sin\theta$. If in $r = a(1 + \cos\theta)$, $\cos\theta$ is replaced by $-\sin\theta$, the curve remains the same but is rotated 270° counterclockwise because

$\cos\left(\frac{3\pi}{2} - \theta\right) = -\sin\theta$. To see this, compare the graph of $r = 2(1 - \sin\theta)$ shown here to the cardioid in the table. The identity can be verified by using the cosine of a difference identity.

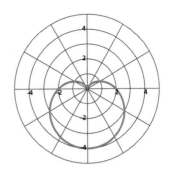

EXAMPLE 2 Sketch the graph of $r = 3\sin 2\theta$ using polar coordinates.

Answer

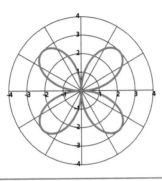

This is a four-petal rose rotated $45°\left(\frac{90°}{2}\right)$ as compared to the four-petal rose in the table. Note that the petals reach out to $r = 3$ (because $a = 3$) and there are four petals ($2n$), since $n = 2$ (even).

If θ is replaced by 2θ, 3θ, . . . , the rotation becomes $45°$, $30°$, . . . , respectively; or, in general, the substitution of $n\theta$ for θ results in a rotation of $\frac{90°}{n}$.

EXAMPLE 3 Sketch the polar graph $r^2 = 9\sin 2\theta$.

Answer

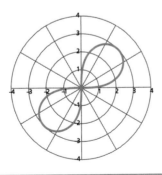

This is a lemniscate. The graph is symmetric about the line $\theta = \frac{\pi}{4}\left(\frac{90°}{2} = 45°\text{ rotation}\right)$. Plot the points, $\left(3, \frac{\pi}{4}\right)$ and $\left(-3, \frac{\pi}{4}\right)$ or $\left(3, \frac{5\pi}{4}\right)$, on the line $\theta = \frac{\pi}{4}$. Also plot the origin and then sketch the curve.

Systems of polar equations can also be graphed, but the points where the curves intersect on their graph may be represented by more than one ordered pair, since points in the polar plane do not have a unique representation. This means one ordered pair representation may satisfy one equation and not the other. Points of intersection that are not solutions occur frequently. For instance, two curves may intersect at the pole, but $(0, \pi)$ may be the coordinates that make one equation true, while $\left(0, \frac{\pi}{6}\right)$ may satisfy the other equation. Similarly, the solution to one equation may be $(-5, 300°)$ while the other solution is $(5, 120°)$. In these cases the solutions are different ordered pairs, but they represent the same point on the graph and therefore result in a point of intersection. For this reason, all points of intersection must be tested in both equations.

EXAMPLE 4   Sketch the graph of the following system. Test the points of intersection in each equation.
$r = -2 \sin \theta$
$r = 2(1 - \sin \theta)$

Answer

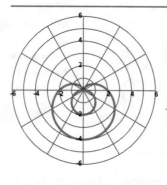

1. Graph both equations. The first is a unit circle translated 1 unit from the pole at 270° ($\cos \theta$ was replaced by $-\sin \theta$). The second is a cardioid, also translated 270°.

2. Identify the pole as the only point of intersection. Check whether it is a solution. Since the first equation is true at $(0, 0)$ and $(0, \pi)$ but the second is true at $\left(0, \frac{\pi}{2}\right)$ there are no simultaneous solutions.

▶ A. Exercises

Match the polar equation to the type of curve.

1. $r = 3\theta$ A. Cardioid
2. $r = \cos 3\theta$ B. Circle
3. $r = 3 \cos \theta$ C. Lemniscate
4. $r = 3 + 3 \cos \theta$ D. Limaçon with loop
5. $r^2 = 3 \cos 2\theta$ E. Rose
6. $r = 3 + 4 \cos \theta$ F. Spiral

▶ B. Exercises

Sketch the graph, and name the curve.

7. $r = 2 + 3 \cos \theta$

8. $r = 3(1 - \cos \theta)$

9. $r = 6$

10. $r = -2$

11. $r^2 = 9 \cos 2\theta$

12. $r^2 = 16 \sin 2\theta$

13. $r^2 = 4 \cos 2\theta$

14. $r = 4 \sin \theta$

15. $r = -6 \cos \theta$

16. $r = -6 \sin \theta$

17. $r = 2(1 + \sin \theta)$

18. $r = 1 + \cos \theta$

19. $r = 2 \cos 2\theta$

20. $r = 2 \sin 3\theta$

21. $r = 3 + 2 \sin \theta$

22. $r = -\theta$

Solve the following polar systems of equations graphically, and test the results in each equation.

23. $r = 3 \cos \theta$
    $r = 1 + \cos \theta$

24. $r = 4$
    $r = 4 \cos \theta$

25. $r = \sin \theta$
    $r = 1 - \sin \theta$

▶ C. Exercises

Find the area enclosed by each graph.

26. $r = 7$

27. $r = -5 \sin \theta.$

⩗ Dominion Modeling

Refer to the data on microphone reception patterns. Each of the following graphs matches the data for the named polar shape. Find a polar model and then also graph it in rectangular coordinates. You will need to use absolute values along with sine or cosine, and it may help to compare them to your previous polar patterns.

28.

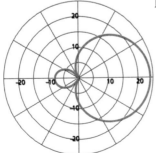

Hypercardioid

29.

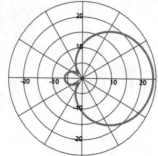

Short shotgun

30.

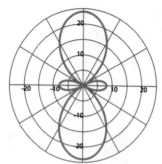

Shotgun (*Hint:* Consider a coefficient for θ other than 1.)

Explain how to modify the given model in the manner indicated.

31.

Rotate the hypercardioid model (exercise 28) **180°**

32. How could you modify the shotgun microphone pattern (exercise 30) to make all the loops the same size?

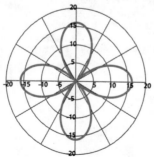

33. Perform the synthetic divisions shown by doing each multiplication and subtraction mentally. Then give the value of $f(x)$ for -2, -1, 1, and 2.

	2	−3	2	−1
−2				
−1				
1				
2				

34. Give all real solutions of the polynomial equation $2x^3 - 3x^2 + 2x - 1 = 0$.

35. What is the difference in the graphs of $f(x) = e^{x+1}$ and $g(x) = e^x + 1$?

36. What is the slope of a line whose angle of inclination is 20°? 40°?

37. Are the functions $f(x) = \dfrac{(x-3)(x+4)}{x+4}$ and $g(x) = x - 3$ equivalent?

Derive a formula for finding distance between two points in the polar plane.

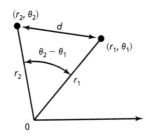

Math *and* Scripture

Bible Chronology

Astronomy helps to verify the chronology of the Assyrian kings. The Assyrians recorded Sennacherib's invasion of Judah as 701 B.C.

1. What year was this to the kings of Judah (2 Kings 18:13)?

This relation to a confirmed Assyrian date permits us to establish many biblical dates by comparing the chronologies of the Assyrians, Egyptians, and Babylonians with those of the kings of Judah and Israel. The five military events below can be found in the records of the foreign powers and dated precisely. These key events are critical for clarifying dates (B.C.) of several kings.

2. In 853, at the Battle of Qarqar, Shalmanezer III of Assyria defeated a coalition of 12 kings, including which king of Israel (I Kings 20:34)?

3. In 841, according to reliefs and inscriptions, Shalmanezer III fought Hazael of Damascus and received tribute from a king of Israel. Which king of Israel thus avoided battle with Shalmanezer but did not successfully diminish Hazael's attacks (2 Kings 10:31-33)?

4. In 722, Samaria fell to the Assyrians under Shalmanezer V and Sargon II during the reign of which king of Israel? (2 Kings 18:9-11)?

5. In 605, at the Battle of Carchemish, Nebuchadnezzar of Babylon decisively defeated Egypt. Four years previously, Pharoah Necho of Egypt had taken Carchemish to harass Babylon and was provoked to kill which king of Judah (2 Chr. 35:20-24)?

6. In 597, which king of Judah was deported by Nebuchadnezzar of Babylon (2 Kings 24:10-15)?

Using the reigns of the kings of Judah, and counting backwards from the deportation to Babylon, Solomon began to reign in 970 B.C. Read 1 Kings 6:1 and Exodus 12:40 to find the:

7. year Solomon started the temple.

8. year of the Exodus.

9. year Joseph's family arrived in Egypt.

From the dates above and your work in Chapter 2, approximate the:

10. birth of Abraham.

11. Tower of Babel.

12. Flood.

13. Creation.

14. What patriarch could have spoken to all his ancestors, including Adam, and passed his knowledge to Shem, who entered the ark?

15. Who is the last patriarch that Shem could have spoken with?

These facts refute those who ridicule the Bible as oral traditions that developed over the millennia. There were only about 2500 years from Adam to Moses, who wrote much of the Bible. All the records could have been passed down from Adam to Joseph with just two intermediate stages. These records did not have to be strictly oral. These computations can help you defend the faith and put to silence such ridiculous criticisms.

MAXIMIZING

Here is a Bible chronology that is easy to remember. It is thought that Zechariah was in his mid-thirties in 500 B.C. Determine the age of the others in the given year.

Year B.C.	Person then Living	Age
1	Christ	
500	Zechariah	35
1000	David	
1500	Moses	
2000	Abraham	
3000	Noah	
4000	Adam	

> **Vital Sines**
>
> **K**NOWING THAT **I** AM SET for the defence of the gospel. ❧
>
> PHIL. 1:17b

Chapter 6 Review

Graph.

1. $x^2 - y^2 + 6x + 4y = 11$
2. $25x^2 + 9y^2 - 100x + 18y = 116$
3. $2y^2 - x + 4y - 3 = 0$
4. $x^2 + y^2 - 10x - 10y = -25$
5. $r = -7$
6. $r = 6 \cos \theta$
7. $4r^2 \cos^2 \theta + 25r^2 \sin^2 \theta = 100$
8. $xy = -25$

Graph each system.

9. $(x - 2)^2 + (y - 2)^2 \geq 4$
   $x \geq (y - 2)^2 - 2$
10. $x^2 + 9y^2 - 2x - 54y \geq -73$
    $x^2 + y^2 - 12x - 6y \geq -41$

Write the equation of the conic described; then find the eccentricity $\left(e = \frac{c}{a}\right)$ of each. (*Hint:* Graphing the data may help.)

11. A circle with center $(-2, -5)$ and containing the point $(0, -5 + 2\sqrt{3})$
12. An ellipse with center $(2, 8)$, focus $(-2, 8)$, and containing the point $(-3, 8)$
13. A parabola with vertex $(5, 0)$, directrix $x = 1$, and focus $(9, 0)$
14. A hyperbola with foci $(2, 12)$ and $(2, -18)$, and containing the vertex $(2, 9)$
15. A circle of radius 3 with center at the pole, in polar coordinates

Change rectangular to polar form and vice versa. Round r to the nearest tenth and θ to the nearest degree in exercises 19 and 20.

16. $\theta = 45°$
17. $r = 8 \cos \theta$
18. $r \sin \theta = -3$
19. $(3, -3)$
20. $(24, -7)$

Plot the points in the appropriate system.

21. $(2, -6)$
22. $\left(-3, \frac{\pi}{6}\right)$

Rewrite each point in two other polar forms; then change to exact rectangular coordinates. (*Hint:* Check using the graphs of each point in both systems.)

23. $\left(5, \frac{2\pi}{3}\right)$

24. $(-2, -60°)$

Graph each function.

25. $f(x) = \frac{3\sqrt{4 + x^2}}{2}$

26. $f(x) = \frac{\sqrt{x - 6}}{2}$

Graph in the polar coordinate system.

27. $r = 5$

28. $r = 4(1 + \cos \theta)$

29. $r = 2 + 3 \cos \theta$

30. $r = 6 \sin 2\theta$

Match.

31. $r = 2 + 2 \sin \theta$ A. Archimedes Spiral

32. $r = 2 + 3 \sin \theta$ B. Cardioid

33. $r = 3 + 2 \sin \theta$ C. Circle centered at pole

34. $r = 2 \sin \theta$ D. Circle not centered at pole

35. $r = 3 \sin 2\theta$ E. Lemniscate

36. $r = 2 \sin 3\theta$ F. Limaçon with loop

37. $r = 2\theta$ G. Limaçon without loop

38. $r = 2$ H. Line

39. $\theta = 2$ I. Rose with even number of petals

40. $r^2 = 2 \sin 2\theta$ J. Rose with odd number of petals

41. Design a microphone reception pattern shaped like butterfly wings. Give the rule for the sinusoidal function and graph it in polar and rectangular form.

42. Give the mathematical significance of Phil. 1:17b.

7 Complex Numbers

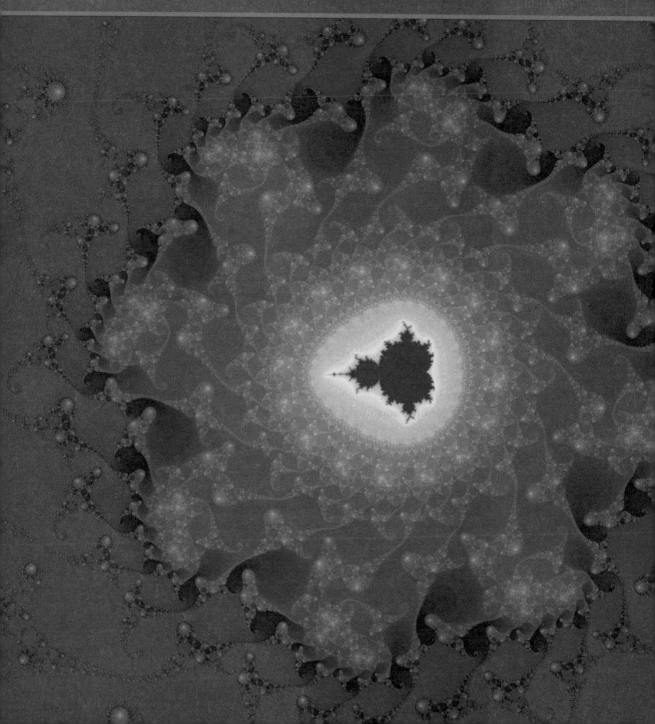

One of the most beautiful developments in pure mathematics has been Benoit Mandelbrot's work with fractals.

Fractals are shapes that are infinitely broken (or *fractured*) at their boundary. Recent technology opens new frontiers in the study of fractals, and the results can be stunningly beautiful. Fractals make it possible for computers to create lifelike virtual worlds.

The best-known fractal is the *Mandelbrot set,* which depends on a quadratic relationship. When you graph the set on the complex plane you obtain the heart-shaped region shown on these pages. The dark center is called the "Mandelbrot Lake."

Successive computations require you to substitute each answer back into the formula repeatedly. The pattern in computation *recurs,* so the formula is called a *recursion formula.*

Julia sets are closely related to the Mandelbrot set and use the same recursion formula.

After this chapter you should be able to

1. use imaginary numbers in solving equations and factoring.
2. perform the four basic operations on complex numbers.
3. graph any complex number on a complex plane as a vector.
4. find the modulus and argument of a complex number.
5. convert between the polar form and the rectangular form of any complex number.
6. multiply and divide complex numbers, using polar form.
7. find powers and roots of a given complex number.
8. find the sum, difference, scalar multiple, and dot product of two vectors.
9. use the dot product to find a perpendicular to a given vector and the angle between two vectors.
10. apply vectors to problems on navigation and forces.

7.1 Standard Form

You know that $x^2 + 1 = 0$ has no solution in the set of real numbers. However, the solution set is not empty when the set of numbers is expanded to the complex number system, $\mathbb{C}$. You should remember this from *Algebra 2*.

$$x^2 + 1 = 0$$
$$x^2 = -1$$
$$\sqrt{x^2} = \pm\sqrt{-1}$$
$$x = \pm\sqrt{-1}$$

The solutions to this equation are $\pm\sqrt{-1}$, but -1 is not the square of any real number. Instead, you must express the answer in terms of an imaginary unit.

Definitions

Imaginary unit i, where $i^2 = -1$ ($i = \sqrt{-1}$).

Pure imaginary number   A nonzero multiple of the imaginary unit (any number of the form ai, where $a \in \mathbb{R}$ and $a \neq 0$).

Imaginary number   Any number containing the imaginary unit (either a pure imaginary number or the sum of a real number and a pure imaginary number).

According to these definitions, the solutions to the equation $x^2 + 1 = 0$ are $\pm i$.

EXAMPLE 1   Solve $x^2 + x + 1 = 0$

Answer $x^2 + x + 1 = 0$

$$x = \frac{-b \pm \sqrt{b^2 - 4ac}}{2a}$$

$$x = \frac{-1 \pm \sqrt{1 - 4}}{2}$$

$$x = \frac{-1 \pm \sqrt{-3}}{2}$$

1. Apply the quadratic formula and simplify.

$$x = \frac{-1 \pm \sqrt{3}\sqrt{-1}}{2}$$

$$x = \frac{-1 \pm \sqrt{3}i}{2}$$

2. Recognize the imaginary number and write it using i.

Continued ▶

$$x = -\frac{1}{2} \pm \frac{\sqrt{3}}{2}i$$

3. Separate the number into the sum of a real number and a pure imaginary number.

The solutions $-\frac{1}{2} + \frac{\sqrt{3}}{2}i$ and $-\frac{1}{2} - \frac{\sqrt{3}}{2}i$ are examples of complex numbers.

Definition

Complex number   The set of complex numbers is the union of the sets of real numbers and imaginary numbers. The standard form is $a + bi$, where $a, b \in \mathbb{R}$ and $i^2 = -1$ ($i = \sqrt{-1}$). The value a is called the *real part* of the complex number, and b (not bi) is called the *imaginary part*.

The set of complex numbers, $\mathbb{C}$, has most of the properties that have been established for the set of real numbers. As a matter of consistency, mathematicians always simplify complex numbers and write them in standard form. This means that you should use the definition of the imaginary unit to simplify powers of i.

$$i = i$$
$$i^2 = -1$$
$$i^3 = i^2 \cdot i = -1 \cdot i = -i$$
$$i^4 = i^2 \cdot i^2 = -1 \cdot -1 = 1$$

$$i^5 = i^4 \cdot i = 1 \cdot i = i$$
$$i^6 = i^4 \cdot i^2 = 1 \cdot -1 = -1$$
$$i^7 = i^4 \cdot i^3 = 1 \cdot -i = -i$$
$$i^8 = i^4 \cdot i^4 = 1 \cdot 1 = 1$$

Do you notice a pattern developing? After i^4 the pattern repeats. To simplify a power of i, divide the exponent by 4. This determines how many i^4 factors there are. Since $i^4 = 1$, the remainder, which will be 3 or less, is applied as the new power of i. Simplify this power of i.

EXAMPLE 2   Simplify i^{63}.

Answer i^{63}

$$\begin{array}{r} 15 \\ 4\overline{)63} \\ \underline{4} \\ 23 \\ \underline{20} \\ 3 \end{array}$$

1. Since $i^4 = 1$, determine how many fourth powers can be simplified in the 63rd power. Division of 63 by 4 leaves a remainder of 3.

$i^{63} = (i^4)^{15} \cdot i^3$

2. Use exponent rules to rewrite the exponent.

$$= 1^{15} \cdot i^3$$
$$= i^3$$
$$= -i$$

3. Substitute $i^4 = 1$ and simplify. The new power of i is the remainder, 3.

All of the basic operations of real numbers can also be done with complex numbers. The following chart summarizes these operations.

Operation	Rule
Addition	$(a + bi) + (c + di) = (a + c) + (b + d)i$
Subtraction	$(a + bi) - (c + di) = (a - c) + (b - d)i$
Multiplication	$(a + bi)(c + di) = (ac - bd) + (ad + bc)i$
Division	$\dfrac{(a + bi)}{(c + di)} = \dfrac{(ac + bd) + (bc - ad)i}{c^2 + d^2}$

The multiplication rule is obtained from the FOIL method for multiplying polynomials, and the division rule by rationalizing the denominator, using the conjugate of $c + di$. Remember that the conjugate of $c + di$ is $c - di$. You will prove these two rules in the exercises.

EXAMPLE 3   Let $z_1 = 2 + 4i$ and $z_2 = 5 - 7i$. Find the following:

  a. $z_1 + z_2$ b. $z_1 - z_2$ c. $z_1 \cdot z_2$ d. $z_1 \div z_2$

Answer

a. $\begin{aligned} z_1 + z_2 &= (2 + 4i) + (5 - 7i) \\ &= (2 + 5) + (4 - 7)i \\ &= 7 + (-3)i \\ &= 7 - 3i \end{aligned}$

1. Combine the real parts and imaginary parts as you would combine like terms.

b. $\begin{aligned} z_1 - z_2 &= (2 + 4i) - (5 - 7i) \\ &= (2 - 5) + [4 - (-7)]i \\ &= -3 + 11i \end{aligned}$

2. Apply the subtraction rule above or add the opposite of the subtrahend.

c. $\begin{aligned} z_1 \cdot z_2 &= (2 + 4i)(5 - 7i) \\ &= 10 - 14i + 20i - 28i^2 \\ &= 10 + 6i - 28(-1) \\ &= 10 + 6i + 28 \\ &= 38 + 6i \end{aligned}$

3. Use the FOIL method, substitute for i^2, and then simplify.

d. $\begin{aligned} z_1 \div z_2 &= \frac{2 + 4i}{5 - 7i} \\ &= \frac{2 + 4i}{5 - 7i} \cdot \frac{5 + 7i}{5 + 7i} \\ &= \frac{10 + 14i + 20i + 28i^2}{25 - 49i^2} \\ &= \frac{-18 + 34i}{74} \end{aligned}$

4. Rationalize the denominator by multiplying both the numerator and the denominator by the conjugate of the denominator. Use the FOIL method to multiply.

Continued ▶

$$= \frac{2(-9 + 17i)}{74}$$

$$= \frac{-9 + 17i}{37}$$

5. Factor a 2 from the numerator, and cancel with the denominator.

$$= \frac{-9}{37} + \frac{17}{37}i$$

6. Write two fractions to obtain standard form with $a = \frac{-9}{37}$ and $b = \frac{17}{37}$.

EXAMPLE 4   Solve $6 - 3x = 7ix$.

Answer

$6 - 3x = 7ix$

$6 = 3x + 7ix$

1. Be sure all terms with the variable are on one side of the equation.

$6 = (3 + 7i)x$

2. Factor out the x to be able to isolate it, since the terms cannot be combined.

$x = \frac{6}{3 + 7i} \cdot \frac{3 - 7i}{3 - 7i}$

$x = \frac{18 - 42i}{9 - 49i^2}$

3. Divide; rationalize the denominator.

$x = \frac{2(9 - 21i)}{58}$

4. Factor out the 2 to reduce.

$x = \frac{9}{29} - \frac{21}{29}i$

5. Express the complex solution in standard form.

The next four theorems show properties of complex numbers and their *conjugates*. If $z = a + bi$, then its conjugate, denoted by $\bar{z}$, is $a - bi$.

Theorem 7.1
$\forall z \in \mathbb{C}, z \cdot \bar{z} \in \mathbb{R}$

Theorem 7.2
$\forall z \in \mathbb{C}, z + \bar{z} \in \mathbb{R}$

Theorem 7.3
$\forall z, w \in \mathbb{C}, \overline{z + w} = \bar{z} + \bar{w}$

Theorem 7.4
$\forall z, w \in \mathbb{C}, \overline{z \cdot w} = \bar{z} \cdot \bar{w}$

The proof of theorem 7.3 follows, and you will prove the rest as exercises.

EXAMPLE 5   Prove theorem 7.3, which states $\forall\, z,\, w \in \mathbb{C},\, \overline{z + w} = \overline{z} + \overline{w}$.

Answer

Let $z,\, w \in \mathbb{C}$	1. Given
$z = a + bi$ where $a,\, b \in \mathbb{R}$ $w = c + di$ where $c,\, d \in \mathbb{R}$	2. Definition of complex number
$\overline{z + w} = \overline{(a + bi) + (c + di)}$	3. Substitution
$\quad = \overline{(a + c) + (b + d)i}$	4. Definition of addition for complex numbers
$\quad = (a + c) - (b + d)i$	5. Definition of conjugate
$\overline{z} + \overline{w} = \overline{(a + bi)} + \overline{(c + di)}$ $\quad = (a - bi) + (c - di)$ $\quad = (a + c) + (-b - d)i$	6. Substitute; apply the definition of conjugate to both terms; add the terms, using the definition of addition for complex numbers.
$\quad = (a + c) - (b + d)i$	7. Factor -1 from the imaginary part.
$\therefore \overline{z + w} = \overline{z} + \overline{w}$	8. Use the transitive property of equality to reach a conclusion. (The symbol $\therefore$ means "therefore").

By using complex numbers, you will be able to factor some polynomials that you were previously unable to factor. For example, the binomial $x^2 + 4$ cannot be factored in the set of real numbers. But it can be factored over the set of complex numbers. Instead of a difference of squares, this is a sum of squares; therefore, $x^2 + 4 = (x + 2i)(x - 2i)$. If you check this by multiplication, you will see that the i^2 will change the last sign.

$$(x + 2i)(x - 2i) = x^2 - 2xi + 2xi - 4i^2$$
$$= x^2 - 4i^2$$
$$= x^2 + 4$$

Other polynomials that have imaginary numbers as coefficients may also be factored over the set of complex numbers.

EXAMPLE 6   Factor $x^2 + 3xi + 10$.

Answer $x^2 + 3xi + 10$	Factor as you would a polynomial with real coefficients. Remember that the i^2
$(x + 5i)(x - 2i)$	will change the sign of the last term.

► A. Exercises

Perform the indicated operation, and simplify.

1. $(5 + 7i) + (2 - 8i)$
2. $(-4 - i) - (3 - 2i)$
3. $(6 + 5i) - (2i)$
4. $8i(2 + 3i)$
5. $\frac{7 + i}{2 - 3i}$
6. $(1 + 2i)(3 + 4i)$
7. $(8 + i) + (3 - 7i)$
8. $\frac{4 + 3i}{2 + 3i}$
9. $(-4 - 5i)(3 + 2i)$
10. $10(4 + 2i)$
11. $\frac{5 + 6i}{4 + 5i}$
12. $(7 + 3i)(7 - 3i)$
13. $(3.4\overline{3} + \sqrt{2}i) - \left(\frac{5}{9} - 12.14i\right)$
14. $(3.978 - 2.4112i)(-0.0256 - 12.5628i)$
15. i^{82}
16. i^{12}
17. i^{139}

► B. Exercises

Solve each equation. If answers are complex, write the answer in standard form.

18. $4ix + 8 = 12i$
19. $x^2 + 4 = 0$
20. $2x^2 + 3x + 8 = 0$
21. $5x + 3ix = 9$
22. $2x - 8ix + 4x = 2(9 + 4i)$

23. $3x^2 + 6x - 4 = 0$
24. $x^2 - 3x + 9 = 0$
25. $8x(2 + 4i) - 7x = 9 - 5i$
26. $5x^2 + x + 1 = 0$

Factor over the set of complex numbers.

27. $x^2 + 9$
28. $x^2 - 10ix - 25$
29. $x^2 + 8ix - 12$

30. $x^2 + 25$
31. $x^2 - 9ix - 18$
32. $x^2 - 14ix - 49$

33. Prove theorem 7.1.
34. Prove theorem 7.2.
35. Prove that $\forall z \in \mathbb{R}, \bar{z} = z$.

► C. Exercises

36. Prove theorem 7.4.

37. Calculate $(2 - 3i)^5$.

38. From the circle mapping shown, give a circle mapping of the inverse relation. Is it a function?

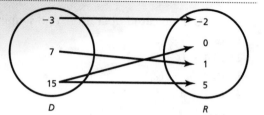

39. Which type of conic section has the greatest eccentricity?

40. What are the maximum and minimum number of distinct real zeros a polynomial function of degree $2n$ could have, where $n \in \mathbb{N}$? Of degree $2n + 1$?

41. Solve for x ($0 \le x < 360°$): $\sin^2 x = \cos x$.

42. Graph the given piece function.

$$f(x) = \begin{cases} -x^2 - 4x - 4 & \text{if} & x < -2 \\ |x + 1| & \text{if} & -2 < x \le 0 \\ \sqrt{x} & \text{if} & 0 < x \le 3 \\ 3 & \text{if} & x > 3 \end{cases}$$

7.2 Graphs of Complex Numbers

Nature is full of physical pictures of spiritual truths. When we get hungry or thirsty it reminds us that Jesus said, "I am the bread of life: he that cometh to me shall never hunger; and he that believeth on me shall never thirst" (John 6:35). The fact that we need food and water daily pictures our need for daily communion with God through prayer and Bible study. Just as no one can drink five gallons of water at once, it is impossible to store up enough spiritual nourishment on Sunday to get through the entire week.

Graphing is the method used to picture mathematics. When you picture real numbers, you graph them on a real number line. However, when you graph a complex number, you must use an *Argand diagram* (another name for the complex plane). The complex plane has a horizontal axis called the *real axis* and a vertical axis called the *imaginary axis*. A complex number *a* + *bi* has two parts: *a* is the real part and *b* is the imaginary part. These two parts determine an ordered pair, (*a*, *b*). Therefore, to graph a complex number, you graph its associated ordered pair.

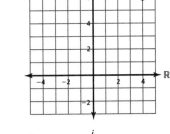

The point graphed on the complex plane is 4 + 6*i*. Two additional numbers are associated with a complex number and are related to its graph. The first number is its *absolute value*, represented by |*a* + *bi*|. The absolute value of a complex number is the distance from the origin to the graph of the number on the complex plane.

If you let $r = |a + bi|$ the absolute value can be found by an application of the Pythagorean theorem.

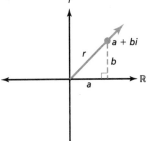

$$r^2 = a^2 + b^2$$
$$r = \sqrt{a^2 + b^2}$$
$$|a + bi| = \sqrt{a^2 + b^2}$$

Therefore, to find the absolute value of a complex number, you must find the square root of the sum of the squares of the real part and the imaginary part. This absolute value is also called the *modulus*.

Another important number associated with the graph of a complex number is the *argument*. The argument is the angle formed by the positive real axis with the terminal ray passing through the graph of the complex number. In the following graph the argument is θ, and the modulus is *r*. Drop a perpendicular from the point to the real axis, then find the argument using the inverse tangent function.

$$\tan \theta = \frac{b}{a}$$
$$\theta = \tan^{-1} \frac{b}{a}$$

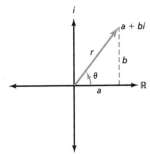

EXAMPLE 1   Find the modulus of 3 + 3*i*.

Answer |3 + 3*i*|

1. The modulus is the absolute value of the complex number.

$\sqrt{3^2 + 3^2}$

$\sqrt{18}$

$3\sqrt{2}$

2. Apply the formula, $|a + bi| = \sqrt{a^2 + b^2}$.

For a specific complex number there is a unique modulus. This is not true for the argument. Look at the following graphs of 3 + 3*i*.

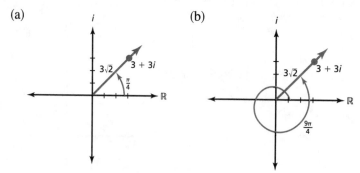

(a)   (b)

The values for the modulus and argument in (a) are $r = 3\sqrt{2}$, $\theta = \frac{\pi}{4}$, while the values in (b) are $r = 3\sqrt{2}$, $\theta = \frac{9\pi}{4}$. There are an infinite number of values for θ that would make the terminal ray pass through 3 + 3*i*. In fact, θ could be replaced by $\theta + 2n\pi$, where $n \in \mathbb{Z}$. The value of θ in the interval $[0, 2\pi)$ is usually used when referring to the argument, therefore the argument for 3 + 3*i* is $\frac{\pi}{4}$.

Definition

Equal complex numbers   Two complex numbers are equal if

1. their moduli are equal and

2. their arguments differ by integral multiples of 2π.

A complex number can also be represented graphically by a geometric figure called a *vector*. A vector is a directed line segment and looks similar to a ray because it has direction; but, unlike a ray, it has length (or magnitude). The *magnitude* of a vector is the absolute value of the complex number that it represents. A vector has an initial point and a terminal point. A vector in standard position has its initial point at the origin. Notice that the vector has only half an arrowhead on the end. This distinguishes it from a ray.

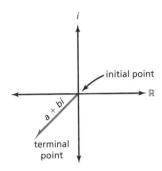

EXAMPLE 2   Graph the vector for the complex number $-2 + 3i$.

Answer

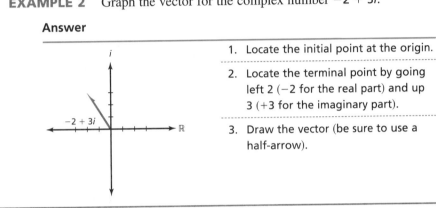

1. Locate the initial point at the origin.

- -

2. Locate the terminal point by going left 2 (-2 for the real part) and up 3 ($+3$ for the imaginary part).

- -

3. Draw the vector (be sure to use a half-arrow).

Equal vectors   Vectors are equal if they have the same magnitude and the same direction.

Notice that equal magnitude and the same direction corresponds to equal moduli and coterminal arguments for equal complex numbers. The positions of the initial points do not matter. (Two vectors can have different locations on a coordinate plane and still be equal.) Direction can be determined from the slope of the vector ($\tan \theta$, where θ is the argument of the complex number) along with the direction that the arrow is pointing. Since vectors in opposite directions have the same slope, both are necessary.

Symbols for vectors include either a half arrow or boldface font on a lower case letter: $\vec{u}$ or **u**. The bold letter will be used in this text, and its coordinates will be given in angle brackets $<a, b>$. Thus, **u** $= <a, b>$. The angle brackets always represent vectors, which will help you distinguish vectors from points represented as ordered pairs. Since you can't change fonts with a pencil, you should always use the half-arrow notation in your homework. $\vec{u} = <a, b>$.

EXAMPLE 3   Find the complex number associated with the given vector.

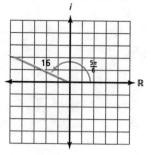

Answer

$$r = 16, \theta = \frac{5\pi}{6}$$

1. Identify r and θ from the graph.

$$\tan \theta = \frac{b}{a}$$

$$\tan \frac{5\pi}{6} = -\frac{1}{\sqrt{3}} = \frac{b}{a}$$

$$a = -\sqrt{3}b$$

$$r = \sqrt{a^2 + b^2}$$

$$16 = \sqrt{(-\sqrt{3}b)^2 + b^2}$$

$$16 = \sqrt{4b^2}$$

$$16 = 2b$$

$$b = 8$$

2. Apply the formulas that relate the magnitude (modulus) and argument with the real and imaginary parts of the complex number.

   Solve the argument formula for a and substitute that value into the modulus formula to solve for b.

$$a = -8\sqrt{3}$$

3. Substitute to find a.

$$-8\sqrt{3} + 8i$$

4. Note the quadrant location (2nd quadrant: a is negative, b is positive). Write the complex number in the form $a + bi$.

▶ A. Exercises

Graph.

1. $-4 + 2i$

2. $6 + 3i$

3. $-1 - 2i$

4. $5 - 5i$

Write the following complex numbers in vector notation, and then graph each vector.

5. $7 + 3i$

6. $-4 - 2i$

7. $6i$

8. $1 - 5i$

▶ B. Exercises

Find the absolute value of each number.

9. $|2 + 8i|$

10. $|-7|$

11. $|10 - 8i|$

12. $|-1 - 5i|$

13. $|9i|$

14. $|3 - 4i|$

Find the complex number for each graph.

15.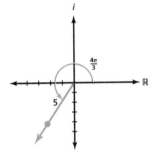

17.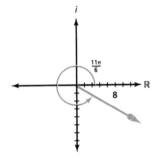

16.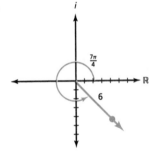

18.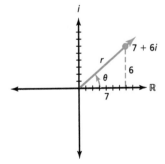

Find the modulus of each complex number.

19. $9 + 2i$

20. $-4 - 6i$

21. $3 - i$

22. $-5 + 7i$

23. Find the argument to the nearest minute of the complex number shown in the graph.

24. State the general formula to find the argument of a complex number.

25. If the argument, θ, of a complex number is $\frac{\pi}{7}$, state three other argument values that would produce equal complex numbers, given equal moduli.

26. Which vectors graphed here are equal? Write the complex number that describes each vector.

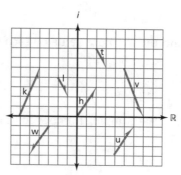

27. If $u = a + bi$ and $v = c + di$, write a program for a graphing utility in which the output is $|u + v|$.

▶ C. Exercises

28. Can $20 + 17i$, $50 - 18i$, and $3 + 24i$ be the lengths of the sides of a triangle? Explain your answer.

29. Let $z = a + bi$. Describe the following set geometrically:
$$\{z \mid |z - 1| = |z - 2|\}.$$

Dominion Modeling

To decide if a complex number k is in the Mandelbrot set, use $z_{n+1} = (z_n)^2 + k$ as follows.

a. Begin with z_0 as the complex origin, $0 + 0i$. Substitute z_0 into the recursion formula above to find z_1 and then find its modulus $|z_1|$.
b. Substitute z_1 into the same formula to find z_2. Then find its modulus.
c. Continue with z_3, z_4, etc. until a pattern in the moduli emerges.
d. If the absolute values (moduli) stay within about 2 units of the origin (instead of getting larger and larger), the original complex number k is in the Mandelbrot set.

Determine whether each value of k is in the Mandelbrot set.

30. $k = 0 + 0i$ 32. $k = 1 - 1i$
31. $k = \frac{1}{2} - \frac{1}{2}i$

33. Verify the results of exercises 30-32 by plotting the values of k on the complex plane showing the Mandelbrot set. What color is used for the set?

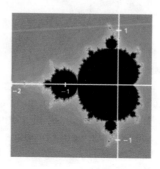

Mandelbrot set

34. Graph $f(x) = 3 \cos 2x$.

35. Write the tangent function with a $\frac{\pi}{8}$ shift to the right and a period of 3π.

36. Simplify $f(x) = \frac{\sin 4x}{\cos 2x}$ to a trig function in only one ratio. Give its amplitude and period.

37. Which number cannot be the number of petals for a rose?

    a. 3   b. 6   c. 9   d. 12

38. Which radical function for $f(x)$ has no inverse relation on $[1, 4]$?

    a. $\sqrt[3]{x - 7}$ b. $\sqrt{5 - x}$ c. $\sqrt{x}$ d. $\sqrt{x - 5}$

7 Approximation Methods

Iteration

An *iteration* is one step in a repeated process and can be easily programmed. You have seen iterations of a recursion formula used with complex numbers to obtain fractals such as the Mandelbrot set. In early math classes, you may have also used an iterative process for finding square roots. The iterative formulas below for radicals can be proved using calculus.

If $a > 1$, $\sqrt{a}$ is approximately given by $x_{i+1} = \frac{1}{2}x_i + \frac{a}{2x_i}$.

Moreover $\sqrt[n]{a}$ is approximated by $x_{i+1} = \frac{n-1}{n}x_i + \frac{a}{nx_i^{n-1}}$

where x_1 is an initial estimate of $\sqrt{a}$ or $\sqrt[n]{a}$.

EXAMPLE 1   Apply the iteration formula three times on the initial estimate to find an approximation for $\sqrt{5}$.

Answer

$\sqrt{5}$ is between 2 and 3. Let $x_1 = 2$.	1. Set the initial estimate, x_1.
$x_2 = \frac{1}{2}(2) + \frac{5}{2(2)} = 1 + \frac{5}{4} = \frac{9}{4} = 2.25$	2. Apply the iteration formula, using $x_1 = 2$ and $a = 5$ to get the second estimate.
$x_3 = \frac{1}{2}\left(\frac{9}{4}\right) + \frac{5}{2\left(\frac{9}{4}\right)} = \frac{9}{8} + \frac{10}{9} = \frac{161}{72} = 2.236\overline{1}$	3. Use the result for x_2 to find x_3.
$x_4 = \frac{1}{2}(2.236) + \frac{5}{2(2.236)} = 2.236067979$	4. To calculate x_4 round x_3 to 3 places. The same result occurs, rounded or not.

Check the accuracy with your calculator. The estimate is accurate to eight decimal places after only three iterations.

Of course, using a calculator to check the accuracy defeats the purpose of such a method. The goal is to obtain desired accuracy in order to program the calculator. This means that we need to know how good the estimate is without depending on the correct value obtained by some other method. You can tell quickly by comparing estimates from successive iterations. As soon as you compute x_4, you can see that x_3 was correct to three decimal places. To see how good x_4 is, simply compute x_5. You can obtain any desired degree of accuracy by performing further iterations.

EXAMPLE 2   Find $\sqrt[3]{75}$ accurate to nine decimal places.

Answer

$\sqrt[3]{75}$ is between 4 and 5. Let $x_1 = 4$.	1. Set the initial estimate at 4.
$x_2 = \frac{2}{3}(4) + \frac{75}{3(4)^2} \approx 4.229166667$	2. Apply the formula with $x_1 = 4$, $n = 3$, and $a = 75$ to calculate x_2. The value of x_1 was accurate to the nearest integer.
$x_3 = \frac{2}{3}(4.2292) + \frac{75}{3(4.2292)^2} \approx 4.217197551$	3. Find x_3; note that the first decimal place has stabilized.
$x_4 = \frac{2}{3}(4.217197) + \frac{75}{3(4.217197)^2} \approx 4.217163327$	4. By x_4, the fourth decimal place is now accurate.
$x_5 = \frac{2}{3}(4.2171633) + \frac{75}{3(4.2171633)^2} \approx 4.217163327$	5. After the fifth iteration it is accurate to nine decimal places.

$\sqrt[3]{75} \approx 4.217163327$

▶ Exercises

Find the third approximation, x_3, from the formulas for the following radicals.

1. $\sqrt{33}$ 2. $\sqrt[4]{29}$

Approximate each radical to nine decimal places using iterative methods.

3. $\sqrt{51}$ 4. $\sqrt[5]{200}$

Consider the iterative formula $x_{i+1} = x_i + x_{i-1}$.

5. If $x_1 = x_2 = 1$, find x_{10}. Do you recall the name for this pattern?

BLAISE PASCAL

Blaise Pascal, born June 19, 1623, was the son of Etîenne Pascal, an able mathematician for whom the limaçon of Pascal is named. Etîenne kept his son away from mathematical studies, but at the age of 12, Blaise found references to geometry and asked his father what the term meant.

Based only on his father's explanation, young Pascal began to prove theorems in geometry. He figured out for himself that the sum of the measures of the angles of a triangle is 180°. This convinced his father that Blaise should develop his talent, so he provided him with a copy of Euclid's *Elements*, thus motivating young Blaise to study more.

Pascal made a number of important new discoveries in his early years. At 16, he discovered Pascal's theorem, which guarantees that points *A*, *B*, and *C* (formed by intersections of diagonals of adjacent quadrilaterals)

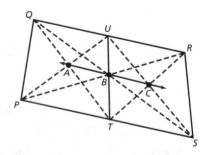

are collinear. The theorem was published in 1640 as "Essai pour les Coniques" (Essay on the Conics). At 18 he invented the world's first computing machine, the forerunner of modern calculators. At 25 (1648) he demonstrated the law of atmospheric pressure by sending a column of mercury with his brother-in-law, Mr. Périer, to the top of the Puy de Dôme. Pascal later repeated the experiment himself after he moved to Paris.

From the age of 17, Pascal suffered from acute dyspepsia. His health problems included digestive problems, temporary paralysis, insomnia, bad teeth, and a brain lesion, eventually culminating in convulsions and death at the age of 39 on August 19, 1662. However, he had not let these problems hinder his work or embitter him against God.

Pascal's spiritual life apparently began at 23, when he became involved with the Jansenists. This group shared certain important characteristics with the Protestants: they emphasized the need for moral absolutes and moral living as well as the impossibility of doing so without God's help. Pascal's Christian masterpiece of French literature, *Pénsees*, was written three years before the Jansenists were declared heretical by papal decree. Three years after the decree, he vigorously attacked the Jesuits with his satire *The Provincial Letters*.

Pascal recognized God's sovereignty over his life. Once his lead horses bolted and ran off the side of a bridge. The carriage did not follow because the connections from horse to carriage had broken. Pascal knew God had protected him, and it strengthened his determination to live for God. Another time God used circumstances to encourage Pascal to write a treatise on the cycloid. Pascal had a desire to keep God first and he would not have pursued his initial thoughts on this curve if he had not first been encouraged by God's providence.

Pascal is best known for "Pascal's triangle" (see *Algebra 2 for Christian Schools*, p. 552), which did not originate with him but which he used frequently, especially in his development of the theory of probability. This theory was developed through his correspondence with Pierre de Fermat, both men sharing the honor of discovery. It is fitting that God would use a man like Blaise Pascal to show that even those things which appear to be "chance" events have an order.

Pascal recognized God's sovereignty over his life.

7.3 Polar Form

The polar coordinates of a point (r, θ) consist of its distance from the pole, r, and the angle, θ, from the polar axis to the terminal ray containing the point. The r and θ from the polar graph relate to complex numbers as the modulus and argument, respectively.

Does this Julia set correspond to a point in the interior or exterior of the Mandelbrot set?

In the last section you learned to write complex numbers in standard form, $a + bi$, or with rectangular coordinates, (a, b). You will now convert the rectangular coordinates to polar coordinates to obtain the polar form of a complex number.

Recall the conversion formulas from Chapter 6 for obtaining the polar coordinates (r, θ) from the rectangular coordinates (x, y) and vice versa.

$$r = \sqrt{x^2 + y^2} \text{ and } \theta = \tan^{-1} \frac{y}{x}$$
$$x = r \cos \theta \text{ and } y = r \sin \theta$$

Rectangular coordinates of complex numbers are changed to polar coordinates by using similar conversion formulas.

$$r = \sqrt{a^2 + b^2} \text{ and } \theta = \tan^{-1} \frac{b}{a}.$$

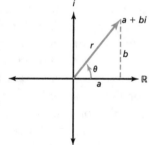

Likewise, to convert from polar form to standard form, use $a = r \cos \theta$ and $b = r \sin \theta$. By substituting these formulas into the rectangular form of a complex number, you obtain the *polar form* of the complex number.

$$a + bi$$
$$r \cos \theta + (r \sin \theta)(i)$$
$$r(\cos \theta + i \sin \theta)$$

Because this form occurs so often, it is commonly abbreviated as

$$r \text{ cis } \theta.$$

To change the polar form of a complex number to rectangular form, determine the cosine and sine values for θ and simplify.

EXAMPLE 1 Change $2 + 2\sqrt{3}i$ to polar form.

Answer

$r = \sqrt{a^2 + b^2}$	$\theta = \tan^{-1} \frac{b}{a}$	1. Find r and θ.
$r = \sqrt{2^2 + (2\sqrt{3})^2}$		
$r = \sqrt{4 + 12}$	$\theta = \tan^{-1} \frac{2\sqrt{3}}{2}$	
$r = \sqrt{16}$	$\theta = \tan^{-1} \sqrt{3}$	
$r = 4$	$\theta = \frac{\pi}{3}$	

$$r(\cos \theta + i \sin \theta) = 4\left(\cos \frac{\pi}{3} + i \sin \frac{\pi}{3}\right)$$ 2. Write in polar form.
$$= 4 \text{ cis } \frac{\pi}{3}$$

EXAMPLE 2 Change $\frac{1}{2}\left(\cos \frac{\pi}{6} + i \sin \frac{\pi}{6}\right)$ to rectangular form.

Answer

$\frac{1}{2}\left(\cos \frac{\pi}{6} + i \sin \frac{\pi}{6}\right)$

$\frac{1}{2} \cos \frac{\pi}{6} + \frac{1}{2} i \sin \frac{\pi}{6}$	1. Use the distributive property.
$\frac{1}{2}\left(\frac{\sqrt{3}}{2}\right) + \frac{1}{2}\left(\frac{1}{2}\right)i$	2. Determine the sine and cosine of θ.
$\frac{\sqrt{3}}{4} + \frac{1}{4}i$	3. Write in standard form.

Use caution when θ is greater than $\frac{\pi}{2}$. Remember that the cosine is negative in the second and third quadrants and the sine is negative in the third and fourth quadrants. Study the following example.

EXAMPLE 3 Change $3\left(\text{cis } \frac{3\pi}{4}\right)$ to rectangular form.

Answer $3\left(\text{cis } \frac{3\pi}{4}\right)$

$3\left(\cos \frac{3\pi}{4} + i \sin \frac{3\pi}{4}\right)$	1. Change abbreviated form to full polar form and distribute r.
$3 \cos \frac{3\pi}{4} + 3i \sin \frac{3\pi}{4}$	
$3\left(\frac{-\sqrt{2}}{2}\right) + 3\left(\frac{\sqrt{2}}{2}\right)i$	2. Since $\frac{3\pi}{4}$ is in quadrant II, the cosine is negative and the sine is positive.
$\frac{-3\sqrt{2}}{2} + \frac{3\sqrt{2}}{2}i$	3. Write in standard form.

EXAMPLE 4   Change $-1 - 4i$ to polar form.

Answer

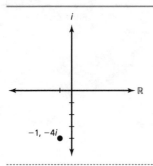

1. Make a quick sketch of the point in rectangular form. Notice that the point lies in the third quadrant. Therefore, θ must be a third quadrant angle $(180° < \theta < 270°)$.

$r = \sqrt{a^2 + b^2}$
$\quad = \sqrt{(-1)^2 + (-4)^2}$
$\quad = \sqrt{1 + 16}$
$\quad = \sqrt{17}$

2. Find r.

$\theta = \tan^{-1} \frac{-4}{-1} = \tan^{-1} 4$
$\alpha \approx 76.0°$ or 1.33 radians
$\theta \approx 76 + 180 = 256°$ or $1.33 + \pi \approx 4.47$ radians

3. Be careful to find the angle in the correct quadrant. Refer to your sketch. First determine the reference angle (α) and then use it to find θ.

$\sqrt{17}(\cos 4.47 + i \sin 4.47)$
$\sqrt{17}$ cis 4.47

4. Write the polar form. In polar form, θ is usually given in radians.

It is fairly easy to find the product or quotient of complex numbers in polar form. Two formulas will be developed here to help you.

Let two complex numbers be

$$r_1(\cos \theta_1 + i \sin \theta_1) \text{ and } r_2(\cos \theta_2 + i \sin \theta_2)$$

The product is

$$r_1(\cos \theta_1 + i \sin \theta_1) \, r_2(\cos \theta_2 + i \sin \theta_2)$$

$$= r_1 r_2(\cos \theta_1 + i \sin \theta_1)(\cos \theta_2 + i \sin \theta_2)$$

$$= r_1 r_2(\cos \theta_1 \cos \theta_2 + i \cos \theta_1 \sin \theta_2 + i \sin \theta_1 \cos \theta_2 + i^2 \sin \theta_1 \sin \theta_2)$$

$$= r_1 r_2[(\cos \theta_1 \cos \theta_2 + i^2 \sin \theta_1 \sin \theta_2) + (i \cos \theta_1 \sin \theta_2 + i \sin \theta_1 \cos \theta_2)]$$

$$= r_1 r_2[(\cos \theta_1 \cos \theta_2 - \sin \theta_1 \sin \theta_2) + i(\cos \theta_1 \sin \theta_2 + \sin \theta_1 \cos \theta_2)]$$

$$= r_1 r_2[\cos (\theta_1 + \theta_2) + i \sin (\theta_1 + \theta_2)]$$

The trigonometric sum identities were used to obtain the last step of the product formula. The derivation of the quotient formula is similar, but uses the trigonometric difference identities and the Pythagorean identity $(\cos^2 \theta + \sin^2 \theta = 1)$. The first step is to rationalize the denominator (use the conjugate of the denominator to write a form of 1).

$$\frac{r_1(\cos \theta_1 + i \sin \theta_1)}{r_2(\cos \theta_2 + i \sin \theta_2)}$$

$$= \frac{r_1(\cos \theta_1 + i \sin \theta_1)}{r_2(\cos \theta_2 + i \sin \theta_2)} \cdot \frac{(\cos \theta_2 - i \sin \theta_2)}{(\cos \theta_2 - i \sin \theta_2)}$$

$$= \frac{r_1}{r_2}\left(\frac{\cos \theta_1 \cos \theta_2 - i \cos \theta_1 \sin \theta_2 + i \sin \theta_1 \cos \theta_2 - i^2 \sin \theta_1 \sin \theta_2}{\cos^2 \theta_2 - i^2 \sin^2 \theta_2} \right)$$

$$= \frac{r_1}{r_2}\left[\frac{(\cos \theta_1 \cos \theta_2 + \sin \theta_1 \sin \theta_2) + i(\sin \theta_1 \cos \theta_2 - \cos \theta_1 \sin \theta_2)}{\cos^2 \theta_2 + \sin^2 \theta_2} \right]$$

$$= \frac{r_1}{r_2}[\cos (\theta_1 - \theta_2) + i \sin (\theta_1 - \theta_2)]$$

In summary,

$$(r_1 \text{ cis } \theta_1)(r_2 \text{ cis } \theta_2) = r_1 r_2 \text{ cis } (\theta_1 + \theta_2)$$

$$\frac{r_1 \text{ cis } \theta_1}{r_2 \text{ cis } \theta_2} = \frac{r_1}{r_2} \text{ cis } (\theta_1 - \theta_2)$$

The following example applies these formulas.

EXAMPLE 5   Find the product and the quotient of $5\left(\cos \frac{\pi}{4} + i \sin \frac{\pi}{4}\right)$ and $3\left(\cos \frac{\pi}{6} + i \sin \frac{\pi}{6}\right)$.

Answer

$5 \text{ cis } \frac{\pi}{4} \cdot 3 \text{ cis } \frac{\pi}{6} = 5 \cdot 3 \text{ cis } \left(\frac{\pi}{4} + \frac{\pi}{6}\right)$ 1.   Find the product by applying
$\qquad\qquad\qquad\quad = 15 \text{ cis } \frac{5\pi}{12}$ the product formula.

$\dfrac{5 \text{ cis } \frac{\pi}{4}}{3 \text{ cis } \frac{\pi}{6}} = \frac{5}{3} \text{ cis } \left(\frac{\pi}{4} - \frac{\pi}{6}\right)$ 2.   Find the quotient by apply-
$\qquad\qquad = \frac{5}{3} \text{ cis } \frac{\pi}{12}$ ing the quotient formula.

▶ A. Exercises

Change each complex number to polar form.

1. $-1 + i$

2. $4i$

3. 9

4. $\frac{\sqrt{3}}{4} - \frac{1}{4}i$

5. $-\sqrt{2} - \sqrt{2}i$

6. $-3 - 3i$

7. $-6i$

8. $\frac{\sqrt{3}}{2} + \frac{3}{2}i$

9. $4 - 3i$

10. $6 + i$

Change each complex number to rectangular form.

11. $3\left(\cos \frac{\pi}{2} + i \sin \frac{\pi}{2}\right)$

12. $5\left(\cos \frac{5\pi}{4} + i \sin \frac{5\pi}{4}\right)$

13. $12\left(\cos \frac{5\pi}{3} + i \sin \frac{5\pi}{3}\right)$

14. $2(\cos 1.7 + i \sin 1.7)$

15. $5(\cos 2 + i \sin 2)$

▶ B. Exercises

Perform the indicated operation with each pair of numbers in two ways. First, perform the operation using rectangular form; then use polar form. You can change each rectangular-form answer to polar form to check the answer.

16. $(1 + i)(1 - i)$

17. $(\sqrt{3} + i)(2 - 2i)$

18. $3\sqrt{2}\left(\cos \frac{5\pi}{6} + i \sin \frac{5\pi}{6}\right) \div \sqrt{2}\left(\cos \frac{\pi}{4} + i \sin \frac{\pi}{4}\right)$

19. $3\left(\cos \frac{\pi}{6} + i \sin \frac{\pi}{6}\right) \cdot 4\left(\cos \frac{7\pi}{6} + i \sin \frac{7\pi}{6}\right)$

20. $4(\cos 1.5 + i \sin 1.5) \div 8(\cos 0.8 + i \sin 0.8)$

▶ C. Exercises

21. Find $\dfrac{\left(3 \operatorname{cis} \frac{\pi}{3}\right)\left(5 \operatorname{cis} \frac{\pi}{6}\right)}{0.5 \operatorname{cis} \frac{\pi}{2}}$

22. Convert $z_1 = -1 - i$ and $z_2 = -4 + 4\sqrt{3}i$ to polar form, and compute $(z_1 z_2)^2$ in polar form. Convert the answer to rectangular form.

⩓ Dominion Modeling

The shades of yellow and orange in the exterior of the Mandelbrot set (shown in Section 7.2) depend on the number of iterations required for the modulus to exceed 2. Since it may require dozens or hundreds of iterations, a program can be helpful.

```
        Disp "KREAL"
        Input A
        Disp "KIMAG"
        Input B
        0→X:0→Y:0→I:0→N
        While N≤2
        X²−Y²+A→Z
        2*X*Y+B→Y
        Z→X
        I+1→I
        √(X²+Y²)→N
        Disp N
        End
        Disp I-1
(TI-83 Plus program)
```

Using $k = a + bi$ with $a = -0.5$, can you find b so that z_n exceeds 2 after the number of iterations given (or shortly thereafter).

23. 10 iterations

24. 25 iterations

25. 50 iterations

26. Find the points on the graph of the Mandelbrot set. What do you notice about the color scheme in the exterior of the set?

■Cumulative Review

Solve the following equations for $0 \le x < 2\pi$.

27. $3 \sin^2 x + 3 \sin x - 6 = 0$

28. $3 \tan^2 2x - 1 = 0$

29. $2 \sec x = 5$

30. Which complex number is farther from the origin: $1 - 5i$ or $4 + 3i$?

31. If $f(x)$ and $g(x)$ are both constant functions, what is the composition (give both possible orders)?

When asked about his age, the 19th century mathematician Augustus DeMorgan replied, "I was x years old in the year x^2." When was he born? Would anyone born in the 20th or 21st century be able to repeat his statement? Can similar statements involving higher powers ever be made in the 21st century?

7.4 Powers and Roots of Complex Numbers

Finding a power of a complex number such as $(-1 + i)^4$ is much easier in polar form. De Moivre's theorem enables you to find powers with less difficulty. The proof requires mathematical induction, which you will learn later. However, the following instances will show you the basic idea.

Consider raising a complex number in polar form to the second power. Apply the product property from the previous section.

$$[r(\cos \theta + i \sin \theta)]^2 = [r(\cos \theta + i \sin \theta)][r(\cos \theta + i \sin \theta)]$$
$$= r^2[\cos (\theta + \theta) + i \sin (\theta + \theta)]$$
$$= r^2(\cos 2\theta + i \sin 2\theta)$$

Now consider the third power.

$$[r(\cos \theta + i \sin \theta)]^3 = [r(\cos \theta + i \sin \theta)]^2[r(\cos \theta + i \sin \theta)]$$
$$= [r^2(\cos 2\theta + i \sin 2\theta)][r(\cos \theta + i \sin \theta)]$$
$$= r^2r[\cos (2\theta + \theta) + i \sin (2\theta + \theta)]$$
$$= r^3(\cos 3\theta + i \sin 3\theta)$$

You should see that the fourth power will be $r^4(\cos 4\theta + i \sin 4\theta)$ or r^4 cis 4θ. DeMoivre's theorem summarizes the general case for the nth power of a complex number.

> **DeMoivre's Theorem**
> $[r(\cos \theta + i \sin \theta)]^n = r^n(\cos n\theta + i \sin n\theta)$ or r^n cis $n\theta$, where $n \in \mathbb{Z}$.

EXAMPLE 1   Find $(-1 + i)^4$.

Answer

$(-1 + i)^4$

$r = \sqrt{(-1)^2 + 1^2} = \sqrt{2}$

$\theta = \tan^{-1} \frac{1}{-1} = \tan^{-1} -1 = \frac{3\pi}{4}$

$(-1 + i) = \sqrt{2}$ cis $\frac{3\pi}{4}$

1. Change the complex number to polar form. Notice θ is a 2nd quadrant angle.

$$(-1 + i)^4 = \left[\sqrt{2} \text{ cis } \frac{3\pi}{4}\right]^4$$

2. Apply DeMoivre's theorem to find the answer in polar form.

$$= (\sqrt{2})^4 \text{ cis } 4\left(\frac{3\pi}{4}\right)$$

$$= 4 \text{ cis } 3\pi$$

$$= 4 \text{ cis } \pi$$

3. Be sure to express θ as an angle in the interval $[0, 2\pi)$.

$$= 4(\cos \pi + i \sin \pi)$$

4. Change the answer back to rectangular form.

$$= 4(-1 + i(0))$$

$$= (4)(-1)$$

$$= -4$$

DeMoivre's theorem holds for exponents that are rational numbers as well as integers. Since $a^{\frac{1}{n}} = \sqrt[n]{a}$ and $\left(\frac{1}{n}\right)\theta = \frac{\theta}{n}$, the following corollary permits you to find the principal nth root of a complex number.

Corollary 7.5

$[r(\cos \theta + i \sin \theta)]^{\frac{1}{n}} = \sqrt[n]{r}\left(\cos \frac{\theta}{n} + i \sin \frac{\theta}{n}\right)$, where $n \in \mathbb{Z}$.

How many roots does a complex number have? The principal square root of 1 is 1, but -1 is also a square root of 1. A number has two square roots: its principal root and another root. Furthermore, every number has three cube roots, four fourth roots, five fifth roots, and so on. Generalizing, a complex number has n nth roots, some real and some imaginary. The formula above gives the principal nth root (the nth root in the first quadrant closest to zero).

Since adding multiples of 2π to θ does not change the angle, the n roots can be found using the angles $\theta + 2\pi k$ ($k = 0, 1, 2, \ldots, n - 1$). If you are taking the fourth root, the angles used in the equation above will be $\theta, \theta + 2\pi, \theta + 4\pi$, and $\theta + 6\pi$ (where $k = 0, 1, 2, 3$). Each of these angle measures are then divided by n as indicated in the corollary. Using these angle values will give the four roots evenly divided about the circle from 0 to 2π. This equal spacing of roots occurs for all complex numbers regardless of the index of the root.

Theorem 7.6

$\sqrt[n]{r(\cos \theta + i \sin \theta)} = \sqrt[n]{r}\left(\cos \frac{\theta + 2k\pi}{n} + i \sin \frac{\theta + 2k\pi}{n}\right)$,

where $k = 0, 1, 2, \ldots, n - 1$.

EXAMPLE 2   Find $\sqrt[3]{i}$.

Answer

$\sqrt[3]{i} = i^{\frac{1}{3}}$	1. Change the radical form to fractional exponent form.
$r = \sqrt{0^2 + 1^2} = 1$ $\theta = \tan^{-1}\frac{1}{0}$; tan is undefined at $\frac{\pi}{2}$. $i = 1 \operatorname{cis} \frac{\pi}{2} = \operatorname{cis} \frac{\pi}{2}$	2. Change the complex number to polar form.
$i^{\frac{1}{3}} = \left[1 \operatorname{cis} \frac{\pi}{2} \right]^{\frac{1}{3}}$ $= 1^{\frac{1}{3}} \operatorname{cis} \frac{\frac{\pi}{2}}{3}$ $= \operatorname{cis} \frac{\pi}{6}$	3. Find the principal cube root.
$= \cos \frac{\pi}{6} + i \sin \frac{\pi}{6}$ $= \frac{\sqrt{3}}{2} + \frac{1}{2}i$	4. Find the complex number in rectangular form. This is the principal cube root.
$i^{\frac{1}{3}} = 1^{\frac{1}{3}} \operatorname{cis} \frac{\frac{\pi}{2} + 2\pi}{3}$ $= 1 \operatorname{cis} \frac{5\pi}{6}$ $= \cos \frac{5\pi}{6} + i \sin \frac{5\pi}{6}$ $= -\frac{\sqrt{3}}{2} + \frac{1}{2}i$	5. Find the other roots by adding multiples of 2π to the angle. Begin by letting $k = 1$ to find a second root. Express the root in rectangular form.
$i^{\frac{1}{3}} = 1^{\frac{1}{3}} \operatorname{cis} \frac{\frac{\pi}{2} + 4\pi}{3}$ $= \operatorname{cis} \frac{9\pi}{6} = \operatorname{cis} \frac{3\pi}{2}$ $= \cos \frac{3\pi}{2} + i \sin \frac{3\pi}{2}$ $= 0 + (-1)i$ $= -i$	6. Add $2(2\pi) = 4\pi$. This will give the third and last root, since adding $3(2\pi)$ will repeat the principal root. Express the root in rectangular form. (The three cube roots are evenly spaced around the circle of 2π.)

The three distinct cube roots of i are $\frac{\sqrt{3}}{2} + \frac{1}{2}i$, $-\frac{\sqrt{3}}{2} + \frac{1}{2}i$, and $-i$.

Always leave your answer in the same form as the problem unless a certain form is specified. If the problem is given in rectangular form, then you should convert your answers back to rectangular form. If the radical is given in polar form, you may leave your answers in polar form.

> *There is no branch of mathematics, however abstract, which may not some day be applied to phenomena of the real world.*
> —Nikolai Lobatchevsky
> (1792-1856)

EXAMPLE 3 Find $\sqrt[5]{32 \text{ cis } 50°}$.

Answer

$\sqrt[5]{32 \text{ cis } 50°} = \sqrt[5]{32} \text{ cis } \frac{50}{5}$ $= 2 \text{ cis } 10°$	1. Find the principal root.
2 cis 10° 2 cis 82° 2 cis 154° 2 cis 226° 2 cis 298°	2. Since the 5 roots are evenly spaced about the circle, 2π or 360°, determine how many degrees between each root. The roots are $\frac{360°}{5} = 72°$ apart. Add 72° to the argument repeatedly until you have $n = 5$ roots. Calculating the sixth one (2 cis 370°) goes over 360° and would repeat the principal root (2 cis 10°).

▶ A. Exercises

Use DeMoivre's theorem to find the following. Write the answer in rectangular form.

1. $(1 + i)^3$
2. $(1 + \sqrt{3}i)^4$
3. $(-4 + 4i)^3$

4. $(-2 - 2i)^5$
5. $(3 + 2i)^8$

Find the principal root of each complex number. Leave answers in polar form.

6. $\sqrt[5]{2\sqrt{3} + 2i}$
7. $\sqrt[3]{-4i}$
8. $\sqrt[4]{i}$

9. $\sqrt[3]{1 + i}$
10. $\sqrt{-1 + \sqrt{3}i}$

▶ B. Exercises

List the roots of the complex numbers in polar form.

11. $\sqrt{49 \text{ cis } 50°}$
12. $\sqrt[3]{125 \text{ cis } \frac{4\pi}{3}}$
13. $\sqrt[4]{81 \text{ cis } \frac{\pi}{2}}$

14. $\sqrt[5]{\text{cis } 65°}$
15. $\sqrt[6]{64 \text{ cis } 42°}$

16. Graph the roots found in Example 3 to verify that they are evenly spaced about a circle.

Find all the roots for the following complex numbers. Write your answers in rectangular form.

17. $\sqrt[4]{16}$
18. $\sqrt[3]{-i}$
19. $\sqrt{2i}$

20. $\sqrt[3]{1 + i}$
21. $\sqrt{3 - 3i}$

22. What angle would consecutive 12th roots of a number form?
23. Solve exercise 5 using the FOIL method.

▶ C. Exercises

24. Find $\sqrt[3]{\left(25 \text{ cis } \frac{\pi}{6}\right)^2}$.

25. Find $(2 - 5i)^{100}$ in polar form.

■ Cumulative Review

Solve the following equations.

26. $\dfrac{3x + 1}{x^2 - 11x + 24} + \dfrac{5}{x^2 - 9} = \dfrac{3x}{x^2 - 5x - 24}$

27. $\sqrt{x - 3} + \sqrt{x} = 8$

28. What solutions would have been extraneous if they had appeared as answers in exercise 26? Why?

29. In what domain must answers to exercise 27 fall to avoid extraneous solutions?

30. Solve $\ln x - \ln 8 = 7$.

7.5 Complex Numbers as Vectors

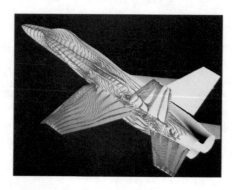

Physicists, navigators, pilots, and many other people use vectors in their work. Professionals in such occupations add and subtract vectors routinely and also find multiples of them. You can add vectors graphically as shown in Example 1.

Pressure-sensitive paint registers the force of winds on an airplane in a wind tunnel.

When the wind forces and directions are determined by using computer simulations or wind tunnels, the forces can be represented as vectors or complex numbers. Such representation is important in streamlining aircraft designs.

EXAMPLE 1   Add the vectors described by <5, 2> and <−3, 1>.

Answer

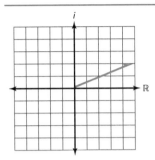

1. Graph the first vector on the complex plane, using the origin as the initial point.

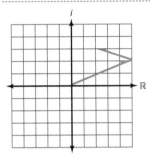

2. Graph the second vector with its initial point at the terminal point of the first vector.

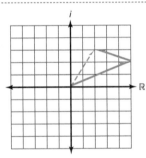

3. To find the sum, draw a vector from the origin to the terminal point of the second vector. Identify the coordinates of the answer vector from your graph, <2, 3>.

$(5 + 2i) + (−3 + i) = 2 + 3i$
$2 + 3i$ corresponds to the vector <2, 3>.

4. You can check your answer by taking the complex numbers represented by the vectors and adding them to see if the sum is the complex number represented by the answer vector.

The vector that is the final answer to a problem is called the *resultant vector*. The method of addition in Example 1 extends to adding any number of vectors. The method also permits you to perform subtraction by adding the opposite of the second vector.

EXAMPLE 2 Subtract <−3, 4> − <4, −1>.

Answer   <−3, 4> − <4, −1>

<−3, 4> + <−4, 1>   1. Change this to an addition problem by finding the opposite of <4, −1>.

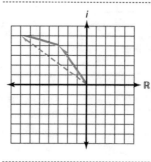

2. Add the vectors graphically and determine the resultant vector.

<−3, 4> − <4, −1> = <−7, 5>   3. Check the result mentally using complex numbers.

You can stretch or shrink the length of a vector without changing its direction if you multiply it by an appropriate constant. Multiplication of a vector by a constant (or scalar) is called *scalar multiplication*. The length of the vector increases if the scalar is a constant whose absolute value is greater than 1. It decreases if the constant has an absolute value less than 1. If the constant k is negative, then the direction of the vector reverses. In general, the scalar multiple of a vector is found as follows: k<*a, b*> = <*ka, kb*>.

EXAMPLE 3 Find 3<1, −2> and $-\frac{1}{2}$<5, 2> graphically.

Answer

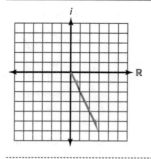

1. Graph the given vector. The scalar 3 has an absolute value greater than 1, so the vector will be three times as long and in the same direction as the original vector.

3<1, −2> = <3, −6>   2. Determine the resultant vector.

Continued ▶

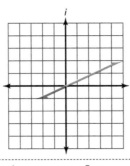

3. Graph the given vector. The scalar $-\frac{1}{2}$ will reverse the direction of the vector and reduce it to half its original length.

$-\frac{1}{2}<5, 2> = <-\frac{5}{2}, -1>$

4. Determine the resultant vector.

Remember that each vector corresponds to a complex number. The following table summarizes the operations on vectors.

Vector Operations	Complex Number Operations
$<a, b> + <c, d> = <a + c, b + d>$	$(a + bi) + (c + di) = (a + c) + (b + d)i$
$<a, b> - <c, d> = <a - c, b - d>$	$(a + bi) - (c + di) = (a - c) + (b - d)i$
$k<a, b> = <ka, kb>$	$k(a + bi) = ka + kbi$

A *unit vector* is a vector whose length is 1. There are many unit vectors, but the two you will use most are $<1, 0>$ and $<0, 1>$. These two vectors are represented by **i** and **j**.

$$\mathbf{i} = <1, 0> \qquad\qquad \mathbf{j} = <0, 1>$$

The vector **i** is called the *horizontal unit vector*, and **j** the *vertical unit vector*. Note that **i** is the vector representing the number 1, whereas the imaginary number *i* is represented by the vector **j**.

Every vector can be broken down (or *decomposed*) into horizontal and vertical *components*. Because any vector can be written as a sum of multiples of the two unit vectors, the vectors **i** and **j** form what is called the *basis* for the set of all vectors. Consider the vector corresponding to 4 + 7*i*. To find the components for this vector, drop a line from the terminal point of the vector perpendicular to the real axis and another line perpendicular to the imaginary axis.

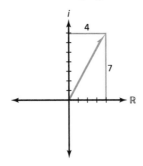

The horizontal component of 4 and the vertical component of 7 serve as the scalar multiples of the unit vectors in order to get the original vector as the sum. The horizontal component vector is <4, 0> and the vertical component vector is <0, 7>.

$$4\mathbf{i} + 7\mathbf{j} = 4<1, 0> + 7<0, 1> = <4, 0> + <0, 7> = <4, 7>$$

The complex number $4 + 7i$ corresponds to <4, 7> and thus to the sum $4\mathbf{i} + 7\mathbf{j}$. In general, any complex number can be expressed as the sum of the scalar products of the two unit vectors.

$$a + bi = <a, b> = a<1, 0> + b<0, 1> = a\mathbf{i} + b\mathbf{j}$$

▶ A. Exercises

Let $\mathbf{u} = <7, 3>$, $\mathbf{v} = <-6, 2>$, and $\mathbf{w} = <-1, -4>$. Perform the following operations graphically.

1. $\mathbf{u} + \mathbf{v}$
2. $\mathbf{w} - \mathbf{u}$
3. $\mathbf{u} + \mathbf{v} + \mathbf{w}$
4. $2\mathbf{w}$
5. $(\mathbf{v} + \mathbf{w}) - \mathbf{u}$

6. $\frac{1}{3}\mathbf{v}$
7. $-2\mathbf{w}$
8. $\mathbf{v} + \mathbf{w}$
9. $\mathbf{u} - \mathbf{w}$

▶ B. Exercises

Let $\mathbf{u} = <8, -5>$, $\mathbf{v} = <2, 6>$, and $\mathbf{w} = <0, 7>$. Perform the following operations.

10. $\mathbf{u} + \mathbf{w}$
11. $\mathbf{v} + \mathbf{u} + \mathbf{w}$
12. $6\mathbf{u}$

13. $\mathbf{v} - \mathbf{w}$
14. $\frac{-1}{2}\mathbf{v}$
15. $(\mathbf{u} + \mathbf{w}) - \mathbf{v}$

Write the following complex numbers as the sum of scalar multiples of unit vectors.

16. $7 + 2i$
17. $-4 - 9i$

18. $6 - 3i$
19. $-4 + 10i$

▶ C. Exercises

20. Prove that vector addition is commutative.
21. Use vectors to find a point P one-third of the way from $A(1 + 4i)$ to $B(6 + 6i)$.

⚙ Dominion Modeling

A Julia set can be obtained for any complex number k using the same recursion formula as was used for the Mandelbrot set. Exclude the point z_0 from the Julia set if the recursion formula results in $|z_n| > 2$. The remaining Dominion Modeling questions explore the relation between Julia sets and the Mandelbrot set.

22. The Julia set for $k = 0 + 0i$ appears below. Describe the set.

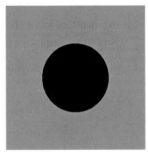

Julia set on $k = 0 + 0i$

23. How many iterations does it take for $|z_n| > 2$ if $k = 0 + 0.3i$? if $k = 0 + 0.6i$? Locate these points in relation to the Mandelbrot set.

Julia set on $k = 0 + 0.3i$

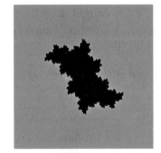

Julia set on $k = 0 + 0.6i$

■ Cumulative Review

24. Solve the equation $x^4 + 4x^3 - 29x^2 - 120x + 432 = 0$.

25. Graph the associated polynomial function for exercise 24.

26. If $\sin A = \frac{5}{7}$, $\sin B = \frac{5}{6}$, and A and B are 1st quadrant angles, find the exact values of $\sin (A + B)$, $\sin (A - B)$, $\sin 2A$, and $\sin \frac{A}{2}$.

27. Give any zeros or asymptotes: $f(x) = \frac{3x^2 - 9}{2x^2 - x - 1}$.

28. Graph the function in exercise 27.

7.6 Dot Products

Physics, engineering, electronics, chemistry, biology, and computer science depend to a large degree on one common tool. As you might suspect, the common tool for each of these sciences is mathematics. Of what use is a tool in the hands of someone who does not know what it does or is incapable of handling it? For any technical field, you must understand the tool that will be essential in your work—mathematics.

Another tool that every Christian must know and be able to use in his work is the Bible. No matter what occupation you have, the Bible should be your principal guidebook. You should have the desire that David had when he wrote in Psalm 119:15-16, "I will meditate in thy precepts, and have respect unto thy ways. I will delight myself in thy statutes: I will not forget thy word." Meditating on God's Word will allow you to develop understanding of your primary work tool, the Bible.

One mathematical tool related to vectors is the dot product.

Definition

Dot product The dot product of two vectors $\mathbf{u}$ and $\mathbf{v}$ is $\mathbf{u} \cdot \mathbf{v} = |\mathbf{u}||\mathbf{v}|\cos \theta$, where θ is the angle between $\mathbf{u}$ and $\mathbf{v}$, and $|\mathbf{u}|$ and $|\mathbf{v}|$ are the lengths of the respective vectors.

EXAMPLE 1 Find the dot product of $\mathbf{u}$ and $\mathbf{v}$ if $\mathbf{u} = <-3, 5>$, $\mathbf{v} = <1, 3>$, and $\theta = 49.4°$.

Answer $\mathbf{u} \cdot \mathbf{v} = |\mathbf{u}||\mathbf{v}| \cos \theta$

$|\mathbf{u}| = \sqrt{(-3)^2 + 5^2} = \sqrt{34}$ 1. Find $|\mathbf{u}|$ and $|\mathbf{v}|$.

$|\mathbf{v}| = \sqrt{1^2 + 3^2} = \sqrt{10}$

$\mathbf{u} \cdot \mathbf{v} = \sqrt{34}\sqrt{10} \cos 49.4°$ 2. Substitute the needed values
$= 12$ and calculate the dot product.

Notice that the dot product is an operation that matches two vectors to a unique real number. The dot-product formula can be written in terms of the real and imaginary parts of the vectors. This formula is derived below.

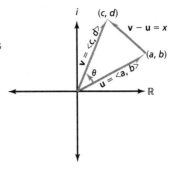

Let $\mathbf{u} = <a, b>$ and $\mathbf{v} = <c, d>$, and the angle between $\mathbf{u}$ and $\mathbf{v}$ be θ. Represent the vector joining their terminal points as $\mathbf{x}$. You can see that $\mathbf{u} + \mathbf{x} = \mathbf{v}$, so the vector $\mathbf{x}$ is the vector $\mathbf{v} - \mathbf{u}$. These three vectors form a triangle, so you can apply the law of cosines. (Since the formula uses vector lengths, it contains absolute value symbols representing their moduli.)

$$|\mathbf{v} - \mathbf{u}|^2 = |\mathbf{u}|^2 + |\mathbf{v}|^2 - 2|\mathbf{u}||\mathbf{v}|\cos\theta$$

$$|\mathbf{v} - \mathbf{u}|^2 - |\mathbf{u}|^2 - |\mathbf{v}|^2 = -2|\mathbf{u}||\mathbf{v}|\cos\theta$$

$$|\mathbf{u}|^2 + |\mathbf{v}|^2 - |\mathbf{v} - \mathbf{u}|^2 = 2|\mathbf{u}||\mathbf{v}|\cos\theta$$

$$\frac{|\mathbf{u}|^2 + |\mathbf{v}|^2 - |\mathbf{v} - \mathbf{u}|^2}{2} = |\mathbf{u}||\mathbf{v}|\cos\theta$$

From the definition of dot product, $|\mathbf{u}||\mathbf{v}|\cos\theta = \mathbf{u} \cdot \mathbf{v}$; therefore,

$$\frac{|\mathbf{u}|^2 + |\mathbf{v}|^2 - |\mathbf{v} - \mathbf{u}|^2}{2} = \mathbf{u} \cdot \mathbf{v}$$

But $|\mathbf{v} - \mathbf{u}|$ is the distance between (a, b) and (c, d); so by the distance formula

$$|\mathbf{v} - \mathbf{u}| = \sqrt{(c - a)^2 + (d - b)^2}, \quad |\mathbf{u}| = \sqrt{a^2 + b^2}, \text{ and } |\mathbf{v}| = \sqrt{c^2 + d^2}.$$

By substitution,

$$\mathbf{u} \cdot \mathbf{v} = \frac{\left(\sqrt{a^2 + b^2}\right)^2 + \left(\sqrt{c^2 + d^2}\right)^2 - \left[\sqrt{(c - a)^2 + (d - b)^2}\right]^2}{2}$$

$$= \frac{(a^2 + b^2) + (c^2 + d^2) - [(c - a)^2 + (d - b)^2]}{2}$$

$$= \frac{a^2 + b^2 + c^2 + d^2 - [c^2 - 2ac + a^2 + d^2 - 2bd + b^2]}{2}$$

$$= \frac{a^2 + b^2 + c^2 + d^2 - c^2 + 2ac - a^2 - d^2 + 2bd - b^2}{2}$$

$$= \frac{2ac + 2bd}{2}$$

$$= ac + bd$$

The following formula summarizes the dot product of two vectors in the plane where $\mathbf{u} = <a, b>$ and $\mathbf{v} = <c, d>$.

$$\mathbf{u} \cdot \mathbf{v} = ac + bd$$

EXAMPLE 2 Find $\mathbf{u} \cdot \mathbf{v}$ if $\mathbf{u} = <0, 4>$, $\mathbf{v} = <4\sqrt{3}, 4>$, and the angle between $\mathbf{v}$ and $\mathbf{u}$ is $60°$.

Answer

Method 1

$$|\mathbf{u}| = \sqrt{a^2 + b^2} \qquad |\mathbf{v}| = \sqrt{c^2 + d^2}$$
$$= \sqrt{0^2 + 4^2} \qquad\quad = \sqrt{(4\sqrt{3})^2 + 4^2}$$
$$= \sqrt{16} \qquad\qquad\quad = \sqrt{16(3) + 16}$$
$$= 4 \qquad\qquad\qquad = \sqrt{48 + 16}$$
$$= \sqrt{64}$$
$$= 8$$

1. Find $|\mathbf{v}|$ and $|\mathbf{u}|$.

$$\mathbf{u} \cdot \mathbf{v} = |\mathbf{u}||\mathbf{v}| \cos \theta$$
$$= 4 \cdot 8 \cos 60°$$
$$= 4 \cdot 8 \cdot \frac{1}{2}$$
$$= 16$$

2. Use the formula in the definition to find the dot product.

Method 2

$$\mathbf{u} = <a, b> = <0, 4>$$
$$\mathbf{v} = <c, d> = <4\sqrt{3}, 4>$$
$$\mathbf{u} \cdot \mathbf{v} = ac + bd$$
$$= 0(4\sqrt{3}) + 4(4)$$
$$= 0 + 16$$
$$= 16$$

Use the formula that involves the coordinates of the vector.

You can use either formula to find the dot product of two vectors. Examine the given information and decide which formula is appropriate.

Perpendicular vectors have a dot product of zero. Applying the definition yields the equation below. Since $\cos 90°$ equals **0**, the product will be **0**.

$$\mathbf{u} \cdot \mathbf{v} = |\mathbf{u}||\mathbf{v}|\cos 90°$$
$$= |\mathbf{u}||\mathbf{v}| \cdot 0$$
$$= 0$$

The converse is also true. If the dot product of two vectors is **0**, the vectors are perpendicular. If two vectors are perpendicular, they are said to be *orthogonal*.

EXAMPLE 3 Find a vector that is orthogonal to the vector $\mathbf{u} = <-3, 1>$.

Answer

$$\mathbf{u} \cdot \mathbf{v} = 0$$
$$\mathbf{u} \cdot \mathbf{v} = ac + bd$$
$$0 = -3c + 1d$$
$$3c = d$$

1. Let $\mathbf{v} = <c, d>$ be the desired vector. The dot product must be 0 if they are perpendicular.

Continued ▶

Let $c = 2$, then $d = 6$.   2. Choose any value for c and compute d.

<2, 6> is a vector orthogonal to **u**.

The dot product also permits you to find the angle, θ, between the two vectors. Since $\mathbf{u} \cdot \mathbf{v} = |\mathbf{u}||\mathbf{v}|\cos\theta$, it follows that $\cos\theta = \frac{\mathbf{u} \cdot \mathbf{v}}{|\mathbf{u}||\mathbf{v}|}$.

EXAMPLE 4 Find the angle between the vectors $\mathbf{u} = <-3, 4>$ and $\mathbf{v} = <1, 5>$.

Answer

$\mathbf{u} \cdot \mathbf{v} = ac + bd$ 1. Find the dot product.
$\phantom{\mathbf{u} \cdot \mathbf{v}} = (-3)(1) + (4)(5)$
$\phantom{\mathbf{u} \cdot \mathbf{v}} = -3 + 20$
$\phantom{\mathbf{u} \cdot \mathbf{v}} = 17$

$|\mathbf{u}| = \sqrt{a^2 + b^2}$ $|\mathbf{v}| = \sqrt{c^2 + d^2}$ 2. Find the lengths of the vectors.
$\phantom{|\mathbf{u}|} = \sqrt{(-3)^2 + (4)^2}$ $\phantom{|\mathbf{v}|} = \sqrt{1^2 + 5^2}$
$\phantom{|\mathbf{u}|} = \sqrt{9 + 16}$ $\phantom{|\mathbf{v}|} = \sqrt{1 + 25}$
$\phantom{|\mathbf{u}|} = \sqrt{25}$ $\phantom{|\mathbf{v}|} = \sqrt{26}$
$\phantom{|\mathbf{u}|} = 5$

$\cos\theta = \frac{\mathbf{u} \cdot \mathbf{v}}{|\mathbf{u}||\mathbf{v}|}$ 3. Substitute to find $\cos\theta$, and then find θ.
$\cos\theta = \frac{17}{5\sqrt{26}}$
$\cos\theta \approx 0.6668$
$\theta \approx 48°11'$

▶ A. Exercises

Find the dot products mentally. Identify any orthogonal vectors.

1. <2, 3> · <5, 7>
2. <-1, -4> · <2, -3>
3. <4, 8> · <4, -2>
4. <5, 2> · <-3, 4>
5. <1, 1> · <3, 3>
6. $<6, \frac{1}{2}> \cdot <\frac{1}{3}, -12>$
7. $<\frac{3}{5}, \frac{-4}{7}> \cdot <\frac{5}{6}, \frac{7}{8}>$
8. $<\sqrt{5}, \frac{10}{3}> \cdot <\sqrt{5}, \frac{1}{2}>$
9. $<7, \pi> \cdot <\frac{3}{5}, 4\sqrt{2}>$
10. **i** · **j**

▶ B. Exercises

Find **u · v**, given the following information. Round answers to the nearest tenth.

11. **u** = <5, 9>, **v** = <−3, −6>
12. **u** = <−6, −8>, **v** = <4, 9>
13. **u** = <0, 6>, **v** = <4, 3>
14. **u** = <5, 1>, **v** = <−2, 7>
15. |**u**| = 2, **v** = <7, 5>, θ = 31°
16. |**u**| = 4, |**v**| = 1, θ = 45°
17. **u** = <−2, 4>, |**v**| = 3, θ = 52°
18. **u** = <3, 0>, |**v**| = 3√2, θ = 45°

Find a vector that is orthogonal to the given vector.

19. **v** = <1, 7>
20. **v** = <2, 8>
21. **v** = <−7, 4>
22. **v** = <−3, −1>

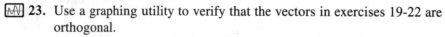 23. Use a graphing utility to verify that the vectors in exercises 19-22 are orthogonal.

Find the angle between the given vectors. Give answers to the nearest minute.

24. **u** = <1, 4>, **v** = <−3, −2>
25. **u** = <7, 6>, **v** = <2, 9>
26. **u** = <5, −8>, **v** = <9, 1>

▶ C. Exercises

27. What can be concluded about angle θ if **u · v** < 0?
28. Given **u** = <u_1, u_2>, **v** = <v_1, v_2>, and **w** = <w_1, w_2>, prove **u · (v + w) = u · v + u · w**. Express in words what the equation means.

▪ Cumulative Review

29. Solve $2^{3x+1} = 7$.
30. Solve $e^{\frac{x}{2}} = 4$.
31. Graph $x^2 - y^2 = 16$.
32. Give the polar form of all three cube roots of 8.
33. To the nearest degree, find the measures of the angles of a right triangle if the legs are 4 and 11 units long.

7.7 Applications of Vectors

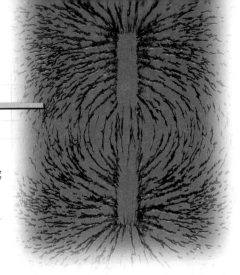

Vectors are very practical for representing paths. For example, if an airplane flies 100 miles west, the vector having a length of 100 units and pointing west provides a good representation. Compass directions (called *bearings*) are often used in such applications. Each bearing is an angle measured clockwise from due north.

Vectors represent the magnitude and directions of the magnetic force at each point. The farther from the bar magnet, the smaller the magnitude (weaker force). The alignments of the iron filings indicate directions.

EXAMPLE 1   An airplane flies due north 125 miles from Newark to Albany, then to Detroit, 450 miles due west. What is the plane's distance and bearing from its starting point?

Answer

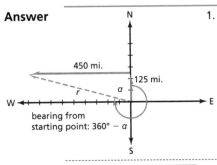

1. Represent the stages of the plane's journey as vectors and add them graphically.

$$r = \sqrt{(450)^2 + (125)^2}$$
$$\approx 467 \text{ mi.}$$
$$\tan \alpha = \frac{450}{125} \approx 3.6$$
$$\alpha \approx 74.5°$$

2. Find the length and direction of the resultant vector.

---

bearing = 360° − 74.5°
       = 285.5°

3. Convert the angle to a bearing (degrees clockwise from north).

The plane is 467 miles from its starting point at a bearing of 285.5° from its starting point.

Another useful vector is the velocity vector—representing an object's speed and direction. Often the velocity of an object depends on what you use for comparison. For example, a blimp's *air speed*—speed compared to the air around it—may be 20 mph; but if the blimp is sailing into a 15-mph headwind, its speed compared to the ground—the ground speed—is only $20 - 15 = 5$ mph. A vessel traveling through air (or water) directly with the wind (or current) has a ground velocity equal to the sum of its velocity and the velocity of the medium through which it travels. If traveling directly into the wind (or current), the ground velocity is the difference of the two velocities.

EXAMPLE 2 A wide river flows due south. A boat crosses the river traveling upstream at a bearing of 60° and at a speed of 30 knots. The speed of the current is 10 knots. What are the bearing and velocity of the boat as measured from the ground?

Answer

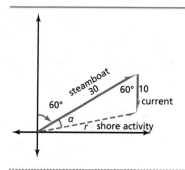

1. Represent these velocities as vectors and add them.

$r^2 = 30^2 + 10^2 - 2(30)(10) \cos 60°$

$r \approx 26.5$ knots

$\frac{\sin \alpha}{10} = \frac{\sin 60°}{26.5}$

$\sin \alpha = \frac{10 \sin 60°}{26.5}$

$\alpha = 19.1°$

2. Find the length and direction of the sum. Notice that the 60° angle and the angle opposite r in the triangle are alternate interior angles. Thus, they are both 60°. Use the law of cosines to find r and the law of sines to find α.

bearing $= 60° + 19.1° = 79.1°$

3. Translate the bearing. Remember velocity includes speed and direction.

The boat travels at a speed of 26.5 knots at a bearing of 79.1°.

EXAMPLE 3   A pilot plots his course from Fernwood to Glendale at a bearing of 65°. If the wind is 40 mph from 300°, at what compass heading and air speed should he fly to maintain a ground speed of 350 mph to compensate for the wind?

Answer

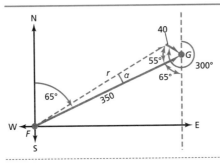

1. Represent the velocities as vectors. Note that the plane's heading must be more northerly than the destination so that when the wind pushes it from 300° the plane will be on course. Add the vectors.

$r^2 = 40^2 + 350^2 - 2(40)(350) \cos 55°$

$r \approx 329$

$\dfrac{\sin \alpha}{40} = \dfrac{\sin 55°}{329}$

$\sin \alpha = \dfrac{40 \sin 55°}{329}$

$\alpha \approx 6°$

bearing: $65 - 6 = 59°$

2. Find the length, r, and direction, α, of the vector.

The pilot must fly at an air speed of 329 mph with a compass heading of 59°.

Vectors can represent forces. If the sum of all the forces on an object is zero, then the forces are balanced and the object is either motionless or moving at a constant velocity. Weight is a force vector that points straight down, toward the center of the earth.

EXAMPLE 4   Two chains support a 10-pound sign so that it hangs motionless. The chains are each at an angle of 45° above the horizontal. The weight of the sign can be represented by a vector with a magnitude of 10 pounds pointing straight down. The chains exert a force upward along their lengths. What force does each chain exert?

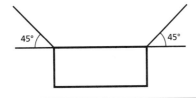

Continued ▶

Answer

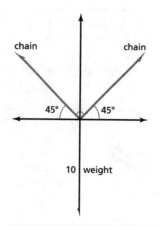

1. Represent the three forces as vectors.

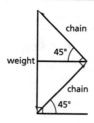

2. Arrange the vectors to show that they add to equal zero. (The terminal ray of the resultant vector ends at the origin.)

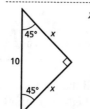

$$x^2 + x^2 = 10^2$$
$$2x^2 = 100$$
$$x^2 = 50$$
$$x \approx 7.07$$

3. Treat this arrangement as a right triangle, and use the Pythagorean theorem.

Each chain exerts a force of 7.07 pounds.

EXAMPLE 5 A 20-pound box of nails rests unmoving on a 30° ramp. Friction exerts a force up the ramp. The ramp itself exerts a force, called the normal force, on the box perpendicular to the ramp. What is the magnitude of this normal force?

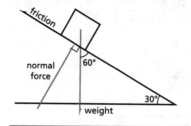

Continued ▶

Answer

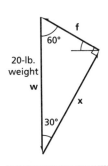

1. By first adding the normal vector **x** (the one perpendicular to the ramp) to the vertical weight vector **w**, then adding the friction force **f** to the sum a right triangle is formed. Since no movement has occurred, the sum of the forces is zero. **x** + **f** + **w** = 0.

$$\cos 30° = \frac{x}{20}$$
$$x = 20 \cos 30°$$
$$x = 17.32$$

2. Use right triangle trigonometry to find $|\mathbf{x}|$.

The ramp exerts a force of 17.32 pounds on the box of nails.

▶ A. Exercises

1. If the bearing of a ship is 287° sailing from Newport to Rockport, what should be the bearing on the return trip?

2. A helicopter flies 50 miles due south and then 80 miles due west. What bearing will return him to his point of origin?

3. A crane lifts a one-ton (2000-lb) block of granite straight up with constant speed. What force does the crane exert on the granite?

4. A fisherman reels in a trout in stages. Consider a moment when the trout is stationary. Suppose the force exerted by the trout is **t**, the force exerted by the fisherman is **f**, the force exerted by the current is **c**, and the force of the water resistance is **r**. Give an equation relating the forces.

▶ B. Exercises

5. A boy attempts to swim directly across a river at a speed of 3 mph. The river current flows at a speed of 4 mph. What is the boy's velocity as measured from the shore?

6. A boat sails 60 miles due east from the island of Unus to the island of Dosland, then 25 miles due south to Tres Island. How far is the boat from Unus? What is the boat's bearing from Unus?

7. A bush pilot flies 200 miles on a compass heading of 45° from the trading post to a small village. After leaving supplies, he flies 141 miles due south to a second village to leave supplies. How far and in what direction must he fly to arrive back at the trading post?

8. A boat leaves port and sails 50 miles due west to avoid a storm, then turns to a compass heading of 200° and proceeds 120 miles to its next port. If the storm had not altered the path of the steamer, the boat would have moved in a straight path to its new port. What distance and course would the boat have traveled?

9. A plane flies with an air velocity of 200 mph at a bearing of 225° through a 50-mph wind from the south. What is the plane's velocity as measured from the ground?

10. A 1-pound mailbox and platform are supported by a horizontal force of 0.5 pound and a diagonal force. What is the magnitude and direction of this diagonal force?

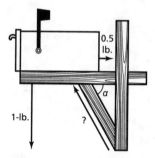

▶ C. Exercises

11. A 50-pound child sits on a tilted seesaw. The force of friction on the child is 30 pounds up the seesaw, and the seesaw exerts a force of 40 pounds on the child, perpendicular to its surface. At what angle is the seesaw tilted?

12. A 40-pound crate rests on a 30° ramp. The force of friction is up the ramp, and the force of the ramp is perpendicular to the ramp. What is the force of friction on the ramp?

⨉ Dominion Modeling

13. The Julia sets for $k = 0 + 0.6514i$ and $k = 0 + 0.75i$ appear below. Locate these points with respect to the Mandelbrot set (see p. 352). How many iterations are needed for $|z_n| > 2$?

Julia set on k = 0 + 0.6514i, just beyond the lake

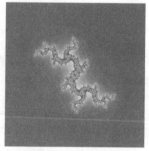

Julia set on k = 0 + 0.75i, to the right of the ball on top

14. The Julia sets for $k = 0 + 1i$ and for $k = 0 + 1.5i$ appear below. Locate these points with respect to the Mandelbrot set (see p. 352). How many iterations are needed for $|z_n| > 2$?

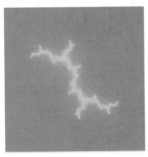
Julia set on k = 0 + 1i

Julia set on k = 0 + 1.5i

15. What do you notice about the Julia sets as the complex number moves from the origin up the imaginary axis?

Cumulative Review

16. Graph $f(y) = y^2 - 8y + 12$ and show the directrix and focus.
17. State the relationship between the area and the radius of a circle in terms of variation.
18. Suppose z varies directly with y and inversely with the square of x. Write the general equation of the variation. Determine k if $z = 0.04$ when $x = 10$ and $y = 8$, then find z when $x = 7$ and $y = 12$.

Let $\mathbf{u} = <4, 7>$ and $\mathbf{v} = <-1, 3>$, then find the following.

19. $2\mathbf{u} - 3\mathbf{v}$
20. $\mathbf{u} \cdot \mathbf{v}$

Math *and* Scripture

Philosophies of Math

What is the foundation or basis of math? The twentieth century saw at least four views of mathematics.

Four Philosophies of Math

1. *Platonists* said that mathematics is the order behind nature. Gifted individuals can have unmediated access to this cosmic knowledge. Christians such as Augustine have sometimes taken this order to be the Mind of God.
2. *Logicists* claimed that the foundation of math is symbolic logic.
3. *Formalists* said that the foundation of math is itself. Math is a game in which one manipulates symbols according to well-defined rules. It has and needs no basis other than itself.
4. *Intuitionists* wrote that the justification of math is the human intuition; anything fundamentally non-intuitive is not true. (This does *not* mean that anything difficult is not true!) For instance, since infinity is not intuitive, it cannot be an actual number.

While Christians have sometimes endorsed some of these views, these views fail to be fully *Christian* since they make the redemptive work of Christ irrelevant. Taken alone, these views assume that Christ's reason for coming to earth is unimportant for mathematics. Therefore, each is a version of humanism.

Classify each quote according to the philosophy it reflects.

1. Out of nothing I have created a strange new universe [non-euclidean geometry.] —János Bolyai
2. Mathematics is a game played according to certain simple rules with meaningless marks on paper. —David Hilbert

3. I believe that mathematical reality lies outside us, that our function is to discover or observe it, and that the theorems which we prove, and which we describe grandiloquently as our "creations," are simply the notes of our observations. —G. H. Hardy, 1941

4. The fact that all Mathematics is Symbolic Logic is one of the greatest discoveries of our age; and when this fact has been established, the remainder of the principles of mathematics consists in the analysis of Symbolic Logic itself. —Bertrand Russell

5. Mathematics is man's own handiwork, subject only to the limitations imposed by the laws of thought . . . we have overcome the notion that mathematical truths have an existence independent and apart from our own minds. It is even strange to us that such a notion could ever have existed. —E. Kasner and J. Newman, 1940

6. There exists, if I am not mistaken, an entire world which is the totality of mathematical truths, to which we have access only with our mind, just as a world of physical reality exists, the one like the other independent of ourselves, both of divine creation. —Charles Hermite

7. God made the integers; all else is the work of man. —Leopold Kronecker

8. The knowledge at which geometry aims is the knowledge of the eternal. —Plato

9. In my opinion, a mathematician, in so far as he is a mathematician, need not preoccupy himself with philosophy. —Henri Lebesgue

10. The chief aim of all investigations of the external world should be to discover the rational order and harmony which has been imposed on it by God and which He revealed to us in the language of mathematics. —Johannes Kepler

The Word of Christ, the Bible, is our only foundation. Mathematics is no exception.

MAXIMIZING
Quote the words of Christ to show that it is impossible to do mathematics without Him.

Vital Sines

IN WHOM ARE HID all the treasures of wisdom and knowledge. ❧

COL. 2:3

Chapter 7 Review

1. Simplify $(2 + 3i) - (5 - 2i)$.
2. Simplify $i - i^3(5i + 6)$.
3. Factor $49x^2 + 1$.
4. Solve $x(7x - 5) = -1$.
5. Find α and β if $\frac{3 + 4i}{2 - i} = \alpha + \beta i$.
6. What is the argument $(0 \le \theta < 2\pi)$ of $-\sqrt{3} + 3i$?
7. What is the modulus of $-\sqrt{3} + 3i$?
8. If the real part of a certain complex number is -1 and its modulus is 4, what is the imaginary part?
9. What is the magnitude of the vector $v = {<}{-7}, 3{>}$?
10. Convert $-8 - 15i$ to polar form.
11. Convert $8\left(\cos \frac{5\pi}{3} + i \sin \frac{5\pi}{3}\right)$ to rectangular form.
12. Convert 12 cis $\frac{\pi}{3}$ to rectangular form.
13. Express the following sum in rectangular form: $3\left(\cos \frac{3\pi}{4} + i \sin \frac{3\pi}{4}\right) + \left(\frac{\sqrt{2}}{2} - \frac{\sqrt{2}}{2}i\right)$.
14. Multiply 4 cis $\pi \cdot 3$ cis $\frac{5\pi}{3}$.
15. Find $(1 - i)^4$ in rectangular form.
16. Find $\left(\frac{-\sqrt{3}}{2} - \frac{1}{2}i\right)^6$ in rectangular form.
17. Find $\sqrt[4]{-1}$ in rectangular form.
18. Find $\sqrt[3]{8i}$ in polar form.
19. Find $\left(-1 + \sqrt{3}i\right)^6$ in polar form.
20. If $\mathbf{u} = {<}3, -5{>}$ and $\mathbf{w} = {<}{-6}, 1{>}$, find the following:
    a. $\mathbf{u} + \mathbf{w}$ b. $\mathbf{w} - \mathbf{u}$ c. $6\mathbf{u} + 2\mathbf{w}$
21. Write in polar form the complex number represented by
    a. $\mathbf{i} - \mathbf{j}$ b. $15i + 15\sqrt{3}j$ c. $-3j$
22. Find $\mathbf{u} \cdot \mathbf{v}$ if $\mathbf{u} = {<}4, 4{>}$ and $\mathbf{v} = {<}{-1}, -6{>}$.
23. Find the angle formed by $\mathbf{u} = 2 + 2\sqrt{3}i$ and $\mathbf{v} = -8 + \sqrt{17}i$.
24. A man in a boat wants to cross a river flowing at 6 mph. He compensates for this current by taking a heading that makes a 9° angle with a line perpendicular to the current ($\alpha = 9°$). If the man wants to go from A to B at this angle, how fast must he go?

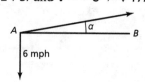

25. Compare and contrast the Mandelbrot and Julia sets.

26. What is the mathematical significance of Col. 2:3?

8 Matrix Algebra

Edwin Hubble published a landmark paper in 1929 that gave strong impetus to the claim that the universe is expanding. Hubble claimed that closer galaxies move away from us slowly while further galaxies rapidly move away from us. "It is he . . . that stretcheth out the heavens as a curtain, and spreadeth them out as a tent to dwell in" (Isaiah 40:22).

Below are several galaxies, listed by their New Galaxy Catalog (NGC) number. The distance (or radius) d from the earth is in units of 10^6 parsecs (or megaparsecs), and velocity v is in kilometers per second. (A parsec is 3.26 light-years.) Hubble labeled this table as "Nebulae Whose Distances Are Estimated from Radial Velocities."

NGC Object	Distance (megaparsecs)	Velocity (km/sec)	NGC Object	Distance (megaparsecs)	Velocity (km/sec)
278	1.52	650	3368	1.74	940
404	—	−25	3379	1.49	810
584	3.45	1800	3489	1.10	600
936	2.37	1300	3521	1.27	730
1023	0.62	300	3623	1.53	800
1700	1.16	800	4111	1.79	800
2681	1.42	700	4526	1.20	580
2683	0.67	400	4565	2.35	1100
2841	1.24	600	4594	2.23	1140
3034	0.79	290	5005	2.06	900
3115	1.00	600	5866	1.73	650

After this chapter you should be able to

1. solve a system of equations algebraically, using matrices, and by Cramer's rule.

2. do basic operations involving matrices.

3. perform elementary row operations.

4. find the determinant of a matrix.

5. evaluate determinants by using properties of determinants.

6. find the inverse of a matrix.

8.1 Solving Systems Algebraically

Many applications in mathematics require a set of equations, each having more than one variable. Such a set is called a *system of equations.*

A linear equation is of the form $a_1x_1 + a_2x_2 + \cdots + a_nx_n = b$, where $a_1, a_2, \ldots, a_n$ are real numbers that are not all zero and b is also a real number. When all of the equations are linear, the system is referred to as a system of linear equations. The following are examples of linear and nonlinear equations.

Linear	Nonlinear
$2x + 3y = 7$	$4x^2 + y^2 = 16$
$5x_1 - 6x_2 + 3x_3 = -37$	$xy = 12$

A solution to a system of equations is an ordered grouping of values for each of the variables that satisfies all of the equations of the system. For example, the ordered pair $(5, -4)$ is a solution to the following system of linear equations.

$$2x + 3y = -2$$
$$6x - y = 34$$

The values $x = 5$ and $y = -4$ satisfy both equations as illustrated.

$$2(5) + 3(-4) = 10 - 12 = -2$$
$$6(5) - (-4) = 30 + 4 = 34$$

A system of equations is *consistent* if it has a solution. This means that the equations are all true for a particular set of values of the variables, but the number of solutions could be finite or infinite. A system with no solutions is *inconsistent.*

Each linear equation in a two-variable system represents a line; a unique solution to such a system is the ordered pair representing the point of intersection. When more than two variables are involved in a system or if the ordered pair involves fractions or large numbers, it is almost impossible to determine the solution by graphing.

Review the two algebraic methods that you learned in Algebra 1 and Algebra 2. The *substitution* method is easy when one equation can be solved for x or y without introducing fractions. Otherwise, this method can be difficult, as shown in Example 1. In such cases, the addition method is easier, as illustrated in Example 2.

EXAMPLE 1   Use substitution to solve the system. $6x - 5y = -43$
$$7x + 2y = -11$$

Answer

$7x + 2y = -11$ $2y = -7x - 11$ $y = \dfrac{-7x - 11}{2}$	1. Solve one of the equations for one of the variables. Solving for the variable with the lowest coefficient results in smaller denominators for fractions.
$6x - 5\left(\dfrac{-7x - 11}{2}\right) = -43$ $12x - 5(-7x - 11) = -86$ $12x + 35x + 55 = -86$ $47x = -141$ $x = -3$	2. Substitute the result into the other equation and solve for x.
$7(-3) + 2y = -11$ $-21 + 2y = -11$ $2y = 10$ $y = 5$	3. Substitute the value -3 back into either original equation and solve for the other variable.
$(-3, 5)$	4. Write the ordered pair solution.
$6(-3) - 5(5) = -18 - 25 = -43$ $7(-3) + 2(5) = -21 + 10 = -11$	5. Your solution should check in both of the original equations. You can do a mental check.

EXAMPLE 2   Solve the following system by the addition method.
$$6x - 5y = -43$$
$$7x + 2y = -11$$

Answer

$6x - 5y = -43$ (2) $7x + 2y = -11$ (5)	1. Multiply one or both equations to obtain opposite coefficients for one of the variables. In this example, multiply the first by 2 and the second by 5.
$12x - 10y = -86$ $\underline{35x + 10y = -55}$ $47x = -141$ $x = -3$	2. Using the addition property of equality, add respective sides of the equation to eliminate the variable y.
$6(-3) - 5y = -43$ $-18 - 5y = -43$ $-5y = -25$ $y = 5$	3. Substitute the value obtained (-3) back into either original equation. Solve for the other variable.
$(-3, 5)$	4. Write the solution as an ordered pair.

EXAMPLE 3 Solve the following system of equations. $3x - 4y = -8$
$6x - 8y = 12$

Answer

$3x - 4y = -8 \, (-2)$ $6x - 8y = 12$	1. Multiply both sides of the first equation by -2.
$-6x + 8y = 16$ $\underline{6x - 8y = 12}$ $0 = 28$	2. Add the result to the second equation.
$\varnothing$	3. The *false statement* shows that there are no solutions.

When no points satisfy both equations (as in Example 3), the lines are parallel and the empty set (or null set) is the solution. This is an example of an inconsistent system.

EXAMPLE 4 Solve the following system of equations.
$4x + 6y = 12$
$y = \frac{-2}{3}x + 2$

Answer

$2x + 3y = 6$ $y = \frac{-2}{3}x + 2$	1. Notice that all terms of the first equation are divisible by 2. Simplify it before solving the system.
$2x + 3\left(\frac{-2}{3}x + 2\right) = 6$ $2x - 2x + 6 = 6$ $6 = 6$	2. Substitute the expression for y from the second equation into the first equation and solve.
infinitely many solutions $\{(x, y) \,\vert\, 2x + 3y = 6\}$	3. The *true statement* shows that any value of x results in a solution. Because the two original equations are equivalent, the solution set is every point on the line.

When equations have infinitely many solutions (as in Example 4), the system is called *dependent*. In order for a linear system to be *independent* (have a unique solution), there must be as many equations as variables.

To solve a system of three linear equations in three variables, select two equations from the system and use the addition method to eliminate one of the variables. Next, take another pair of equations and again use addition to eliminate the same variable that you eliminated from the first pair of equations. The two resulting equations will form a new system of two equations in two variables. Solve this new system as before; then substitute the results back into one of the original equations to find the value of the third variable. The following example illustrates the method.

EXAMPLE 5 Solve the system.

$$2x - y + 3z = 7 \quad \text{(a)}$$
$$x + 2y - 4z = -19 \quad \text{(b)}$$
$$-3x + 4y - z = 12 \quad \text{(c)}$$

Answer

$$x + 2y - 4z = -19 \ (-2)$$

$$\underline{\begin{aligned}-2x - 4y + 8z &= 38 \\ 2x - y + 3z &= 7\end{aligned}}$$

$$-5y + 11z = 45 \quad \text{(d)}$$

1. Multiply equation (b) by -2 and add the result to equation (a). This eliminates x and results in equation (d).

$$x + 2y - 4z = -19 \ (3)$$

$$\underline{\begin{aligned}3x + 6y - 12z &= -57 \\ -3x + 4y - z &= 12\end{aligned}}$$

$$10y - 13z = -45 \quad \text{(e)}$$

2. Using equations (b) and (c), eliminate x again. Multiply equation (b) by 3 and add the result to equation (c) to obtain equation (e).

$$-5y + 11z = 45 \ (2)$$

$$\underline{\begin{aligned}-10y + 22z &= 90 \\ 10y - 13z &= -45\end{aligned}}$$

$$9z = 45$$
$$z = 5$$

3. Solve the two-variable system formed by equations (d) and (e). Multiply equation (d) by 2 and add the result to equation (e). Find z.

$$10y - 13(5) = -45$$
$$10y - 65 = -45$$
$$10y = 20$$
$$y = 2$$

4. Finish solving the two-variable system by finding y. Substitute the value of z into equation (e) and solve for y.

$$x + 2(2) - 4(5) = -19$$
$$x - 16 = -19$$
$$x = -3$$

5. Substitute the values of y and z into one of the original equations (b) and solve for x.

$$(-3, 2, 5)$$

6. Write the solution as an ordered triple. The system is consistent.

EXAMPLE 6 Solve the following system of linear equations.

$$2x + 3y - 7z = 8$$
$$6x + 8y - 11z = 4$$

Answer

$2x + 3y - 7z = 8 \ (-3)$	1. Multiply the first equation by -3 and add to the second equation to eliminate x. Since there are no other equations, no other variable can be eliminated and the system is dependent, having infinitely many solutions.
$-6x - 9y + 21z = -24$	
$\underline{6x + 8y - 11z = 4}$	
$-y + 10z = -20$	
$y = 10z + 20$	
$z = t$	2. Express the solution to a dependent system by writing each variable in terms of a single arbitrary constant, t. In this example let $z = t$, since you can then express y in terms of it.
$y = 10t + 20$	
$2x + 3(10t + 20) - 7t = 8$	3. Substitute for y and z in the first equation to express x in terms of t.
$2x + 30t + 60 - 7t = 8$	
$2x = -23t - 52$	
$x = \dfrac{-23t - 52}{2}$	
$x = \dfrac{-23}{2}t - 26$	
$\left(\dfrac{-23}{2}t - 26,\ 10t + 20,\ t\right)$	4. A general ordered triple represents any point on the line where the graph of the planes intersect. Write the *general solution*.

You can find *particular solutions* to the system in Example 6 by substituting any real number for t. For example, if $t = -2$, the solution is

$$\left(\left(\dfrac{-23}{2}\right)(-2) - 26,\ 10(-2) + 20,\ -2\right) = (-3, 0, -2).$$

The solution checks in both equations. The ordered triple $(-3, 0, -2)$ is one of infinitely many solutions to this system.

▶ A. Exercises

Solve the following system of equations, and express your answers as ordered pairs.

1. $6x - 4y = 60$
$3x + 2y = 18$

2. $\frac{1}{2}x - 3y = \frac{73}{8}$
$4x + 5y = -14$

3. $8x + 3y = 38\frac{1}{2}$
$7x + 4y = 33$

4. $5x + 2y = 20$
$7\frac{1}{2}x + 3y = 30$

5. $2x + y = 3$
$4x + 2y = 7$

6. Find the intersection of the graphs of $x = \frac{7}{2} + \frac{1}{2}y$ and $2x - y = 7$.

Solve each system.

7. $0.6x + 2y = 3.66$
$1.3x - 0.5y = 2.13$

8. $4x - 6y + 6z = -21$
$3x + 4y - z = -6$
$x - 2y + 4z = -8$

▶ B. Exercises

9. Solve the system. (*Hint:* Let $a = \frac{1}{x}$ and $b = \frac{1}{y}$.)
$\frac{5}{x} - \frac{2}{y} = 6$
$\frac{3}{x} + \frac{4}{y} = 1$

10. Let $f(x) = ax + 4$, $g(x) = cx - 1$, $2f(x) + g(x) = 12x + 7$, and $f(x) - 3g(x) = -x + 7$. Find a and c.

The general solution of a system is $(3t + 4, t - 6, t)$.

11. Find particular solutions for $t = -1$ and $t = 2$.

12. What value of t corresponds to the point with an x-coordinate of -8?

13. What solution has an x-coordinate of 13?

14. Give the general solution and a particular solution for the following system.
$x + 5y - z = 8$
$2x - 4y + 4z = 2$

15. Solve $\frac{1}{2}x + \frac{2}{3}y + 4z = 6$. Give the general solution (using two arbitrary constants) and also give a particular solution.

16. The following are vertices of a triangle: $A(-2, 5)$, $B(-6, 1)$, $C(4, -1)$. Find the intersection of the altitude from vertex A with side BC.

17. Use two arbitrary constants to represent the solution of $x - y + 3z = 5$.

18. Find x, y such that $0 \leq x < 2\pi$ and $0 \leq y < 2\pi$ where $2 \sin x + 4 \cos y = 4$ and $\sin x = 2 \cos y$.

▶ C. Exercises

19. $x^2 + y^2 + Ax + By + C = 0$ is the equation of a circle. Find A, B, C, if the circle goes through $(3, -6)$, $(-1, 2)$, and $(6, 3)$.

20. Solve the system, giving all solutions. Describe the general appearance of the graph of the system based on your answer.

$$2x + 3y = 8$$
$$xy = 12$$

▥ Dominion Modeling

21. From the Hubble data, make a scatterplot with velocity as a function of distance, find the linear model and r^2, and plot the residuals. (*Hint:* Omit Object 404, since the distance was not reported.)

22. Hubble wrote in his original paper that the "run of the residuals is about as smooth as can be expected. . . ." What did this mean?

▮ Cumulative Review

23. Given a triangle with sides of 9, 10, and 14, find the angles to the nearest degree.

24. Place $y = 3x^2 - 7x + 1$ in work form; find the maximum or minimum and where it occurs.

25. Write the equation of the cosine function translated $\frac{\pi}{3}$ to the right with an amplitude of 3 and a period of $\frac{\pi}{2}$.

26. Find the dot product if $\mathbf{u} = <3, 1>$ and $\mathbf{v} = <7, -2>$.

27. Give the polar form of $2 - 2i$.

8.2 Matrices

A *matrix* is a rectangular array of numbers designated with an upper case letter. Each number in a matrix is called an *entry*, and a matrix with m rows and n columns is an m by n matrix (written $m \times n$). The notation a_{ij} denotes the entry in row i and column j of matrix A.

This British marching band employs rows and columns.

Definition

Equal matrices   If A and B are both $m \times n$ matrices, then $A = B$ when $a_{ij} = b_{ij}$ for all $i = 1, 2, \ldots, m$ and $j = 1, 2, \ldots, n$.

For two matrices to be equal, they must have the same number of rows, the same number of columns, and all corresponding entries must be equal.

EXAMPLE 1   Under what conditions will

$$\begin{bmatrix} 2 & -1 & a_{13} \\ 5 & a_{22} & 7 \end{bmatrix} = \begin{bmatrix} b_{11} & -1 & 8 \\ 5 & -3 & b_{23} \end{bmatrix}?$$

Answer $a_{13} = 8$, $a_{22} = -3$, $b_{11} = 2$, and $b_{23} = 7$.

Definition

Matrix addition   If A and B are both $m \times n$ matrices, then $A + B = C$ where $c_{ij} = a_{ij} + b_{ij}$ for all $i = 1, 2, \ldots, m$ and $j = 1, 2, \ldots, n$.

In summary, to add two matrices of the same size, you must add corresponding entries.

EXAMPLE 2 If $A = \begin{bmatrix} 3 & -2 & 1 \\ -4 & 5 & 7 \end{bmatrix}$ and $B = \begin{bmatrix} -11 & 0 & -4 \\ 5 & 9 & -3 \end{bmatrix}$, find $A + B$.

Answer $A + B = \begin{bmatrix} 3 - 11 & -2 + 0 & 1 - 4 \\ -4 + 5 & 5 + 9 & 7 - 3 \end{bmatrix} = \begin{bmatrix} -8 & -2 & -3 \\ 1 & 14 & 4 \end{bmatrix}$

Matrices have *some* of the properties of real numbers. One such property is the *commutative property of addition*.

If $A = \begin{bmatrix} -9 & -4 \\ 24 & 16 \end{bmatrix}$ and $B = \begin{bmatrix} 11 & 2 \\ -13 & -8 \end{bmatrix}$,

$A + B = \begin{bmatrix} -9 + 11 & -4 + 2 \\ 24 - 13 & 16 - 8 \end{bmatrix} = \begin{bmatrix} 2 & -2 \\ 11 & 8 \end{bmatrix} = \begin{bmatrix} 11 - 9 & 2 - 4 \\ -13 + 24 & -8 + 16 \end{bmatrix} = B + A.$

The commutative property of addition of matrices is based on the commutative property of addition of real numbers. $A + B$ is obtained by adding $a_{ij} + b_{ij}$ for all i and j. $B + A$ is obtained by adding $b_{ij} + a_{ij}$ for all i and j. Since $a_{ij} + b_{ij} = b_{ij} + a_{ij}$ by the commutative property of real numbers, corresponding entries in $A + B$ and $B + A$ are equal, so $A + B = B + A$.

Definition

Zero matrix A matrix, denoted by O, with zeros for all of its entries.

The number of rows and columns of O can vary according to the application.

EXAMPLE 3 If $A = \begin{bmatrix} 2 & -1 & 3 & 4 \\ 4 & 5 & 8 & -9 \end{bmatrix}$, find $A + O$.

Answer In this case $O = \begin{bmatrix} 0 & 0 & 0 & 0 \\ 0 & 0 & 0 & 0 \end{bmatrix}$ and $A + O = \begin{bmatrix} 2 & -1 & 3 & 4 \\ 4 & 5 & 8 & -9 \end{bmatrix}$.

Since $A + O = O + A = A$ for any 4×2 matrix A, O is an *additive identity* for them. An identity matrix exists for the set of $m \times n$ matrices.

Every matrix A has a corresponding matrix designated as $-A$, where each entry is the additive inverse of the corresponding entry of A. Note that A and $-A$ must have the same number of rows and columns.

Additive inverse of a matrix   Each entry in $-A$ is the additive inverse of the corresponding entry in A.

This definition leads to a property of matrices analogous to that of real numbers; that is $A + (-A) = (-A) + A = 0$. We then define matrix subtraction in a way similar to that of real numbers.

Definition

Matrix subtraction $A - B = A + (-B)$.

Just as subtraction of real numbers is not commutative, neither is subtraction of matrices.

$$\text{If } A = \begin{bmatrix} -8 & 7 \\ 2 & 4 \end{bmatrix} \text{ and } B = \begin{bmatrix} 14 & -3 \\ 9 & -5 \end{bmatrix},$$

$$\text{then } A - B = \begin{bmatrix} -22 & 10 \\ -7 & 9 \end{bmatrix} \text{ and } B - A = \begin{bmatrix} 22 & -10 \\ 7 & -9 \end{bmatrix}.$$

Note that $A - B = -(B - A)$ but $A - B \neq B - A$.

Definition

Scalar multiplication   If A is an $m \times n$ matrix and k is a real number, then kA is the $m \times n$ matrix obtained by multiplying each entry of A by k. This product is represented either as kA or using brackets, as $[ka_{ij}]$.

EXAMPLE 4   Compute $4\begin{bmatrix} 3 & 2 & -4 \\ 5 & 1 & -2 \end{bmatrix}$.

Answer $4\begin{bmatrix} 3 & 2 & -4 \\ 5 & 1 & -2 \end{bmatrix} = \begin{bmatrix} 4 \cdot 3 & 4 \cdot 2 & 4 \cdot -4 \\ 4 \cdot 5 & 4 \cdot 1 & 4 \cdot -2 \end{bmatrix}$ Multiply each element of the matrix by the scalar 4.

$$= \begin{bmatrix} 12 & 8 & -16 \\ 20 & 4 & -8 \end{bmatrix}$$

For $m \times n$ matrices A, B, and C and any scalars e and f, the following properties of matrices hold.

1. $(A + B) + C = A + (B + C)$ associative property of addition

2. $(e + f)A = e \cdot A + f \cdot A$ distributive property—matrix over two scalars

3. $e(A + B) = e \cdot A + e \cdot B$ distributive property—scalar over two matrices

4. $1 \cdot A = A$ scalar identity property

You may think that you could find the product of two $m \times n$ matrices by multiplying corresponding entries. However, that process does not turn out to be useful because it does not relate to any real-life process. Instead, we define matrix multiplication so that it has practical uses in areas such as inventory control. Consider the two arbitrary matrices $A_{2 \times 2}$ and $B_{2 \times 3}$.

$$A = \begin{bmatrix} a & b \\ c & d \end{bmatrix} \quad B = \begin{bmatrix} e & f & g \\ h & i & j \end{bmatrix}$$

The product of A and B is AB, where each entry is the sum of the products of the entries from row i of A and corresponding entries from column j of B. For example, the entry of AB in the second row and the third column is the sum of the products of corresponding entries from the second row of A and the third column of B.

$$AB = \begin{bmatrix} a & b \\ \boxed{c} & \boxed{d} \end{bmatrix} \begin{bmatrix} e & f & \boxed{g} \\ h & i & \boxed{j} \end{bmatrix}$$

$$AB = \begin{bmatrix} * & * & * \\ * & * & cg + dj \end{bmatrix}$$

Similarly, the entry of AB in the first row and the second column is the sum of the products of corresponding entries in the first row of A and the second column of B.

$$AB = \begin{bmatrix} \boxed{a} & \boxed{b} \\ c & d \end{bmatrix} \begin{bmatrix} e & \boxed{f} & g \\ h & \boxed{i} & j \end{bmatrix}$$

$$AB = \begin{bmatrix} * & af + bi & * \\ * & * & * \end{bmatrix}$$

EXAMPLE 5 Find AB if $A = \begin{bmatrix} 2 & -3 \\ 1 & 5 \end{bmatrix}$ and $B = \begin{bmatrix} 4 & 6 & 2 \\ -3 & 1 & -5 \end{bmatrix}$.

Answer $AB = \begin{bmatrix} 2 & -3 \\ 1 & 5 \end{bmatrix} \begin{bmatrix} 4 & 6 & 2 \\ -3 & 1 & -5 \end{bmatrix}$

$$= \begin{bmatrix} 2 \cdot 4 + (-3)(-3) & 2 \cdot 6 + (-3)1 & 2 \cdot 2 + (-3)(-5) \\ 1 \cdot 4 + 5(-3) & 1 \cdot 6 + 5 \cdot 1 & 1 \cdot 2 + 5(-5) \end{bmatrix}$$

$$= \begin{bmatrix} 17 & 9 & 19 \\ -11 & 11 & -23 \end{bmatrix}$$

In order to multiply two matrices, the number of columns of the first matrix must equal the number of rows of the second matrix. The matrices $D_{m \times n}$ and $E_{r \times p}$ can be multiplied only if n equals r, and the product will be $m \times p$.

EXAMPLE 6 Let $A = \begin{bmatrix} 2 & 3 \\ -1 & 4 \\ 5 & -2 \end{bmatrix}$ and $B = \begin{bmatrix} -3 & 1 & 3 \\ 6 & -2 & -1 \end{bmatrix}$.

a. Determine whether AB is defined.
b. If the product is defined, give its size.
c. If possible, find the product.

Answer a. The number of columns of $A_{3 \times 2}$ equals the number of rows of $B_{2 \times 3}$; so AB is defined.

b. $A_{3 \times 2} \cdot B_{2 \times 3}$ is a 3×3 matrix.

c. $AB = \begin{bmatrix} 2 & 3 \\ -1 & 4 \\ 5 & -2 \end{bmatrix} \begin{bmatrix} -3 & 1 & 3 \\ 6 & -2 & -1 \end{bmatrix}$

$= \begin{bmatrix} -6 + 18 & 2 + (-6) & 6 + (-3) \\ 3 + 24 & -1 + (-8) & -3 + (-4) \\ -15 + (-12) & 5 + 4 & 15 + 2 \end{bmatrix}$

$= \begin{bmatrix} 12 & -4 & 3 \\ 27 & -9 & -7 \\ -27 & 9 & 17 \end{bmatrix}$

God says in I Corinthians 14:40, "Let all things be done decently and in order." This principle encompasses your Bible study, your work, your relationships, and your homework. You can see its importance in matrix multiplication, which can get very confusing if you don't keep track of entries in a neat and orderly fashion.

Is multiplication of matrices commutative? To answer this question, let us use the matrices of Example 6.

$BA = \begin{bmatrix} -3 & 1 & 3 \\ 6 & -2 & -1 \end{bmatrix} \begin{bmatrix} 2 & 3 \\ -1 & 4 \\ 5 & -2 \end{bmatrix} = \begin{bmatrix} -6 - 1 + 15 & -9 + 4 - 6 \\ 12 + 2 - 5 & 18 - 8 + 2 \end{bmatrix} = \begin{bmatrix} 8 & -11 \\ 9 & 12 \end{bmatrix}_{2 \times 2}$

As you can see, $AB \neq BA$. In fact, the size of AB and BA is not the same. It frequently happens that one of the two products is defined but the other is not. For example, $A_{3 \times 5} \cdot B_{5 \times 7} = C_{3 \times 7}$; however, $B_{5 \times 7} \cdot A_{3 \times 5}$ is undefined. You will check whether matrix multiplication is associative in the exercise set.

EXAMPLE 7 If $A = \begin{bmatrix} -14 & 5 \\ 6 & -2 \\ 9 & 3 \end{bmatrix}$ and $I = \begin{bmatrix} 1 & 0 & 0 \\ 0 & 1 & 0 \\ 0 & 0 & 1 \end{bmatrix}$, find IA.

Answer $IA = \begin{bmatrix} 1 & 0 & 0 \\ 0 & 1 & 0 \\ 0 & 0 & 1 \end{bmatrix} \begin{bmatrix} -14 & 5 \\ 6 & -2 \\ 9 & 3 \end{bmatrix} = \begin{bmatrix} -14 & 5 \\ 6 & -2 \\ 9 & 3 \end{bmatrix}$

The matrix I behaves like the multiplicative identity 1 of the real numbers ($a \cdot 1 = 1 \cdot a = a$). However, even though $IA = A$, the product AI does not exist in this case, since multiplying a 3×2 matrix by a 3×3 matrix is impossible. This problem does not exist when A is a square matrix. A *square matrix* is $n \times n$, having the same number of rows and columns. Notice that I is a square matrix with ones down the *main diagonal* (main diagonal is a_{ij}, where $i = j$) and zeros elsewhere.

$$I = \begin{bmatrix} 1 & 0 & \cdot & \cdot & \cdot & 0 \\ 0 & 1 & \cdot & \cdot & \cdot & 0 \\ \cdot & \cdot & & & & \cdot \\ \cdot & \cdot & & & & \cdot \\ \cdot & \cdot & & & & \cdot \\ 0 & 0 & \cdot & \cdot & \cdot & 1 \end{bmatrix}$$

Definition

Identity matrix A square matrix with 1 as every entry on the main diagonal and 0 as all other entries.

If A is an $n \times n$ (square) matrix and I is an $n \times n$ identity matrix, then $AI = IA = A$.

Now that we have introduced matrix multiplication, let us reexamine how we might express the following system of equations.

$$2x_1 - 3x_2 - 4x_3 = -4$$
$$5x_1 + 4x_2 - x_3 = -7$$
$$-8x_1 + 0x_2 + 3x_3 = 0$$

This system of equations is equivalent to the following matrix equation.

$$\begin{bmatrix} 2 & -3 & -4 \\ 5 & 4 & -1 \\ -8 & 0 & 3 \end{bmatrix} \begin{bmatrix} x_1 \\ x_2 \\ x_3 \end{bmatrix} = \begin{bmatrix} -4 \\ -7 \\ 0 \end{bmatrix}$$

If $A = \begin{bmatrix} 2 & -3 & -4 \\ 5 & 4 & -1 \\ -8 & 0 & 3 \end{bmatrix}$, $X = \begin{bmatrix} x_1 \\ x_2 \\ x_3 \end{bmatrix}$, and $B = \begin{bmatrix} -4 \\ -7 \\ 0 \end{bmatrix}$, the given system can be abbreviated as $AX = B$. This form is used often with systems of linear equations.

▶ A. Exercises

Determine the necessary conditions for the following matrices to be equal.

1. $\begin{bmatrix} -1 & 3 & b \\ a & -5 & \frac{1}{2} \end{bmatrix} = \begin{bmatrix} -1 & 3 & c \\ 4 & -5 & d \end{bmatrix}$

2. $\begin{bmatrix} 8 & 4 & -1 \\ 3 & a & -2 \\ 2 & -1 & 6 \\ 5 & -9 & b \end{bmatrix} = \begin{bmatrix} 8 & 4 & c \\ 3 & -9 & -2 \\ 4 & -1 & 6 \\ 5 & -9 & 7 \end{bmatrix}$

Perform the following computations.

3. $\begin{bmatrix} 4 & -7 & 1 \\ -2 & 5 & 8 \end{bmatrix} + \begin{bmatrix} -9 & -1 & 3 \\ 5 & 2 & -4 \end{bmatrix}$

4. $\begin{bmatrix} 3 & -6 \\ 8 & -1 \end{bmatrix} - \begin{bmatrix} -4 & 9 \\ 6 & -13 \end{bmatrix}$

5. $-2 \begin{bmatrix} 8 \\ -7 \\ -3 \end{bmatrix} + 4 \begin{bmatrix} 2 \\ -6 \\ 7 \end{bmatrix}$

6. $\begin{bmatrix} 13 & -9 & 14 \\ 8 & 7 & -5 \end{bmatrix} - 3 \begin{bmatrix} 3 & 7 & -6 \\ 4 & \frac{1}{3} & 10 \end{bmatrix}$

7. $\begin{bmatrix} 3.4 & -2.15 & 5.7 \\ -54 & 2.9 & 7.34 \end{bmatrix} + 5.4 \begin{bmatrix} -5.8 & 3.19 & 4.3 \\ -6.2 & -32 & 0.45 \end{bmatrix}$

Solve for the unknown variables.

8. $5 \begin{bmatrix} a & -2 \\ 3 & 4 \\ -6 & b \end{bmatrix} - 2 \begin{bmatrix} 2 & 3 \\ c & -2 \\ 7 & 4 \end{bmatrix} = \begin{bmatrix} 16 & -16 \\ 19 & 24 \\ d & -23 \end{bmatrix}$

9. $-4 \begin{bmatrix} 6 & e & -3 \\ 2 & 7 & 5 \end{bmatrix} + 3 \begin{bmatrix} -2 & 8 & g \\ f & -9 & 4 \end{bmatrix} = \begin{bmatrix} -30 & 4 & 6 \\ 16 & h & -8 \end{bmatrix}$

Multiply the following matrices.

10. $\begin{bmatrix} 3 & -1 & 4 \\ 5 & 0 & 2 \end{bmatrix} \begin{bmatrix} -3 & 2 & 6 \\ 0 & 2 & -4 \\ 1 & 4 & 2 \end{bmatrix}$

11. $\begin{bmatrix} 3 & -5 \\ 6 & 4 \end{bmatrix} \begin{bmatrix} -2 & 3 \\ 4 & 7 \end{bmatrix}$

12. $\begin{bmatrix} 6 & -2 & 7 \end{bmatrix} \begin{bmatrix} 2 & 6 \\ 3 & -2 \\ -5 & 2 \end{bmatrix}$

13. $\begin{bmatrix} 3 & 2 & -1 & 6 \\ 2 & 2 & -2 & 4 \end{bmatrix} \begin{bmatrix} 2 \\ 5 \\ 6 \\ -1 \end{bmatrix}$

14. $\begin{bmatrix} -2.3 & 9.6 & 5.4 & -5 \\ 6.1 & -2.5 & 30 & 8.4 \end{bmatrix} \begin{bmatrix} 17 & -9 \\ 5.64 & -12.3 \\ -25 & 6.14 \\ 0.4 & 3.6 \end{bmatrix}$

▶ B. Exercises

Verify the given properties, using the given matrices and scalars.

15. Associative property of addition

$\begin{bmatrix} 5 & -2 \\ -4 & 11 \end{bmatrix} \begin{bmatrix} 8 & 3 \\ -6 & 9 \end{bmatrix} \begin{bmatrix} -9 & 7 \\ 12 & 3 \end{bmatrix}$

16. Associative property of multiplication

$\begin{bmatrix} 1 & -3 \\ 4 & 2 \end{bmatrix} \begin{bmatrix} 2 & 3 & 2 \\ 1 & 0 & 4 \end{bmatrix} \begin{bmatrix} 5 \\ -2 \\ 6 \end{bmatrix}$

17. Distributive property of matrix multiplication over scalar addition

$5, 6, \begin{bmatrix} 4 & -2 & 3 \\ 2 & 3 & 1 \end{bmatrix}$

18. Distributive property of scalar multiplication over matrix addition

$3, \begin{bmatrix} 8 & -6 \\ 1 & 7 \end{bmatrix}, \begin{bmatrix} -5 & 4 \\ 3 & 11 \end{bmatrix}$

19. Use the following matrices to show that the statement "If $A \cdot C = B \cdot C$, then $A = B$" is not necessarily true.

$A = \begin{bmatrix} 4 & -2 \\ -6 & 2 \end{bmatrix}, B = \begin{bmatrix} -6 & 4 \\ -1 & -1 \end{bmatrix}, C = \begin{bmatrix} 3 \\ 5 \end{bmatrix}$

20. Use the following matrices to show that the statement "If $A + C = B + C$, then $A = B$" is true.

$$A = \begin{bmatrix} a & b \\ c & d \end{bmatrix}, B = \begin{bmatrix} -2 & 6 \\ 7 & 1 \end{bmatrix}, C = \begin{bmatrix} 5 & 4 \\ -3 & 8 \end{bmatrix}$$

21. Show that $\begin{bmatrix} 6 \\ -3 \\ -2 \end{bmatrix}$ is a solution to the matrix equation $AX = B$, where

$$A = \begin{bmatrix} 3 & 1 & 4 \\ 2 & 1 & 6 \end{bmatrix} \text{ and } B = \begin{bmatrix} 7 \\ -3 \end{bmatrix}.$$

22. Solve the matrix equation $AX = B$ if $A = \begin{bmatrix} 2 & 7 \\ 3 & -5 \end{bmatrix}$ and $B = \begin{bmatrix} 2 \\ 34 \end{bmatrix}.$

▶ C. Exercises

23. If the three matrices $A_{2\times3}$, $B_{3\times4}$, and $C_{4\times2}$, are to be multiplied together, list all possible orders of multiplication (ABC, etc.) with the resulting matrix size of each. Also list all possible multiplications of two of the matrices with the matrix size of the products.

24. Explain how the product of two matrices can result in a scalar.

■ Cumulative Review

25. Find the zeros of $x^5 + 5x^4 - 7x^3 - 43x^2 - 8x - 48$.

26. Change $r \sin \theta = (r \cos \theta)^{\frac{2}{3}}$ to rectangular coordinates.

27. Find the height of a building if a six-foot-tall observer 500 feet away views the top at a 52° angle of elevation.

28. Prove $\frac{1}{2} \sec^2 x = \tan x \csc 2x$.

29. Is $\text{Tan}^{-1} x$ increasing, decreasing, or neither?

8 Approximation Methods

Interpolating Polynomials

Curve fitting describes the process of finding a function that passes through given data points. You have already seen how to find linear and quadratic splines for a set of data, but polynomials are much more convenient than piece functions. In this section you will learn to fit a polynomial to data. Such a polynomial function is called an *interpolating polynomial*. The following theorem is basic to such applications.

> **Theorem**
>
> **Given *n* points, there exists a polynomial having a degree no larger than *n* − 1 that passes through all *n* data points.**

For any three points, there is a second degree (quadratic) polynomial function of the form $y = ax^2 + bx + c$ that contains the three points.

EXAMPLE Find an interpolating polynomial such that $f(1) = -4$, $f(-2) = -19$, and $f(4) = -25$.

Answer

Since there are 3 given points, find a quadratic function $f(x) = ax^2 + bx + c$. Substitute each ordered pair into the general form to form a system of three equations in three variables and solve for the values of a, b, and c.

1. Find the system.

$$a + b + c = -4 \qquad f(1) = a(1)^2 + b(1) + c = -4$$
$$4a - 2b + c = -19 \qquad f(-2) = a(-2)^2 + b(-2) + c = -19$$
$$16a + 4b + c = -25 \qquad f(4) = a(4)^2 + b(4) + c = -25$$

2. To eliminate c, multiply the first equation by -1 and add to the second equation. Divide the resulting equation by 3 to simplify.

$$-a - b - c = 4$$
$$\underline{4a - 2b + c = -19}$$
$$3a - 3b = -15$$
$$a - b = -5$$

3. Multiply the original third equation by -1 and add to the first equation to again eliminate c. Divide the equation by -3 to simplify.

$$a + b + c = -4$$
$$\underline{-16a - 4b - c = 25}$$
$$-15a - 3b = 21$$
$$5a + b = -7$$

Continued ▶

$$a - b = -5$$
$$\underline{5a + b = -7}$$
$$6a = -12$$
$$a = -2$$
$$-2 - b = -5$$
$$b = 3$$

4. Add the two resulting equations from steps 2 and 3 to solve for a. Substitute the value into either equation and find b.

$$a + b + c = -4$$
$$-2 + 3 + c = -4$$
$$c = -5$$

5. Now substitute the values for a and b into one of the original equations to find c.

$$f(x) = ax^2 + bx + c$$
$$f(x) = -2x^2 + 3x - 5$$

6. Answer the original question by supplying the 3 parameters for the desired function.

The same system could be solved with matrices. In fact, given 10 data points, the ninth degree polynomial would require a system of 9 equations in 9 variables. A graphing calculator is very convenient for solving such a system.

The advantage of interpolating polynomials is that they are smooth curves. However, the disadvantage is that as the number of data points increases, so does the degree of the polynomial and therefore the total number of maxima and minima. This means that the curve may have erratic ups and downs between data points, which is hardly a good fit to the data. This disadvantage explains why splines or best fit curves are preferred in some contexts.

▶ Exercises

Give the maximum degree of the interpolating polynomial for the following numbers of data points.

1. 4

2. 20

Find the interpolating polynomial for each set of data points.

3. $f(1) = 3$, $f(2) = 5$, and $f(3) = 11$

4. $f(0) = 7$, $f(1) = 2$, $f(3) = 9$, and $f(4) = 1$

5. $f(-1) = 4$, $f(1) = -3$, $f(2) = -3$, and $f(3) = 5$

Math Through History

THE TREE OF MATH

In Christ are hid all the treasures of wisdom and knowledge. All truth is in Christ, and humans only manage what He made. The three main branches of modern math are algebra, analysis, and topology. Mathematicians consider each in a very abstract and purely theoretical sense. Just as your algebra classes generalized arithmetic properties using variables, modern mathematicians use abstract ideas to generalize algebraic properties whether the objects are matrices, complex numbers, or functions. The result is abstract algebra. Analysis arises by drawing similar generalizations from calculus, and topology arises by generalizing geometry.

Archimedes (287-212 B.C.), depicted on a bas-relief in the Capitoline Museum at Rome, was the greatest mathematician of the ancient world. He developed ideas that were precursors of calculus.

Isaac Newton (1642-1727), whose statue stands at Trinity Chapel, Cambridge, invented calculus and is considered one of the greatest mathematicians in history.

Two other branches are treated as peripheral but every bit as important. Applied math includes probability and statistics as well as numerical analysis and modeling theory. Theoretical math ideas are essential to all modern applications. The other branch is foundations, which includes both logic and set theory as well as philosophy. Unfortunately, modern philosophies reject Christ as the foundation, yet the replacements they offer are inconsistent.

The table below shows developments in the 5 branches.

Of course, no classification is perfect. Some research straddles categories and causes some overlap among the branches. Descartes's analytic geometry merged algebra and geometry, as does Poincaré's algebraic topology. Likewise, Banach applied topology to analysis. Differential topology links analysis and topology.

Many of the mathematicians listed as key figures in a given branch of math contributed to other branches as well. Gauss, for instance, contributed to almost every field. In fact, Archimedes, Newton, and Gauss are some of the greatest mathematicians in history.

Karl Friedrich Gauss (1777-1855), honored in bronze in his home town of Göttingen for inventing the telegraph with Wilhelm Weber, is regarded as among the greatest mathematicians ever. His math will long outlast his telegraph.

Algebra	Analysis	Foundations	Topology	Applied	
Galois and Noether (abstract algebra)	Weierstrass and Cauchy (calculus axiomatized)	Cantor (set theory)	Poincaré and Hausdorff (algebraic and point-set topology)	Gauss (numerical analysis; theory of errors)	**Modern**
Peano (algebra axiomatized)	Newton and Leibniz (calculus)	Boole (symbolic logic axiomatized)	Riemann and Lobachevsky (non-Euclidean geometry)	Pascal and Fermat (probability and statistics)	
Diophantus (equations)	Archimedes (calculus concepts)	Aristotle (logic)	Euclid (geometry axiomatized)	Hipparchus (trig theory applied to astronomy)	**Ancient**

Christ

8.3 Solving Systems by Gaussian Elimination

This section introduces *Gaussian elimination*, which is a method of solving systems of equations. The name of the method honors Karl Friedrich Gauss (1777-1855), a German mathematician who helped develop the branch of mathematics called linear algebra.

To represent an arbitrary system of n equations in n variables, use the variables x_1 to x_n. Next, number the constants on the right side of the equations from b_1 to b_n. Each coefficient requires two subscripts to identify which variable in which equation it multiplies. The first subscript identifies the equation number and therefore matches the subscript of the constant on the right side. The second subscript identifies the variable it multiplies and therefore matches the variable's subscript.

$$a_{11}x_1 + a_{12}x_2 + \cdots + a_{1n}x_n = b_1$$
$$a_{21}x_1 + a_{22}x_2 + \cdots + a_{2n}x_n = b_2$$
$$\vdots \qquad \vdots \qquad \qquad \vdots \qquad \vdots$$
$$a_{n1}x_1 + a_{n2}x_2 + \cdots + a_{nn}x_n = b_n$$

In solving a system of linear equations, the variables remain the same and in the same order; therefore, it suffices to keep track of only the coefficients. The *coefficient matrix* will be an $n \times n$ matrix containing only the coefficients of the variables.

$$\begin{bmatrix} a_{11} & a_{12} & \cdots & a_{1n} \\ a_{21} & a_{22} & \cdots & a_{2n} \\ \vdots & \vdots & & \vdots \\ a_{n1} & a_{n2} & \cdots & a_{nn} \end{bmatrix}$$

Combine the column of constants with the coefficient matrix to obtain the following *augmented matrix*.

$$\left[\begin{array}{cccc|c} a_{11} & a_{12} & \cdots & a_{1n} & b_1 \\ a_{21} & a_{22} & \cdots & a_{2n} & b_2 \\ \vdots & \vdots & & \vdots & \vdots \\ a_{n1} & a_{n2} & \cdots & a_{nn} & b_n \end{array}\right]$$

EXAMPLE 1 Give the augmented matrix for the following system of
equations.

$$2x - 3y = 4z - 4$$
$$5x + 4y - z = -7$$
$$-8x + 3z - 1 = 0$$

Answer

$$2x - 3y - 4z = -4$$
$$5x + 4y - z = -7$$
$$-8x + 0y + 3z = 1$$

1. Rearrange the equations in the system into the appropriate form.

$$\begin{bmatrix} 2 & -3 & -4 & | & -4 \\ 5 & 4 & -1 & | & -7 \\ -8 & 0 & 3 & | & 1 \end{bmatrix}$$

2. Augment the coefficient matrix with a column of constants.

The same type of operations used to solve systems algebraically can
be performed on an augmented matrix. These three operations are called
elementary row operations. The subscripted r's designate rows.

Elementary Row Operations

1. Any two rows can be interchanged. $(r_1 \leftrightarrow r_2)$
2. Any row can be multiplied by a nonzero real number. $(2r_1)$
3. Any multiple of one row can be added to another row. $(-3r_1 + r_2)$

If the row operations are used to transform a matrix into one that has all
entries below the main diagonal as zeros (called *echelon form*), the system
will be easy to solve. Example 2 illustrates this fact.

EXAMPLE 2 Solve the following system of equations.

$$3x - 4y + z = 13$$
$$2y - 5z = -11$$
$$7z = 14$$

Answer

$$\begin{bmatrix} 3 & -4 & 1 & | & 13 \\ 0 & 2 & -5 & | & -11 \\ 0 & 0 & 7 & | & 14 \end{bmatrix}$$

1. Write the system in augmented-matrix form.

$$7z = 14$$
$$z = 2$$

2. Solve for z.

$$2y - 5z = -11$$
$$2y - 5(2) = -11$$
$$2y = -1$$
$$y = \frac{-1}{2}$$

3. Substitute to solve for the remaining variables.

Continued ▶

$$3x - 4y + z = 13$$
$$3x - 4\left(\frac{-1}{2}\right) + 2 = 13$$
$$3x + 2 + 2 = 13$$
$$3x = 9$$
$$x = 3$$

$$\left(3, \frac{-1}{2}, 2\right)$$

4. Write the solution as an ordered triple.

As you saw in Example 2, when an augmented matrix is in echelon form, it is easy to solve. You find the value of the last variable and substitute to find the value of the remaining variables. This provides a strategy known as Gaussian elimination for solving a system of linear equations.

1. Write the augmented matrix for the system of equations.
2. Use elementary row operations to convert the augmented matrix into echelon form.
3. If the last equation has one variable, solve for it and substitute to find the other values. Otherwise, the system is inconsistent or dependent. It is inconsistent only when all the variables in one equation have coefficients of zero but the constant is non-zero. If it is dependent, use arbitrary constants to express the solution (Section 8.1, Example 6).

EXAMPLE 3 Use Gaussian elimination to solve the following system of linear equations.
$$-2x + 5y + 2z = 23$$
$$4x - y + 2z = -13$$
$$x - 3y + 6z = -17$$

Answer

$$\begin{bmatrix} -2 & 5 & 2 & | & 23 \\ 4 & -1 & 2 & | & -13 \\ 1 & -3 & 6 & | & -17 \end{bmatrix}$$

1. Write the system as an augmented matrix.

2. Row-reduce to echelon form, using elementary row operations.

$$\xrightarrow{r_1 \leftrightarrow r_3} \begin{bmatrix} 1 & -3 & 6 & | & -17 \\ 4 & -1 & 2 & | & -13 \\ -2 & 5 & 2 & | & 23 \end{bmatrix} \xrightarrow{-4r_1 + r_2} \begin{bmatrix} 1 & -3 & 6 & | & -17 \\ 0 & 11 & -22 & | & 55 \\ -2 & 5 & 2 & | & 23 \end{bmatrix} \xrightarrow{2r_1 + r_3} \begin{bmatrix} 1 & -3 & 6 & | & -17 \\ 0 & 11 & -22 & | & 55 \\ 0 & -1 & 14 & | & -11 \end{bmatrix}$$

Continued ▶

$$\xrightarrow{r_2 \leftrightarrow r_3} \begin{bmatrix} 1 & -3 & 6 & | & -17 \\ 0 & -1 & 14 & | & -11 \\ 0 & 11 & -22 & | & 55 \end{bmatrix} \xrightarrow[\frac{1}{11}r_3]{-r_2} \begin{bmatrix} 1 & -3 & 6 & | & -17 \\ 0 & 1 & -14 & | & 11 \\ 0 & 1 & -2 & | & 5 \end{bmatrix} \xrightarrow{-r_2 + r_3} \begin{bmatrix} 1 & -3 & 6 & | & -17 \\ 0 & 1 & -14 & | & 11 \\ 0 & 0 & 12 & | & -6 \end{bmatrix}$$

$12z = -6$

$z = \frac{-1}{2}$

$y - 14z = 11$

$y - 14\left(\frac{-1}{2}\right) = 11$

$y + 7 = 11$

$y = 4$

$x - 3y + 6z = -17$

$x - 3(4) + 6\left(\frac{-1}{2}\right) = -17$

$x - 12 - 3 = -17$

$x = -2$

$\left(-2, 4, \frac{-1}{2}\right)$

3. Now solve for z, and substitute to find values for the other variables.

4. Write the solution as an ordered triple.

The following example illustrates how to use multiples to avoid fractions when using the Gaussian method.

EXAMPLE 4 Use the Gaussian method to solve the following system of linear equations.

$2a + 3b + 5c = -9$

$3a + 3b + 2c = 4$

$5a + 2b + 3c = -1$

Answer

$$\begin{bmatrix} 2 & 3 & 5 & | & -9 \\ 3 & 3 & 2 & | & 4 \\ 5 & 2 & 3 & | & -1 \end{bmatrix} \xrightarrow[2r_3]{-2r_2} \begin{bmatrix} 2 & 3 & 5 & | & -9 \\ -6 & -6 & -4 & | & -8 \\ 10 & 4 & 6 & | & -2 \end{bmatrix}$$

$$\xrightarrow[-5r_1 + r_3]{3r_1 + r_2} \begin{bmatrix} 2 & 3 & 5 & | & -9 \\ 0 & 3 & 11 & | & -35 \\ 0 & -11 & -19 & | & 43 \end{bmatrix}$$

1. To avoid fractions, do row operations $-2r_2$ and $2r_3$, making the first entries of row 2 and row 3 multiples of the first entry of row 1.

$$\xrightarrow{3r_3} \begin{bmatrix} 2 & 3 & 5 & | & -9 \\ 0 & 3 & 11 & | & -35 \\ 0 & -33 & -57 & | & 129 \end{bmatrix} \xrightarrow{11r_2 + r_3} \begin{bmatrix} 2 & 3 & 5 & | & -9 \\ 0 & 3 & 11 & | & -35 \\ 0 & 0 & 64 & | & -256 \end{bmatrix}$$

2. To avoid fractions, do row operation $3r_3$, making the second entry in row 3 a multiple of the second entry in row 2.

Continued ▶

$$64c = -256$$
$$c = -4$$

$$3b + 11c = -35$$
$$3b + 11(-4) = -35$$
$$3b = 9$$
$$b = 3$$

$$2a + 3b + 5c = -9$$
$$2a + 3(3) + 5(-4) = -9$$
$$2a - 11 = -9$$
$$2a = 2$$
$$a = 1$$

3. Solve for c and substitute to find the values for a and b.

$(1, 3, -4)$

4. Write the solution as an ordered triple.

It should be pointed out that row reduction could be carried out to the point where the coefficient matrix (left portion of the augmented matrix) becomes an identity matrix. The constant column then is the solution to the system.

The following example shows a dependent system solved by Gaussian elimination. A general solution in terms of the arbitrary constant t is found.

EXAMPLE 5   Solve.
$$x - 2y - 4z = 2$$
$$-3x + 10y + 4z = 10$$

Answer

$$\begin{bmatrix} 1 & -2 & -4 & | & 2 \\ -3 & 10 & 4 & | & 10 \end{bmatrix} \xrightarrow{3r_1 + r_2} \begin{bmatrix} 1 & -2 & -4 & | & 2 \\ 0 & 4 & -8 & | & 16 \end{bmatrix}$$

$$\xrightarrow{\frac{1}{4}r_2} \begin{bmatrix} 1 & -2 & -4 & | & 2 \\ 0 & 1 & -2 & | & 4 \end{bmatrix}$$

1. Write in augmented matrix form, and row-reduce to echelon form with $a_{11} = a_{21} = 1$. This will add to the ease of the solution.

$$y - 2z = 4$$
$$y - 2t = 4$$
$$y = 4 + 2t$$

2. Let z equal an arbitrary constant, t. Solve for y.

$$x - 2y - 4z = 2$$
$$x - 2(4 + 2t) - 4(t) = 2$$
$$x - 8 - 4t - 4t = 2$$
$$x = 10 + 8t$$

3. To find x, substitute for y and z and solve.

$(10 + 8t, 4 + 2t, t)$

4. Write the general solution as an ordered triple.

The system has infinitely many solutions. Every real value of t corresponds to an ordered triple that is a particular solution to the system. The particular solution corresponding to $t = 1$ is (18, 6, 1). You can check it in the original system.

▶ A. Exercises

Based on the augmented matrices representing linear systems below, give the solution and classify any inconsistent or dependent systems.

1. $\begin{bmatrix} 5 & 3 & | & 2 \\ 0 & 1 & | & 4 \end{bmatrix}$

2. $\begin{bmatrix} 8 & 4 & | & 6 \\ 12 & 6 & | & 9 \end{bmatrix}$

3. $\begin{bmatrix} 7 & 2 & 3 & | & 5 \\ 0 & 1 & 2 & | & -1 \\ 0 & 0 & 1 & | & 4 \end{bmatrix}$

4. $\begin{bmatrix} 3 & 5 & 2 & | & -7 \\ 0 & -2 & 8 & | & 4 \\ 0 & 0 & 0 & | & 6 \end{bmatrix}$

5. $\begin{bmatrix} 2 & -3 & 1 & | & 3 \\ 0 & 1 & 3 & | & 2 \\ 0 & 0 & 0 & | & 0 \end{bmatrix}$

6. $\begin{bmatrix} 4 & 1 & 3 & | & 5 \\ 0 & 2 & 5 & | & 6 \\ 0 & 0 & 3 & | & 1 \end{bmatrix}$

▶ B. Exercises

Use matrix methods to solve the following systems of equations. If the problem has infinite solutions, give a general solution and a particular solution.

7. $3x + 5y = 9$
   $6x + 7y = 9$

8. $8x - 7y = -32$
   $12x + 3y = 6$

9. $8a - b = 9$
   $2a - \frac{1}{4}b = 5$

10. $15c + 2d = -15$
    $6c - 5d = 23$

11. $-2x + 3y + 5z = -1$
    $6x - 2y - 3z = 5$

12. $3x + 4y + 5z = 4$
    $x + 2y - 2z = 2$

13. $2x - 3y + z = -15$
    $-4x + y + 5z = 13$

14. $3a - 2b - 5c = -9$
    $3a + 4b - 4c = 1$
    $-2a + 3b + 5c = 6$

15. $4x_1 - 3x_2 + 2x_3 = -7$
    $6x_1 + 2x_2 + 3x_3 = 9$
    $-8x_1 + 3x_2 - 5x_3 = 3$

16. $5x_1 - 2x_2 + 4x_3 = -9$
    $3x_1 - 4x_2 + 2x_3 = -2$
    $2x_1 + 6x_2 + 5x_3 = -7$

17. $2x_1 + 3x_2 + x_3 + 2x_4 = 1$
    $4x_1 - x_2 + 3x_3 = 4$
    $-6x_1 + 4x_2 + 2x_3 + 3x_4 = -2$
    $-4x_1 - 2x_2 + 3x_3 + 2x_4 = 8$

18. $6x_1 + x_2 - 4x_3 - 5x_4 = 1$
    $2x_1 + 3x_2 - 2x_3 - 2x_4 = 6$
    $4x_1 - 2x_2 - 2x_3 - 3x_4 = -5$
    $4x_1 + 2x_2 - 3x_3 - 5x_4 = -1$

19. $\frac{1}{8}x + \frac{1}{4}y = \frac{7}{5}$

$\quad\; \frac{1}{2}x - \frac{1}{5}y = -\frac{7}{8}$

20. Create a matrix *A* of coefficients and a matrix *B* of constants, and then augment them. Use reduced row-echelon form to solve the system. (Round coordinates of the solution to the nearest tenth.)

$1.5x - 3.3y + 0.7z = 9.9$

$0.2x + 4.1y - 1.3z = 10.5$

$2.4x + 0.4y - 7.5z = 2.2$

▶ C. Exercises

21. A Christian school earned $150 the first week of a paper drive. The second and third weeks it earned $400 and $750, respectively. The business manager noticed that this followed a parabolic curve. Find the quadratic function whose graph fits the description and predict the income of the paper drive for the fourth week, given the general equation of a parabola: $y = ax^2 + bx + c$.

22. Auto Mart has two varieties of antifreeze, one that is **30%** alcohol and another that is **80%** alcohol. How many gallons of each should be mixed together to get **30** gallons of **50%** alcohol?

Dominion Modeling

23. A regression line rarely passes through all the data points; plotting residuals shows the difference between the actual data and the fitted model. The linear regression line *minimizes* the sum of the squared residuals. (Sometimes "residuals" are called "errors.")

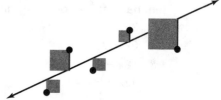

Example of 5 data points with squared errors

The figure shown is an example of five data points, with errors from the data to the model in red and the squares of the errors in blue. Using your Hubble scatterplot (with model), sketch the squared error for each data point.

24. What is the sum of the squared errors for Hubble's data? Does the data fit the model?

Cumulative Review

Given: $\sin \theta = a$, $\cos \theta = b$, $\sin \phi = c$, and $\cos \phi = d$, find the following.

25. $\sin 2\theta$ and $\cos 2\theta$

26. $\cos 4\theta$

27. $\cot \phi$ and $\tan (-\phi)$

28. $\sin (\theta + \phi)$ and $\cos (2\theta - \phi)$

29. $\cos \frac{\theta}{2}$ and $\sin \frac{\theta}{4}$

8.4 Determinants

The determinant of a matrix maps a matrix to a real number. The determinant is therefore a real valued function that pairs each square matrix $A_{n \times n}$ with a real number known as the determinant of A, denoted $|A|$. The formula for finding the determinant of a 2×2 matrix is given here.

$$\text{If } A = \begin{bmatrix} a & b \\ c & d \end{bmatrix}, \text{ then } |A| = \begin{vmatrix} a & b \\ c & d \end{vmatrix} = ad - bc$$

EXAMPLE 1 If $A = \begin{bmatrix} 6 & -2 \\ 5 & 8 \end{bmatrix}$, find $|A|$.

Answer $|A| = 6(8) - 5(-2) = 48 + 10 = 58$

Evaluating 3×3 determinants is a bit harder; consider the two methods below.

Method 1: Using Diagonal Products

Let $A = \begin{bmatrix} a_{11} & a_{12} & a_{13} \\ a_{21} & a_{22} & a_{23} \\ a_{31} & a_{32} & a_{33} \end{bmatrix}$.

List the first two columns of A in order after the matrix.

$$\begin{bmatrix} a_{11} & a_{12} & a_{13} \\ a_{21} & a_{22} & a_{23} \\ a_{31} & a_{32} & a_{33} \end{bmatrix} \begin{matrix} a_{11} & a_{12} \\ a_{21} & a_{22} \\ a_{31} & a_{32} \end{matrix}$$

The determinant of A requires the calculation of six products. Find the first three by multiplying the entries in the diagonals running from upper left to lower right. Add these three products together.

$$\begin{bmatrix} a_{11} & a_{12} & a_{13} \\ a_{21} & a_{22} & a_{23} \\ a_{31} & a_{32} & a_{33} \end{bmatrix} \begin{matrix} a_{11} & a_{12} \\ a_{21} & a_{22} \\ a_{31} & a_{32} \end{matrix} \qquad a_{11}a_{22}a_{33} + a_{12}a_{23}a_{31} + a_{13}a_{21}a_{32}$$

Then find the other three terms by multiplying the entries in the diagonals running from lower left to upper right. Subtract each of these products.

$$\begin{bmatrix} a_{11} & a_{12} & a_{13} \\ a_{21} & a_{22} & a_{23} \\ a_{31} & a_{32} & a_{33} \end{bmatrix} \begin{matrix} a_{11} & a_{12} \\ a_{21} & a_{22} \\ a_{31} & a_{32} \end{matrix} \quad -a_{31}a_{22}a_{13} - a_{32}a_{23}a_{11} - a_{33}a_{21}a_{12}$$

$$|A| = a_{11}a_{22}a_{33} + a_{12}a_{23}a_{31} + a_{13}a_{21}a_{32} - a_{31}a_{22}a_{13} - a_{32}a_{23}a_{11} - a_{33}a_{21}a_{12}$$

EXAMPLE 2   If $A = \begin{bmatrix} 2 & -3 & 4 \\ 0 & 5 & -1 \\ 4 & 6 & 1 \end{bmatrix}$, find $|A|$.

Answer $\begin{bmatrix} 2 & -3 & 4 \\ 0 & 5 & -1 \\ 4 & 6 & 1 \end{bmatrix} \begin{matrix} 2 & -3 \\ 0 & 5 \\ 4 & 6 \end{matrix}$ $|A| = 10 + 12 + 0 - 80 - (-12) - 0$

$ = -46$

Method 1 applies only to 3×3 matrices. Another method is needed to find the determinant for a larger square matrix. To use the more general method you must understand minors and cofactors. The *minor of an entry* in a matrix A is the determinant of the matrix formed by crossing out the row and column of the given entry. For matrix $A = \begin{bmatrix} 2 & -3 & 4 \\ 0 & 5 & -1 \\ 4 & 6 & 1 \end{bmatrix}$, the minor for $a_{13} = 4$ is the determinant left after you cross out the first row and third column.

$$\begin{bmatrix} 2 & -3 & 4 \\ 0 & 5 & -1 \\ 4 & 6 & 1 \end{bmatrix}$$

The minor of entry a_{13} is $\begin{vmatrix} 0 & 5 \\ 4 & 6 \end{vmatrix} = 0 \cdot 6 - 4 \cdot 5 = -20$.

EXAMPLE 3   Find the minor of 6 in matrix $A = \begin{bmatrix} 2 & -3 & 4 \\ 0 & 5 & -1 \\ 4 & 6 & 1 \end{bmatrix}$.

Answer $\begin{bmatrix} 2 & -3 & 4 \\ 0 & 5 & -1 \\ 4 & 6 & 1 \end{bmatrix}$ 1. The 6 is in position a_{32}, therefore, cross out the third row and the second column to find the minor.

$\begin{vmatrix} 2 & 4 \\ 0 & -1 \end{vmatrix} = 2(-1) - 0(4) = -2$ 2. Evaluate the determinant.

The *cofactor of an entry* a_{ij} is $(-1)^{i+j}$ times the minor of a_{ij}.

EXAMPLE 4   Find the cofactor of 2 in the matrix $A = \begin{bmatrix} 2 & -3 & 4 \\ 0 & 5 & -1 \\ 4 & 6 & 1 \end{bmatrix}$.

Answer

$(-1)^{1+1} \begin{vmatrix} 5 & -1 \\ 6 & 1 \end{vmatrix} = (1)[5 \cdot 1 - 6 \cdot -1] = 11$ Since 2 is the a_{11} entry, $i = 1$ and $j = 1$. Remember that i and j are row and column numbers.

EXAMPLE 5   Find the cofactor of 0 in the matrix $A = \begin{bmatrix} 2 & -3 & 4 \\ 0 & 5 & -1 \\ 4 & 6 & 1 \end{bmatrix}$.

Answer

$(-1)^{2+1} \begin{vmatrix} -3 & 4 \\ 6 & 1 \end{vmatrix} = (-1)(-3 \cdot 1 - 6 \cdot 4) = 27$ 0 is the a_{21} entry; so $i = 2$ and $j = 1$.

Note that $(-1)^{i+j}$ will have the following pattern for signs of entries in an $n \times n$ matrix.

$$\begin{bmatrix} + & - & + & \cdots \\ - & + & - & \cdots \\ + & - & + & \cdots \\ \cdots & \cdots & \cdots & \cdots \\ \cdots & \cdots & \cdots & \cdots \end{bmatrix}$$

By observing the alternating pattern, you can see that the cofactor of 1 in

$$A = \begin{bmatrix} 2 & -3 & 4 \\ 0 & 5 & -1 \\ 4 & 6 & 1 \end{bmatrix} \text{ is } (1) \begin{vmatrix} 2 & -3 \\ 0 & 5 \end{vmatrix} = 1(10 - 0) = 10.$$

Now let us return to evaluating a determinant. Method 2 uses minors to evaluate the determinant of a square matrix in the following 3 steps.

Method 2: Expansion by Minors

1. Select a row or column.
2. Multiply each entry in the row or column by its cofactor.
3. Add the products from step 2.

EXAMPLE 6   If $A = \begin{bmatrix} 2 & -3 & 4 \\ 0 & 5 & -1 \\ 4 & 6 & 1 \end{bmatrix}$, find $|A|$ by the use of *minors*.

Answer

$|A| = 2 \cdot$ cofactor of $2 + (-3) \cdot$ cofactor of $-3 +$ 1. Use the entries
       $4 \cdot$ cofactor of 4   in the first row.

$|A| = 2(-1)^{1+1} \begin{vmatrix} 5 & -1 \\ 6 & 1 \end{vmatrix} + (-3)(-1)^{1+2} \begin{vmatrix} 0 & -1 \\ 4 & 1 \end{vmatrix} + 4(-1)^{1+3} \begin{vmatrix} 0 & 5 \\ 4 & 6 \end{vmatrix}$

$\quad = 2(1)(5 + 6) + (-3)(-1)(0 + 4) + 4(1)(0 - 20)$ 2. Multiply each

$\quad = 22 + 12 - 80$ entry by its

$\quad = -46$ cofactor and add.

Alternate answer

$|A| = 2 \begin{vmatrix} 5 & -1 \\ 6 & 1 \end{vmatrix} - 0 \begin{vmatrix} -3 & 4 \\ 6 & 1 \end{vmatrix} + 4 \begin{vmatrix} -3 & 4 \\ 5 & -1 \end{vmatrix}$ A better method would be
to expand by the first col-
umn, since one term would

$\quad = 2(11) + 4(-17) = 22 - 68 = -46$ be 0. Also notice the $(-1)^{i+j}$
was replaced by alternating
signs, +, −, +.

The value of the determinant is the same no matter which row or column you use in the expansion. Row 2 or column 1 are better choices, since one entry is zero. Zero times a cofactor will always be zero regardless of the value of the cofactor. Therefore, only two cofactors need be calculated. Unlike Method 1 (for 3×3 matrices only), Method 2 (expansion by minors) can be used on any larger square matrix.

EXAMPLE 7   If $B = \begin{bmatrix} 1 & 2 & -1 & 0 \\ -3 & 2 & 4 & 1 \\ -2 & -1 & 2 & 5 \\ 0 & 4 & 1 & 3 \end{bmatrix}$, find $|B|$.

Answer

$|B| = +(1) \begin{vmatrix} 2 & 4 & 1 \\ -1 & 2 & 5 \\ 4 & 1 & 3 \end{vmatrix} - (2) \begin{vmatrix} -3 & 4 & 1 \\ -2 & 2 & 5 \\ 0 & 1 & 3 \end{vmatrix}$ 1. Evaluate the determinant, using the minors
of the first row. Since
one entry is zero, there

$\quad + (-1) \begin{vmatrix} -3 & 2 & 1 \\ -2 & -1 & 5 \\ 0 & 4 & 3 \end{vmatrix} - 0$ will be only 3 cofactors
to calculate. Patterns of
signs +, −, + are shown.

Continued ▶

$$|B| = 1\left[2\begin{vmatrix}2 & 5 \\ 1 & 3\end{vmatrix} - 4\begin{vmatrix}-1 & 5 \\ 4 & 3\end{vmatrix} + 1\begin{vmatrix}-1 & 2 \\ 4 & 1\end{vmatrix}\right]$$

$$- 2\left[-3\begin{vmatrix}2 & 5 \\ 1 & 3\end{vmatrix} - (-2)\begin{vmatrix}4 & 1 \\ 1 & 3\end{vmatrix} + 0\right]$$

$$+ (-1)\left[0 - 4\begin{vmatrix}-3 & 1 \\ -2 & 5\end{vmatrix} + 3\begin{vmatrix}-3 & 2 \\ -2 & -1\end{vmatrix}\right]$$

$$= 1[2(1) - 4(-23) + 1(-9)] - 2[-3(1)$$
$$+ 2(11)] - 1[-4(-13) + 3(7)]$$

$$= 1(85) - 2(19) - 1(73)$$

$$= 85 - 38 - 73$$

$$= -26$$

2. Evaluate each 3 × 3 determinant using minors.

   a. Expand using the first row of the first 3 × 3 determinant.

   b. Expand using the first column of the second 3 × 3 determinant.

   c. Expand using the last row of the third 3 × 3 determinant.

As you can see, even though expansion works on any square matrix, calculating determinants with larger numbers of rows and columns can be very laborious. In the next section you will study some properties of determinants which will reduce this work.

The *transpose* of a matrix A, denoted by A^T, is obtained by using the respective rows of A as the columns of A^T.

EXAMPLE 8   If $A = \begin{bmatrix} 3 & -1 & 4 \\ 2 & 5 & -6 \end{bmatrix}$, find A^T.

Answer $A^T = \begin{bmatrix} 3 & 2 \\ -1 & 5 \\ 4 & -6 \end{bmatrix}$ The first row of A becomes the first column of A^T, and the second row of A becomes the second column of A^T.

The determinant of a square matrix can be found by the expansion method. Since it can be expanded using minors of either a row or a column, $|A| = |A^T|$. This means that you should be alert for column relationships to shortcut determinant calculations. Methods used on rows can also be used on columns.

Evaluate the determinants of the following matrices.

1. $\begin{bmatrix} 8 & -3 \\ 5 & 9 \end{bmatrix}$

2. $\begin{bmatrix} \frac{1}{2} & 5 \\ 6 & 8 \end{bmatrix}$

3. $\begin{bmatrix} 11 & 7 \\ -13 & -9 \end{bmatrix}$

4. $\begin{bmatrix} -14 & 3.5 \\ -42 & -5.6 \end{bmatrix}$

5. $\begin{bmatrix} 2 & 1 & -4 \\ 3 & 2 & -5 \\ 6 & 2 & 1 \end{bmatrix}$

6. $\begin{bmatrix} 5 & -3 & 4 \\ 2 & 3 & -2 \\ 4 & -2 & 4 \end{bmatrix}$

7. If $A = \begin{bmatrix} 2 & -3 & 4 \\ 7 & 5 & -5 \\ 8 & 2 & 6 \end{bmatrix}$, write A^T.

8. If $|B| = 78$, what is $|B^T|$?

► B. Exercises

Evaluate the following determinants, using row or column expansion and cofactors.

9. $\begin{vmatrix} 4 & 2 & -2 \\ 0 & -4 & 5 \\ 5 & 6 & 1 \end{vmatrix}$

10. $\begin{vmatrix} -7 & 1 & -2 \\ 5 & -8 & 0 \\ 3 & -3 & 3 \end{vmatrix}$

11. $\begin{vmatrix} 10 & -1 & 4 \\ 2 & 1 & 6 \\ 4 & -2 & -3 \end{vmatrix}$

12. $\begin{vmatrix} 2 & 3 & 1 & -1 \\ 0 & 2 & 0 & 3 \\ -4 & 1 & 0 & 5 \\ 3 & 2 & 3 & -2 \end{vmatrix}$

13. $\begin{vmatrix} 6 & -3 & 4 & -2 \\ 1 & -1 & 3 & 2 \\ 0 & 0 & 2 & 0 \\ 1 & 3 & 1 & -2 \end{vmatrix}$

14. $\begin{vmatrix} 5 & -2 & 1 & 3 & 4 \\ 0 & 6 & 2 & -4 & 5 \\ 0 & 0 & -2 & 3 & 1 \\ 0 & 0 & 0 & 4 & 2 \\ 0 & 0 & 0 & 0 & 1 \end{vmatrix}$

15. If matrix A has a row of zeros, find $|A|$. Explain your answer.

16. If $A = \begin{bmatrix} a_{11} & a_{12} & a_{13} & a_{14} \\ 0 & a_{22} & a_{23} & a_{24} \\ 0 & 0 & a_{33} & a_{34} \\ 0 & 0 & 0 & a_{44} \end{bmatrix}$, find $|A|$.

17. If A is an $n \times n$ matrix in echelon form, find $|A|$.

18. Give the determinant of any identity matrix.

Evaluate the following determinants.

19. $\begin{vmatrix} 0 & 2 & 0 \\ 0 & 0 & -3 \\ 4 & 0 & 0 \end{vmatrix}$

21. $\begin{vmatrix} 0 & 2 & 0 \\ 5 & -3 & 6 \\ 0 & 9 & 0 \end{vmatrix}$

20. $\begin{vmatrix} 0 & 0 & 5 & 0 \\ \frac{1}{2} & 0 & 0 & 0 \\ 0 & 0 & 0 & -3 \\ 0 & 8 & 0 & 0 \end{vmatrix}$

22. $\begin{vmatrix} -\frac{1}{8} & \frac{1}{4} & \frac{7}{5} \\ -2 & -\frac{1}{5} & \frac{5}{8} \\ -\frac{1}{2} & 3 & -5 \end{vmatrix}$

▶ C. Exercises

23. Which properties below are satisfied for all square matrices? Provide an example or counterexample as appropriate.
$$|AB| = |A| \cdot |B|$$
$$|A + B| = |A| + |B|$$

24. Prove or disprove: $|A| = 0$ if A is a square matrix with zero for each corner entry.

Dominion Modeling

Answer each question according to the linear regression model for Hubble's data. Interpret and evaluate each answer.

25. How rapidly would a galaxy move away from us if it is 0 megaparsecs distant? (Also give your answer in miles per hour.)

26. How distant must an object be for its velocity to be zero? (*Hint:* Hubble did not measure the direction of the nebula in his calculations.)

27. At what distance will the velocity of the object reach the speed of light (about 3.0×10^5 km/sec.)?

Cumulative Review

28. Without graphing, specify all asymptotes and give the domain and range for the following functions.
$$f(x) = \tfrac{1}{x}, \ g(x) = \tfrac{1}{x^2}, \ h(x) = \tfrac{x + 1}{x^2 + 4x + 3}$$

29. For the functions in exercise 28, find $(f \circ h)(x)$ and $(h \circ f)(x)$.

30. For the functions in exercise 28, find $(f + g)(x)$, $fg(x)$ and $(f - g)(x)$.

31. Graph $f(x) = 3e^x$.

32. Give the inverse function for the function in exercise 31 and graph it.

8.5 Properties of Determinants

The properties of determinants in this section will help you evaluate them. Let's consider the effect of each elementary row operation on the value of the determinant.

Obtain matrix B from matrix A by switching two rows (the first elementary row operation). Let $A = \begin{bmatrix} -3 & 4 \\ 5 & 2 \end{bmatrix}$ and $B = \begin{bmatrix} 5 & 2 \\ -3 & 4 \end{bmatrix}$. The determinants of these matrices are $|A| = -6 - 20 = -26$ and $|B| = 20 - (-6) = 26$. Notice that the determinants are opposites. This suggests that when A is a square matrix and B is obtained by interchanging two rows of matrix A, then $|B| = -|A|$.

Next, consider a matrix B obtained from matrix A by multiplying a specific row by a scalar (second elementary row operation). For example, let $A = \begin{bmatrix} -3 & 4 \\ 5 & 2 \end{bmatrix}$ and $B = \begin{bmatrix} -3 & 4 \\ 15 & 6 \end{bmatrix}$ (obtained by multiplying row 2 by scalar 3). The determinants of A and B follow.

$$|A| = \begin{vmatrix} -3 & 4 \\ 5 & 2 \end{vmatrix} = -6 - 20 = -26 \text{ and } |B| = \begin{vmatrix} -3 & 4 \\ 15 & 6 \end{vmatrix} = -18 - 60 = -78$$

Notice that $|B| = 3|A|$ and that we multiplied the second row of A by 3. The implication is that if matrix B is obtained from a square matrix A by multiplying one of its rows by a constant k, then $|B| = k|A|$.

For the third elementary row operation, consider matrices A and B, where the second row of B is obtained from matrix A by computing $2r_1 + r_2$. For example,

$$A = \begin{bmatrix} -3 & 4 \\ 5 & 2 \end{bmatrix} \text{ and } B = \begin{bmatrix} -3 & 4 \\ -1 & 10 \end{bmatrix}.$$

The determinants are $|A| = -26$ and $|B| = -30 + 4 = -26$. This example illustrates that if A is a square matrix and matrix B is obtained by adding a multiple of one row of A to another row, then $|A| = |B|$.

A fourth property is also worth some attention. Examine a square matrix in which one row is a multiple of another row.

$$A = \begin{bmatrix} -3 & 4 \\ 15 & -20 \end{bmatrix}$$

In this case, $|A| = 60 - 60 = 0$. Notice that the second row is -5 times the first row. Conclusion: If A is a square matrix with one row being a multiple of another, then $|A| = 0$.

You will now see how to use these properties to find determinants more easily.

EXAMPLE 1 If $B = \begin{bmatrix} 1 & 2 & -1 & 0 \\ -3 & 2 & 4 & 1 \\ -2 & -1 & 2 & 5 \\ 0 & 4 & 1 & 3 \end{bmatrix}$, find $|B|$.

Answer

$$B = \begin{bmatrix} 1 & 2 & -1 & 0 \\ -3 & 2 & 4 & 1 \\ -2 & -1 & 2 & 5 \\ 0 & 4 & 1 & 3 \end{bmatrix} \xrightarrow[2r_1 + r_3]{3r_1 + r_2} \begin{bmatrix} 1 & 2 & -1 & 0 \\ 0 & 8 & 1 & 1 \\ 0 & 3 & 0 & 5 \\ 0 & 4 & 1 & 3 \end{bmatrix}$$

1. Multiplying a row of a matrix by a constant and adding it to another row will give a matrix with the same determinant value as the original matrix. Use this property to make the determinant easier to evaluate.

$$\xrightarrow{-r_2 + r_4} \begin{bmatrix} 1 & 2 & -1 & 0 \\ 0 & 8 & 1 & 1 \\ 0 & 3 & 0 & 5 \\ 0 & -4 & 0 & 2 \end{bmatrix}$$

$$|B| = 1(-1)^{1+1} \begin{vmatrix} 8 & 1 & 1 \\ 3 & 0 & 5 \\ -4 & 0 & 2 \end{vmatrix} + 0 + 0 + 0$$

2. Use expansion by minors to find $|B|$, using the first column of the new 4×4 matrix.

$$|B| = 1(-1)^{1+2} \begin{vmatrix} 3 & 5 \\ -4 & 2 \end{vmatrix} + 0 + 0$$

$$= -1(6 + 20)$$

$$= -26$$

3. Now expand using the middle column of the new 3×3 determinant.

Elementary row operations can make the computations of determinants easier. Example 1 used only the third elementary row operation (a multiple of one row added to another), which does not change the determinant. If other row operations are used, be careful to compensate for the effect of the operation. Recall that once the matrix is in echelon form, the determinant is the product of the entries on the main diagonal (Section 8.4, exercises 16 and 17).

EXAMPLE 2 If $A = \begin{bmatrix} 3 & 1 & -2 \\ 4 & 8 & -12 \\ 2 & 0 & -1 \end{bmatrix}$, find $|A|$.

Answer

$$|A| = \begin{vmatrix} 3 & 1 & -2 \\ 4 & 8 & -12 \\ 2 & 0 & -1 \end{vmatrix}$$

$$= 4\begin{vmatrix} 3 & 1 & -2 \\ 1 & 2 & -3 \\ 2 & 0 & -1 \end{vmatrix}$$

1. Find $\frac{1}{4}r_2$. Remember that this makes the determinant one-fourth as large. Balance this by multiplying by 4.

$$= -4\begin{vmatrix} 1 & 2 & -3 \\ 3 & 1 & -2 \\ 2 & 0 & -1 \end{vmatrix}$$

2. $r_1 \leftrightarrow r_2$ (Interchange the top two rows.) Switching rows reverses the sign of the determinant, so change the sign on the outside of the determinant to compensate.

$$= -4\begin{vmatrix} 1 & 2 & -3 \\ 0 & -5 & 7 \\ 0 & -4 & 5 \end{vmatrix}$$

$$= -4\begin{vmatrix} 1 & 2 & -3 \\ 0 & -1 & 2 \\ 0 & -4 & 5 \end{vmatrix}$$

3. Use the third row operation to obtain zeros at the start of rows 2 and 3: $\xrightarrow[-2r_1 + r_3]{-3r_1 + r_2}$. Next, work on row 2 by finding $-r_3 + r_2$. These operations did not affect the determinant.

$$= 4\begin{vmatrix} 1 & 2 & -3 \\ 0 & 1 & -2 \\ 0 & -4 & 5 \end{vmatrix}$$

4. Find $-r_2$, which requires a sign change. The multiplier -4 becomes 4.

$$= 4\begin{vmatrix} 1 & 2 & -3 \\ 0 & 1 & -2 \\ 0 & 0 & -3 \end{vmatrix}$$

$$= 4(-3) = -12$$

5. To obtain echelon form, find $4r_2 + r_3$, which does not affect the determinant. Then multiply the outside scalar by the product of the entries on the main diagonal.

EXAMPLE 3 Find $\begin{vmatrix} 7 & 6 & 9 & 3 \\ 2 & -4 & -6 & 5 \\ 5 & 2 & 3 & 8 \\ -4 & 8 & 12 & -4 \end{vmatrix}$.

Answer Recall that when one row is a multiple of another, the determinant is zero. Since this property applies to columns as well as rows, and since column 3 is 1.5 times as large as column 2, the determinant is 0.

> **Effects of Elementary Row Operations on Determinants**
>
> 1. Interchange rows → sign of the determinant changes
> 2. Multiply a row by a nonzero constant k → determinant is multiplied by k
> 3. Add a multiple of one row to another row → determinant remains the same
> 4. One row is a multiple of another → determinant is zero
> 5. Matrix is in echelon form → determinant is the product of the main diagonal

▶ A. Exercises

Find the determinants.

1. $\begin{vmatrix} 2 & 0 & 0 & 0 & 0 & 0 \\ 0 & 2 & 0 & 0 & 0 & 0 \\ 0 & 0 & 2 & 0 & 0 & 0 \\ 0 & 0 & 0 & 2 & 0 & 0 \\ 0 & 0 & 0 & 0 & 2 & 0 \\ 0 & 0 & 0 & 0 & 0 & 2 \end{vmatrix}$

2. $\begin{vmatrix} 7 & -1 & 1 & 2 \\ 5 & 2 & 4 & -1 \\ 0 & 0 & 0 & 0 \\ 3 & 6 & -3 & 5 \end{vmatrix}$

If $A = \begin{bmatrix} a & 2 & 7 \\ -3 & 1 & 4 \\ 5 & b & -2 \end{bmatrix}$ and $|A| = 6$, find

3. $\begin{vmatrix} a & 2 & 7 \\ 5 & b & -2 \\ -3 & 1 & 4 \end{vmatrix}$.

4. $\begin{vmatrix} a & 2 & 7 \\ -15 & 5 & 20 \\ 5 & b & -2 \end{vmatrix}$.

5. $\begin{vmatrix} a & 2 & 7 \\ -3 & 1 & 4 \\ 2 & 1+b & 2 \end{vmatrix}$.

6. $\begin{vmatrix} a & -3 & 5 \\ 2 & 1 & b \\ 7 & 4 & -2 \end{vmatrix}$.

▶ B. Exercises

Evaluate the following determinants, using the properties of determinants.

7. $\begin{vmatrix} 3 & -2 & 4 \\ 1 & 2 & 3 \\ 2 & 2 & 5 \end{vmatrix}$

8. $\begin{vmatrix} 2 & 3 & 5 \\ 4 & -5 & -1 \\ 5 & 2 & 7 \end{vmatrix}$

9. $\begin{vmatrix} -5 & 3 & 6 \\ 7 & 4 & 2 \\ -1 & 5 & -4 \end{vmatrix}$

10. $\begin{vmatrix} 3 & -1 & 2 & -2 \\ 4 & -2 & 3 & 3 \\ 5 & 1 & 4 & 2 \\ 2 & 2 & -3 & 2 \end{vmatrix}$

12. $\begin{vmatrix} 2 & 5 & 3 \\ 2 & 5 & 3 \\ 6 & 1 & 4 \end{vmatrix}$

11. $\begin{vmatrix} -2 & 1 & 2 & -1 \\ 3 & 2 & -3 & 2 \\ 1 & -3 & -1 & 3 \\ 4 & 0 & -4 & 8 \end{vmatrix}$

13. $\begin{vmatrix} 3 & 9 & 6 \\ 5 & 7 & 1 \\ 1 & 3 & 2 \end{vmatrix}$

If A is an $n \times n$ matrix and $|A| = 10$, find the following determinants.

14. $|2A|$ if $n = 3$

16. $|5A|$ if $n = 2$

15. $|3A|$ if $n = 4$

▶ C. Exercises

17. If A is an $n \times n$ matrix and k is a constant, give a formula for $|kA|$ in terms of $|A|$.

18. Justify your answer to exercise 17.

Dominion Modeling

19. Astronomers call the slope of the regression equation *Hubble's constant*, or H_0. What is the value of H_0 from Hubble's data, and what are the units? (*Hint:* Reduce the units from kilometer/second per megaparsec to a unit of time. A megaparsec is a million parsecs, a parsec is about 3.262 light years, and a light year is about 9.461×10^{12} km.)

20. What is the value of the reciprocal of H_0? Give your answer in *years*.

21. What assumption underlies the calculation of the age of the universe by this means? How does it result in circular reasoning?

Cumulative Review

Graph the following.

22. $f(x) = 3 + \sqrt{x - 1}$

25. $k(x) = \text{Sin}^{-1} x$

23. $g(x) = \dfrac{x + 1}{x^2 - 4}$

26. $p(x) = x^3 - x$

24. $h(x) = \frac{1}{2}e^{-x} - 1$

Seven rows of seven seats are arranged in a lecture hall. After the forty-nine students are seated, the professor asks that every student move up one seat, back one seat, to the left one seat, or to the right one seat. Is this possible? Explain.

8.6 Solving Systems by Cramer's Rule

Gabriel Cramer (1704-1752) worked with determinants and popularized their use. He introduced a method of solving systems of equations by calculating determinants.

Switzerland's Matterhorn would have been familiar to Gabriel Cramer and other Swiss mathematicians such as Leonhard Euler and the Bernoulli family.

Cramer's Rule

Let

$$a_{11}x_1 + a_{12}x_2 + \cdots + a_{1n}x_n = b_1$$
$$a_{21}x_1 + a_{22}x_2 + \cdots + a_{2n}x_n = b_2$$
$$\vdots \qquad \vdots \qquad \cdots \qquad \vdots \qquad \vdots$$
$$a_{n1}x_1 + a_{n2}x_2 + \cdots + a_{nn}x_n = b_n$$

represent a consistent and independent system of n linear equations in n variables. Then $x_1 = \dfrac{|A_1|}{|A|}$, $x_2 = \dfrac{|A_2|}{|A|}$, . . . , $x_n = \dfrac{|A_n|}{|A|}$, where A is the coefficient matrix of the system:

$$\begin{bmatrix} a_{11} & a_{12} & \cdots & a_{1n} \\ a_{21} & a_{22} & \cdots & a_{2n} \\ \vdots & \vdots & & \vdots \\ a_{n1} & a_{n2} & \cdots & a_{nn} \end{bmatrix}.$$

Each A_i is a modification of matrix A formed by replacing the ith column with the column of constants.

$$A_i = \begin{bmatrix} a_{11} & a_{12} & \cdots & b_1 & \cdots & a_{1n} \\ a_{21} & a_{22} & \cdots & b_2 & \cdots & a_{2n} \\ \vdots & \vdots & & \vdots & & \vdots \\ a_{n1} & a_{n2} & \cdots & b_n & \cdots & a_{nn} \end{bmatrix}.$$

Gabriel Cramer (1704-1752), seen in a rare depiction without his wig, proved Cramer's rule.

EXAMPLE 1 Use Cramer's rule to find the solution to the following system of equations: $-3x + 7y + 2z = 44$
$$9x + 4y - 5z = -27$$
$$2x + 3y + 4z = 28$$

Answer

$$A = \begin{bmatrix} -3 & 7 & 2 \\ 9 & 4 & -5 \\ 2 & 3 & 4 \end{bmatrix}$$

$$A_1 = A_x = \begin{bmatrix} 44 & 7 & 2 \\ -27 & 4 & -5 \\ 28 & 3 & 4 \end{bmatrix}$$

$$A_2 = A_y = \begin{bmatrix} -3 & 44 & 2 \\ 9 & -27 & -5 \\ 2 & 28 & 4 \end{bmatrix}$$

$$A_3 = A_z = \begin{bmatrix} -3 & 7 & 44 \\ 9 & 4 & -27 \\ 2 & 3 & 28 \end{bmatrix}$$

1. Find, A, A_1, A_2, and A_3. For A_1, replace the first column (coefficients of x) of A with the constants; for A_2, replace the second column; and for A_3, replace the third column. Since the variables are not subscripted, A_1 can be written as A_x, A_2 as A_y, and A_3 as A_z.

2. Apply Cramer's rule.

$$x = \frac{|A_x|}{|A|} = \frac{\begin{vmatrix} 44 & 7 & 2 \\ -27 & 4 & -5 \\ 28 & 3 & 4 \end{vmatrix}}{\begin{vmatrix} -3 & 7 & 2 \\ 9 & 4 & -5 \\ 2 & 3 & 4 \end{vmatrix}} = \frac{754}{-377} = -2$$

$$y = \frac{|A_y|}{|A|} = \frac{\begin{vmatrix} -3 & 44 & 2 \\ 9 & -27 & -5 \\ 2 & 28 & 4 \end{vmatrix}}{-377} = \frac{-1508}{-377} = 4$$

$$z = \frac{|A_z|}{|A|} = \frac{\begin{vmatrix} -3 & 7 & 44 \\ 9 & 4 & -27 \\ 2 & 3 & 28 \end{vmatrix}}{-377} = \frac{-1885}{-377} = 5$$

The solution is $(-2, 4, 5)$.

EXAMPLE 2 Use Cramer's rule to solve the following system of equations.

$$3x + 8y = 5$$
$$6x + 16y = 7$$

Answer $A = \begin{vmatrix} 3 & 8 \\ 6 & 16 \end{vmatrix} = 0, \quad A_x = \begin{vmatrix} 5 & 8 \\ 7 & 16 \end{vmatrix} = 24, \quad A_y = \begin{vmatrix} 3 & 5 \\ 6 & 7 \end{vmatrix} = -9$

$$x = \frac{|A_x|}{|A|} = \frac{24}{0} \text{ (undefined)} \quad y = \frac{|A_y|}{|A|} = \frac{-9}{0} \text{ (undefined)}$$

The solution to the system is $\varnothing$. This inconsistent system is represented graphically by two parallel lines. The zero determinant for the coefficient matrix shows that the system is either dependent or inconsistent and that Cramer's rule does not apply.

EXAMPLE 3 Use Cramer's rule to solve the following system of equations.

$$3x + 8y = 5$$
$$6x + 16y = 10$$

Answer $A = \begin{vmatrix} 3 & 8 \\ 6 & 16 \end{vmatrix} = 0, \quad A_x = \begin{vmatrix} 5 & 8 \\ 10 & 16 \end{vmatrix} = 0, \quad A_y = \begin{vmatrix} 3 & 5 \\ 6 & 10 \end{vmatrix} = 0$

$$x = \frac{|A_x|}{|A|} = \frac{0}{0} \quad y = \frac{|A_y|}{|A|} = \frac{0}{0}$$

Both determinants are undefined because the system is dependent. The two equations represent the same line. The solution is $\{(x, y) \mid 3x + 8y = 5\}$.

The following example illustrates that the determinant of a product is equal to the product of the individual determinants.

EXAMPLE 4 If $A = \begin{bmatrix} 3 & -4 \\ 5 & -6 \end{bmatrix}$ and $B = \begin{bmatrix} -7 & -5 \\ 4 & 8 \end{bmatrix}$, show that $|AB| = |A| \cdot |B|$.

Answer $|A| = -18 - (-20) = 2$ and $|B| = -56 - (-20) = -36$

$$|A| \cdot |B| = -72$$

$$AB = \begin{bmatrix} 3 & -4 \\ 5 & -6 \end{bmatrix} \begin{bmatrix} -7 & -5 \\ 4 & 8 \end{bmatrix} = \begin{bmatrix} -37 & -47 \\ -59 & -73 \end{bmatrix}$$

$$|AB| = \begin{vmatrix} -37 & -47 \\ -59 & -73 \end{vmatrix} = 2701 - 2773 = -72$$

Therefore, $|AB| = |A| \cdot |B|$

The property illustrated in Example 4 does not apply to addition. Notice that

$$|A + B| = \begin{vmatrix} -4 & -9 \\ 9 & 2 \end{vmatrix} = 73 \text{ but } |A| + |B| = 2 - 36 = -34.$$

▶ A. Exercises

Solve each system using Cramer's rule.

1. $3x - 2y = 12$
   $4x + 3y = -1$

2. $6x - 2y = 11$
   $14x + 5y = -13$

3. $8x + 12y = 13$
   $6x + 9y = 15$

4. $-2x - 7y = 26$
   $3x + 2y = -5$

5. $5x - 3y = -11$
   $y = \frac{3}{2}x + 4$

6. $5x + 6y = -13$
   $y = \frac{1}{3}x + \frac{4}{3}$

Cramer's rule makes it easy to solve for selected variables.

7. Solve for y only.
   $x + 8y = 4$
   $2x - 3y = -5$

8. Solve for x only.
   $7x + 4y = 6$
   $2x + 5y = 3$

9. Solve for y only.
   $x + y + z = 5$
   $2x - y + z = 3$
   $x + 3y - 2z = 4$

10. Solve for z only.
    $x + y - 3z = 0$
    $2x + y + z = 3$
    $-x + z = 0$

▶ B. Exercises

Solve each system using Cramer's rule.

11. $2x_1 - 3x_2 + 4x_3 = 16$
    $-x_1 + 4x_2 - 10x_3 = -13$
    $4x_1 + 6x_2 - x_3 = 8$

12. $2x - y - 3z = -4$
    $3x + y - z = 2$
    $-x + y + 2z = 3$

13. $3a - b - c = -5$
    $21a - 3b + c = -7$
    $-9a + 2b - 7c = 0$

14. $3x - 5z = 3$
    $4y + 2z = 2$
    $2x + 3y = -2$

15. $7.4x + 3.2y - 2.5z = -3.1$
    $44x - 15.3y + 4.5z = 32.1$
    $3.2x - 4.8y + 1.1z = 12.45$

Consider the system:
$$v + x + z = 1$$
$$2v + w + 3z = 0$$
$$3w + y = 2$$
$$x - y = 3$$
$$v - 2z = 0$$

16. Find $|A|$.
17. Solve for v only.
18. Solve for z only.

19. Without calculating, solve for y.

$$5x + y + 3z + t = 1$$
$$-2x + 7y + z + 4t = 7$$
$$x + 2y - z + 3t = 2$$
$$3x - 4y + 2z + 4t = -4$$

20. Explain how you know the answer to exercise 19.

▶ C. Exercises

21. Solve the following system using Cramer's rule.

$$230.5x + 147.9y = 1024$$
$$123.7x + 67.34y = 765.0$$

22. A certain linear system has (1, 5) as a solution, but the determinant of A_x is zero, which makes it impossible to get $x = 1$ from Cramer's rule. How can this be?

▥ Dominion Modeling

23. Critique the following aspects of estimating the age of the earth using Hubble's constant.
    a. the data used to obtain Hubble's model
    b. the linear model
    c. the application of the reciprocal of the slope

■ Cumulative Review

24. Use laws of logarithms to evaluate $\log \frac{a^2 b^3}{c}$ if $\log a = 2.3456$, $\log b = 1.4532$, and $\log c = 0.9876$.

Solve the following equations.

25. $5^{2x} = 129$

26. $\ln (-2x) = 8.513$

27. Suppose p varies jointly with q and r and inversely with t. If $p = 3q$ when $r = 4t$, find q when $p = 8$, $r = 12$, and $t = 20$.

28. Find i^0, i^{-1}, i^{-2}, i^{-3}, and i^{-4}.

8.7 Inverses of Matrices

The inverse property of multiplication states that for all real numbers x ($x \neq 0$), there exists a real number y such that $x \cdot y = 1 = y \cdot x$. Similarly, a matrix A has an inverse if there is a matrix B so that $AB = I = BA$, where I is the identity matrix. A matrix for which an inverse exists is called an *invertible matrix*.

For example, $\begin{bmatrix} 2 & 1 \\ 3 & 4 \end{bmatrix}$ is an invertible matrix because

$$\begin{bmatrix} 2 & 1 \\ 3 & 4 \end{bmatrix} \cdot \begin{bmatrix} \frac{4}{5} & \frac{-1}{5} \\ \frac{-3}{5} & \frac{2}{5} \end{bmatrix} = \begin{bmatrix} 1 & 0 \\ 0 & 1 \end{bmatrix} = \begin{bmatrix} \frac{4}{5} & \frac{-1}{5} \\ \frac{-3}{5} & \frac{2}{5} \end{bmatrix} \cdot \begin{bmatrix} 2 & 1 \\ 3 & 4 \end{bmatrix}$$

In this case, $\begin{bmatrix} \frac{4}{5} & \frac{-1}{5} \\ \frac{-3}{5} & \frac{2}{5} \end{bmatrix}$ is the inverse of A, denoted A^{-1}.

Thus, $A \cdot A^{-1} = I = A^{-1} \cdot A$.

If $A = \begin{bmatrix} a & b \\ c & d \end{bmatrix}$ is invertible, $A^{-1} = \begin{bmatrix} \frac{d}{ad-bc} & \frac{-b}{ad-bc} \\ \frac{-c}{ad-bc} & \frac{a}{ad-bc} \end{bmatrix}$ or $A^{-1} = \begin{bmatrix} \frac{d}{|A|} & \frac{-b}{|A|} \\ \frac{-c}{|A|} & \frac{a}{|A|} \end{bmatrix}$.

EXAMPLE 1   If $A = \begin{bmatrix} 2 & -1 \\ 5 & -4 \end{bmatrix}$, find A^{-1}.

Answer $A^{-1} = \begin{bmatrix} \frac{-4}{|A|} & \frac{1}{|A|} \\ \frac{-5}{|A|} & \frac{2}{|A|} \end{bmatrix}$

$|A| = -8 - (-5) = -3$

$A^{-1} = \begin{bmatrix} \frac{4}{3} & \frac{-1}{3} \\ \frac{5}{3} & \frac{-2}{3} \end{bmatrix}$

Since the determinant of A is in the denominator, if $|A| = 0$, then A^{-1} does not exist.

EXAMPLE 2 Find A^{-1} if $A = \begin{bmatrix} 6 & -18 \\ -9 & 27 \end{bmatrix}$.

Answer Since $|A| = 162 - 162 = 0$, A^{-1} does not exist.

An alternate method of finding the inverse is to augment A with the identity matrix and use elementary row operations to reduce A to the identity matrix, I; the original identity matrix will then be A^{-1}.

EXAMPLE 3 If $A = \begin{bmatrix} 2 & 1 \\ 3 & 4 \end{bmatrix}$, find A^{-1}.

Answer

$\begin{bmatrix} 2 & 1 & | & 1 & 0 \\ 3 & 4 & | & 0 & 1 \end{bmatrix} \xrightarrow{2r_1} \begin{bmatrix} 4 & 2 & | & 2 & 0 \\ 3 & 4 & | & 0 & 1 \end{bmatrix}$

1. Place the identity matrix to the right of A and work to convert A to I.

$\xrightarrow{-r_2 + r_1} \begin{bmatrix} 1 & -2 & | & 2 & -1 \\ 3 & 4 & | & 0 & 1 \end{bmatrix}$

$\xrightarrow{-3r_1 + r_2} \begin{bmatrix} 1 & -2 & | & 2 & -1 \\ 0 & 10 & | & -6 & 4 \end{bmatrix}$

$\xrightarrow{\frac{1}{10}r_2} \begin{bmatrix} 1 & -2 & | & 2 & -1 \\ 0 & 1 & | & -\frac{3}{5} & \frac{2}{5} \end{bmatrix} \xrightarrow{2r_2 + r_1} \begin{bmatrix} 1 & 0 & | & \frac{4}{5} & -\frac{1}{5} \\ 0 & 1 & | & -\frac{3}{5} & \frac{2}{5} \end{bmatrix}$

$\therefore A^{-1} = \begin{bmatrix} \frac{4}{5} & -\frac{1}{5} \\ -\frac{3}{5} & \frac{2}{5} \end{bmatrix}$

2. The augmented portion of the matrix is the inverse of A.

EXAMPLE 4 If $A = \begin{bmatrix} 1 & 0 & 2 \\ 2 & -1 & 1 \\ 1 & 1 & 1 \end{bmatrix}$, find A^{-1}.

Answer

$\begin{bmatrix} 1 & 0 & 2 & | & 1 & 0 & 0 \\ 2 & -1 & 1 & | & 0 & 1 & 0 \\ 1 & 1 & 1 & | & 0 & 0 & 1 \end{bmatrix}$

$\xrightarrow[{-r_1 + r_3}]{-2r_1 + r_2} \begin{bmatrix} 1 & 0 & 2 & | & 1 & 0 & 0 \\ 0 & -1 & -3 & | & -2 & 1 & 0 \\ 0 & 1 & -1 & | & -1 & 0 & 1 \end{bmatrix} \xrightarrow[{-r_2}]{r_2 + r_3} \begin{bmatrix} 1 & 0 & 2 & | & 1 & 0 & 0 \\ 0 & 1 & 3 & | & 2 & -1 & 0 \\ 0 & 0 & -4 & | & -3 & 1 & 1 \end{bmatrix}$

Continued ▶

$$\xrightarrow{-\frac{1}{4}r_3} \begin{bmatrix} 1 & 0 & 2 & | & 1 & 0 & 0 \\ 0 & 1 & 3 & | & 2 & -1 & 0 \\ 0 & 0 & 1 & | & \frac{3}{4} & -\frac{1}{4} & -\frac{1}{4} \end{bmatrix} \xrightarrow[-3r_3 + r_2]{-2r_3 + r_1} \begin{bmatrix} 1 & 0 & 0 & | & -\frac{1}{2} & \frac{1}{2} & \frac{1}{2} \\ 0 & 1 & 0 & | & -\frac{1}{4} & -\frac{1}{4} & \frac{3}{4} \\ 0 & 0 & 1 & | & \frac{3}{4} & -\frac{1}{4} & -\frac{1}{4} \end{bmatrix}$$

$$\therefore A^{-1} = \begin{bmatrix} -\frac{1}{2} & \frac{1}{2} & \frac{1}{2} \\ -\frac{1}{4} & -\frac{1}{4} & \frac{3}{4} \\ \frac{3}{4} & -\frac{1}{4} & -\frac{1}{4} \end{bmatrix}$$

In Section 8.6, Example 4, the property $|AB| = |A| \cdot |B|$ was illustrated. This property facilitates the proof of the relationship between the determinants of matrices that are inverses.

$\|A A^{-1}\| = \|A A^{-1}\|$	1. reflexive property of equality
$\|A A^{-1}\| = \|I\|$	2. substitution from definition of inverse
$\|A A^{-1}\| = 1$	3. $\|I\| = 1$ (ones on the diagonal, echelon form)
$\|A\| \cdot \|A^{-1}\| = 1$	4. property that $\|AB\| = \|A\| \cdot \|B\|$
$\|A^{-1}\| = \dfrac{1}{\|A\|}$	5. multiplication property of equality (since the matrix is invertible, $\|A\| \neq 0$.)

Therefore, if A is invertible, $|A^{-1}| = \dfrac{1}{|A|}$

In Example 1, you can see this property where

$$A = \begin{bmatrix} 2 & -1 \\ 5 & -4 \end{bmatrix} \text{ and } A^{-1} \text{ was found to be } \begin{bmatrix} \frac{4}{3} & \frac{-1}{3} \\ \frac{5}{3} & \frac{-2}{3} \end{bmatrix}.$$

$$|A| = -8 - (-5) = -3$$

$$|A^{-1}| = \left(\frac{-8}{9}\right) - \left(\frac{-5}{9}\right) = \frac{-3}{9} = \frac{-1}{3}$$

$$|A^{-1}| = \frac{-1}{3} = \frac{1}{-3} = \frac{1}{|A|}$$

A linear system of equations can be represented by the matrix equation $AX = C$ where A is the coefficient matrix, X is the variable matrix, and C is the constant column matrix. Solving the matrix equation yields $X = A^{-1}C$. Thus, the product of the inverse of the coefficient matrix and the constant matrix will be the solution to the system of linear equations.

EXAMPLE 5 Solve the system using an inverse matrix.

$$3x - 2y = 12$$
$$4x + 3y = -1$$

Answer

$\begin{bmatrix} 3 & -2 \\ 4 & 3 \end{bmatrix} \begin{bmatrix} x \\ y \end{bmatrix} = \begin{bmatrix} 12 \\ -1 \end{bmatrix}$	1. Write the system as a matrix equation.
$A^{-1} = \begin{bmatrix} \frac{3}{17} & \frac{2}{17} \\ -\frac{4}{17} & \frac{3}{17} \end{bmatrix} = \frac{1}{17} \begin{bmatrix} 3 & 2 \\ -4 & 3 \end{bmatrix}$	2. Find the inverse of the coefficient matrix.
$X = A^{-1}C = \frac{1}{17} \begin{bmatrix} 3 & 2 \\ -4 & 3 \end{bmatrix} \begin{bmatrix} 12 \\ -1 \end{bmatrix} = \frac{1}{17} \begin{bmatrix} 34 \\ -51 \end{bmatrix} = \begin{bmatrix} 2 \\ -3 \end{bmatrix}$	3. Find the matrix product $X = A^{-1}C$.
The solution is $(2, -3)$.	4. Write the solution as an ordered pair.

This chapter has focused on the solution of linear systems of equations. In the first section, we reviewed the algebraic methods of addition and substitution. We then introduced matrices and developed the Gaussian elimination method using row-reduction to solve a linear system. After studying determinants, we then used Cramer's rule as another method. Finally, we developed the matrix inverse method. Although the Gaussian elimination and matrix inverse methods are the hardest to do manually, they are the best methods for calculators and computers, especially when the systems are 3 × 3 or larger.

▶ A. Exercises

Find each determinant.

1. $\begin{vmatrix} 2 & -2 & 2 \\ 5 & 3 & -4 \\ -3 & 2 & 1 \end{vmatrix}$

2. $\begin{vmatrix} 4 & 2 & -2 \\ 6 & 3 & -5 \\ -7 & -5 & 4 \end{vmatrix}$

3. $\begin{vmatrix} 5 & 1 & 12 \\ 10 & 0 & 24 \\ 15 & 5 & -6 \end{vmatrix}$

4. $\begin{vmatrix} 0 & 0 & 0 & -2 \\ 4 & 0 & 0 & 0 \\ -12 & 0 & -4 & 0 \\ 0 & 5 & 0 & 0 \end{vmatrix}$

Find the determinant of each matrix, and determine whether the matrix is invertible.

5. $\begin{bmatrix} 3 & -4 \\ -12 & 16 \end{bmatrix}$

7. $\begin{bmatrix} 5 & 2 & 14 \\ 1 & -2 & -2 \\ 6 & -4 & 4 \end{bmatrix}$

6. $\begin{bmatrix} 10 & 90 \\ 4 & -36 \end{bmatrix}$

8. $\begin{bmatrix} 5 & 6 & -2 & 1 \\ 13 & 8 & 7 & 0 \\ 2 & -3 & 5 & 0 \\ 9 & 14 & -3 & 0 \end{bmatrix}$

▶ B. Exercises

If $|A| = 6$ and $|B| = \frac{3}{4}$, find the determinants of the following matrices.

9. A^{-1}

11. A^T

10. AB

12. $A^T B^{-1}$

Find the inverse of each of the following matrices.

13. $\begin{bmatrix} 8 & 3 \\ 4 & 2 \end{bmatrix}$

18. $\begin{bmatrix} 3 & 5 & 6 \\ 1 & 2 & 2 \\ 2 & 4 & 5 \end{bmatrix}$

14. $\begin{bmatrix} 3 & 7 \\ -5 & -9 \end{bmatrix}$

19. $\begin{bmatrix} 4 & 8 & -6 \\ -6 & -13 & 12 \\ 2 & 4 & -4 \end{bmatrix}$

15. $\begin{bmatrix} 2 & 1 \\ 1 & \frac{2}{3} \end{bmatrix}$

20. $\begin{bmatrix} 2 & -7 & -9 \\ 3 & -12 & -6 \\ -4 & 17 & 11 \end{bmatrix}$

16. $\begin{bmatrix} \frac{-5}{3} & \frac{4}{3} \\ \frac{-8}{3} & \frac{7}{3} \end{bmatrix}$

21. $\begin{bmatrix} 1 & 1 & 2 & 1 \\ 1 & 2 & 2 & 1 \\ -2 & -2 & -3 & 0 \\ 0 & 1 & 2 & 3 \end{bmatrix}$

17. $\begin{bmatrix} 1 & 2 & 0 \\ 2 & 1 & -3 \\ 0 & 3 & 2 \end{bmatrix}$

22. $\begin{bmatrix} 1 & 0 & 0 & -1 & 0 \\ 0 & 3 & 2 & 0 & 0 \\ 0 & 1 & 1 & 0 & 1 \\ 0 & 0 & 0 & 2 & 0 \\ 1 & 0 & 3 & 0 & 10 \end{bmatrix}$

23. If $A = \begin{bmatrix} 12 & -14 & 3 \\ -5 & 9 & -7 \\ 10 & 7 & -13 \end{bmatrix}$, find A^{-1} by augmenting A and I, then row reducing.

Solve the following systems using the inverse matrix method.

24. $x - 5y = -30$
$2x - y = 3$

27. $x + 3y - 4z = 41$
$2x - y + 5z = 0$
$4x + 2y + 4z = 44$

25. $2x - 5y = -39$
$x + 4y = 26$

28. $2x + 3y - z = 21$
$x + y + 2z = 18$
$x - 3y + 2z = 12$

26. $4x + 2y = -8$
$x + 6y = 1$

▶ C. Exercises

If $|A| = 3$, $|B| = \frac{1}{4}$, $|C| = 6$, and all three matrices are 3×3, find:

29. $|4A \cdot B^{-1} \cdot C^T|$

30. $|A^T \cdot B^2 \cdot C^{-1}|^{-1}$

■ Cumulative Review

Solve the following equations.

31. $\sqrt{x - 3} = 4 - \sqrt{x + 5}$

32. $2x^2 - 3x + 8 = 0$

33. $3x + 5\sqrt{2} = 7 - 4\sqrt{3}x$

34. Solve the system.
$3x + 2y = 25$
$5x - y = 7$

35. Find the determinant. $\begin{vmatrix} -2 & 4 & 3 \\ 1 & 5 & -4 \\ -3 & 2 & -1 \end{vmatrix}$

> *God exists since mathematics is consistent, and the Devil exists since we cannot prove it.*
> —ANDRE WEIL
> (1906-1998)

Math and Scripture

Foundation of Math

Review the philosophies of math presented in Chapter 7. Most were popular at some point in the twentieth century.

The first view, platonism, claims that we peer into the naked mind of God. Thus, according to this view, we can know what He thinks about mathematics without regard to our knowledge of Him. In the woodcut is a good description of platonism: the shepherd peers beyond created reality into the Cosmos, the pure world of ideas, especially mathematical ideas, to understand nature below.

Logicism and formalism suppose that logic or mathematics itself can serve as the foundation for mathematics. These claims have been problematic since 1934 when Kurt Gödel proved his incompleteness theorem (or undecideability theorem). This well-accepted theorem shows that any system of math, including the integers, may contain inconsistencies. In the era before Gödel's theorem, scientists and mathematicians hoped to attain complete knowledge in these fields. Now they understand this will never happen.

1. Mathematicians instantly distinguish important new results from unimportant ones. How is this a problem for formalists?

Finally, intuitionism posited the human intuition as the foundation of math. Thus complicated ideas (such as arithmetic with infinity) are the work of man.

What do these four views have in common? They tend to be *foundationalist* views in that they believed that autonomous man, having no need for God, could give coherence to all order in creation.

2. Antichristian philosophies make autonomous man the measure of all things. What is the name of this viewpoint?

MAXIMIZING

Give a Bible verse to prove that no field of knowledge can have a foundation for truth other than Christ.

Some have even supposed that reality is ultimately disorderly, that knowledge is fundamentally incoherent. But all the order in mathematics belies this view.

Christians know that creation is orderly because the God of order made it: He created the world by His decree. All fields of knowledge, to the extent that they are Christian, point to Christ, who holds all things together by the Word of his power. Today, unfortunately, many mathematicians refuse to acknowledge God. Having rejected the Creator, they are "willingly ignorant."

3. How does Romans 1 describe the ungodly approach to math?

Christians can glorify God for His order in Creation, and must be careful to build the entire tree of math on the firm foundations of Scripture rather than on the crumbling foundations of secular philosophy.

> ## Vital Sines
>
> Beware lest any man spoil you through philosophy and vain deceit, after the tradition of men, after the rudiments of the world, and not after Christ. For in him dwelleth all the fulness of the Godhead bodily. ❧
>
> Colossians 2:8-9

Chapter 8 Review

1. Solve the system.

    $6x - 2y = 22$
    $5x + 7y = 1$

2. Solve for a, b, and c if $3\begin{bmatrix} -6 & a \\ 8 & -2 \end{bmatrix} + \begin{bmatrix} 2 & -2 \\ b & 4 \end{bmatrix} = \begin{bmatrix} c & 10 \\ 19 & -2 \end{bmatrix}$.

3. Multiply: $\begin{bmatrix} 6 & -2 & 1 \\ 3 & 4 & -2 \end{bmatrix} \begin{bmatrix} -5 & 4 \\ -1 & 3 \\ 6 & 3 \end{bmatrix}$.

4. Evaluate $\begin{vmatrix} 8 & -2 \\ -4 & 7 \end{vmatrix}$.

5. Evaluate $\begin{vmatrix} 4 & -2 & 6 \\ 7 & 5 & -4 \\ 3 & 1 & 5 \end{vmatrix}$ by two different methods: diagonals and expansion using minors.

6. Find the inverse of $\begin{bmatrix} 3 & 6 \\ 2 & 5 \end{bmatrix}$.

7. Find the inverse of $\begin{bmatrix} 2 & -1 & 3 \\ 6 & -1 & 9 \\ -4 & 3 & -11 \end{bmatrix}$ by using the identity matrix and the given matrix.

8. Use a determinant to show that $\begin{bmatrix} 3 & 4 & -1 \\ 2 & 5 & 7 \\ 8 & -2 & 6 \end{bmatrix}$ is invertible.

9. $\begin{bmatrix} 2 & 1 \\ 6 & 0 \\ 1 & -5 \end{bmatrix} - \begin{bmatrix} 4 & 3 \\ 2 & 7 \\ -3 & 1 \end{bmatrix}$

10. Use Cramer's rule to solve.

    $x - y + z = 7$
    $x + 3y + z = -1$
    $2x + y - 3z = 3$

11. Solve by the Gaussian method.

$$x - 3y + 5z = 33$$
$$2x - y + 4z = 32$$
$$x - 2y - z = -17$$

12. Use the inverse matrix to solve.

$$3x + y - z = 16$$
$$x + y + 2z = 12$$
$$x - y + z = 8$$

Given $|A| = 8$, $|B| = \frac{1}{4}$, $|C| = 2$, and all three matrices are 4×4, find the following.

13. $|A^T|$

14. $|B^{-1}|$

15. $\left|\frac{1}{4}C\right|$

16. $|AC|$

17. $|B^4|$

18. $|(AB)^{-1}|$

19. $|2C^T|$

20. $\left|(2A \cdot B^2 \cdot C^{-1})^T\right|$

21. $|C|I$

22. Which of the 3 matrices A, B, or C could have a row of zeros?

23. Some use the reciprocal of Hubble's constant to determine the age of the universe. Evaluate this application of Hubble's data.

24. What is the mathematical significance of Col. 2:8-9?

9 Statistics

$\mathbf{C}$ollege admissions offices consider exam scores to evaluate a student's potential to succeed in college. The SAT data below shows average scores for the verbal and math portions.

Year	Verbal (Male)	Verbal (Female)	Verbal Total	Math (Male)	Math (Female)	Math Total
1972	531	529	530	527	489	509
1973	523	521	523	525	489	506
1974	524	520	521	524	488	505
1975	515	509	512	518	479	498
1976	511	508	509	520	475	497
1977	509	505	507	520	474	496
1978	511	503	507	517	474	494
1979	509	501	505	516	473	493
1980	506	498	502	515	473	492
1981	508	496	502	516	473	492
1982	509	499	504	516	473	493
1983	508	498	503	516	474	494
1984	511	498	504	518	478	497
1985	514	503	509	522	480	500
1986	515	504	509	523	479	500
1987	512	502	507	523	481	501
1988	512	499	505	521	483	501
1989	510	498	504	523	482	502
1990	505	496	500	521	483	501
1991	503	495	499	520	482	500
1992	504	496	500	521	484	501
1993	504	497	500	524	484	503
1994	501	497	499	523	487	504
1995	505	502	504	525	490	506
1996	507	503	505	527	492	508
1997	507	503	505	530	494	511
1998	509	502	505	531	496	512
1999	509	502	505	531	495	511

National Mean SAT/SAT I Scores for College-Bound Seniors, 1972-1999 (Scores from 70s, 80s, and early 90s are shown as Recentered).

After this chapter you should be able to

1. compute measures of central tendency and variation.
2. determine the percentage of data falling in various intervals, using Chebyshev's theorem or the normal distribution.
3. calculate and interpret *z*-scores and SAT scores.
4. determine best-fit lines and correlation for a set of data.
5. test hypotheses.

9.1 Samples and Central Tendency

John 20:30-31 says that "many other signs truly did Jesus in the presence of his disciples, which are not written in this book: But these are written, that ye might believe that Jesus is the Christ, the Son of God; and that believing ye might have life through his name." It is not important for us to know every miracle that Jesus did, but it is important that we understand the kinds of miracles He did. John included, under the guidance of the Holy Spirit, a representative sample.

Political surveys, marketing surveys, educational research, medical research, sociology, psychology, and many other fields use samples to approximate information about larger groups. The larger group of interest is called the *population,* and the selected subset is a *sample.* In a political survey, the population consists of all the votes that will be cast. As John penned his gospel, he considered the population of all the miracles Jesus performed, and the Holy Spirit guided his selection, arrangement, and narrative.

If every member of the population has an equal chance of being included in the sample, then it is a *random sample.* Such samples avoid bias in the selection process. Drawing names from a hat is an example of a random sample if the name of each member of the population is put into the hat exactly once.

Sometimes groups or strata within a population are essential to the study, and the researcher cannot risk the possibility that they may be under- or over-represented among the random selections. John was directed to use such a stratified sample, since he included examples of Christ's miracles from all categories (healing the blind, healing the lame, feeding the 5000, etc.). John was directed in the selection, but most researchers employ a random sample within each stratum to obtain a *stratified random sample.* For instance, to predict a presidential election, the pollster may randomly sample each state in proportion to its electoral vote. Likewise, a tax researcher may sample people from each income bracket in the same proportion that the income bracket bears to all taxpayers.

Suppose a national chain of T-shirt stores has most of its locations in shopping malls. Mrs. Shanda opens a new franchise near a large university of 30,000 students, and the national headquarters provides guidelines on how many shirts of each size to stock. She suspects that she should stock more larger sizes because the national data (based mostly on malls catering to families with children) may not accurately reflect her university market. Since she cannot ask all **30,000** students for their sizes, she decides to obtain shirt sizes from a random sample of **500** students. Only God knows the average shirt size for the entire population, but the sample average will be an estimate of the actual average. This will help Mrs. Shanda decide if she really needs more of the larger-sized shirts.

Definitions

Parameter   The actual value of a quantity for the population, usually known only to God.

Statistic   An estimate of the population parameter based on a sample.

Greek letters usually represent parameters, while English letters represent statistics. For instance, the Greek letter mu, μ (corresponding to English *m* for mean), represents the population mean, while $\bar{x}$ (*x* bar) represents a sample mean. The bar over the *x* distinguishes the sample mean from an individual value of the variable *x*.

You probably already know how to calculate the sample mean. You add up the data values and divide by the total number of values. The number (n) of values is the *sample size,* the number in the population is *N*, and the data values are numbered with subscripts $x_1, x_2, x_3, \ldots, x_n$. More simply, you can refer to these values as x_i for $i = 1, 2, \ldots, n$. The letter *i* is a counter variable or *index.* The symbol Σ is used to represent the addition of data values because it is the capital Greek letter *sigma* that corresponds to our letter *s* as an abbreviation for *sum.* The starting value of the index appears below the Σ, and the ending value above the Σ. The summation in the following definition is read "summation of *x* sub *i* as *i* goes from one to *n*."

Definition

Mean $\bar{x} = \dfrac{\sum\limits_{i=1}^{n} x_i}{n}$

The mean is one of several statistics that are called *measures of central tendency.*

Median   The middle value (or average of the middle two values) after listing the data in order of size.

Mode   The most frequent value(s) (if any).

Midrange   The average of the highest and lowest value.

EXAMPLE 1   Find the mean, median, mode, and midrange of these values.
15, 17, 17, 19, 20, 20, 21, 24, 24, 24, 25

Answer

$\sum_{i=1}^{11} x_i = 226$

$\bar{x} = \dfrac{\sum_{i=1}^{11} x_i}{n} = \dfrac{226}{11} \approx 20.55$

1. Mean. Use the formula to find the mean of the $n = 11$ data values.

15, 17, 17, 19, 20, 20, 21, 24, 24, 24, 25
median = 20

2. Median. The values must be in order. Since n is odd, locate the middle value.

---

mode = 24

3. Mode. The most frequent value occurs three times.

---

midrange $= \dfrac{15 + 25}{2} = \dfrac{40}{2} = 20$

4. Midrange. Average the extreme values.

You should be aware that multiple modes could occur. If Example 1 had one less "24," there would be three modes (17, 20, and 24). It is also possible that no mode exists. This occurs when no two data points are the same.

EXAMPLE 2   Find four measures of central tendency for the following list of data.
97, 59, 67, 82, 73, 95, 88, 91

Answer

$\bar{x} = \dfrac{\sum_{i=1}^{8} x_i}{8} = \dfrac{652}{8} = 81.5$

1. Mean. Average all eight values.

Continued ▶

59, 67, 73, <u>82, 88</u>, 91, 95, 97 median $= \dfrac{82 + 88}{2} = \dfrac{170}{2} = 85$	2. Median. Order the data. Since n is even, average the middle two.
no mode	3. Mode. Each value occurs with equal frequency so there is no mode.
midrange $= \dfrac{59 + 97}{2} = \dfrac{156}{2} = 78$	4. Midrange. Average the extreme values.

Finally, you will need to know two rules of summation. The first is an extension of the commutative and associative laws. The second expresses the definition of the product n times k. For both rules, k is any real number and n is a natural number. You will be asked to prove them as *C Exercises*.

Summation Rules

1. $\displaystyle\sum_{i=1}^{n} (x_i + y_i) = \sum_{i=1}^{n} x_i + \sum_{i=1}^{n} y_i$

2. $\displaystyle\sum_{i=1}^{n} k = nk$ for any $k \in \mathbb{R}$.

▶ A. Exercises

28, 28, 31, 35, 35, 36, 39, 40, 43, 43, 43, 43, 47

For the quiz scores listed above, find the
1. sample size.
2. mean.
3. median.
4. midrange.
5. mode.

33, 33, 33, 35, 38, 39, 41, 42, 43, 43, 46, 46, 46, 47, 48, 50

For the set of data given above, find
6. $\displaystyle\sum_{i=1}^{16} x_i$.
7. the mean.
8. the median.
9. the mode.
10. the midrange.

▶ B. Exercises

Give four measures of central tendency for these exam scores from a small class:

96, 87, 91, 90, 88, 83

11. Mean
12. Median
13. Midrange
14. Mode

Suppose that the data values are listed in order.

15. Give a formula for the midrange.
16. A measure of a sample characteristic is called what?
17. A measure of a corresponding population characteristic is called what?

⊞ Use a graphing calculator and the following list of data to answer exercises 18-21.

12.24, 16.19, 32.04, 25.58, 17.41, 27.95, 19.09, 22.22

18. List the data in order using your graphing calculator.

19. $\displaystyle\sum_{i=1}^{8} x_i$

20. What is the mean?
21. What is the median?

Explain why each sample below may not be representative of the town or city.

22. Announcements are made on the town's radio and TV stations and in all the local newspapers, calling for people to volunteer to take a survey and receive free discount coupons in return.
23. A survey team stands at the corner of Broadway and Main and obtains information from everyone passing by.
24. All names in the phone book are placed in a hat and a random sample is drawn.

▶ C. Exercises

Prove these two important rules of summation.

25. $\displaystyle\sum_{i=1}^{n} (x_i + y_i) = \sum_{i=1}^{n} x_i + \sum_{i=1}^{n} y_i$

26. $\displaystyle\sum_{i=1}^{n} k = nk$ for any $k \in \mathbb{R}$.

27. Solve $\triangle ABC$ if $b = 29$, $c = 21$, and $\angle C = 42°$.

28. Find the central angle of a circle of radius 10.2 m if the angle intercepts an arc of length 47.9 m. Give the answer in both radians and degrees.

29. Which elementary row operation changes the sign of the determinant?

30. Find $5<2, 7> - 2<1, -6>$

31. Write the equation of an ellipse with center $(5, -2)$, horizontal major axis of 10, and eccentricity of 0.75.

9.2 Variability

Look at the three lists of numbers below.

A	B	C
x_i	x_i	x_i
8	10	10
7	8	6
6	6	6
5	4	6
4	2	2

Each list has a mean and median of 6, but you can see that the lists are not the same. The numbers are spread out in different ways around the mean.

The *range* is the highest value minus the lowest value. For list A, the range is $8 - 4 = 4$ units. For lists B and C, the range is $10 - 2 = 8$ units. This shows that the numbers in list A are not as spread out as the other lists. However, you can see that lists B and C are not equally spread out even though they have the same range. List B is equally spaced, whereas list C is clustered at the mean.

Lists B and C show that we should measure the spread of data as related to the mean. The *deviation* of a data value from the mean is the difference between the data value and the mean, $x - \bar{x}$. The deviations from the mean of 6 are shown in the following table.

A		B		C	
x_i	$x_i - \bar{x}$	x_i	$x_i - \bar{x}$	x_i	$x_i - \bar{x}$
8	2	10	4	10	4
7	1	8	2	6	0
6	0	6	0	6	0
5	−1	4	−2	6	0
4	−2	2	−4	2	−4

Notice that the total of each list of deviations is zero. You will prove as an exercise that $\sum_{i=1}^{n} (x_i - \bar{x}) = 0$ for any set of data. Since the positives and negatives cancel each other, we must obtain positive values before adding to get a meaningful measurement. Two options for making the deviations positive are to use their absolute values or to square them.

The *mean deviation* averages the absolute values of the deviations $\dfrac{\sum_{i=1}^{n} |x_i - \bar{x}|}{n}$.

For list A, you would get $\dfrac{2 + 1 + 0 + 1 + 2}{5} = 1.2$ This calculation is less useful than the next one and will not be discussed further.

The *variance* applies the squaring method. The parameter (population measure) is σ^2, and the statistic (estimate based on a sample) is s^2. The formula for σ^2 uses population parameters and calculates the average of the squared deviations: $\sigma^2 = \dfrac{\sum_{i=1}^{N} (x_i - \mu)^2}{N}$. Since the parameters are rarely known, you will use the sample variance more frequently. Its calculation is similar but the subtraction in the denominator gives a better estimate of the parameter: $s^2 = \dfrac{\sum_{i=1}^{n} (x_i - \bar{x})^2}{n - 1}$.

The sum of the squared deviations (numerator) is important and is often abbreviated to SS for *sum of squares:* $SS = \sum_{i=1}^{n} (x_i - \bar{x})^2$.

For list A, $s^2 = \dfrac{SS}{n - 1} = \dfrac{4 + 1 + 0 + 1 + 4}{4} = 2.5$

You can see how this statistic indicates that the spread of list C is less than the spread of list B.

B			C		
x_i	$x_i - \bar{x}$	$(x_i - \bar{x})^2$	x_i	$x_i - \bar{x}$	$(x_i - \bar{x})^2$
10	4	16	10	4	16
8	2	4	6	0	0
6	0	0	6	0	0
4	−2	4	6	0	0
2	−4	16	2	−4	16
		$SS = 40$			$SS = 32$

$$s^2 = \frac{\sum_{i=1}^{5} (x_i - \bar{x})^2}{n - 1} = \frac{40}{4} = 10 \qquad s^2 = \frac{\sum_{i=1}^{5} (x_i - \bar{x})^2}{n - 1} = \frac{32}{4} = 8$$

All the deviations were squared in finding the variance s^2, but the square root of the variance is the most useful calculation. It is called the *standard deviation*. Lowercase Greek letters represent parameters and English letters represent statistics. Therefore, σ (sigma, Greek "s") is the standard deviation parameter and s is the standard deviation statistic. Don't confuse capital sigma, used for sum (Σ), with small sigma for standard deviation (σ). Since standard deviation is the square root of the variance, you can write these formulas.

$$\sigma = \sqrt{\frac{\sum_{i=1}^{N}(x_i - \mu)^2}{N}} \qquad s = \sqrt{\frac{\sum_{i=1}^{n}(x_i - \bar{x})^2}{n-1}}$$

The variance and standard deviation follow for lists B and C.

		B	C
Variance	s^2	10	8
Standard deviation	s	3.16	2.83

Definitions

Variance   The average of squared deviations. For a population, $\sigma^2 = \dfrac{\sum_{i=1}^{N}(x_i - \mu)^2}{N}$.

For a sample, $s^2 = \dfrac{\sum_{i=1}^{n}(x_i - \bar{x})^2}{n-1}$. Population variance can be estimated based on sample variance.

Standard deviation   The square root of the variance.

EXAMPLE 1   Find SS, s^2, and s for the data below.

23, 29, 34, 37, 40, 41, 43, 51

Answer

x	$x_i - \bar{x}$	$(x_i - \bar{x})^2$
23	-14.25	203.0625
29	-8.25	68.0625
34	-3.25	10.5625
37	-0.25	0.0625
40	2.75	7.5625
41	3.75	14.0625
43	5.75	33.0625
51	13.75	189.0625
298	0	525.5

1. In the first column of a table list the values, x_i. Add to obtain Σx_i then find the mean. $\bar{x} = \frac{298}{8} = 37.25$

2. Subtract the mean from each data value to get the deviations for the second column. (The sum of this column is always zero.) If you needed the mean deviation you would use absolute values of this column. The mean deviation is 6.5.

3. Square the deviations to fill in the 3rd column; total to find the sum of squares, SS.

Continued ▶

$$s^2 = \frac{525.5}{7} = 75.07$$ 4. Find s^2 by dividing SS by $n - 1$.

$$s = \sqrt{s^2} = \sqrt{75.07} = 8.66$$ 5. Find the standard deviation by taking the square root of the variance.

Remember to use statistics—not parameters—because we use sample statistics to study populations.

▶ A. Exercises

Find the indicated statistics for the set of data below (by making a table).
18, 21, 17, 15, 20, 16, 13

1. $\displaystyle\sum_{i=1}^{n} x_i$

2. Mean

3. Order the data and find the deviation of the fifth data value in the above list: $x_5 - \bar{x}$.

4. $\displaystyle\sum_{i=1}^{n} (x_i - \bar{x})$

5. $\displaystyle\sum_{i=1}^{n} |x_i - \bar{x}|$

6. Mean deviation

7. SS

8. s^2

9. s

10. Range

▶ B. Exercises

Use the given data values to find the following statistics.
87, 52, 87, 78, 65, 91, 77, 84, 93, 87, 89, 72

11. Range

12. Mean deviation

13. Sum of squares

14. Variance

15. Standard deviation

A class of 10 takes a 40-point quiz. The mean is 32 with a standard deviation of 4.

16. What is the variance?
17. What is the sum of squares?
18. How many standard deviations above the mean is a perfect score?

A set of 35 scores has a variance of 25, find the

19. sum of squares.
20. standard deviation.

Use the list of data from Section 9.1, exercises 18-21.

21. Find the sum of squares.
22. Find the standard deviation.
23. Find the variance.

▶ C. Exercises

24. Give a short formula for the variance and standard deviation using *SS*.
25. Prove that the sum of deviations from the mean is always zero.

Dominion Modeling

26. Make a scatterplot of total SAT-Math as a function of year. What kind of model might be appropriate?
27. Construct a linear model for the SAT data, taking total SAT-Math as a function of the year. Draw the model on a scatterplot. Plot the residuals and evaluate the model.

Cumulative Review

28. Given points $A(9, -3)$ and $B(2, -5)$, find AB, the midpoint of $\overline{AB}$, and the point $\frac{1}{4}$ of the way from A to B.
29. Write the equation of the line through A and B in exercise 28. Give your answer in standard form.
30. Which type of function is always continuous?
    a. trigonometric b. rational c. radical d. piece
31. If $f(x)$ is continuous and $f(a) = 0$, what happens at $x = a$ on the graph of $g(x) = \frac{1}{f(x)}$?
32. Write the equation of a hyperbola opening vertically that is centered at the origin with $b = 6$ and with perpendicular asymptotes.

9.3 Transformations of Data

Look at the quiz scores below.

> 4, 6, 7, 9, 9, 10

You should be able to check that $\bar{x} = 7.5$ and $s = 2.26$. Now suppose that you added 5 to everyone's score.

> 9, 11, 12, 14, 14, 15

You can see that the range is the same, $10 - 4 = 6 = 15 - 9$. It should not surprise you that the standard deviation has not changed either. The scores are no more or less spread out than they were originally. However, the mean has changed—it is five units larger. Check this on your calculator. Did you get $\bar{x} = 12.5$ and $s = 2.26$?

Theorem 9.1: Translated Data

Let $x_1, x_2, \ldots, x_n$ represent the original data. If $y_1, y_2, \ldots, y_n$ are obtained by adding a constant k to the original data values, then $\bar{y} = \bar{x} + k$ and $s_y = s_x$.

Proof

The proof applies the summation rules from the end of Section 9.1.

$$\bar{y} = \frac{\sum_{i=1}^{n} y_i}{n} = \frac{\sum_{i=1}^{n}(x_i + k)}{n} = \frac{\sum_{i=1}^{n} x_i + \sum_{i=1}^{n} k}{n} = \frac{\sum_{i=1}^{n} x_i + nk}{n} = \frac{\sum_{i=1}^{n} x_i}{n} + k = \bar{x} + k$$

Therefore, $\bar{y} = \bar{x} + k$.

$$s_y^2 = \frac{\sum_{i=1}^{n}(y_i - \bar{y})^2}{n-1} = \frac{\sum_{i=1}^{n}[(x_i + k) - (\bar{x} + k)]^2}{n-1} = \frac{\sum_{i=1}^{n}(x_i - \bar{x})^2}{n-1} = s_x^2$$

Therefore, $s_y = s_x$.

Now consider what happens when you multiply every score by the same constant.

							Mean	Standard Deviation
Original	4	6	7	9	9	10	7.5	2.26
Transformed	12	18	21	27	27	30	22.5	6.77

You can see that multiplying by 3 triples the average and also makes the values 3 times more spread out.

> **Theorem 9.2: Scaled Data**
> If $y_1, y_2, \ldots, y_n$ are found from $x_1, x_2, \ldots, x_n$ by multiplying each by the same constant k, then $\bar{y} = k\bar{x}$ and $s_y = ks_x$.

You will prove this in the exercises in a manner similar to the proof of theorem 9.1.

Definition

z-score The transformed score found by subtracting the mean from the individual score, and dividing by the standard deviation: $z = \frac{x - \bar{x}}{s}$.

The statistic z is a measure of the deviation of an individual score from the mean in units of standard deviation.

EXAMPLE 1   Mary got a 9 on her quiz. The class average was 7 and the standard deviation was 1.5. How many standard deviations away from the mean (z-score) was Mary's score?

Answer $9 - 7 = 2$ units above the mean.

$\frac{2}{1.5} = 1.3$ standard deviations above the mean.

or $z = \frac{x - \bar{x}}{s} = \frac{9 - 7}{1.5} = \frac{2}{1.5} = 1.3$

Both of the above theorems are used in the definition of a z-score. It is first translated by the subtraction of $\bar{x}$ and then scaled through the division by s. Let's use the theorems to determine the mean and standard deviation of z-scores.

Since $z = \frac{x - \bar{x}}{s}$, consider the mean of data translated by adding $-\bar{x}$ and scaled by multiplying by $\frac{1}{s}$. By theorems 9.1 and 9.2, the original mean is increased by $-\bar{x}$ and multiplied by $\frac{1}{s}$. $[\bar{x} + (-\bar{x})](\frac{1}{s}) = \frac{\bar{x} - \bar{x}}{s} = \frac{0}{s} = 0$. Also consider the standard deviation for the translated data. Adding $-\bar{x}$ to the original data values does not affect the standard deviation (theorem 9.1). Multiplying by $\frac{1}{s}$ does, however. By theorem 9.2, the standard deviation of the translated data is $\frac{1}{s}(s) = 1$. Therefore, the mean of z-scores is 0 and the standard deviation is 1.

In Example 1, where $z = 1.3$, it means that the score of 9 is 1.3 standard deviations above the mean. If the individual score x is the same as the mean, the z-score will be 0. If the individual score is less than the mean, the z-score will be negative.

EXAMPLE 2   If John scored 79 on a test having a mean of 84 and a standard deviation of 4, find his z-score.

Answer $z = \frac{x - \bar{x}}{s} = \frac{79 - 84}{4} = -1.25$

John's score is 1.25 standard deviations below the mean.

▶ A. Exercises

If the mean is 83 and the standard deviation is 7, find the z-score for each test score below.

1. 88
2. 96
3. 79
4. 83
5. 73
6. 55

▶ B. Exercises

If the mean of a set of data values is 75 and the standard deviation is 10, find the mean and standard deviation for the data transformed as follows.

7. $y = x + 5$
8. $y = 2x$
9. $y = \frac{1}{5}x - 10$
10. $y = \frac{x - \bar{x}}{5}$

Use the given set of scores to find the following values.
37, 44, 39, 48, 44, 47, 45, 42, 44

11. The mean
12. The standard deviation
13. The z-score of the lowest score
14. The z-score of the highest score
15. Transform the rest of the scores to z-scores.

SAT scores are calculated from z-scores using the transformation
SAT = 100z + 500.

16. Give the mean score on the SAT.
17. Give the standard deviation of the SAT.
18. Give the SAT score of someone who scored 2.5 standard deviations above the mean.
19. What does an SAT score of 563 mean?
20. What does an SAT score of 381 mean?

Refer to the data from Section 9.1, exercise 18-21 and find the z-score of

21. 27.95.
22. 17.41.
23. 22.22.

▶ C. Exercises

Prove the following relations for sets of transformed data $y_i = kx_i$.

24. $\bar{y} = k\bar{x}$
25. $s_y = ks_x$

■ Cumulative Review

26. A line passes through (3, 4) with an angle of inclination of 20°. Write its equation in slope-intercept form.
27. State the three Pythagorean identities.
28. In a class, three quiz scores range from 10 to 20 with a median of 18. Find the mean, midrange, and mode.
29. Graph $r = 2 + 3 \cos \theta$.
30. If $\sin \theta = \frac{a}{b}$, give the other five trig functions in terms of a and b.

9.4 Theorems About Variability

Pafnuti Chebyshev (also spelled Tchebycheff), a Russian mathematician, proved the following theorem, which applies to any set of data. It tells what fraction of the measurements falls within various ranges.

Carl F. Gauss (1777-1855) derived the central limit theorem. He also developed the method of least squares and proved the fundamental theorem of algebra.

Theorem 9.3: Chebyshev's Theorem

Given any n measurements, at least $1 - \frac{1}{k^2}$ of the measurements must lie within k standard deviations of the mean for $k > 1$. (At most $\frac{1}{k^2}$ of the data can lie outside the interval $[\bar{x} - ks, \ \bar{x} + ks]$.)

EXAMPLE 1 What portion of data must always lie within 3 standard deviations of the mean?

Answer Apply Chebyshev's theorem with $k = 3$.
$$1 - \frac{1}{k^2} = 1 - \frac{1}{3^2} = \frac{8}{9}$$

EXAMPLE 2 Check the theorem for the following set of data when $k = 3$.
1, 6, 7, 8, 8, 8, 9, 9, 9, 10, 10, 10, 10, 11, 11, 11, 12, 12

Answer

$\bar{x} = 9$ and $s = 2.59$	1. Find $\bar{x}$ and s.
$[\bar{x} - 3s, \bar{x} + 3s]$ $[9 - 3(2.59), 9 + 3(2.59)]$ $[1.23, 16.77]$	2. Write the interval of values within 3 standard deviations of the mean.
Only one value (the number 1) is not in the interval.	3. Count the data values outside the interval.

Continued ▶

$\frac{1}{9}(18) = 2$ values allowed outside. Since only one was, the theorem is verified for this data.

4. Compare to Chebyshev's theorem. In Example 1, the portion for 3 standard deviations was found to be $\frac{8}{9}$. So $\frac{1}{9}$ of the 18 values can be outside.

As mentioned above, Chebyshev's theorem applies to every set of data. It is a very broad statement. A more specific statement can be proved for special kinds of data, such as *mound-shaped data*.

Definition

Mound-shaped data   Mound-shaped data is a set of data in which the graph of frequencies is roughly symmetrical and the mode is in the middle.

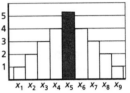

The empirical rule is a more specific rule for mound-shaped data.

Theorem 9.4: Empirical Rule

Given a set of data that is mound-shaped, approximately 68% of the data will fall within 1 standard deviation of the mean, 95% of the data will fall within 2 standard deviations of the mean, and 99.7% of the data will fall within 3 standard deviations of the mean.

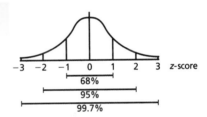

EXAMPLE 3   Using the data shown, check that it is roughly mound-shaped and show that the empirical rule applies.

8, 9, 10, 8, 7, 5, 11, 6, 8, 7, 9, 7, 8, 10, 9, 8, 3, 9, 6, 4

Answer

3 — 1	
4 — 1	
5 — 1	
6 — 2	
7 — 3	
8 — 5	
9 — 4	
10 — 2	
11 — 1	

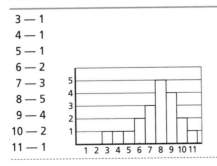

1. Find $\bar{x} = 7.6$, $s = 2.0$, and list the frequencies.

2. Graph the frequencies and notice the mound shape.

Continued ▶

$[\bar{x} - s, \bar{x} + s] = [5.6, 9.6]$ contains 14 of the 20 values or 70% of the data.

$[\bar{x} - 2s, \bar{x} + 2s] = [3.6, 11.6]$ contains 19 of the 20 values or 95% of the data.

$[\bar{x} - 3s, \bar{x} + 3s] = [1.6, 13.6]$ contains all 20 values or 100% of the data.

3. Find the intervals of 1, 2, and 3 standard deviations around the mean. Count the values in each interval. See if the totals are approximately the percentages in the empirical rule.

In the next section you will see that the empirical rule is based on the bell-shaped or normal curve.

Theorem 9.5: Central Limit Theorem

If you repeatedly choose random samples each of size n ($n \geq 30$) from the same population and compute the mean for each sample, the graph of the frequency distribution of the population of all sample means will be mound-shaped.

The larger n is, the closer the graph of the distribution of sample means will be to a normal (bell-shaped) curve. In other words, for averages (and many other kinds of statistical data), the larger the size of the samples, the more the data accumulates at the center. As the sample size increases, the approximation gets closer to the bell curve. This is why it is called the central limit theorem.

▶ A. Exercises

What percentage of any set of data must always fall within
1. 1 standard deviation of the mean?
2. 2 standard deviations of the mean?
3. 3 standard deviations of the mean?
4. 4 standard deviations of the mean?
5. How many full standard deviations are necessary to guarantee that 97% of the data is included?

If a set of data is mound-shaped with $\bar{x} = 110$ and $s = 3$,
6. what percentage of data must lie in $[104, 116]$?
7. give the interval containing 68% of the data.
8. how many full standard deviations are necessary to guarantee that 97% of the data is included?
9. give the interval containing at least 97% of this data.
10. If the data were not mound-shaped, how spread out could 97% of the data be? Give the interval.

▶ B. Exercises

Use the data below.

11, 15, 11, 15, 16, 17, 15, 11, 10, 12, 16, 15, 20, 11, 15

11. Is the data mound-shaped? Why?
12. Find the interval 2 standard deviations about the mean.
13. Find the interval 3 standard deviations about the mean.
14. What percentage of the data lies within 2 standard deviations of the mean? Is this consistent with Chebyshev's theorem?
15. What percentage of the data lies within 3 standard deviations of the mean? Is this consistent with Chebyshev's theorem?

Verify the empirical rule on the following data.

41, 43, 46, 43, 39, 40, 43, 45, 41, 44, 47, 43, 44, 42

16. Show that the data is mound-shaped.
17. For 1 standard deviation
18. For 2 standard deviations
19. For 3 standard deviations
20. Since test scores for national tests such as the SAT are typically mound-shaped, what percentage of students score 700 or above?

▶ C. Exercises

21. What is the practical range for SAT scores? Why?
22. How does this differ from a true range?

Dominion Modeling

23. Find the quartic model of total SAT-Math as a function of year. Are the residuals better than the linear model?
24. According to the quartic model, when was the SAT-Math score lowest? Does this agree with the data?

■ Cumulative Review

25. Give the three smallest positive and three largest negative angles coterminal with 42°.
26. Give the exact values of the sine, cosine, and tangent of 210° and of 135°.

Identify the horizontal asymptote of each function.

27. $g(x) = 4 + e^x$
28. $h(x) = \text{Tan}^{-1} x$
29. $f(x) = \frac{8x - 5}{9x + 10}$

RUSSIAN MATH

Pafnuti Chebyshev (1821-1894)

The Goldbach conjecture remains unproven in spite of a million-dollar prize offer.

Can you name any Russian mathematicians? You may have heard of Nikolai Ivanovich Lobachevsky (1792-1856) of Nizhniy Novgorod, one of the founders of non-Euclidean geometry. Another Russian mathematician, Sonya Vasilyevna Kovalevsky (1850-91) of Moscow, contributed to differential equations. You may also have heard of the Goldbach conjecture, posed by Christian Goldbach (1690-1764) of Königsberg. This professor from St. Petersburg guessed that every even integer is the sum of two primes. Although he conjectured this almost two centuries ago, no proof has been found in spite of a million-dollar prize offer. Many other Russian mathematicians have also made important contributions.

Chebyshev's Theorem is named after the Russian mathematician Pafnuti Lvovich Chebyshev (1821-94). Born in Okatovo, he began teaching at the University of St. Petersburg in 1847 and founded the school of mathematics. His theorem is evidence of his work in probability theory, but mathematicians better know him for his work on the distribution of prime numbers. To supplement his university salary, he worked on minimizing fabric waste for a textile company that was producing army uniforms for the Crimean War.

Chebyshev's students included Markov and Ljapunov. Aleksandr Mikhailovich Ljapunov (1857-1918) of Yaroslavl contributed to probability, differential equations, and approximation techniques. Andrei Andreyevich Markov (1856-1922) of Ryazan studied number theory, approximation theory, limits of integrals, series convergence, and sequences of random variables, which have been named

Markov chains in his honor. These led to the development of the concept of stochastic processes.

Andrei Nikolaevich Kolmogorov (1903-87) of Tambov did for probability what Euclid did for geometry. His 1933 monograph *Grundbegriffe der Wahrscheinlichkeitsrechnung* (Foundational Concepts of Probability Calculations) axiomatized probability theory. He also extended the theory of Markov chains. Kolmogorov contributed to many other branches in mathematics as well. While still an undergraduate, he published eight papers; by the time he finished his doctorate in 1929 he had 18 papers to his credit, spanning a wide range of topics from sets and logic to topics in calculus. His later research contributed to the solution of Hilbert's sixth problem and also proved that Hilbert's thirteenth problem was impossible. He also made major contributions to topology by defining cohomology groups and T_0 spaces, also called *Kolmogorov spaces* in his honor.

The palace at St. Petersburg, Russia, would have been a familiar sight to the many mathematicians who taught there.

The Russian contributions to topology are not limited to Kolmogorov. In fact, $T_{2.5}$ and $T_{3.5}$ spaces are also named for the Russian mathematicians Pavel Samuilovich Urysohn (1898-1924) and Andrei Nikolaevich Tikhonov (1906-93) respectively. Urysohn's birthplace in Odessa, Ukraine, was at that time part of the U.S.S.R., and he studied at Moscow. Though he drowned in France at 26, he had already contributed essential theorems to topology such as Urysohn's lemma. Tikhonov (or Tychonoff) hailed from Gzhatska and, like Kolmogorov, contributed to many branches of math and physics (topology, functional analysis, and partial differential equations). In his most famous theorem, he defined a topology on a Cartesian product of topological spaces and proved that if the separate spaces are compact, the product is also compact. This result, which he proved before he graduated, is named Tikhonov's theorem in his honor.

Nikolai Lobachevsky (1792-1856)

9.5 The Bell Curve

The bell-shaped curve is a mound-shaped frequency distribution called the *normal distribution*. It is given by the function $y = \frac{1}{\sqrt{2\pi}}\, e^{-\frac{1}{2}z^2}$.

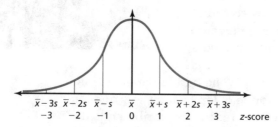

Do you see that **50%** of the values correspond to positive *z*-scores and the other half result in negative values? This means that a *z*-score of zero is not a bad score—it is average.

Recall that approximately **68%** of the values fall within **1** standard deviation of the mean. This means that **34%** of the *z*-scores are between **0** and **1** and the other **34%** are between **0** and −**1**. To calculate this, you would need to find the shaded area shown below. The table of *z*-scores on the next page conveniently list the calculated values.

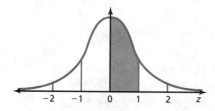

In the table, find **1.00.** Look down the first column to the row marked **1.0.** Then go to the column .**00,** which signifies that the second decimal place is zero. You should find the value **0.3413,** which represents the percentage of values in the shaded region written as a decimal. The empirical rule rounds this off to **34%.** The percentages in the table are computed using calculus and printed in table form to permit you to find percentages for parts of standard deviations.

Table of Normal Curve Areas

Z	.00	.01	.02	.03	.04	.05	.06	.07	.08	.09
0.0	.0000	.0040	.0080	.0120	.0160	.0199	.0239	.0279	.0319	.0359
0.1	.0398	.0438	.0478	.0517	.0557	.0596	.0636	.0675	.0714	.0753
0.2	.0793	.0832	.0871	.0910	.0948	.0987	.1026	.1064	.1103	.1141
0.3	.1179	.1217	.1255	.1293	.1331	.1368	.1406	.1443	.1480	.1517
0.4	.1554	.1591	.1628	.1664	.1700	.1736	.1772	.1808	.1844	.1879
0.5	.1915	.1950	.1985	.2019	.2054	.2088	.2123	.2157	.2190	.2224
0.6	.2257	.2291	.2324	.2357	.2389	.2422	.2454	.2486	.2517	.2549
0.7	.2580	.2611	.2642	.2673	.2704	.2734	.2764	.2794	.2823	.2852
0.8	.2881	.2910	.2939	.2967	.2995	.3023	.3051	.3078	.3106	.3133
0.9	.3159	.3186	.3212	.3238	.3264	.3289	.3315	.3340	.3365	.3389
1.0	.3413	.3438	.3461	.3485	.3508	.3531	.3554	.3577	.3599	.3621
1.1	.3643	.3665	.3686	.3708	.3729	.3749	.3770	.3790	.3810	.3830
1.2	.3849	.3869	.3888	.3907	.3925	.3944	.3962	.3980	.3997	.4015
1.3	.4032	.4049	.4066	.4082	.4099	.4115	.4131	.4147	.4162	.4177
1.4	.4192	.4207	.4222	.4236	.4251	.4265	.4279	.4292	.4306	.4319
1.5	.4332	.4345	.4357	.4370	.4382	.4394	.4406	.4418	.4429	.4441
1.6	.4452	.4463	.4474	.4484	.4495	.4505	.4515	.4525	.4535	.4545
1.7	.4554	.4564	.4573	.4582	.4591	.4599	.4608	.4616	.4625	.4633
1.8	.4641	.4649	.4656	.4664	.4671	.4678	.4686	.4693	.4699	.4706
1.9	.4713	.4719	.4726	.4732	.4738	.4744	.4750	.4756	.4761	.4767
2.0	.4772	.4778	.4783	.4788	.4793	.4798	.4803	.4808	.4812	.4817
2.1	.4821	.4826	.4830	.4834	.4838	.4842	.4846	.4850	.4854	.4857
2.2	.4861	.4864	.4868	.4871	.4875	.4878	.4881	.4884	.4887	.4890
2.3	.4893	.4896	.4898	.4901	.4904	.4906	.4909	.4911	.4913	.4916
2.4	.4918	.4920	.4922	.4925	.4927	.4929	.4931	.4932	.4934	.4936
2.5	.4938	.4940	.4941	.4943	.4945	.4946	.4948	.4949	.4951	.4952
2.6	.4853	.4955	.4956	.4957	.4959	.4960	.4961	.4962	.4963	.4964
2.7	.4965	.4966	.4967	.4968	.4969	.4970	.4971	.4972	.4973	.4974
2.8	.4974	.4975	.4976	.4977	.4977	.4978	.4979	.4979	.4980	.4981
2.9	.4981	.4982	.4982	.4983	.4984	.4984	.4985	.4985	.4986	.4986
3.0	.4987	.4987	.4987	.4988	.4988	.4989	.4989	.4989	.4990	.4990

This table is abridged from Table 1 of *Statistical Tables and Formulas,* by A. Hald (New York: John Wiley & Sons, Inc., 1952). Reproduced by permission of A. Hald and the publishers, John Wiley & Sons, Inc.

EXAMPLE 1   Find the percentage of values in the interval $0 \leq z \leq 1.63$.

Answer   According to the table, you should get 0.4484 or 44.8%.

You can use diagrams to compute more difficult percentages. The following example shows how to take advantage of the symmetry of the curve.

EXAMPLE 2   Find the percentage of values lying within 0.6 standard deviations of the mean.

Answer

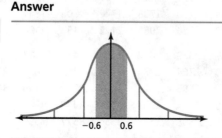

1. Sketch the desired area.

2. The table gives values of z such that $0 \leq z \leq 0.6$, but due to symmetry we need only double the table value to find z, such that $-0.6 \leq z \leq 0.6$.

2 (0.2257)
0.4514 or 45.1%

EXAMPLE 3   Find the percentage of values such that $z \geq 0.98$.

Answer

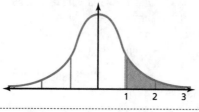

1. Sketch the desired area.

0.5 − (0.3365)
0.1635 or 16.4%

2. Find the shaded area by subtracting the value in the table (for $0 \leq z \leq 0.98$) from 0.5 since half the values lie above 0.

Definition

Percentile rank   The percentage of values less than or equal to a given value.

A percentile rank of 73% indicates that the student did at least as well as 73% of all students taking a test.

EXAMPLE 4 Find the percentile rank of a student whose quiz score is 29 in a class with a mean of 27 and a standard deviation of 4.

Answer

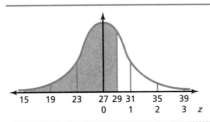

1. Sketch the desired area.

$$z = \frac{x - \bar{x}}{s} = \frac{29 - 27}{4} = 0.5$$

2. Convert to a z-score

0.5 + 0.1915

0.6915

69.2%

This student is in the 69th percentile.

3. Find the percentage of $0 \leq z \leq 0.5$ from the table and add to 50% or 0.5 (the percentage of scores below zero).

You should see that a sketch is very helpful in order to know how to use the table. Sometimes the table value is the answer, but other times, you must double it, add **0.5**, subtract **0.5**, or even add or subtract two values from the table value. A sketch will help you decide what to do.

Finally, you should be able to use the table in reverse.

EXAMPLE 5 Find the interval of z-scores around the mean that contains 44% of the scores.

Answer

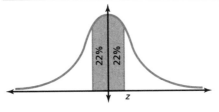

1. Sketch the desired area.

$0.2190 \leq 0.22 \leq 0.2224$

0.22 is closer to 0.2190

z = 0.58

2. Find the closest value to 0.22 in the body of the table and read the corresponding z-score.

[−0.58, 0.58]

3. Give the interval.

▶ A. Exercises

Find the percentage of values in each interval.

1. $0 \leq z \leq 1.7$
2. $0 \leq z \leq 0.69$
3. $-1.21 \leq z \leq 0$
4. $-2.47 \leq z \leq 0$
5. $-0.74 \leq z \leq 0.74$
6. $-1.85 \leq z \leq 1.85$
7. $z \geq 1.06$
8. $z \geq 2.37$
9. $z \leq -1.56$
10. $z \leq -0.92$
11. $z \geq -1.4$
12. $z \geq -0.7$
13. $z \leq 2.0$
14. $z \leq 1.44$
15. $-0.3 \leq z \leq 0.3$

▶ B. Exercises

Find the interval of z-scores around the mean that contain the following percentage of values.

16. 34%
17. 39%
18. 97%
19. 82%
20. 49.7%

Find the percentage of values in each interval.

21. $-1.4 \leq z \leq 2.3$
22. $-1.03 \leq z \leq 0.25$
23. $-2.83 \leq z \leq 1.11$

Find the percentile rank for each student.

24. Joe's z-score is 1.07
25. Mary's z-score is -0.26
26. Leesha's score was 90 in a class with a mean of 85 and a standard deviation of 3.
27. Mark's score was 14 in a class with a mean of 31 and a standard deviation of 9.

▶ C. Exercises

28. Find the *z*-score corresponding to a percentile rank of 28%.

29. Bryan had a percentile rank of 91 on a test having a mean of 77 and a standard deviation of 8. What was his score on the original test?

〰 Dominion Modeling

30. Make a linear model to compare the SAT-Math scores for young men and women over all the given years. (*Hint:* Let Girls-Math be a function of Boys-Math.)

31. As the young men increase their SAT-Math by one point, how could we expect the young women's scores to change? Explain.

At what score does this model predict men and women would be the same?

▪ Cumulative Review

Given a triangle with sides of 17, 29, and 40, find

32. its area.

33. the measures of its angles to the nearest degree.

Graph the following in polar coordinates.

34. $r = \cos \theta$

35. $r = \sin 2\theta$

36. $r = 2 - 2 \cos \theta$

9.6 Linear Correlation

Imagine that you check the population of a bacteria culture after every generation. The table below displays the results, as does the graph at the right, where *y* is measured in logarithms.

Generation	Population
1	1
2	3
3	2
4	3
5	5
6	4
7	5

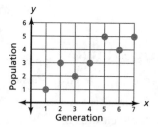

Find the average population size:

$$\bar{y} = \frac{\sum\limits_{i=1}^{n} y_i}{n} = \frac{1 + 3 + 2 + 3 + 5 + 4 + 5}{7} = \frac{23}{7} \approx 3.29.$$

You could draw a horizontal line $y = 3.29$ to predict the number of bacteria after any given generation, but you can see from the graph that this population is growing. If you could determine the rate of growth, you could make a better prediction for the population after a particular generation. In other words, the points on the graph appear to lie on a line and the slope of that line would represent the growth rate. The problem is determining which line best represents the set of points. Finding the best-fit line is called *linear regression*.

The horizontal line is shown at the average $\bar{y} = 3.29$. If there is any relation between generations and population, one of the other lines will improve the prediction. *Correlation* measures the strength of the relationship between two variables. To understand it, though, you will need some background.

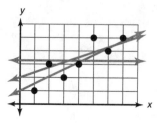

Suppose that $y = mx + b$ is the equation of the best-fit line. For each data point (x_i, y_i), you could calculate the predicted y-value, $\hat{y}_i$ (y_i-hat), by the line $\hat{y}_i = mx_i + b$. To have a good model, the $\hat{y}_i$ on the best-fit line should be close to the y_i of the original data for each x_i. Thus, you want the deviations $|y_i - \hat{y}_i|$ (shown in red on the graph) to be small. Remember that the sum of the deviations will be zero, so you must minimize either the sum of the absolute values of the deviations or the sum of the squared deviations. As before, in the case of variance, using the squares turns out to be better. This method is called the *method of least squares*.

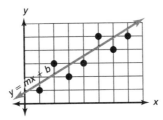

Since the sum of the squared deviations represents the *error* between the line (model) and the actual data, *SSE* is used as an abbreviation for the sum of squares error.

$$SSE = \sum_{i=1}^{n} (y_i - \hat{y}_i)^2 = \sum_{i=1}^{n} (y_i - mx_i - b)^2$$

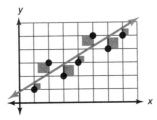

You can also compute the sum of squared deviations for the x and y variables separately.

$$SS_x = \sum_{i=1}^{n} (x_i - \bar{x})^2 \qquad SS_y = \sum_{i=1}^{n} (y_i - \bar{y})^2 \qquad SS_{xy} = \sum_{i=1}^{n} (x_i - \bar{x})(y_i - \bar{y})$$

Since adding squares always results in positive numbers, $SSE \geq 0$, $SS_x \geq 0$, and $SS_y \geq 0$. SS_{xy} may be either positive or negative since it does not involve actual squares.

Theorem 9.6: Linear Regression
Using the method of least squares, the best-fit line $y = mx + b$ has slope $m = \dfrac{SS_{xy}}{SS_x}$ and y-intercept $b = \bar{y} - m\bar{x}$.

The theorem above requires calculus for its proof.

EXAMPLE 1 Give the equation of the line for the bacteria population. Predict the population after the eighth generation.

Answer

x_i	y_i	$x_i - \bar{x}$	$y_i - \bar{y}$	$(x_i - \bar{x})^2$	$(y_i - \bar{y})^2$	$(x_i - \bar{x})(y_i - \bar{y})$
1	1	−3	−2.29	9	5.22	6.86
2	3	−2	−0.29	4	0.08	0.57
3	2	−1	−1.29	1	1.65	1.29
4	3	0	−0.29	0	0.08	0.00
5	5	1	1.71	1	2.94	1.71
6	4	2	0.71	4	0.51	1.43
7	5	3	1.71	9	2.94	5.14
$\Sigma = 28$	$\Sigma = 23$			$\Sigma = 28$	$\Sigma \approx 13.43$	$\Sigma = 17.00$

$$\bar{x} = \frac{\sum\limits_{i=1}^{7} x_i}{n} = \frac{28}{7} = 4 \qquad \bar{y} = \frac{\sum\limits_{i=1}^{7} y_i}{n} = \frac{23}{7} = 3.29$$

$$SS_x = 28 \qquad SS_y = 13.43 \qquad SS_{xy} = 17.00$$

$$m = \frac{SS_{xy}}{SS_x} = \frac{17}{28} = 0.61$$

$b = \bar{y} - m\bar{x} = 3.29 - (0.61)(4) = 0.86$

The equation of the line $y = mx + b$ is $y = 0.61x + 0.86$.

To predict y for $x = 8$, find $f(8)$.

$$f(8) = 0.61(8) + 0.86 = 5.71$$

Definitions

Correlation A measure of the strength of the relation between two variables using the formula $r = \dfrac{SS_{xy}}{\sqrt{SS_x SS_y}}$.

Coefficient of determination The square of the correlation, r^2.

You have seen the value of these statistics for evaluating models throughout this book in the Dominion Modeling exercises. The following formula can be proved, and it is useful for finding SSE when the other values are known. More importantly, though, it is the key to understanding the meaning of r and r^2.

$$r^2 = \frac{SS_y - SSE}{SS_y}$$

The idea of correlation is that using x to predict y will be more accurate than not using x. If we ignored x, we would have to use the mean of the y-values. SS_y measures the squared deviations of the y-values from the mean, so it is a measure of the error involved when using the average $\bar{y}$ as a model. Since SSE measures the error involved in using the linear model, $SS_y - SSE$ is the reduction in error obtained by using the linear model instead of the mean to predict y. The ratio given for r^2, then, is the percent reduction (in decimal form) using the linear model instead of the mean.

You can now see the ranges for these measures are $0 \le r^2 \le 1$ and $-1 \le r \le 1$. When all the data points fall exactly on the least squares line, the model has no error and $SSE = 0$. This means that $r^2 = 1$ (and r is 1 or -1). Notice that if the model does not help at all and there is no reduction in error, then $SSE = SS_y$, making $r^2 = 0$ (and $r = 0$). Thus, 0 means the model is worthless, and ± 1 means that it is perfect.

Finally, what does the sign of the correlation tell us? Compare the formulas for m and r.

$$m = \frac{SS_{xy}}{SS_x} \qquad r = \frac{SS_{xy}}{\sqrt{SS_x SS_y}}$$

Since SS_x and SS_y are always positive, m and r will always have the same sign, depending on SS_{xy}. Since the sign of the slope determines whether the line is increasing or decreasing, you can get the same information from the sign of r.

EXAMPLE 2 Find the correlation between generation and population size for the bacteria. Interpret your answer.

Answer $r = \dfrac{SS_{xy}}{\sqrt{SS_x SS_y}} = \dfrac{17}{\sqrt{28(13.43)}} = 0.88$

Since $r > 0$, the positive correlation tells us that the slope of the best-fit line is positive. Since $r^2 = 0.77$, using the line provides a 77% reduction in error over using the average, the horizontal line.

▶ A. Exercises

If $SS_x = 100$, $SS_y = 25$, $SS_{xy} = -50$, $\bar{y} = 4$, and $\bar{x} = 6$, find
1. the slope of the best-fit line.
2. the intercept of the best-fit line.
3. the equation of the best-fit line.
4. the correlation r and its meaning.
5. the error SSE of the model.

If $y = 4x + 3$ is the best-fit line by the method of least squares, $SS_x = 2$, and $SS_y = 71$, then
6. predict y when x is 8.
7. find SS_{xy}.
8. find r.
9. interpret r.
10. find SSE.

▶ B. Exercises

Use the given data and the method of least squares to find the following.

x	y
2	10
3	8
4	6
6	5
8	1

11. $\bar{x}$ and $\bar{y}$
12. SS_x
13. SS_y
14. SS_{xy}
15. Slope of best-fit line
16. y-intercept of best-fit line
17. Equation of best-fit line
18. Correlation
19. Interpret the correlation.
20. SSE

Use the following data and your graphing calculator to find the following.

x	y
85.41	12
66.43	9
93.56	14
55.30	7
112.43	17
81.25	11

21. Slope of the best-fit line
22. y-intercept of the best-fit line
23. Equation of the best-fit line
24. Correlation
25. Coefficient of determination
26. The x-values are weights and the y-values are ages. Is the best-fit line a good model of the relationship between these measures?

► C. Exercises

27. Obtain a formula for *SSE* by solving a formula in this section for it.

28. Suppose that $r = -0.87$ and that $SS_y = 100$. What can you say about the slope of the best-fit line? What about its improvement in comparison to using the mean as a predictor?

Dominion Modeling

Review your linear and quartic models for total SAT-Math scores as a function of year.

29. What is the *SSE* for the linear model?

30. What is the *SSE* for the quartic model? Compare it to that of the linear model.

Cumulative Review

Consider the function $f(x) = x^4 + 2x^3 - 35x^2 - 36x + 180$.

31. Find the zeros of the function.

32. Is the function even? odd? Identify any symmetry.

33. Graph the function.

34. Solve the equation $x^3 + 125 = 0$.

35. Solve the system using Cramer's rule.

$$4x - 5y = 8$$
$$3x + 2y = 4$$

The graph shows the profits for Blue Springs Electronics. The company has operated only 5 years and wants to predict their profit for next year in order to make a budget. What profit should they expect?

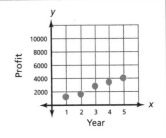

Year	Profit
1	1300
2	1700
3	2900
4	3500
5	4100

9 Approximation Methods

Method of Least Squares

Look at the graph shown.

The best-fit line for this data is $y = 9.54x + 7.69$. You can see that the data does not even appear linear, so it's no surprise that the correlation is only $r = 0.681$ (reduces error only 46% from $\bar{y} = 22$).

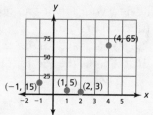

The method of least squares applies to functions other than linear functions. For instance, to find the best-fit parabola, you would use the quadratic model $y = ax^2 + bx + c$. Then you would minimize

$$SSE = \sum_{i=1}^{n} (y_i - \hat{y}_i)^2 = \sum_{i=1}^{n} \left(y_i - [ax_i^2 + bx_i + c] \right)^2.$$ Again this requires calculus, but the result is the system shown.

$$a\sum_{i=1}^{n} x_i^4 + b\sum_{i=1}^{n} x_i^3 + c\sum_{i=1}^{n} x_i^2 = \sum_{i=1}^{n} x_i^2 y_i$$

$$a\sum_{i=1}^{n} x_i^3 + b\sum_{i=1}^{n} x_i^2 + c\sum_{i=1}^{n} x_i = \sum_{i=1}^{n} x_i y_i$$

$$a\sum_{i=1}^{n} x_i^2 + b\sum_{i=1}^{n} x_i + cn = \sum_{i=1}^{n} y_i$$

For the data above you obtain the system
$$274a + 72b + 22c = 1072$$
$$72a + 22b + 6c = 256$$
$$22a + 6b + 4c = 88$$

Using Cramer's rule, the solutions are
$$a = \frac{11{,}232}{1872} = 6 \qquad b = \frac{-15{,}840}{1872} \approx -8.46 \qquad c = \frac{3168}{1872} \approx 1.69$$

The best-fit quadratic (parabola) is $y = 6.00x^2 - 8.46x + 1.69$.

Using the method of least squares, the functions do not pass through the original data points. They approximate the data, which is very useful for some scientific research, where the data is subject to experimental error and is not expected to be exact. It is possible to find functions that pass exactly through the data, though. You already know how to find the linear spline (Chapter 5).

The linear spline for the previous data is:

$$f(x) = \begin{cases} -5x + 10 & \text{if } x < 1 \\ -2x + 7 & \text{if } 1 \le x \le 2. \\ 31x - 59 & \text{if } x > 2 \end{cases}$$

The linear spline has sharp corners where the segments connect. You can obtain a smooth function by finding a polynomial. Since 4 points were given, a third degree (cubic) polynomial is determined. Substitute the coordinates into the model $y = ax^3 + bx^2 + cx + d$ and solve the system formed.

$$-a + b - c + d = 15$$
$$a + b + c + d = 5$$
$$8a + 4b + 2c + d = 3$$
$$64a + 16b + 4c + d = 65$$

Solving the system, $a = 2$, $b = -3$, $c = -7$, $d = 13$. Therefore, the following cubic passes through the data points: $y = 2x^3 - 3x^2 - 7x + 13$.

In summary, the following four models have been developed.

linear regression: $y = 9.54x + 7.69$
quadratic regression: $y = 6.00x^2 - 8.46x + 1.69$
cubic curve: $y = 2x^3 - 3x^2 - 7x + 13$
linear spline: $f(x) = \begin{cases} -5x + 10 & \text{if } x < 1 \\ -2x + 7 & \text{if } 1 \le x \le 2 \\ 31x - 59 & \text{if } x > 2 \end{cases}$

▶ Exercises

1. Use the 4 models above to predict $f(3)$.

Given three points $(-1, 2)$, $(0, 3)$, $(2, 1)$, find

2. the best-fit line.
3. the linear spline.
4. the polynomial that passes through them.
5. If you had 50 data points, what kind of polynomial would you need?

9.7 Tests of Hypotheses (optional)

Suppose that Mrs. Jackson has algebra classes during the first and second periods. The class averages on the last exam were 89 and 85, respectively. Is the first period class smarter? At first you may think so, since the first period class had a higher average score. However, because these are average scores, this is not necessarily true. What if everyone in the second class had perfect scores except one person who did very poorly?

Blaise Pascal (1623-1662)

A problem in comparing averages is seen when the standard deviation is examined. If the standard deviation of both tests is 1 and the scores are normally distributed, then 95% of the first-period students scored between 91 and 87, whereas 95% of the second-period class scored between 87 and 83. In this case the first-period class appears to be superior. On the other hand, what if the standard deviation is 12 on both tests? Then the second-period average is within $\frac{1}{3}$ of a standard deviation of the first period. In other words, the spreads within 1 standard deviation (77 to 101 vs. 73 to 97) are about the same. Each is well within the bounds of an average score for the other class. In this case it would be wrong to say that the first-period class did better.

> *Let us weigh the gain and the loss in wagering that God is. . . If you gain, you gain all; if you lose, you lose nothing. Hesitate not, then, to wager that He is.*
> —BLAISE PASCAL
> (1623-1662)

You can see that standard deviations must be considered when comparing averages. You must ask not only whether the averages are different, but whether the averages are *significantly* different (in light of the standard deviations). The apparent difference between 85 and 89 must be checked for relevance.

Hypothesis testing is one way to check for significance. This method uses indirect proof (proof by contradiction). It also requires you to specify a *level of significance* or error. The symbol for level of significance is α and it can be given as a decimal or a percent.

You will use $\alpha = 0.05$ as the allowable error, unless otherwise specified. This 5% error corresponds to 95% accuracy as in the intervals containing 95% of the test scores discussed above.

The term *critical value* (z_c) is used for that value of z beyond which the hypothesis is rejected. The steps in the test of a hypothesis follow.

Test of a Hypothesis

1. State the hypothesis. H_0: $\mu_1 = \mu_2$; there is no significant difference between the means.

2. Find z_c, the critical value of z. Using $\alpha = 0.05$, the 5% error must be split evenly in the tails. Thus, $2\frac{1}{2}\%$ is in each end of the graph. The corresponding percentage for the shaded area is 47.5%. From the table, then, $z_c \approx 1.96$.

3. Calculate the test statistic. To compare two means, find

$$z = \frac{\bar{x}_1 - \bar{x}_2}{\sqrt{\frac{s_1^2}{n_1} + \frac{s_2^2}{n_2}}}.$$ The formula

compares the means in light of the standard deviations.

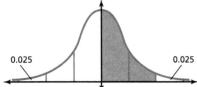

0.025   0.025

4. Check the rejection region. If $|z| > z_c$, then the result is so unlikely that it is easier to believe the assumption was false. In other words, reject the hypothesis and conclude that the means are significantly different.

The hypothesis is called the *null hypothesis* (null means zero and refers to the default). In step 4, if $|z| \leq z_c$, then there is not enough evidence to reject the null hypothesis. This does not prove that the means are equal; it indicates that the test was inconclusive. Do not say that you accept or retain the null hypothesis; say only that you fail to reject the null hypothesis.

EXAMPLE 1 Suppose that the first period class average of 89 included 45 students with a standard deviation of 5. Also suppose that the second period mean of 85 averaged 30 scores with a standard deviation of 7. Is there a significant difference? Do a two-tailed test with $\alpha = 0.05$.

Answer

1. Null hypothesis H_0: $\mu_1 = \mu_2$.

---

2. $z_c = 1.96$

---

3. $z = \dfrac{\bar{x}_1 - \bar{x}_2}{\sqrt{\frac{s_1^2}{n_1} + \frac{s_2^2}{n_2}}} = \dfrac{89 - 85}{\sqrt{\frac{5^2}{45} + \frac{7^2}{30}}} = \dfrac{4}{\sqrt{2.1889}} = 2.704$

---

4. Since $|2.704| > 1.96$, we reject H_0 and conclude that the class averages are significantly different.

The above test is *two-tailed* because it searches for significant differences in either direction. An example of a *one-tailed* test follows.

EXAMPLE 2 Suppose that at a certain school, the senior class took the SAT and averaged 526 with a standard deviation of 100. If there are 79 seniors, is their average significantly above the national mean of 500? Test using $\alpha = 0.01$.

Answer

1. H_0: $\mu = 500$. Note that μ is used because it represents a national average, not a sample mean.

2. To find z_c, note $\alpha = 0.01$ and that you are checking for significance above the mean. Use a one-tailed test by putting all of the error in the upper tail. Thus, $z_c = 2.33$. The shaded area is 0.49 for which the table gives $z_c \approx 2.33$.

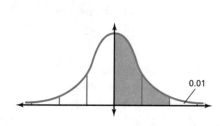

0.01

3. For a population in the millions, such as the population of all students who take the SAT, the value of n is so large that $\frac{s_2^2}{n_2}$ is virtually zero. Thus, you do not need to know s_2 or n_2 to do this problem.

$$z = \frac{\bar{x}_1 - \bar{x}_2}{\sqrt{\frac{s_1^2}{n_1} + \frac{s_2^2}{n_2}}} = \frac{526 - 500}{\sqrt{\frac{(100)^2}{79} + 0}} = \frac{26}{\sqrt{126.58}} \approx 2.31$$

4. Since $|z| < z_c$ (2.31 < 2.33), we cannot reject the null hypothesis. There is not sufficient evidence for this school to conclude that they do better than the national average (even though their average was 26 points higher).

This method is appropriate only if both sample sizes are at least 30 ($n_1 \geq 30$, $n_2 \geq 30$). Similar methods apply to smaller samples, as you will learn in college statistics.

▶ A. Exercises

Mrs. Yiuchi and Mr. Ostrowski teach the same course. They are having a friendly competition in which the class that does best on the mid-term will get a pizza party. The only perfect score on the test was in Mr. O's class of 37 students (mean of 79 and standard deviation of 10), but Mrs. Y's class of 33 students had a higher average with a mean score of 85 and a standard deviation of 6. To settle the issue, they test their means at the .05 level.

1. What is the null hypothesis?
2. Give the critical value z_c.
3. Calculate the test statistic z.
4. What do you conclude regarding the null hypothesis?
5. Interpret your answer for the competition.

An office has 25 applicants for a secretarial position. Using character references, previous experience, college transcripts, and personal testimony, they narrow it down to two candidates. Each candidate takes a comprehensive word processing test involving 30 samples from typical forms and correspondence. Sharon averaged 94 with a standard deviation of 5. Jodi's average was 96 with a standard deviation of 6. Test for a significant difference using $\alpha = 0.025$.

6. Give the null hypothesis.
7. Give the critical value of z_c.
8. Calculate the test statistic.
9. What do you conclude about H_0?
10. Interpret your answer for the company.

▶ B. Exercises

The average SAT score at Cloverdale Christian High School was 537 with a standard deviation of 100. If there are 47 seniors, did they significantly exceed the national mean (use $\alpha = 0.05$)?

11. What is H_0?
12. Find z_c.
13. Find z.
14. What do you conclude about H_0?
15. Interpret your answer for CCHS.

Since sewage absorbs oxygen, some states regulate oxygen content in rivers as a pollution control standard for industries. Suppose the regulation requires at least 5 parts per million. If 30 water samples downstream from *XYZ* manufacturing yield a mean oxygen content of 4.9 parts per million and a standard deviation of 0.17, is the oxygen content significantly below state standards? Should the state prosecute *XYZ* Manufacturing for breaking pollution laws? For a stronger court case, use $\alpha = 0.01$.

16. State H_0.
17. Find z_c.
18. Find z.
19. What do you conclude about H_0?
20. What do you suggest to the state?

The graphing calculator can also be used for hypothesis testing. If a *p*-value greater than α is obtained, you cannot reject the null hypothesis. Repeat the examples below using a graphing calculator. Verify the value of z from the example and compare the *p*-value to α to determine whether the null hypothesis should be rejected.

21. Example 1
22. Example 2

▶ C. Exercises

Test a hypothesis to answer each question. Write all parts of the test and interpret your results.

23. A certain airline offers a daily flight at 7 A.M. on weekdays from Kansas City to Denver. The jet holds 80 passengers and must be two-thirds full (53 passengers) for the airline to profit. After 3 months (60 flights), the airline finds that the 7 A.M. flight averaged 51 passengers with a standard deviation of 9. Is this sufficient evidence to suggest that the flight is unprofitable and should be canceled?

24. A new weight loss program hopes to develop an ad campaign showing itself more effective than the leading program. They randomly assign 90 dieters into 2 groups of 45 and record their weights. At the end of the week, weights of those in the new program showed an average loss of 10.3 pounds with a standard deviation of 4.2 pounds, while those in the rival program showed an average loss of 8.2 pounds with a standard deviation of 5.9. Does the evidence suggest that the difference in effectiveness between the two diet programs is significant?

Dominion Modeling

25. What is the average SAT-Math score for young men? for young women? Is there a significant difference in the achievement of men and women? Show all the parts of testing a hypothesis, including an interpretation of the results.
26. Is there a difference between the groups of males and females on the math test in this data? Explain whether a z-test is informative here. (*Hint:* Recall the difference between a sample and a population.)

Cumulative Review

27. Find all asymptotes and all intercepts of the function $f(x) = \dfrac{x^2 - x - 12}{x^2 - 2x - 3}$.
28. Graph the function in exercise 27.
29. Find the area of a triangle with sides of 17 and 23, with an included angle of 34°.
30. Give the increasing and decreasing intervals for the function graphed here.
31. Barton scored 82 on a standardized test with a mean of 70 and a standard deviation of 15. What is his percentile rank?

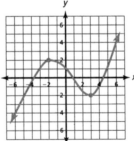

Math *and* Scripture

Least Squares Line

Now you will be able to find the equation of the best-fit line for the logarithms of the patriarchs' life spans. Remember that $\sum$ is the symbol for a sum and SS is an abbreviation for sum of squares. Use a calculator or keep track of your calculations in a table.

1. These sums of squares are the total squared deviation from the mean. What did you get?

$$SS_x = \sum (x - \bar{x})^2 \qquad\qquad SS_{xy} = \sum (x - \bar{x})(y - \bar{y})$$

$$SS_y = \sum (y - \bar{y})^2 \qquad\qquad SS_{xY} = \sum (x - \bar{x})(Y - \bar{Y})$$

$$SS_Y = \sum (Y - \bar{Y})^2$$

The formula for the slope and Y-intercept of the best-fit line using the formula of least squares is $m = \frac{SS_{xY}}{SS_x}$ and $b = \bar{Y} - m\bar{x}$.

Find the equation of the best-fit line

2. for generations and log of life spans.

3. for generation and life span.

Find the SSE for each model.

4. Generation and life span (y)

5. Generation and logs of life span (Y)

Find the correlation and the coefficient of determination for each set of data.

6. Generation and life span

7. Generation and log of life span

8. Compare the error reductions of the two models. Which reduces error more?

With only 15 data points, a correlation of 0.62 is significantly different than zero with 99% confidence.

9. Are the correlations in exercises 6 and 7 significant?

10. Which set of data points is closer to lying on the line?

11. Find the best-fit line for the pre-Flood data.

12. Calculate the correlation and interpret it (with 9 data points, correlations of 0.6 are significant with 95% confidence).

The study of statistics builds on probability and chance. Some argue that it is not an acceptable topic of study for a Christian. However, Ecclesiastes 9:11 provides an example of the word "chance" in the Bible. Such usage shows that the word is appropriate in a Christian's vocabulary at least in certain contexts. On the other hand, Proverbs 16:33 shows that chance events are impossible in the sovereignty of God and James 4:13-15 shows that Christians should never say anything that would detract from the sovereignty of God.

MAXIMIZING

Scripture uses the word *chance* but also seems to prohibit its use. Explain why this is not a contradiction. Reconcile the verses mentioned above to show that there is no contradiction between them.

Vital Sines

I RETURNED, AND SAW under the sun, that the race is not to the swift, nor the battle to the strong, neither yet bread to the wise, nor yet riches to men of understanding, nor yet favour to men of skill; but time and chance happeneth to them all.

ECCLESIASTES 9:11

Chapter 9 Review

Use the data shown to find the following statistics.
49, 38, 41, 47, 42, 44, 46, 47
1. The median
2. The mode
3. The midrange
4. The mean
5. The range
6. The variance
7. The standard deviation

Given a set of 36 scores with $\bar{x} = 23$ and $s = 8$, answer the following.
8. If all the scores are increased by five what will the mean and standard deviation be?
9. If all the scores are multiplied by 2, what will the mean and standard deviation be?
10. What is the z-score for a score of 18?

Find the percentage of z-scores so that
11. $0 \leq z \leq 0.51$
12. $z \geq 1.16$
13. $-1.2 \leq z \leq 1.2$
14. $-0.4 \leq z \leq 2.15$

Find the interval of z-scores containing each percentage of values.
15. 56%, centered at mean
16. 12%, centered at mean
17. 15% in upper tail
18. 9% in lower tail

If $\bar{x} = 10$, $s = 3$, and $n = 32$,
19. find the interval containing 95% of the scores.
20. find the percentile rank for the score of 12.
21-24. Test the hypothesis that $\mu = 11$ at the 5% level. Give each part of the test.

Use the data shown below for exercises 25-26.

x	5	8	3	6	10	2	7	12	4
y	18	21	11	17	25	9	18	27	12

25. Find the best-fit line.
26. Find the correlation and interpret.

27. No matter what data you start with, what percentage of values will fall within 4 standard deviations of the mean? Why?

28. Given mound-shaped data, what percentage of values falls within 2 standard deviations of the mean? Why?

29. Given a large group of means, what percentage of them falls within 1.34 standard deviations of the mean? Why?

30. If $x_1, x_2, \ldots, x_n$ is a set of measurements with mean $\bar{x}$ and variance s_x^2 and $y_i = kx_i + c \; \forall \; i$, give and justify a formula for s_y^2.

31. Consider the linear and quartic models for SAT-Math versus year. Can the SSE help us decide which model is best? Explain.

32. Explain the mathematical significance of Ecclesiastes 9:11.

Suppose that you graduate from college when you are 22 years old, and that you then save $1000 at the beginning of each year. Further suppose that you invest in stocks with a 6% return on your investment. How large could you expect your investment to be when you reach 35? What about when you are 65?

You could answer these questions without much difficulty, although it might take some time. You could also use software to answer such questions. But what if you changed your assumptions about the rate of return? What about a *general* solution, one that helps you understand how payments, rates of return, and frequency of payment interact? To develop such formulas, you will use the following abbreviations.

A	**Future value**: the *amount* you will have someday	*P*	**Principal**: the *present* value (amount you have now)
n	**Number** of interest or payment periods annually	*t*	**Time** (length of investment)
r	Annual interest **rate**	*R*	Periodic **payment** or *rent*

Keep in mind that Christ honored the kind of financial wisdom you can learn throughout this analysis (Luke 16:8).

After this chapter you should be able to

1. find any term of a sequence, given an explicit or recursive formula.
2. identify special sequences: Fibonacci, harmonic, factorial, geometric, and arithmetic.
3. find explicit or recursive formulas for a sequence.
4. prove theorems using mathematical induction.
5. find partial sums of a sequence.

10.1 Recursive Formulas

The Fibonacci sequence relates to rabbit populations. Each rabbit pair produces one pair each month. Each baby rabbit will mature and begin producing more rabbits in its second month. Begin with one pair of rabbits and assume that none die during the span of the study.

A weatherman for a local news station keeps track of the high temperature for each day of a particular month. Part of the month is listed below.

Day	1	2	3	4	5	6	7	8	9	...	30
High Temperature	78	81	80	85	83	88	90	87	91	...	

You can arrange the daily highs in a *sequence* (78, 81, 80, 85, 83, 88, 90, 87, 91, . . .), in which the first number that appears is understood to be associated with the first day, the second number associated with the second day, and so on. We can relate a term's value (such as 78) with the number of the term (*position*) in the sequence. Then $A(1) = 78$ or $A_1 = 78$ gives the position 1 as a domain element or subscript and the term 78 as the range element. The difference between a sequence and an arbitrary set is that the *order* in which the elements appear is important in a sequence, but not in a set. A sequence can be defined as a function whose domain is the set of natural numbers.

Definition

Sequence   A function whose domain is the natural numbers, $\mathbb{N}$. The function values $A_1, A_2, \ldots, A_n, \ldots$ are the *terms* of the sequence, being the first, second, and nth terms, respectively. The nth term is called the *general term*.

Recall that a function is a set of ordered pairs in which the first coordinates are from the domain and the second coordinates are from the range. Thus, the sequence $S = 1, \sqrt{2}, \sqrt{3}, \ldots, \sqrt{n}, \ldots$ means $S = \{(1, 1), (2, \sqrt{2}), (3, \sqrt{3}), \ldots, (n, \sqrt{n}), \ldots \}$.

The list of range elements is more convenient, and you will rarely need to write the set form. The *listing* of a sequence always attaches importance to the order. For instance, the fifth term is always the range element associated with the domain element 5.

Many sequences have patterns to them, and it is the patterns that mathematicians study. A listed sequence may not indicate the pattern for finding terms further down the list. A more useful way to describe a sequence is to use a *recursive formula*. A recursive formula expresses the general term in terms of previous terms. For example,

$$A_n = A_{n-1} + 3, \text{ where } A_1 = 1 \text{ (and } n \geq 2\text{)}.$$

A_{n-1} is the term right before the nth term, thus the general term is described using the previous term. This means that in order to find A_5 you must compute A_4. But to find A_4 you must know A_3. Since each term requires a previous term, it is essential that a starting value be provided. The formula above states that the first term, A_1, is 1.

EXAMPLE 1   Find the first five terms of the sequence above.

Answer $A_1 = 1$

$A_2 = A_1 + 3 = 1 + 3 = 4$

$A_3 = A_2 + 3 = 4 + 3 = 7$

$A_4 = A_3 + 3 = 7 + 3 = 10$

$A_5 = A_4 + 3 = 10 + 3 = 13$

The sequence listing is 1, 4, 7, 10, 13, . . .

EXAMPLE 2   Let $A_1 = 1$, and $A_2 = 2$; $A_n = A_{n-1} \cdot A_{n-2}$ for $n = 3, 4, 5, \ldots$. Find A_3, A_4, and A_5.

Answer $A_n = A_{n-1} \cdot A_{n-2}$

$A_3 = A_2 \cdot A_1 = 2 \cdot 1 = 2$

$A_4 = A_3 \cdot A_2 = 2 \cdot 2 = 4$

$A_5 = A_4 \cdot A_3 = 4 \cdot 2 = 8$

While it may seem bothersome, recursive formulas are quite useful. First, there are many relationships that can be modeled only recursively. Second, if you can write a recursive formula for a sequence, you can easily program a computer to perform the necessary calculations to find the terms of the sequence. In fact, recursion is an important tool in computer programming. The following program in BASIC generates the first 300 terms of the sequence 1, 4, 7, 10, 13, ...

```
05 DIM A(500)
10 LET A(1) = 1
15 PRINT A(1)
20 FOR I = 2 TO 300
25 A(I) = A(I − 1) + 3
30 PRINT A(I)
35 NEXT I
```

You should be able to find recursive formulas for many sequences. Simply compare consecutive terms to find the pattern.

EXAMPLE 3   Give a recursive formula for the sequence 2, 4, 16, 256, ...

Answer

$4 = 2^2$
$16 = 4^2$
$256 = 16^2$

1. Compare each term to previous terms.

$A_n = (A_{n-1})^2$, where $A_1 = 2$

2. Express the pattern; include the starting point.

The sequence above has no special name, but the following patterns arise so often that they do have names.

Definitions

Arithmetic sequence   Consecutive terms differ by a constant. Each is obtained from the previous by adding the same constant, called the *common difference d*. $A_n = A_{n-1} + d$

Geometric sequence   The ratio of consecutive terms is constant. The constant is the *common ratio r*. Each term is the ratio times the previous term. $A_n = rA_{n-1}$

Fibonacci sequence   Each term is obtained by adding the previous two terms. $A_n = A_{n-1} + A_{n-2}$

Factorial sequence   Each term is obtained by multiplying the position by the previous term. $A_n = nA_{n-1}$

Harmonic sequence   The reciprocal of an arithmetic sequence. $A_n = \dfrac{1}{\dfrac{1}{A_{n-1}} + d}$

EXAMPLE 4 Give the first five terms of $A_n = \dfrac{1}{\frac{1}{A_{n-1}} + 5}$ if $A_1 = \frac{1}{3}$. What kind of sequence is it?

Answer Find the next four terms:

$$A_2 = \dfrac{1}{\frac{1}{\frac{1}{3}} + 5} = \frac{1}{8}, \quad A_3 = \dfrac{1}{\frac{1}{\frac{1}{8}} + 5} = \frac{1}{13},$$

$$A_4 = \dfrac{1}{\frac{1}{\frac{1}{13}} + 5} = \frac{1}{18}, \quad A_5 = \dfrac{1}{\frac{1}{\frac{1}{18}} + 5} = \frac{1}{23}.$$

List the terms of the sequence: $\frac{1}{3}, \frac{1}{8}, \frac{1}{13}, \frac{1}{18}, \frac{1}{23}, \ldots$

The terms of A_n are the reciprocals of the terms of $B_n = 3, 8, 13, 18, 23, \ldots$; that is, $A_n = \frac{1}{B_n}$. This means that A_n is a harmonic sequence.

▶ A. Exercises

Write each sequence in list form (include six terms). Identify any sequence that is arithmetic, geometric, Fibonacci, factorial, or harmonic.

1. $A_n = \frac{1}{A_{n-1}}$, $A_1 = 2$
2. $A_n = n(A_{n-1})$, $A_1 = 1$
3. $A_n = A_{n-1} - 4$, $A_1 = 11$
4. $A_n = 2^{n-1}(A_{n-1})$, $A_1 = 3$
5. $A_n = A_{n-1} + A_{n-2}$, $A_1 = 3$, $A_2 = 4$
6. $A_n = 2A_{n-1} + A_{n-3}$, $A_1 = 1$, $A_2 = 5$, $A_3 = 2$
7. $A_n = \frac{2}{3}A_{n-1}$, $A_1 = 27$
8. $A_n = \frac{1}{A_{n-1} + 2}$, $A_1 = 5$
9. $A_n = \dfrac{1}{\frac{1}{A_{n-1}} + 2}$, $A_1 = \frac{1}{2}$
10. $A_n = 2A_{n-1} + 1$, $A_1 = 0$

▶ B. Exercises

Find a recursive formula for each of the following sequences. Identify special sequences.

11. 6, 6, 6, 6, . . .
12. 3, 6, 9, 12, 15, . . .
13. 3, 6, 12, 24, 48, . . .
14. 3, 6, 9, 15, 24, 39, . . .
15. 3, 5, 8, 12, 17, 23, 30, . . .
16. 1, $\frac{1}{2}$, $\frac{1}{4}$, $\frac{1}{8}$, $\frac{1}{16}$, . . .
17. 8, 1.8, 1.18, 1.118, 1.1118, . . .
18. 1, 2, 6, 24, 120, . . .

19. $1, \frac{1}{2}, \frac{1}{3}, \frac{1}{4}, \ldots$

20. 3, 4, 9, 64, 3969, . . .

21. Give the first seven values of the sequence $A_n = 5A_{n-1} + 3$, $A_1 = 2$

22. Give the 12th element in the sequence in exercise 21.

▶ C. Exercises

Find a recursive formula for each of the following sequences.

23. 2, 10, 26, 58, 122, . . .

24. 5, 9, 49, 2209, . . .

Cumulative Review

25. If a right triangle has legs of 6 and 10, find the exact value of the sine, cosine, and tangent of the smaller acute angle A.

Find the slopes of the following lines.

26. The line that contains $(-4, -9)$ and $(-12, 7)$

27. The line $13x - 4y = 12$

28. The line that has an angle of inclination of $137°$

29. The line $x = 3$

10.2 Explicit Formulas

Another useful way to express a sequence is to give a formula for the general term of the sequence. For example, the terms of the sequence 1, 4, 7, 10, 13, . . . can be found by using the equation $A_n = 3n - 2$.

The formula above is an *explicit formula* for the general term because it tells you how to calculate A_n from the position directly without using previous terms. To find a particular term of the sequence, substitute the appropriate integer for n.

$$A_n = 3n - 2$$
$$A_1 = 3(1) - 2 = 1$$
$$A_2 = 3(2) - 2 = 4$$
$$A_{300} = 3(300) - 2 = 898$$

The explicit formula $A_n = 3n - 2$ represents the same sequence as the recursive formula $A_n = A_{n-1} + 3$, $A_1 = 1$. The advantage of the explicit formula should be clear. It permits you to calculate any term directly without finding the previous terms. Using a recursive formula, the calculation of A_{300} above would have required finding all 299 previous terms first.

EXAMPLE 1   Find the first five terms of $A_n = 2n^3 - 10$, and write the sequence as a list.

Answer $A_1 = 2 \cdot 1^3 - 10 = -8$

$A_2 = 2 \cdot 2^3 - 10 = 6$

$A_3 = 2 \cdot 3^3 - 10 = 44$

$A_4 = 2 \cdot 4^3 - 10 = 118$

$A_5 = 2 \cdot 5^3 - 10 = 240$

$-8, 6, 44, 118, 240, \ldots$

Not every sequence has an explicit formula. However, any sequence that has an explicit formula also has a recursive formula.

EXAMPLE 2   If $A_n = 3n - 2$ is the explicit formula for a sequence, find the recursive formula.

Answer

$A_n - A_{n-1} = [3n - 2] - [3(n - 1) - 2]$ $= [3n - 2] - [3n - 5]$ $= 3n - 2 - 3n + 5$ $= 3$	1. Calculate $A_n - A_{n-1}$ to find a common difference.
$A_n - A_{n-1} = 3$ $A_n = A_{n-1} + 3$	2. Express A_n using the relation just found.
$A_1 = 3(1) - 2 = 1$	3. Find A_1 using the explicit formula.
$A_n = A_{n-1} + 3$ where $A_1 = 1$	4. Give the recursive formula.

You can often find explicit formulas by looking for patterns. Look for changes and compare them to the position numbers.

EXAMPLE 3 Find the explicit formula and give A_{10}.

$$1 + \sqrt{2},\ 4 + \sqrt{2},\ 9 + \sqrt{2},\ 16 + \sqrt{2},\ \ldots$$

Answer

n	1	2	3	4 …	1. Write the position above each term. Note that $\sqrt{2}$ is constant.
A_n	$1 + \sqrt{2}$	$4 + \sqrt{2}$	$9 + \sqrt{2}$	$16 + \sqrt{2}$ …	

$A_5 = 25 + \sqrt{2}$

2. Find the next term, noting that the changing part of the term is the square of the position.

$A_n = n^2 + \sqrt{2}$

3. Express your conclusion, using n.

$A_{10} = 10^2 + \sqrt{2} = 100 + \sqrt{2}$

4. Find A_{10}.

EXAMPLE 4 Find the explicit formula for 17, 20, 23, 26, 29, 32, . . .

Answer

1	2	3	4	5	6	1. The terms differ by the constant 3, so the sequence is arithmetic. Compare positions and terms.
17	20	23	26	29	32	

17	$17 + 3$	$17 + 2 \cdot 3$	$17 + 3 \cdot 3$	$17 + 4 \cdot 3$	$17 + 5 \cdot 3$	2. Write each term using $A_1 = 17$ and the common difference $d = 3$.

$A_n = 17 + 3(n - 1)$
$A_n = 17 + 3n - 3$
$A_n = 14 + 3n$

3. To get the 5th term, you added the difference to A_1 four times $(+ 4 \cdot 3)$. For the nth term, add the difference $n - 1$ times $(+ [n - 1] \cdot 3)$.

To better understand this, think of terms of the sequences as pickets in a fence and the common difference as a uniform gap between any pair of pickets. Between any n pickets there are $n - 1$ gaps.

$4 - 1 =$ 3 gaps $8 - 5 =$ 3 gaps $14 - 10 =$ 4 gaps

The explicit formula for an arithmetic sequence with d as the common difference is as follows.

$$A_n = A_1 + (n - 1)d$$

The same principle applies to geometric sequences, but contains a common ratio r. To find the explicit formula of a geometric sequence, multiply by the common ratio $n - 1$ times as follows.

$$A_n = A_1 r^{n-1}$$

The explicit formula for the factorial sequence is $A_n = 1 \cdot 2 \cdot 3 \cdots \cdot n$, which is abbreviated $A_n = n!$ using the factorial symbol (!); for example, $5! = 1 \cdot 2 \cdot 3 \cdot 4 \cdot 5 = 120$ and $1! = 1$. You will need to know that $0! = 1$. Since factorials are defined as multiplications, it should not surprise you that $0!$ is the multiplicative identity. If it does, recall that exponents are also defined using multiplications, and zero powers result in the multiplicative identity.

A harmonic sequence is the reciprocal of an arithmetic sequence. Its explicit formula is $A_n = \dfrac{1}{\frac{1}{A_1} + (n - 1)d}$ when d represents the difference in denominators.

The explicit formula for the Fibonacci sequence is very difficult. You will find it in the table below.

Summary of Formulas		
Sequence	**Recursive Formula**	**Explicit Formula**
Arithmetic	$A_n = A_{n-1} + d$	$A_n = A_1 + (n - 1)d$
Geometric	$A_n = rA_{n-1}$	$A_n = A_1 r^{n-1}$
Factorial	$A_n = nA_{n-1}$	$A_n = n!$
Harmonic	$A_n = \dfrac{1}{\frac{1}{A_{n-1}} + d}$	$A_n = \dfrac{1}{\frac{1}{A_1} + (n - 1)d}$
Fibonacci	$A_n = A_{n-1} + A_{n-2}$	$A_n = \dfrac{1}{\sqrt{5}}\left[\left(\dfrac{1 + \sqrt{5}}{2}\right)^n - \left(\dfrac{1 - \sqrt{5}}{2}\right)^n\right]$

▶ A. Exercises

List each of the following sequences (give 5 terms).

1. $A_n = 2n - 5$

2. $A_n = \dfrac{3}{(n^2 + 1)}$

3. $A_n = \dfrac{n(n - 1)}{2}$

4. $A_n = (-2)^{n-1}$

5. $A_n = 1 + \dfrac{1}{n}$

6. $A_n = 2^{n!}$

7. $A_n = -2 + 3(n - 1)$

8. $A_n = \dfrac{1}{3 + 2n}$

9. $A_n = n!(x + y)$

10. $A_n = 5$

11. $A_n = -3.3(n + 1.22) - 4.444$

▶ B. Exercises

Find an explicit formula for the following sequences. Identify any special sequences.

12. 1, 4, 9, 16, 25, . . .

13. 3, 6, 12, 24, 48, . . .

14. 1, 2, 6, 24, 120, . . .

15. $1, \sqrt{2}, \sqrt{3}, 2, \sqrt{5}, \ldots$

16. 3, 5, 7, 9, 11, . . .

17. $\dfrac{1}{5}, \dfrac{1}{12}, \dfrac{1}{19}, \dfrac{1}{26}, \dfrac{1}{33}, \ldots$

18. 1, −1, 1, −1, 1, . . .

19. $0, \dfrac{1}{2}, \dfrac{2}{3}, \dfrac{3}{4}, \dfrac{4}{5}, \ldots$

20. $\dfrac{1}{x}, \dfrac{1}{x^2}, \dfrac{1}{x^3}, \ldots$

21. 1, 1, 2, 3, 5, . . .

Find the 7th and 20th terms of each sequence.

22. Exercise 12

23. Exercise 17

24. Exercise 14

25. Exercise 19

Every calculator has a largest number that it can handle (even in scientific notation).

26. What is the largest factorial that your calculator can find?

Convert the following arithmetic sequence into a harmonic sequence.

27. 1, 4, 7, 10, 13, . . .

▶ C. Exercises

28. Find an explicit formula for $\dfrac{1}{2}, \dfrac{\sqrt{3}}{2}, 1, \dfrac{\sqrt{3}}{2}, \dfrac{1}{2}, 0, -\dfrac{1}{2}, \ldots$.

29. Show that the explicit formula of the Fibonacci sequence is equivalent to

$$A_n = \frac{(1 + \sqrt{5})^n - (1 - \sqrt{5})^n}{2^n \sqrt{5}}$$

and then determine its first five terms.

30. Graph $x = y^2 + 4y - 1$.

31. A fourth degree polynomial equation has roots of $3 - i$ and $5 + 2i$. What are the other two roots? What can we say about the graph of its associated polynomial function?

32. Find the equation in exercise 31.

33. A pilot wishes to go from airport A to airport B. He will fly at a rate of 200 mph and airport B is on a heading of 75°, but there is a 30 mph wind blowing from the south. What heading should the pilot take to fly to B?

34. Suppose that a sample of 5 students take a test and that their scores are 60, 70, 80, 90, and 100. Find the standard deviation.

Recall that the probability of an event is the number of ways the event can occur divided by the number of possible outcomes. Guess how large a class would have a 70% probability that at least two people have the same birthday. Figure the actual class size and compare it to your guess. Using n as the class size, give an explicit formula for the sequence of probabilities that at least two of the n students have the same birthday.

10.3 Arithmetic and Geometric Sequences

If you deposit $1000 in an account that earns 8% simple interest for five years, you will earn $400 in that time (total $1400 at the end). This amounts to $80 annually as shown in a sequence: 1080, 1160, 1240, 1320, 1400. This is an arithmetic sequence with $d = 80$. The general simple interest formula gives the amount accrued after t years as an arithmetic sequence.

$A = P + Prt$ (r is annual interest rate)

If your $1000 investment earns compound interest at 8% annually, then the nth term of the sequence 1080.00, 1166.40, 1259.71, . . . represents the balance of the account after the nth year. To determine the general term A_n, multiply the amount after the $(n - 1)$st year, A_{n-1}, by 1.08 (1 + interest rate). You can summarize this process by saying that $A_n = A_{n-1} \cdot r$, where r, *the common ratio*, is the compound interest factor (in this case 1.08). Such a sequence is a geometric sequence. The general formula for compound interest gives the amount accrued after t years at rate r as a geometric sequence.

$A = P(1 + r)^t$

EXAMPLE 1   Find the interest earned on a $100 investment earning 6% annual interest for 10 years if the interest is compounded quarterly.

Answer   Since the interest is compounded quarterly, the rates and times must be calculated in quarters. The quarterly interest rate is $\frac{0.06}{4} = 0.015$, and the number of quarters in 10 years is $10 \cdot 4 = 40$. The total value of the account after 10 years is

$A = P(1 + r)^t = 100(1.015)^{40} \approx 181.40$

Since the question asked for the interest, we must deduct the original $100 investment to obtain the total interest of $81.40 in 10 years.

Since both arithmetic and geometric sequences apply to financial stewardship, they are worth some detailed study. You have already learned their formulas.

	List	Recursive	Explicit
Arithmetic	$A_1, A_1 + d, A_1 + 2d, \ldots$	$A_n = A_{n-1} + d$	$A_n = A_1 + (n - 1)d$
Geometric	$A_1, rA_1, r^2A_1, \ldots$	$A_n = rA_{n-1}$	$A_n = A_1r^{n-1}$

Notice that the explicit formula for an arithmetic sequence always simplifies.

By the formula

$$A_n = A_1 + (n - 1)d$$
$$= A_1 + nd - d$$
$$= nd + (A_1 - d)$$
$$= nd + c, \text{ where } c \text{ is a constant } (c = A_1 - d).$$

Thus, in the formula for the general term A_n of an arithmetic sequence, the coefficient of the position number n is d, and n is raised to no power other than 1. By inspecting the equation of the general term A_n, you can immediately determine whether the sequence is arithmetic.

EXAMPLE 2 State whether the following sequences are arithmetic. If they are, give the common difference.

   a. $A_n = 5n + 4$ c. $A_n = \sqrt{n} - 2$
   b. $A_n = \frac{-n}{2} - 2$ d. $A_n = 3n^2 + 4$

Answer

   a. $A_n = 5n + 4$ is arithmetic with a common difference of 5.

   b. $A_n = \frac{-n}{2} - 2$ is arithmetic with a common difference of $\frac{-1}{2}$.

   c. $A_n = \sqrt{n} - 2$ is not arithmetic (because it is not linear).

   d. $A_n = 3n^2 + 4$ is not arithmetic (because it is not linear).

EXAMPLE 3 Find the explicit formula A_n and A_{10} for
   a. an arithmetic sequence with $A_1 = \sqrt{5}$ and $d = \sqrt{7}$.
   b. a geometric sequence with $A_1 = 12$ and $r = 2$.

Answer

   a. $A_n = A_1 + (n - 1)d$ b. $A_n = A_1r^{n-1}$
   $A_n = \sqrt{5} + (n - 1)\sqrt{7}$ $A_n = 12(2)^{n-1}$
   $A_{10} = \sqrt{5} + 9\sqrt{7}$ $A_n = 12(2)^n(2)^{-1}$
         $A_n = 6 \cdot 2^n$
         $A_{10} = 6 \cdot 2^{10} = 6144$

The next theorem shows how to determine the formula for an arithmetic sequence from two terms.

Theorem 10.1

If A_k is the kth term of an arithmetic sequence with common difference d, then the explicit formula for the sequence is $A_n = A_k + (n - k)d$.

Proof

$$A_n = A_1 + (n - 1)d$$

$$A_k = A_1 + (k - 1)d$$

$$\therefore A_n - A_k = [A_1 + (n - 1)d] - [A_1 + (k - 1)d]$$

$$= A_1 + nd - d - A_1 - kd + d$$

$$= nd - kd$$

$$= (n - k)d$$

$$\therefore A_n = A_k + (n - k)d$$

EXAMPLE 4 Given the two terms of an arithmetic sequence $A_3 = 8$ and $A_7 = -6$, find A_n.

Answer

$A_n = A_k + (n - k)d$	1. Using $n = 7$ and $k = 3$, apply
$A_7 = A_3 + (7 - 3)d$	the theorem and solve for d.
$-6 = 8 + 4d$	
$4d = -14$	
$d = \frac{-7}{2}$	
$A_n = A_k + (n - k)d$	2. Apply the theorem again with
$A_n = 8 + (n - 3)\left(-\frac{7}{2}\right)$	$k = 3$ to find the explicit formula.
$A_n = 8 - \frac{7}{2}n + \frac{21}{2}$	
$A_n = -\frac{7}{2}n + \frac{37}{2}$	

A similar result holds for geometric sequences.

Theorem 10.2

If A_k is the kth term of a geometric sequence with a common ratio r, then the explicit formula for the sequence is $A_n = A_k r^{n-k}$.

EXAMPLE 5 Find the explicit formula for a geometric sequence if $A_3 = 6$ and $A_7 = 96$.

Answer

$A_n = A_k r^{n-k}$

1. Use the theorem above with $n = 7$ and $k = 3$ to find r. There are two possible values.

$A_7 = A_3 r^{7-3}$

$96 = 6r^4$

$16 = r^4$

$r = \pm 2$

$A_n = A_k r^{n-k}$

2. Case 1: $r = 2$. Apply the theorem again with $k = 3$. Note that you can add exponents on like bases by factoring the 6.

$A_n = A_3 r^{n-3}$

$A_n = 6 \cdot 2^{n-3}$

$A_n = 3 \cdot 2^1 \cdot 2^{n-3}$

$A_n = 3 \cdot 2^{n-2}$

$A_n = A_k r^{n-k}$

3. Case 2: $r = -2$. Repeat the process from case 1.

$A_n = A_3 r^{n-3}$

$A_n = 6(-2)^{n-3}$

$A_n = (-3)(-2)(-2)^{n-3}$

$A_n = -3(-2)^{n-2}$

You may by now be able to appreciate the power of theorems, or general principles, in mathematics. In the Christian life as well, there are certain principles which are foundational. Since it is impossible to work and memorize answers to every conceivable math problem, you learn principles that apply. Likewise, you cannot list every situation in life, so it is essential to learn biblical principles and apply them to the situations. Therefore, in your Christian life you must build on the foundational principles of Scripture.

EXAMPLE 6 Prove that if A_n is a geometric sequence, then A_n^2 is also geometric.

Answer

$A_n = rA_{n-1}$

1. Since A_n is geometric, it has a recursive formula with common ratio r.

$\dfrac{A_n}{A_{n-1}} = r$

2. Solve for r.

$\dfrac{A_n^2}{A_{n-1}^2} = r^2$

$A_n^2 = r^2 A_{n-1}^2$

3. Square both sides and simplify; r^2 must be a constant because r is a constant.

A_n^2 is geometric.

4. Use the definition again, since r^2 is the common ratio.

| | EXAMPLE 7 | Suppose a rubber ball is dropped from a height of 20 feet and it rebounds 0.8 of its former height on each bounce. How high will it bounce on the eighth bounce? |

Answer

$A_1 = 20(0.8) = 16$ feet

$A_2 = 16(0.8) = 12.8$ feet

$A_3 = 12.8(0.8) = 10.24$ feet

1. Compute the first few terms.

$A_8 = A_1 r^{8-1} = 16(0.8)^7 \approx 3.36$ feet

2. The height of consecutive bounces forms a geometric sequence with $A_1 = 16$ and $r = 0.8$.

▶ A. Exercises

Write the first five terms of each sequence satisfying the following criteria. Remember that d is the common difference for an arithmetic sequence and r is the common ratio for a geometric sequence.

1. $A_1 = 5, d = 6$
2. $A_1 = -32, r = \frac{1}{2}$
3. $A_1 = 9, r = \frac{-1}{3}$
4. $A_1 = 3 + 2i, d = 4 - i$
5. $A_1 = \log 64, d = \log 2$
6. $A_{10} = 5, d = 3$
7. $A_{12} = 49, A_8 = 25$ for an arithmetic sequence
8. $A_3 = 9, A_6 = 72$ for a geometric sequence
9. $A_2 = -\text{cis } \pi, r = \frac{\text{cis } \pi}{2}$ (give answer in rectangular form)
10. $A_8 = 3^5, r = \frac{1}{3^2}$

▶ B. Exercises

For each sequence, determine if it is arithmetic, geometric, or neither. If it is arithmetic, find the common difference and the explicit formula. If it is geometric, find its common ratio and the explicit formula.

11. $\frac{1}{3}, \frac{2}{3}, \frac{4}{3}, \frac{8}{3}, \ldots$
12. $3 + 2i, 6 - i, 5 - 7i, -2 - 12i, \ldots$
13. $1, 4, 7, 10, 13, \ldots$
14. $10, 8, 6, 4, \ldots$
15. $1, \frac{1}{2}, \frac{1}{3}, \frac{1}{4}, \frac{1}{5}, \ldots$
16. $5.3, 5.7, 6.1, 6.5, \ldots$
17. $1^2, 2^2, 3^2, 4^2, \ldots$

18. $\frac{y}{x}, 1, \frac{x}{y}, \frac{x^2}{y^2}, \ldots$

19. ln 1, ln 2, ln 3, ln 4, . . .

20. 10, 10, 10, 10, . . .

21. Find the twentieth term of the geometric sequence $xy^2, x^2y, x^3, \frac{x^4}{y}, \ldots$.

22. Suppose that a bacterium divides into 2 bacteria every 20 minutes. Assuming the new bacteria do likewise, what is the number of bacteria present after 6 hours? after 1 day?

23. Suppose that a ball is dropped from a height of 100 feet and rebounds 0.6 of its former height on each bounce. Write an expression for the height of the ball on each bounce. How many bounces will it take until the height of each bounce is less than 5 feet?

24. The value of a car depreciates 20% each year (i.e., if a car is worth $5000 at the beginning of the year, it will be worth $4000 at the end of the year). What is a fair price to pay for a five-year-old car if it sold for $8000 when new?

Prove or disprove each of the following statements, where k is a constant.

25. If A_n is an arithmetic sequence, then kA_n is also arithmetic. For example, if $A_n = 1, 2, 3, \ldots$, then $5A_n = 5, 10, 15, \ldots$.

26. If A_n is an arithmetic sequence, then $A_n + B_n$ is an arithmetic sequence.

27. If A_n is a geometric sequence, then $A_n{}^k$ is geometric.

28. If A_n is geometric, then kA_n is geometric.

▶ C. Exercises

Prove or disprove each of the following statements.

29. If A_n is an arithmetic sequence, then $\frac{1}{A_n}$ is arithmetic.

30. If A_n is geometric, then $\frac{1}{A_n}$ is geometric if $A_n \neq 0$.

⟨⟩ Dominion Modeling

31. Suppose you had $1000 in an investment that earned 5% annually. Complete the table below to find how much you would have at the end of 5 years.

Year	Start	Income at 5%	End
1	$1000.00	$50.00	$1050.00
2	$1050.00		
3			
4			
5			

32. Suppose you invested *P* dollars in an account that earned *r*% annually. Complete the table below to find how much you would have at the end of 5 years.

Year	Start	Income at *r*%	End (Add)	Factor	Simplify
1	*P*	*Pr*	*P* + *Pr*	*P*(1 + *r*)	*P*(1 + *r*)
2	*P*(1 + *r*)	*P*(1 + *r*)*r*	*P*(1 + *r*) + *P*(1 + *r*)*r*	*P*(1 + *r*)(1 + *r*)	*P*(1 + *r*)²
3					
4					
5					

33. Based on your calculations above, what kind of sequence develops from the annual values of the investment? Write a formula that expresses the value *A* for a principal *P* invested at *r*% annually for *t* years.

34. Use your formula to answer exercise 31 quickly. If you invested $1000 and earned 5% annual interest, how much would you have after 5 years? after 10 years?

Cumulative Review

35. List all possible rational roots of the given equation $4x^4 - 3x^3 + 8x - 3 = 0$. Do not attempt to solve.

36. Without graphing, explain which way the tails go on the graph of the associated polynomial function of exercise 35.

37. What is the distinguishing feature of an exponential function?

38. What method is used to solve an exponential equation?

39. Find the minor of 7 in the following matrix.

$$\begin{bmatrix} 6 & 4 & 8 \\ 2 & -5 & 7 \\ 3 & 5 & 1 \end{bmatrix}$$

10.4 Mathematical Induction

The proofs of several theorems about sequences require an application of the principle of mathematical induction.

> ### Postulate 10.1: Principle of Mathematical Induction
> Let $P(n)$ be a proposition. $P(n)$ is true for all natural numbers n if
>
> 1. $P(1)$ is true, and
> 2. $P(k + 1)$ is true when $P(k)$ is true.

In other words, you must first check that the proposition is true when $n = 1$, and then you must prove the induction step that each proposition guarantees the next.

It may help to compare mathematical induction to a chain of dominos. The first condition states that you can knock down the first domino [$P(1)$ is true], and the second step states that the kth domino will knock down the next $(k + 1)$ domino [$P(k)$ implies $P(k + 1)$]. In other words, if

1. the first domino falls and
2. every domino always knocks down the next,

then eventually all the dominos will fall. [$P(n)$ is true for all $n \in \mathbb{N}$.]

The idea of mathematical induction is that a sequence of statements can be checked much like a sequence of falling dominos. If the first statement checks (first domino falls), and if each statement's truth guarantees the next one (each domino always knocks down the next one), then all the statements are true (all the dominos fall).

Mathematical induction should remind you of recursive formulas. If you state the first term, A_1 [show that $P(1)$ is true], and if you define A_{n+1} based on the preceding term, A_n, then you can calculate A_n for every value of n.

The second step may seem like you are assuming the proposition that you are trying to prove. However, the step does not prove the proposition for any given value of n. It shows only that every proposition follows from the previous one. It will help you if you write out both $P(k)$ and $P(k + 1)$ to distinguish what you start with and what you are trying to prove.

EXAMPLE 1   Prove the explicit formula for arithmetic sequences.

Answer   For each arithmetic sequence, where A_1 is the first term and d is the common difference, the explicit formula is $A_n = A_1 + (n - 1)d$. Prove $P(n)$: $A_n = A_1 + (n - 1)d \: \forall \: n$.

Proof

STATEMENTS	REASONS
1. Verify $P(1)$. $P(1)$: $A_1 = A_1 + (1 - 1)d = A_1$	1. Check the first statement. Substitute $n = 1$; note that the resulting statement is true.
2. Show that $P(k)$ implies $P(k + 1)$. Assume $P(k)$: $A_k = A_1 + (k - 1)d$ Show $P(k + 1)$: $A_{k+1} = A_1 + ([k + 1] - 1)d$ $A_k = A_1 + (k - 1)d$ $A_{k+1} = A_1 + (k - 1)d + d$ $A_{k+1} = A_1 + [(k - 1) + 1]d$ $A_{k+1} = A_1 + [(k + 1) - 1]d$ $P(k)$ implies $P(k + 1)$	2. Prove the induction step. We have not said that $P(k)$ is true, but will show that *if* it is true, then $P(k + 1)$ is also true. a. Begin with the assumption. Add d to both sides. By definition of arithmetic sequence $A_k + d = A_{k+1}$. b. Factor the d on the right. c. Use the commutative and associative properties to regroup. d. From $P(k)$ in step a, we derived $P(k + 1)$ in step c.
3. Conclude that $P(n)$ is true for all $n \in \mathbb{N}$.	3. Apply the principle of mathematical induction.

The study of mathematics cannot be replaced by any other activity that will train and develop man's purely logical faculties to the same level of rationality.
—C. O. OAKLEY

EXAMPLE 2 Prove the explicit formula for geometric sequences.

Answer If A_n is a geometric sequence with a common ratio r, then
$A_n = A_1 r^{n-1}$. Prove $P(n)$: $A_n = A_1 r^{n-1} \ \forall \ n$.

Proof

STATEMENTS	REASONS
1. Verify $P(1)$. $P(1)$: $A_1 = A_1 r^{1-1} = A_1 r^0 = A_1$	1. Check the first statement. $P(n)$ is true when $n = 1$.
2. Show that $P(k)$ implies $P(k + 1)$. *Assume $P(k)$*: $A_k = A_1 r^{k-1}$ *Show $P(k + 1)$*: $A_{k+1} = A_1 r^{k+1-1}$ $\quad A_k = A_1 r^{k-1}$ $\quad A_k r = A_1 r^{k-1} \cdot r$ $\quad A_{k+1} = A_1 r^{k-1+1}$ $\quad A_{k+1} = A_1 r^{k+1-1}$ $\quad P(k)$ implies $P(k + 1)$	2. Prove the induction step: if $P(k)$ is true, then $P(k + 1)$ is also. a. Begin with the assumption. Multiply both sides by r. b. By definition of geometric sequence $A_k r = A_{k+1}$. Multiply r^{k-1} by r by adding exponents. c. Use the commutative property in the exponent. d. From $P(k)$ in step a, we derived $P(k + 1)$ in step c.
3. Conclude that $P(n)$ is true for all $n \in \mathbb{N}$.	3. Apply the principle of mathematical induction.

You can also prove inequalities, divisibility, and generalizations of real number properties using induction.

EXAMPLE 3 Prove that $n \leq 2^n \ \forall \ n$.

Answer Let $P(n)$: $n \leq 2^n \ \forall \ n$.

Proof

STATEMENTS	REASONS
1. Verify $P(1)$. $P(1)$: $1 \leq 2^1$	1. Check the first statement. $P(n)$ is true when $n = 1$.
2. Show that $P(k)$ implies $P(k + 1)$. *Assume $P(k)$*: $k \leq 2^k$ *Show $P(k + 1)$*: $k + 1 \leq 2^{k+1}$ $\quad k \leq 2^k$ $\quad k + 1 \leq 2^k + 1$	2. Prove the induction step: $P(k)$ implies $P(k + 1)$. a. Begin with $P(k)$. b. Add 1 to both sides to get the correct left side for $P(k + 1)$.

Continued ▶

$$2^k + 1 \leq 2^k + 2^k$$

c. $2^k + 2^k$ is greater than $2^k + 1$, since all powers of 2 are larger than 1.

$$k + 1 \leq 2^k + 2^k$$

d. Combine steps b and c using the transitive property of inequality.

e. Simplify step d.

$$k + 1 \leq 2(2^k)$$
$$k + 1 \leq 2^{k+1}$$

$P(k + 1)$ is true whenever $P(k)$ is true.

f. From $P(k)$ in step a, we derived $P(k + 1)$ in step e.

----

3. Conclude that $P(n)$ is true for all $n \in \mathbb{N}$.

3. Apply the principle of mathematical induction.

EXAMPLE 4 Prove that $n^2 - n$ is divisible by 2 for all positive integers.

Answer Let $P(n)$: $n^2 - n$ is divisible by 2. We must show that for every natural number n, $n^2 - n = 2c$ for some integer c.

Proof

STATEMENTS

REASONS

1. Verify $P(1)$.
   $P(1)$: $1^2 - 1 = 0$

1. Check the first statement. $P(n)$ is true when $n = 1$ since 0 is divisible by 2.

----

2. Show that $P(k)$ implies $P(k + 1)$.
   Assume $P(k)$: $k^2 - k = 2c$ for $c \in \mathbb{Z}$.
   Show $P(k + 1)$: $(k + 1)^2 - (k + 1) = 2c$.
   $$k^2 - k = 2c$$
   $$k^2 + 2k + 1 - k - 1 = 2c + 2k$$

2. Prove the induction step that $P(k)$ implies $P(k + 1)$.

a. Add $2k$ to both sides and add and subtract 1 on the left side

$$(k + 1)^2 - (k + 1) = 2c + 2k$$

b. Factor the left side to get it in the form $P(k + 1)$.

$$P(k + 1) = 2(c + k)$$

c. The factor of 2 proves $P(k + 1)$ is divisible by 2.

----

3. Conclude that $P(n)$ is true for all $n \in \mathbb{N}$.

3. Apply the principle of mathematical induction.

You are now in a position to understand the proof of DeMoivre's theorem from Chapter 7. Recall that cis $\theta = \cos \theta + i \sin \theta$.

DeMoivre's Theorem
For any complex number of the form r cis θ, $(r$ cis $\theta)^n = r^n$ cis $(n\theta)$.

Proof

Let $P(n)$: $(r$ cis $\theta)^n = r^n$ cis $(n\theta)$.

STATEMENTS	REASONS
1. Verify $P(1)$. $(r$ cis $\theta)^1 = r$ cis $\theta = r^1$ cis 1θ	**1.** Check the first statement. $P(n)$ is true when $n = 1$.
2. Show that $P(k)$ implies $P(k + 1)$. *Assume* $P(k)$: $(r$ cis $\theta)^k = r^k$ cis $(k\theta)$. *Show* $P(k + 1)$: $(r$ cis $\theta)^{k+1} = r^{k+1}$ cis $[(k + 1)\theta]$ $(r$ cis $\theta)^k = r^k$ cis $(k\theta)$ $(r$ cis $\theta)^k (r$ cis $\theta) = (r^k$ cis $k\theta)(r$ cis $\theta)$ $(r$ cis $\theta)^{k+1} = r^k r$ cis $(k\theta + \theta)$ $(r$ cis $\theta)^{k+1} = r^{k+1}$ cis $[(k + 1)\theta]$ $P(k + 1)$ is true whenever $P(k)$ is true.	**2.** Prove the induction step that $P(k)$ implies $P(k + 1)$. a. Start with $P(k)$. b. Multiply both sides by $(r$ cis $\theta)$ to obtain the left side of $P(k + 1)$. c. Multiply the two complex numbers in polar form, then factor out θ. d. We proved $P(k + 1)$ based on $P(k)$.
3. Conclude that $P(n)$ is true for all $n \in \mathbb{N}$.	**3.** Apply the principle of mathematical induction.

Another important theorem that requires mathematical induction for its proof is the binomial theorem, which you studied in Algebra 2. This theorem gives the expansion for $(x + y)^n$. While the coefficients can also be obtained from Pascal's triangle, it requires mathematical induction for its proof.

Binomial Theorem
For any natural number n, and for any terms x and y, the binomial expansion is given by the following formula.

$$(x + y)^n = x^n + nx^{n-1}y + \frac{n(n - 1)}{2!}x^{n-2}y^2 + \frac{n(n - 1)(n - 2)}{3!}x^{n-3}y^3$$
$$+ \cdots + nxy^{n-1} + y^n$$

▶ A. Exercises

Prove that $n^3 - n$ is always divisible by 6.

1. State $P(1)$ and determine if it is true.
2. Find $P(2)$ and determine if it is true.
3. Find $P(3)$ and determine if it is true.
4. Find $P(5)$ and determine if it is true.
5. Find $P(7)$ and determine if it is true.
6. Find $P(10)$ and determine if it is true.
7. Find $P(k)$.
8. Find $P(k + 1)$.
9. Assume $P(k)$ is divisible by 6; show $P(k + 1)$ is divisible by 6.
10. Which exercises in steps 1-9 provide a proof using mathematical induction?

▶ B. Exercises

11. Prove that $(1 + n)^2 \geq 1 + n^2$ for all positive integers.
12. Prove that $n! > 2^n$ for $n \geq 4$. (*Hint:* Start the induction proof at 4 instead of 1.)
13. Prove that $2^n > n$ for all positive integers.
14. Prove that $\forall\, z \in \mathbb{C}, \overline{z^n} = (\bar{z})^n$.
15. Prove the generalized distributive property: $a(b_1 + b_2 + b_3 + \cdots + b_n) = ab_1 + ab_2 + ab_3 + \cdots + ab_n$ for $n \geq 2$.
16. Prove the generalized grouping property: $(a_1 + b_1) + (a_2 + b_2) + \cdots + (a_n + b_n) = (a_1 + a_2 + \cdots + a_n) + (b_1 + b_2 + \cdots + b_n)$.

▶ C. Exercises

17. Prove the binomial theorem.

■ Cumulative Review

Consider the following functions.

a. $f(x) = x^4 - 3x^2 + 2$ c. $h(x) = 2x^3 - x$

b. $g(x) = x^3 - x^2$ d. $k(x) = 2 \cos \frac{x}{2}$

18. Classify each function as even, odd, or neither.
19. Which function has a zero at $x = \sqrt{2}$?

Give the intervals of continuity for the following functions.

20. $f(x) = \dfrac{x + 1}{x^2 - 7x + 12}$

21. $g(x) = \dfrac{1}{x - 1}$

22. What distinguishes the graphs of functions that are not continuous?

10.5 Sums and Their Properties

Recall from statistics that Σ (*sigma*, the Greek capital letter) represents summation and i is used as an index or counter.

EXAMPLE 1   Evaluate $\displaystyle\sum_{i=3}^{7} (i^2 - 2i)$.

Answer

The bounds on the index written below and above the summation symbol indicate that the index runs from $i = 3$ to 7. The index always increases by one, so you must successively substitute the values 3, 4, 5, 6, and 7 for i and then add the results.

$$\sum_{i=3}^{7} (i^2 - 2i) = [3^2 - 2 \cdot 3] + [4^2 - 2 \cdot 4] + [5^2 - 2 \cdot 5]$$
$$+ [6^2 - 2 \cdot 6] + [7^2 - 2 \cdot 7]$$
$$= 3 + 8 + 15 + 24 + 35$$
$$= 85$$

In Example 1, the index of summation (i) was actually used in the calculations, but i can also reference terms of a sequence as in Example 2.

EXAMPLE 2   If $A_n = 2, 4, 6, 8, 10, \ldots, 2n, \ldots$, find $\displaystyle\sum_{i=1}^{5} A_i$.

Answer

$\displaystyle\sum_{i=1}^{5} A_i = A_1 + A_2 + A_3 + A_4 + A_5$	1. Substitute the values 1, 2, 3, 4, and 5 for i; find the sum of the sequence elements.
$= 2 + 4 + 6 + 8 + 10$ $= 30$	2. Substitute the corresponding sequence numbers from the given sequence A_n. Find the sum.

Consider the sequence $A = A_1, A_2, A_3, \ldots, A_n, \ldots$. You can form a sequence S_n of *partial sums* as follows.

$$S_1 = A_1$$
$$S_2 = A_1 + A_2$$
$$S_3 = A_1 + A_2 + A_3$$
$$S_n = A_1 + A_2 + A_3 + \cdots + A_n.$$

This is conveniently summarized using summation notation:

$$S_n = A_1 + A_2 + A_3 + \cdots + A_n = \sum_{i=1}^{n} A_i.$$

Summation properties are important when working with partial sums. The first of the following properties is a generalization of the commutative and associative properties while the second is the definition of multiplication (repeated addition). The third generalizes the distributive property and the fourth is a generalization of the associative property.

Properties of Summations

Let A and B be sequences, c and p constants, and n the upper bound of the index of summation.

1. $\displaystyle\sum_{i=1}^{n} (A_i + B_i) = \sum_{i=1}^{n} A_i + \sum_{i=1}^{n} B_i$

2. $\displaystyle\sum_{i=1}^{n} c = nc$

3. $\displaystyle\sum_{i=1}^{n} cA_i = c\sum_{i=1}^{n} A_i$

4. $\displaystyle\sum_{i=1}^{n} A_i = \sum_{i=1}^{p} A_i + \sum_{i=p+1}^{n} A_i$ where $1 < p < n$

EXAMPLE 3   Prove property 3.

Answer   Proving the property for all values of n requires mathematical induction.

$$P(n): \sum_{i=1}^{n} cA_i = c\sum_{i=1}^{n} A_i$$

Proof

STATEMENTS	REASONS
1. Verify $P(1)$. $P(1): \displaystyle\sum_{i=1}^{1} cA_i = c\sum_{i=1}^{1} A_i$, or $cA_1 = cA_1$	1. Check the first statement. $P(n)$ is true when $n = 1$.
2. Show that $P(k)$ implies $P(k + 1)$. Assume $P(k): \displaystyle\sum_{i=1}^{k} cA_i = c\sum_{i=1}^{k} A_i$	2. Prove the induction step that $P(k)$ implies $P(k + 1)$.

Continued ▶

$$\text{Show } P(k+1): \sum_{i=1}^{k+1} cA_i = c\sum_{i=1}^{k+1} A_i$$

$\displaystyle\sum_{i=1}^{k} cA_i = c\sum_{i=1}^{k} A_i$	a. Given $P(k)$.
$cA_{k+1} + \displaystyle\sum_{i=1}^{k} cA_i = cA_{k+1} + c\sum_{i=1}^{k} A_i$ $\displaystyle\sum_{i=1}^{k+1} cA_i = c\!\left(A_{k+1} + \sum_{i=1}^{k} A_i\right) = c\sum_{i=1}^{k+1} A_i$	b. Add cA_{k+1} to both sides to obtain $P(k+1)$; factor the right side.
$P(k+1)$ is true whenever $P(k)$ is true.	c. We proved $P(k+1)$ based on $P(k)$.

---

3. Conclude that $P(n)$ is true for all $n \in \mathbb{N}$.	3. Apply the principle of mathematical induction.

The other properties of summation may be proved in the same way. Mathematical induction can also be used to develop formulas for some summations that arise frequently.

EXAMPLE 4 Prove $\displaystyle\sum_{i=1}^{n} i = 1 + 2 + 3 + 4 + \cdots + n = \frac{n(n+1)}{2} = \frac{n^2 + n}{2}$, $\forall\, n \in \mathbb{N}$.

Answer   Let $P(n)$: $1 + 2 + 3 + 4 + \cdots + n = \dfrac{n^2 + n}{2}$.

Proof

STATEMENTS	REASONS
1. Verify $P(1)$. $\quad P(1)$: $1 = \dfrac{1^2 + 1}{2} = \dfrac{2}{2} = 1$	1. Check the first statement to show that the formula works for $n = 1$.

---

2. Show that $P(k)$ implies $P(k+1)$. Assume $P(k)$: $1 + 2 + 3 + \cdots + k = \dfrac{k^2 + k}{2}$. Show $P(k+1)$: $\quad 1 + 2 + 3 + \cdots + k + (k+1) = \dfrac{(k+1)^2 + (k+1)}{2}$	2. Prove the induction step that $P(k)$ implies $P(k+1)$.
$\qquad\qquad 1 + 2 + 3 + \cdots + k = \dfrac{k^2 + k}{2}$	a. Given $P(k)$.

Continued ▶

$$1 + 2 + 3 + 4 + \cdots + k + (k + 1) = \frac{k^2 + k}{2} + (k + 1)$$

$$= \frac{(k^2 + k)}{2} + \frac{2(k + 1)}{2}$$

$$= \frac{(k^2 + k + 2k + 2)}{2}$$

$$= \frac{(k^2 + 2k + 1) + (k + 1)}{2}$$

$$= \frac{(k + 1)^2 + (k + 1)}{2}$$

b. Add $k + 1$ to both sides. Obtain a common denominator on the right side; then group in terms of $k + 1$.

$P(k + 1)$ is true whenever $P(k)$ is true.

c. We proved $P(k + 1)$ based on $P(k)$.

3. Conclude that $P(n)$ is true $\forall\, n \in \mathbb{N}$.

3. Apply the principle of mathematical induction.

EXAMPLE 5   Find a formula for the nth partial sum of the following sequence. $\dfrac{1}{1 \cdot 2}, \dfrac{1}{2 \cdot 3}, \dfrac{1}{3 \cdot 4}, \cdots, \dfrac{1}{n(n + 1)}, \cdots$
Prove your answer is true for all n.

Answer

$S_1 = \dfrac{1}{1 \cdot 2} = \dfrac{1}{2}$

$S_2 = \dfrac{1}{1 \cdot 2} + \dfrac{1}{2 \cdot 3} = \dfrac{4}{6} = \dfrac{2}{3}$

$S_3 = S_2 + \dfrac{1}{3 \cdot 4} = \dfrac{2}{3} + \dfrac{1}{12} = \dfrac{9}{12} = \dfrac{3}{4}$

$S_4 = S_3 + \dfrac{1}{4 \cdot 5} = \dfrac{3}{4} + \dfrac{1}{20} = \dfrac{16}{20} = \dfrac{4}{5}$

1. While you may wish to use mathematical induction, you have no proposition yet. One drawback to mathematical induction is that it requires the answer before you can begin the proof. Instead, examine a few terms and identify the pattern.

$S_n = \dfrac{1}{1 \cdot 2} + \dfrac{1}{2 \cdot 3} + \dfrac{1}{3 \cdot 4}$
$\qquad + \cdots + \dfrac{1}{n(n + 1)} = \dfrac{n}{n + 1}$

$P(n)\colon \dfrac{1}{1 \cdot 2} + \dfrac{1}{2 \cdot 3} + \dfrac{1}{3 \cdot 4}$
$\qquad + \cdots + \dfrac{1}{n(n + 1)} = \dfrac{n}{n + 1}$

2. Write an explicit formula for S_n. Let $P(n)$ be the proposition, and note that $P(1)$ is already verified above.

$S_k = \displaystyle\sum_{i=1}^{k} \dfrac{1}{i(i + 1)} = \dfrac{1}{1 \cdot 2} + \dfrac{1}{2 \cdot 3}$
$\qquad + \cdots + \dfrac{1}{k(k + 1)} = \dfrac{k}{k + 1}$

3. Write $P(k)$ and seek to derive $P(k + 1)\colon S_{k+1} = \dfrac{k + 1}{k + 1 + 1}.$

Continued ▶

$$S_k = \frac{k}{k+1}$$

4. Write out the summation for S_k and add the $(k+1)$ term to both sides.

$$S_k + \frac{1}{(k+1)(k+1+1)} = \frac{k}{k+1} + \frac{1}{(k+1)(k+1+1)}$$

$$S_{k+1} = \frac{k}{k+1} + \frac{1}{(k+1)(k+2)}$$

$$= \frac{k(k+2)+1}{(k+1)(k+2)}$$

$$= \frac{k^2 + 2k + 1}{(k+1)(k+2)}$$

$$= \frac{(k+1)(k+1)}{(k+1)(k+2)}$$

$$= \frac{k+1}{k+2}$$

$$= \frac{(k+1)}{(k+1)+1}$$

5. Find a common denominator, add the numerators, and reduce the expression.

$P(n)$ is true $\forall\, n \in \mathbb{N}$.

6. Apply mathematical induction.

▶ A. Exercises

Write the first five partial sums for the following sequences.

1. $3, 0.3, 0.03, 0.003, 0.0003, \ldots, 3 \cdot 10^{-n+1}, \ldots$

2. $1, \frac{1}{2}, \frac{1}{4}, \frac{1}{8}, \frac{1}{16}, \ldots, \frac{1}{2^{n-1}}, \ldots$

3. $1, 3, 5, 7, 9, \ldots, 2n-1, \ldots$

4. $A_n = \frac{1}{n}$

5. $A_n = \frac{x^{n-1}}{n!}$

6. $A_n = 3n - 5$

7. $A_n = 1(-1)^n$

8. $A_1 = 2, A_n = A_1\, 3^{n-1}$

Calculate the following.

9. $\sum_{i=1}^{5} 2i + 1$

10. $\sum_{i=1}^{6} i^i$

11. $\sum_{j=0}^{5} i^j$, where $i = \sqrt{-1}$

12. $\sum_{i=1}^{5} \frac{4}{i}$

13. $\sum_{n=1}^{4} 3n^4$

14. $\sum_{n=3}^{10} 3n^4$

15. $\sum_{j=5}^{17} \frac{j^2}{4}$

▶ B. Exercises

Given $\sum\limits_{i=1}^{200} A_i = 20$, $\sum\limits_{i=1}^{200} B_i = 67$, and $\sum\limits_{i=1}^{200} C_i = 404$, use summation properties to find the following.

16. $\sum\limits_{i=1}^{200} 3A_i$

18. $\sum\limits_{i=1}^{200} 7A_i + 3C_i$

17. $\sum\limits_{i=1}^{200} 4B_i + 3$

19. $\sum\limits_{i=1}^{200} i$

20. $\sum\limits_{i=4}^{200} 5B_i$ if $B_1 + B_2 + B_3 = 17$ (*Hint:* use property 4)

Use the principle of mathematical induction to prove the following formulas.

21. $\sum\limits_{i=1}^{n} i^2 = 1^2 + 2^2 + 3^2 + 4^2 + 5^2 + \cdots + n^2 = \dfrac{n(n + 1)(2n + 1)}{6}$

22. $\sum\limits_{i=1}^{n} i^3 = 1^3 + 2^3 + 3^3 + 4^3 + 5^3 + \cdots + n^3 = \dfrac{n^2(n + 1)^2}{4}$

23. $\sum\limits_{i=1}^{n} i^4 = 1^4 + 2^4 + 3^4 + 4^4 + 5^4 + \cdots + n^4 = \dfrac{n(n + 1)(2n + 1)(3n^2 + 3n - 1)}{30}$

24. $\sum\limits_{i=1}^{n} i^5 = 1^5 + 2^5 + 3^5 + 4^5 + 5^5 + \cdots + n^5 = \dfrac{n^2(n + 1)^2(2n^2 + 2n - 1)}{12}$

▶ C. Exercises

Calculate the following.

25. $\sum\limits_{i=1}^{300} (2i^5 + i^4 - 3i^3 + 2i^2 + 3i - 2)$

26. $\sum\limits_{i=1}^{520} (i - 3)^3$

ᛟ Dominion Modeling

27. Suppose you invested $1000 at the beginning of each year in a fund that earned 5% annually. Complete the table below to find how much you would have at the end of 5 years.

Year	Start	Invested at Beginning	Income at 5%	End
1	$0.00	$1000.00	$50.00	$1050.00
2	$1050.00	$1000.00	$102.50	$2152.50
3		$1000.00		
4		$1000.00		
5		$1000.00		

28. Suppose you periodically invest *R* at the end of each year in an account that earns *r*% annually. Complete the table below to find the growth value, *G*, at the end of the investment.

n	Amount Added at End of Year	Value of This Payment at End of 5 Years	Accumulated Growth of These Payments After 5 Years
1	R	$R(1 + r)^4$	$R(1 + r)^4$
2			
3		$R(1 + r)^2$	$R[(1 + r)^2 + (1 + r)^3 + (1 + r)^4]$
4			
5			

29. Following the pattern in the above table, what is the growth value *G* of these payments after *n* years?

30. Use summation notation to express the partial sum in your answer. What kind of sequence is it?

Cumulative Review

31. Find the interest earned after 10 years if $5000 is invested at 5.5% compounded continuously.

32. Find the amount in an account after 10 years if $5000 is invested at 5.5% interest compounded monthly.

33. Graph the function. $f(x) = \begin{cases} x + 3 & \text{if } x < 0 \\ 4 & \text{if } 0 \le x \le 3 \\ \sqrt{x} & \text{if } x > 3 \end{cases}$

34. Suppose a large set of data has the graph shown instead of a bell curve. Based on the graph, order the four measures of central tendency from smallest to largest.

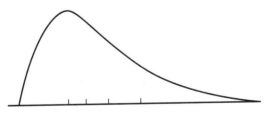

35. Describe a scenario in which data would vary from the bell curve in this manner.

Augustin-Louis Cauchy

Augustin-Louis Cauchy was born on August 21, 1789, in Paris, France and grew up among the battle and strife of the French Revolution. Because of poverty, Augustin was an undernourished child. His father, who was his first teacher, had two close friends, Joseph Louis Lagrange and Pierre Simon de Laplace—two great mathematicians of the period. These two men influenced young Cauchy toward the study of math.

Cauchy's formal education began at École Centrale du Panthéon, where he studied the ancient classical subjects. In 1805 he began studying at École Polytechnique, and in 1807 he entered École des Ponts et Chaussées, where he studied for three years. After finishing his education, he worked as a master engineer for three years and then changed to pure mathematics.

Cauchy devoted his time to teaching and research in pure mathematics, and by 1815 he had become an established figure in the mathematical community, holding a professorship at his alma mater, École Polytechnique. After Charles X was expelled from France in 1830, Cauchy went into voluntary exile in Switzerland. He continued his mathematical research and accepted the chair of mathematical physics at the University of Turin in Italy. In 1833 he took a position devoted to educating the Duke of Bordeaux, the grandson of Charles X. Cauchy returned to Paris in 1838 where he prepared many standard textbooks and greatly influenced the common people in the field of mathematics. In 1848 Cauchy again became a professor at École Polytechnique in Paris. He later held the chair of astronomy at the Sorbonne—a position that he kept until his death on May 23, 1857.

Writing about different areas of mathematics was one of Cauchy's greatest accomplishments. He wrote over 700 memoirs about topics ranging from hydrodynamics and the orbits of planets to the theory of numbers. Cauchy, working on the theory of polyhedra, extended Leonard Euler's formula, which connects the number of edges (E), faces (F), and vertices (V) of a polyhedron, by the equation $E + 2 = F + V$. He also introduced rigor into calculus. Although he often used the indirect form, he demanded flawless proofs.

Cauchy's emphasis on accurate proofs caused major improvements in the study of infinite series and calculus. He can be considered the father of complex variables, which allows one to use complex numbers in calculus, as in the Cauchy-Riemann equations. His precise definitions of calculus concepts (limit, derivative, integral) in his three most important books are still foundational to calculus: *Cours d'analyse de l'École Polytechnique* (1821), *Résumé des leçons sur le calcul infinitésimal* (1823), and *Leçons sur le calcul differential* (1829).

Cauchy's dedication to learning was not limited to the field of mathematics. A man of character and conviction, he also learned Hebrew in his sixties to better study the Bible.

He can be considered the father of complex variables . . .

10.6 Special Sums

The following theorems allow us to find partial sums for arithmetic and geometric sequences. The theorems will also be important in Chapter 11.

> ### Theorem 10.3
> For an arithmetic sequence A_n, the partial sum of the first n terms is given by $\sum_{i=1}^{n} A_i = \frac{n(A_1 + A_n)}{2}$.

Proof

Write the sum of the first n terms of the sequence.
$$S_n = A_1 + A_2 + A_3 + A_4 + A_5 + \cdots + A_n$$

Since A is an arithmetic sequence, each term can be expressed using the explicit formula and common difference: $A_2 = A_1 + d$, $A_3 = A_1 + 2d$, etc. Use these to express S_n. This produces the first of two equations needed for S_n.
$$S_n = A_1 + (A_1 + d) + (A_1 + 2d) + (A_1 + 3d) + (A_1 + 4d) + \cdots + [A_1 + (n - 1)d]$$

Refer to the initial equation and use the commutative and associative properties to reverse the order of the terms.
$$S_n = A_n + A_{n-1} + A_{n-2} + A_{n-3} + \cdots + A_1$$

Each term can be expressed using the common difference by subtracting from the last term. For example, $A_{n-1} = A_n - d$, $A_{n-2} = A_n - 2d$, etc. Substitute these quantities. This produces the second equation needed for S_n.
$$S_n = A_n + (A_n - d) + (A_n - 2d) + (A_n - 3d) + (A_n - 4d) + \cdots + [A_n - (n - 1)d]$$

Add the two equations for S_n, and then divide both sides by 2.
$$S_n = A_n + (A_n - d) + (A_n - 2d) + \cdots + [A_n - (n - 1)d]$$
$$\underline{S_n = A_1 + (A_1 + d) + (A_1 + 2d) + \cdots + [A_1 + (n - 1)d]}$$
$$2S_n = (A_1 + A_n) + (A_1 + A_n) + \cdots + (A_1 + A_n) = n(A_1 + A_n)$$
$$S_n = \frac{n(A_1 + A_n)}{2}$$

Notice that the partial sum of the first n terms of an arithmetic sequence is the product of n and the average of the first and last terms.

Corollary 10.4

$$\sum_{i=1}^{n} A_i = \frac{n[2A_1 + (n - 1)d]}{2}$$

Proof

$A_n = A_1 + (n - 1)d$, by the explicit formula for an arithmetic sequence. Therefore, by substituting for A_n in theorem 10.3,

$$S_n = \sum_{i=1}^{n} A_i = \frac{n[A_1 + A_1 + (n - 1)d]}{2} = \frac{n[2A_1 + (n - 1)d]}{2}.$$

In order to find the sum in theorem 10.3 and corollary 10.4, you must know n, A_1, and A_n (Example 1), or you must know n, A_1, and d.

EXAMPLE 1   Suppose $A_n = 11n - 6$. Find the sum of the first 500 terms.

Answer

$A_1 = 11(1) - 6 = 5, A_{500} = 11(500) - 6 = 5494$ 1. Find A_1 and A_n for $n = 500$.

$S_n = \frac{n(A_1 + A_n)}{2}$ 2. Apply theorem 10.3 and compute.

$S_{500} = \frac{500(A_1 + A_{500})}{2} = \frac{500(5 + 5494)}{2} = 1{,}374{,}750$

EXAMPLE 2   Suppose A_n is an arithmetic sequence with $A_1 = 10$, and the sum of the first 100 terms is $S_{100} = 10{,}900$. Find the general term A_n.

Answer

$S_n = \frac{n[2A_1 - (n - 1)d]}{2}$ 1. Use corollary 10.4 to find the common difference, d.

$S_{100} = \frac{100[2(10) + (100 - 1)d]}{2} = 10{,}900$

$50(20 + 99d) = 10{,}900$ 2. Solve the resulting equation for d.

$20 + 99d = 218$

$d = 2$

Therefore, $A_n = A_1 + (n - 1)d$ 3. Determine the general term, A_n.

$A_n = 10 + (n - 1)2 = 2n + 8$

Theorem 10.5

If S_n is a partial sum for a geometric sequence with A_1 as the first term and r as the common ratio, then $S_n = \dfrac{A_1(1 - r^n)}{1 - r}$.

Proof

Let S_n be the sum of the first n terms.

$$S_n = A_1 + A_1r + A_1r^2 + \cdots + A_1r^{n-1}$$

Multiply both sides by r.

$$rS_n = A_1r + A_1r^2 + A_1r^3 + \cdots + A_1r^n$$

Subtract the second equation from the first. Most terms cancel. Solve for S_n.

$$S_n - rS_n = A_1 - A_1r^n$$
$$S_n(1 - r) = A_1(1 - r^n)$$
$$S_n = \frac{A_1(1 - r^n)}{(1 - r)}$$

Recall the example involving a rubber ball from Section 10.3 which involves a geometric sequence. To determine the total distance traveled by the ball involves partial sums. If the ball is originally thrown to a height of 100 feet and rebounds 80% of its former height on each bounce, then $A_1 = 100$ and $r = 0.8$. By the fourth bounce, $S_4 = \dfrac{100(1 - 0.8^4)}{1 - 0.8} = 295.2$ feet. This value must be doubled to take into account that the ball traveled up after each bounce and then back down the same distance. The final answer is 590.4 feet.

▶ A. Exercises

Find the general formula for the *n*th partial sum, S_n, and determine the partial sum for the first 10 terms.

1. 1, 4, 7, 10, 13, . . .
2. $A_n = A_{n-1} + 4;\ A_1 = 0$
3. $A_n = 4n + 3$
4. 1, −2, 4, −8, 16, . . .
5. $A_n = 3A_{n-1},\ A_1 = 2$
6. $A_n = 3(2)^{n-2}$
7. $H_n = 2^n + 3n$ (*Hint:* If $G_n = 2^n$ and $A_n = 3n$, then H_n is the sum of G_n and A_n.)

▶ B. Exercises

Find the partial sum for the first 10 terms of the following sequences.

8. A_n is a geometric sequence with $A_2 = 3$ and $A_4 = 12$
9. A_n is an arithmetic sequence with $A_{10} = 30$ and $A_{15} = 70$
10. If a rubber ball rebounds 0.6 of its height on each bounce, how far has the ball traveled after the tenth bounce if it was initially thrown up to a height of 40 feet?

Find the following. Use whatever method is appropriate.

11. $\displaystyle\sum_{r=1}^{200} 2^r$

12. $\displaystyle\sum_{k=1}^{500} 2k + 3$

13. $\displaystyle\sum_{n=4}^{8} n^2$

14. $\displaystyle\sum_{n=1}^{15} 3\left(\frac{-1}{2}\right)^n$

15. $\displaystyle\sum_{j=1}^{60} \frac{(j + 6)}{3}$

16. $\displaystyle\sum_{n=3}^{9} 5n - (-2)^{n-2}$

17. $\displaystyle\sum_{n=1}^{15} 3^n + 2n$

18. Find A_{15} of an arithmetic sequence if $S_{15} = 30$ and $A_1 = 3$.
19. Find A_{12} of an arithmetic sequence if $S_{12} = 44$ and $A_3 = 5$.
20. Find A_{12} of an arithmetic sequence if $S_{12} = 30$ and $d = 3$.

▶ C. Exercises

Find the following.

21. $\displaystyle\sum_{n=1}^{1000} e^n$

22. $\displaystyle\sum_{n=1}^{427} \pi n$

⩗ Dominion Modeling

23. What is the partial sum of the *geometric sequence* 1, $(1 + r)$, $(1 + r)^2$, $(1 + r)^3$, ... $(1 + r)^{n-1}$? (The r in this problem represents interest rate, not to be confused with the r in the partial sum formula.)

24. Refer to your expression for G in the previous section, and simplify the partial sum. Show your work.

25. Suppose you wanted to invest a principal value P and you intended to add an additional payment R at the end of each year. What would the sum S of these values be at r% annually after n years? (*Hint:* assume that the funds are compounded annually, and let $S = A + G$.)

26. Suppose $S = 0$. Solve for R. Finally, in what practical instances is $S = 0$?

▌Cumulative Review

Consider the following functions.

a. $f(x) = \frac{1}{2}e^{-x}$ b. $g(x) = \frac{1}{x^2}$ c. $p(x) = x^3 + 1$ d. $q(x) = x^3 + x^2 - 2x$

27. Classify each function as increasing, decreasing, or neither.

28. Which functions are one-to-one?

29. Find the inverses of any one-to-one functions.

30. Classify the greatest integer function, $h(x) = [x]$.

31. Find $\sum_{i=-1}^{5} i^2 - 4$

Constants Using Sums

Partial sums are the main tool used to approximate irrational values. When an engineer needs an irrational solution accurate to a specific number of decimal places, he can use a partial sum. Consider π, for example.

$$A = 4, -\frac{4}{3}, \frac{4}{5}, -\frac{4}{7}, \frac{4}{9}, -\frac{4}{11}, \ldots, (-1)^{n-1}\frac{4}{2n-1}$$

$$\pi \approx S_n = 4 - \frac{4}{3} + \frac{4}{5} - \frac{4}{7} + \frac{4}{9} - \frac{4}{11} + \cdots = \sum_{i=1}^{n} (-1)^{i-1}\frac{4}{2i-1}$$

The sequence of partial sums gets closer and closer to the actual value of π. If an engineer needs the value to 10 decimal places, he simply keeps adding terms until the numbers being added affect only later decimal places. Other partial sums permit the calculation of exponential, log, and trig values to any desired number of decimal places.

$$\ln(1 + x) \approx S_n = x - \frac{x^2}{2} + \frac{x^3}{3} - \frac{x^4}{4} + \cdots + (-1)^{n-1}\frac{x^n}{n}$$

$$= \sum_{k=1}^{n} (-1)^{k-1}\frac{x^k}{k} \text{ if } |x| < 1$$

$$e^x \approx S_n = 1 + x + \frac{x^2}{2!} + \frac{x^3}{3!} + \frac{x^4}{4!} + \cdots + \frac{x^{n-1}}{(n-1)!}$$

$$= \sum_{k=1}^{n} \frac{x^{k-1}}{(k-1)!} = \sum_{k=0}^{n} \frac{x^k}{k!}$$

$$\sin x \approx S_n = x - \frac{x^3}{3!} + \frac{x^5}{5!} - \frac{x^7}{7!} + \cdots + (-1)^{n+1}\frac{x^{2n-1}}{(2n-1)!}$$

$$= \sum_{k=0}^{n} (-1)^k\frac{x^{2k+1}}{(2k+1)!}$$

$$\cos x \approx S_n = 1 - \frac{x^2}{2!} + \frac{x^4}{4!} - \frac{x^6}{6!} + \cdots + (-1)^{n+1}\frac{x^{2n-2}}{(2n-2)!}$$

$$= \sum_{k=0}^{n} (-1)^k\frac{x^{2k}}{(2k)!}$$

Notice in the series for e^x that the powers in the second summation are simpler than those with an index of 1. Write out several terms of the summation to verify that they are the same. For this reason, it is often convenient to begin with an index of zero as shown for the trig functions.

10 Approximation Methods

EXAMPLE 1 Approximate e^2 to two decimal places.

Answer

Use the partial sums for e^x with $x = 2$.

$$e^2 \approx S_n = 1 + 2 + \frac{2^2}{2!} + \frac{2^3}{3!} + \frac{2^4}{4!} + \cdots + \frac{2^{n-1}}{(n-1)!}$$

Add successive terms until the desired decimal place stabilizes.

$$1, 3, 5, 6.\overline{3}, 7, 7.2\overline{6}, 7.3\overline{5}, 7.381, 7.387, 7.389, \ldots$$

Notice that the ones place stabilizes (remains the same thereafter) at the 6th partial sum. By the 8th partial sum, the tenths have stabilized, and by the 9th partial sum the second decimal place has stabilized, but rounds up, as confirmed by the 10th partial sum.

Thus, $e^2 \approx 7.39$.

Partial sums also show us how to define functions of complex numbers. Consider a complex power of e such as e^{a+bi}. You can see that $e^{a+bi} = e^a e^{bi}$. Since e^a is a real number, we will know how to find complex powers of e if we can discover how to find e^{bi}.

EXAMPLE 2 Find e^{xi}.

Answer

$$e^x \approx 1 + x + \frac{x^2}{2!} + \frac{x^3}{3!} + \frac{x^4}{4!} + \frac{x^5}{5!} + \frac{x^6}{6!} + \frac{x^7}{7!} + \cdots + \frac{x^n}{n!}$$

1. Replace x with ix in the formula given above and simplify exponents.

$$e^{ix} \approx 1 + ix + \frac{(ix)^2}{2!} + \frac{(ix)^3}{3!} + \frac{(ix)^4}{4!} + \frac{(ix)^5}{5!} + \frac{(ix)^6}{6!} + \frac{(ix)^7}{7!} + \cdots + \frac{(ix)^n}{n!}$$

$$\approx 1 + ix + \frac{i^2 x^2}{2!} + \frac{i^3 x^3}{3!} + \frac{i^4 x^4}{4!} + \frac{i^5 x^5}{5!} + \frac{i^6 x^6}{6!} + \frac{i^7 x^7}{7!} + \cdots + \frac{i^n x^n}{n!}$$

2. Simplify the powers of i.

$$\approx 1 + ix + \frac{(-1)x^2}{2!} + \frac{(-i)x^3}{3!} + \frac{1x^4}{4!} + \frac{ix^5}{5!} + \frac{(-1)x^6}{6!} + \frac{(-i)x^7}{7!} + \cdots + \frac{i^n x^n}{n!}$$

$$\approx 1 + xi - \frac{x^2}{2!} - \frac{x^3}{3!}i + \frac{x^4}{4!} + \frac{x^5}{5!}i - \frac{x^6}{6!} - \frac{x^7}{7!}i + \cdots + \frac{x^n}{n!}i^n$$

Continued ▶

3. Group the terms into a real part and an imaginary part (recursive formulas assume sequences begin with A_0).

$$\approx 1 - \frac{x^2}{2!} + \frac{x^4}{4!} - \frac{x^6}{6!} + \cdots + \frac{x^{2n}}{(2n)!}$$

$$+ \, xi - \frac{x^3}{3!}i + \frac{x^5}{5!}i - \frac{x^7}{7!}i + \cdots + \frac{x^{2n+1}}{(2n+1)!}i$$

$$\approx \left[1 - \frac{x^2}{2!} + \frac{x^4}{4!} - \frac{x^6}{6!} + \cdots + \frac{x^{2n}}{(2n)!} \right]$$

$$+ \left[x - \frac{x^3}{3!} + \frac{x^5}{5!} - \frac{x^7}{7!} + \cdots + \frac{x^{2n+1}}{(2n+1)!} \right] i$$

$$\approx \left[\sum_{k=0}^{n} \frac{(-1)^k x^{2k}}{(2k)!} \right] + i \left[\sum_{k=0}^{n} \frac{(-1)^k x^{2k+1}}{(2k+1)!} \right] \qquad \text{4. Write using summations.}$$

$$\approx \cos x + i \sin x \qquad\qquad\qquad \text{5. Recognize the partial sums given above.}$$

▶ Exercises

Use partial sums to approximate to three decimals.

1. π
2. $\ln 1.5$
3. e
4. $\sqrt{e}$
5. Find e^{2+3i}

Leonhard Euler (1707-1783) substituted $i\theta$ into the series for e^x and regrouped the terms to obtain the series for sine and cosine, thus proving that $e^{i\theta} = \cos\theta + i\sin\theta$. Since this formula holds for all radian measures, it follows that $1 + e^{i\pi} = 0$.

Math and Scripture

The Beauty of Mathematics

Sequences display the beauty and power of mathematics. The approximation formulas given in the foregoing Approximation Methods relate polynomials to trig, log, and exponential functions. Isn't it amazing that you can approximate sines and logarithms with polynomials?

As you saw in the Approximation Methods section, Euler was responsible for the following well-known relationship.

$$e^{ix} = \cos x + i \sin x$$

Recall that the right side can be abbreviated cis x. This amazing formula reveals a relationship between trig functions and exponential functions based on complex numbers. This is one of the reasons why mathematicians often say there is beauty in mathematics. Do you see that mathematics is analogous to God's created wonders?

Euler's Formula

$$\cos \theta + i \sin \theta = e^{i\theta}$$

1. Evaluate Euler's formula for $\theta = 0$.
2. Evaluate Euler's formula for $\theta = \frac{\pi}{2}$.
3. Evaluate Euler's formula for $\theta = \pi$.
4. How does Phil. 4:8 apply to math?

$\mathcal{B}$y rearranging the terms in the last equation, you obtain $1 + e^{i\pi} = 0$. This formula relates the five most important numbers in mathematics. While these constants are fundamental yet so different, they are related by this amazing but simple formula.

5. Each of the five constants is basic to which math concept?

$\mathcal{N}$ote how Euler's relationship is a wonderful analogy to the intricate complexity in God's created order. God "gave to the sea his decree, that the waters should not pass his commandment" (Proverbs 8:29). At His decree, all creation submits. How are God's decrees expressed in each passage below?

6. Job 28:26
7. Job 38:8-11
8. Jeremiah 5:22
9. Psalm 148:1-6

MAXIMIZING
Find a parallel passage to Romans 11:34.

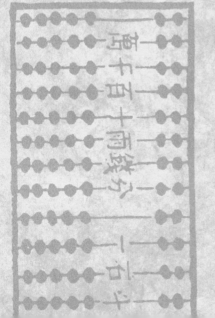

Vital Sines

$\mathcal{F}$INALLY, BRETHREN,

whatsoever things are true,

whatsoever things are honest,

whatsoever things are just,

whatsoever things are pure,

whatsoever things are lovely,

whatsoever things are of good report;

if there be any virtue, and if there be

any praise, think on these things.

PHILIPPIANS 4:8

Chapter 10 Review

Find the indicated terms of the sequence.

1. If $A_n = 5n^2 + 4n + \cos \frac{n\pi}{180}$, find A_{30} and A_{45}.
2. If $A_{n+1} = 2A_n - 3A_n - 1$, $A_1 = 2$, and $A_2 = 2$, find A_6.

Find the explicit formula of the arithmetic sequence A_n, and determine A_8.

3. $A_3 = 8$, $d = -2$
4. $A_4 = 7$, $A_{10} = -5$
5. $A_7 = 6$, $S_{10} = 63$, where S_{10} is the sum of the first 10 terms

Find the explicit formula of the geometric sequence A_n and determine A_{10}.

6. $A_5 = 8$, $r = \frac{1}{2}$
7. $A_5 = 8$, $A_7 = 72$

Convert the arithmetic sequence A_n, where $A_n = 4n - 2$, into a harmonic sequence. Use your harmonic sequence to answer questions 8-10.

8. What are the first five terms?
9. What is the 50th term?
10. What is the general term?
11. Compute 11!
12. If $A_1 = 5$ and $A_6 = 0$ in the arithmetic sequence A_n, find S_{11} where S_{11} is the 11th partial sum.
13. If $A_1 = 8$ and $A_4 = -1$ of the geometric sequence A_n, then find S_6 where S_6 is the sixth term in its sequence of partial sums.

Evaluate.

14. $\displaystyle\sum_{i=1}^{6} 3i^2 + 4i - 2$

15. $\displaystyle\sum_{i=1}^{50} 3\left(\frac{3}{4}\right)^i$

16. $\displaystyle\sum_{i=10}^{162} 4i + 3$

17. Prove theorem 10.3 without using the book.
18. Prove theorem 10.5 without using the book.
19. Prove that $1 + 3 + 5 + \cdots + (2n - 1) = n^2$, using mathematical induction.
20. If $\displaystyle\sum_{i=1}^{n} A_i = 3$ and $\displaystyle\sum_{i=1}^{n} B_i = 6$, find $\displaystyle\sum_{i=1}^{n} (2A_i - B_i)$.
21. Use the exercises in Section 10.5 to find $\displaystyle\sum_{i=1}^{53} i\left(i^3 + 2i^2 - 3i + 2 - \frac{6}{i}\right)$.

22. Your earlier formula for future value (amount you will have someday) was:
$$S_n = R[1 + (1 + r) + (1 + r)^2 + \cdots + (1 + r)^{n-1}] + P(1 + r)^n.$$
If $(1 + r) = x$, what well-known type of function results?

23. Give the mathematical significance of Philippians 4:8.

Snow can bring visions of sleds and skis or of slippery roads and slow traffic. But mathematicians might think of Helge von Koch, a Swedish mathematician who invented the "Koch curve" or the "Koch snowflake."

The Koch curve is the result of an infinite process. Start with a large, equilateral triangle. Then divide each side into three congruent segments and replace the middle segment with two of the same size. The result is the same as gluing an equilateral triangle to the middle of each side. Third, trisect each side again, and replace the middle third with two of that same length. Continue this process.

Iteration 0 *Iteration 1* *Iteration 2* *Iteration 3* *Iteration 4* *Iteration 5*

Since the triangular additions get smaller and smaller, iteration 5 has the same general shape as the infinitely iterated Koch curve, but the differences would be microscopic. Zooming in on the Koch curve would display finer and finer detail in an infinitely wiggly curve; whereas, for Iteration 5, all the sides are congruent segments with a length that is $\frac{1}{243}$ of the length of the original side.

In this chapter, you will calculate the perimeter and area of the Koch curve, and you will need limits to determine them. Since each iteration is a closer approximation to the curve, the perimeters and areas at each iteration get closer to those of the Koch curve.

After this chapter you should be able to

1. find limits of sequences and series.
2. find limits of functions.
3. define and identify continuous functions.
4. find asymptotes using limits.
5. apply limit theorems.
6. define limit and apply it to specific limits.

11.1 Limits of Sequences

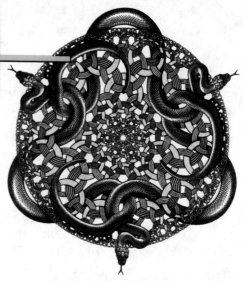

M. C. Escher's work, entitled "Snakes" (1969), incorporates limits at both the center and the edge. Escher's clever use of the tessellating attribute of hexagons and their symmetries allows him to play on suggested infinite processes while locking them together with circles and semicircular loops of reptiles.

Consider the following sequence:

$$A_n = 1, \frac{1}{2}, \frac{1}{3}, \frac{1}{4}, \frac{1}{5}, \frac{1}{6}, \ldots, \frac{1}{n}, \ldots$$

As n increases, the terms of the sequence get smaller. That is, as we consider terms increasingly farther from the beginning of the sequence, the values of the terms become closer and closer to 0. We say then that the sequence has a *limit* and that the limit is zero. In symbols, $\lim\limits_{n \to \infty} \frac{1}{n} = 0$ which is read, "the limit of $\frac{1}{n}$ as n approaches infinity is 0." Notice the symbol ∞, which represents infinity. Similarly, for the sequence $0, \frac{1}{2}, \frac{2}{3}, \frac{3}{4}, \frac{4}{5}, \frac{5}{6}, \ldots, \frac{n-1}{n} \ldots,$ you can see that $\lim\limits_{n \to \infty} \frac{(n-1)}{n} = 1$.

EXAMPLE 1   Give the limit for each of the following sequences.

a. $\frac{5}{2}, \frac{7}{3}, \frac{9}{4}, \frac{11}{5}, \frac{13}{6}, \ldots$

b. A_n is geometric with $A_1 = -4$ and $r = \frac{1}{2}$

c. $A_n = (-1)^n$

d. $A_n = \frac{2n+1}{2n}$

Answer   a. The sequence approaches 2.

b. The sequence contains the following:
$-4, -2, -1, -\frac{1}{2}, -\frac{1}{4}, \ldots$ It approaches 0.

c. The sequence contains the following:
$-1, 1, -1, 1, -1, \ldots$ There is no limit since it does not approach any specific value.

d. The sequence contains the following:
$\frac{3}{2}, \frac{5}{4}, \frac{7}{6}, \frac{9}{8}, \frac{11}{10}, \ldots$ It approaches 1.

EXAMPLE 2   Find $\lim_{n\to\infty} A_n$ for each sequence.

a. $A_n = \dfrac{2n}{n+5}$

b. $A_n = \dfrac{2n+7}{3n-4}$

Answer   a. Consider the first few terms: $\dfrac{2}{6}, \dfrac{4}{7}, \dfrac{6}{8}, \dfrac{8}{9}, \dfrac{10}{10}, \ldots$

Considering just these terms is not helpful. They would cause you to think the limit is 1. But $A_{100} = \dfrac{200}{105}$, $A_{1000} = \dfrac{2000}{1005}$, and $A_{1,000,000} = \dfrac{2,000,000}{1,000,005}$. The limit is 2.

b. Again, considering just the first few terms is not helpful.

$-9, \dfrac{11}{2}, \dfrac{13}{5}, \dfrac{15}{8}, \dfrac{17}{11}, \ldots$ but $A_{100} = \dfrac{207}{296}$, $A_{1000} = \dfrac{2007}{2996}$,

and $A_{1,000,000} = \dfrac{2,000,007}{2,999,996}$

$\therefore \lim_{n\to\infty} \dfrac{2n+7}{3n-4} = \dfrac{2}{3}$

The general idea of "closer and closer" needs to be rigorously defined. After all, the sequence $0, \dfrac{1}{2}, \dfrac{2}{3}, \dfrac{3}{4}, \dfrac{4}{5}, \dfrac{5}{6}, \ldots, \dfrac{n-1}{n}, \ldots$ may be getting closer to 1, but it is also getting closer and closer to 1.1 or 1.2. How do we know which one is the limit? The answer is that $\dfrac{n-1}{n}$ does not get arbitrarily close to 1.1 or 1.2. No matter what value of n you choose, the distance from $\dfrac{n-1}{n}$ to 1.1 will never be less than 0.1 (i.e., $\left|\dfrac{n-1}{n} - 1\right| \geq 0.1$). However, you can find terms of the sequence arbitrarily close to 1.

EXAMPLE 3   Find the smallest N such that each term of the sequence above, where $n > N$, is within $\dfrac{1}{1000}$ of the limit.

Answer

$\left\|\dfrac{n-1}{n} - 1\right\| \leq 0.001$	1. Use absolute values to state that the distance from the term to the limit 1 must be less than 0.001.
$\left\|1 - \dfrac{1}{n} - 1\right\| \leq 0.001$ $\left\|-\dfrac{1}{n}\right\| \leq 0.001$ $\dfrac{1}{n} \leq 0.001$ $n \geq 1000$	2. Simplify the quantity in the absolute value sign. Solve for n.
$A_{1000} = \dfrac{999}{1000}$ which is exactly 0.001 units from the limit 1.	3. Test the nth term. Whenever $n > 1000$, A_n will be even closer to 1.

The above example shows how far out the position must be to get within 0.001 of the limit. However, the idea of the limit requires that we get not just within 0.001, but arbitrarily close to the limit. For this reason, mathematicians use the lower case Greek letter epsilon, ε, to represent an arbitrarily small value. To justify a limit, then, we need to be able to find a position number N for any ε, so the $|A_n - L| < \varepsilon$ when $n > N$. In other words, all the terms of the sequence beyond a certain position number N must be within an arbitrarily small distance of the limit.

Definition

Limit of a sequence A_n has a limit L if and only if for each $\varepsilon > 0$ there exists an N so that $|A_n - L| < \varepsilon$ whenever $n > N$.

Various theorems make it easier to find limits. You will not have to prove limit theorems in this course, but the following theorem shows you how limit theorems of sequences are proved using the arbitrary value ε.

> *Pure mathematics is on the whole distinctly more useful than applied. For what is useful above all is technique, and mathematical technique is taught mainly through pure mathematics.*
>
> —G. H. HARDY
> (1877-1947)

Theorem 11.1

If $A_n = \dfrac{1}{n^p}$, where $p \in \mathbb{N}$, then $\lim\limits_{n \to \infty} A_n = 0$.

Proof

Let $\varepsilon > 0$. Choose $N > \dfrac{1}{\sqrt[p]{\varepsilon}}$. Then whenever $n > N$, we know that $n > \dfrac{1}{\sqrt[p]{\varepsilon}}$.

Solving for ε, we get $\dfrac{1}{n} < \sqrt[p]{\varepsilon}$ or $\dfrac{1}{n^p} < \varepsilon$.

Since $\left| \dfrac{1}{n^p} - 0 \right| < \varepsilon$, the sequence $\dfrac{1}{n^p}$ is always within ε of the limit 0 whenever $n > N$.

Thus, $\lim\limits_{n \to \infty} \dfrac{1}{n^p} = 0$ by definition.

The hardest part of such a proof is finding the correct choice of N, and you must often work backwards to determine it. The proofs of the following properties are similar but much more difficult and well beyond the scope of this book.

Properties of Limits

If A_n and B_n are sequences with limits L_1 and L_2 respectively, and if c is a constant, then the following properties hold.

1. $\lim\limits_{n \to \infty} c = c$

2. $\lim\limits_{n \to \infty} (A_n + B_n) = \lim\limits_{n \to \infty} A_n + \lim\limits_{n \to \infty} B_n = L_1 + L_2$

3. $\lim\limits_{n \to \infty} A_n \cdot B_n = \lim\limits_{n \to \infty} A_n \cdot \lim\limits_{n \to \infty} B_n = L_1 \cdot L_2$

4. $\lim\limits_{n \to \infty} \dfrac{A_n}{B_n} = \dfrac{\lim\limits_{n \to \infty} A_n}{\lim\limits_{n \to \infty} B_n} = \dfrac{L_1}{L_2}$ if $L_2 \neq 0$

EXAMPLE 4   Find the limits of the following sequences.

$$A_n = 7,\ B_n = \frac{1}{n^5},\ \text{and}\ C_n = \frac{7}{n^5}$$

Answer $\lim\limits_{n \to \infty} A_n = \lim\limits_{n \to \infty} 7 = 7$ (property 1)

$\lim\limits_{n \to \infty} B_n = \lim\limits_{n \to \infty} \frac{1}{n^5} = 0$ (theorem 11.1)

$\lim\limits_{n \to \infty} C_n = \lim\limits_{n \to \infty} \frac{7}{n^5} = \lim\limits_{n \to \infty} 7 \cdot \frac{1}{n^5} = \lim\limits_{n \to \infty} 7 \cdot \lim\limits_{n \to \infty} \frac{1}{n^5} = 7 \cdot 0 = 0$

(property 3, property 1, and theorem 11.1)

In the same way we found the last limit in Example 4, it is easy to prove theorem 11.2. You will be asked to do this in the exercises.

Theorem 11.2

If A_n is a sequence with limit L and k is a constant, then

$$\lim\limits_{n \to \infty} kA_n = k \lim\limits_{n \to \infty} A_n = kL.$$

EXAMPLE 5   Find $\lim\limits_{n \to \infty} \dfrac{6n^2 + 3n + 4}{3n^2}$.

Answer

$\lim\limits_{n \to \infty} \dfrac{6n^2 + 3n + 4}{3n^2} = \lim\limits_{n \to \infty} \left(\dfrac{6n^2}{3n^2} + \dfrac{3n}{3n^2} + \dfrac{4}{3n^2} \right)$ 1. Separate the fractions and reduce.

$= \lim\limits_{n \to \infty} \left(2 + \dfrac{1}{n} + \dfrac{4}{3n^2} \right)$

$= \lim\limits_{n \to \infty} 2 + \lim\limits_{n \to \infty} \dfrac{1}{n} + \lim\limits_{n \to \infty} \dfrac{4}{3n^2}$ 2. Apply property 2 to the sums.

Continued ▶

$$= \lim_{n\to\infty} 2 + \lim_{n\to\infty} \frac{1}{n} + \frac{4}{3} \lim_{n\to\infty} \frac{1}{n^2}$$

3. Factor out the constant $\frac{4}{3}$ in the last term (theorem 11.2).

$$= 2 + 0 + \frac{4}{3}(0)$$
$$= 2$$

4. Evaluate the limits. The first limit follows from property 1 and the other two from theorem 11.1.

EXAMPLE 6   Find $\lim_{n\to\infty} \dfrac{3n^2 + 4n + 2}{2n^2 + 8n + 5}$.

Answer

$$\lim_{n\to\infty} \frac{3n^2 + 4n + 2}{2n^2 + 8n + 5} = \lim_{n\to\infty} \frac{3 + \frac{4}{n} + \frac{2}{n^2}}{2 + \frac{8}{n} + \frac{5}{n^2}}$$

1. Multiply both the numerator and the denominator by $\frac{1}{n^2}$.

$$= \frac{\lim_{n\to\infty} \left(3 + \frac{4}{n} + \frac{2}{n^2}\right)}{\lim_{n\to\infty} \left(2 + \frac{8}{n} + \frac{5}{n^2}\right)}$$

2. Apply property 4.

$$= \frac{\lim_{n\to\infty} 3 + \lim_{n\to\infty} \frac{4}{n} + \lim_{n\to\infty} \frac{2}{n^2}}{\lim_{n\to\infty} 2 + \lim_{n\to\infty} \frac{8}{n} + \lim_{n\to\infty} \frac{5}{n^2}}$$

$$= \frac{3 + 4(0) + 2(0)}{2 + 8(0) + 5(0)}$$

$$= \frac{3}{2}$$

3. Apply property 2, then find the limits of the numerator and denominator separately as in Example 5.

Some sequences do not have limits. You can sometimes recognize such cases by writing out the first few terms.

EXAMPLE 7   Find the limit of the sequence if it exists: $A_n = \left(\frac{3}{2}\right)^n$.

Answer   Since this sequence is not one to which any properties apply, write out the first few terms and examine them.

1.5, 2.25, 3.375, 5.0625, . . .

The sequence is geometric with $r = 1.5$.

It is clear since each term is 1.5 times larger than the previous term that the terms will increase without bound. Since the terms do not get arbitrarily close to any fixed number, the sequence has no limit.

▶ A. Exercises

Find the following limits.

1. $\lim\limits_{n \to \infty} 5$

2. $\lim\limits_{n \to \infty} \dfrac{8}{4n^3}$

3. $\lim\limits_{n \to \infty} \dfrac{5n^2 + 4n - 1}{7n^2 - 2n + 3}$

4. $\lim\limits_{n \to \infty} \dfrac{3 - 2n}{n}$

Find the limits of the following sequences if they exist.

5. $A_n = 8$

6. $A_n = 3 + \dfrac{1}{n}$

7. $A_n = \dfrac{8n - 1}{2n}$

8. $A_n = n$

9. $A_n = (-1)^n$

10. $A_n = \dfrac{12n + 16}{2n - 2}$

11. $A_n = \dfrac{5.4n^2 - 2.5n + 1}{21.6n^2 + 29.8}$

▶ B. Exercises

If $\lim\limits_{n \to \infty} A_n = 12$ and $\lim\limits_{n \to \infty} B_n = 4$, find the following limits.

12. $\lim\limits_{n \to \infty} 2A_n$

13. $\lim\limits_{n \to \infty} \left(A_n - B_n \right)$

14. $\lim\limits_{n \to \infty} \dfrac{2A_n}{3B_n}$

15. $\lim\limits_{n \to \infty} \left(A_n B_n - \dfrac{2n}{n - 1} \right)$

16. $\lim\limits_{n \to \infty} \left(3A_n + B_n{}^2 - \dfrac{1}{n^2} \right)$

17. $\lim\limits_{n \to \infty} \dfrac{1}{A_n}$

Find the limits of the sequences whose nth term is given; show your work.

18. $A_n = \dfrac{n^3(n^4 - 2n^3 + n^2 - n + 1)}{2n^7}$

19. $A_n = \dfrac{6n^4 - 3n^3 + 5n^2 + 4n - 1}{5n^4 + 7n^2 - 2n}$

20. $A_n = 1 + (-1)^n$

21. $A_n = \left(\dfrac{-3}{4} \right)^n$

For each sequence, find the limit and then find the smallest N such that each term A_n, where $n > N$, is within $\dfrac{1}{100}$ of the limit.

22. $A_n = \dfrac{1}{n}$

23. $A_n = 10$

24. $A_n = 6 + \dfrac{1}{n^2}$

25. $A_n = \dfrac{1}{n^3}$

▶ C. Exercises

26. Prove $\lim\limits_{n \to \infty} \dfrac{a_1 n^2 + b_1 n + c_1}{a_2 n^2 + b_2 n + c_2} = \dfrac{a_1}{a_2}$.

27. Prove theorem 11.2 using the properties of limits.

Dominion Modeling

The initial stage in constructing the Koch curve is a triangle with sides one unit long. Thus, the perimeter (p_0) and area (A_0) of the triangle comprise the initial estimates of the perimeter and area of the Koch curve.

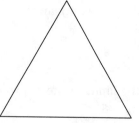

28. Find the *perimeter*, p_0.
29. Find the *area*, A_0.

Koch curve construction, iteration 0

Cumulative Review

30. Use division to find the translation for the graph of $f(x) = \dfrac{x^2 + 8x - 7}{x^2 - 4}$.
31. Graph the function in exercise 30.
32. Using $Ax^2 + Cy^2 + Dx + Ey + F = 0$, specify the conditions for each conic section.

    a. circle b. parabola c. ellipse d. hyperbola

33. Give the period, reciprocal, and cofunction identities for tangent.
34. What is true of two vectors $\mathbf{u}$ and $\mathbf{v}$ for which $\mathbf{u} \cdot \mathbf{v} = 0$?

11.2 Series

If you add a finite number of terms of a sequence, you obtain a partial sum. The term "partial" implies that there is something else. Indeed, if you add *all* the terms of the sequence, you obtain a series. This sum may or may not exist.

Definitions

Series The sum of all the terms of a sequence.

Convergent series A series with a finite sum.

Divergent series A series with no finite sum.

The series that is formed from the constant sequence 3, 3, 3, 3, . . . is
3 + 3 + 3 + 3 + · · · . In this case, you can see that no finite sum exists. You
can also recognize this by investigating the limit of the *partial sums*. For the
series above, the sequence of partial sums is 3, 6, 9, 12, 15, . . . , which has no
limit. Therefore, $\sum_{i=1}^{\infty} 3 = \infty$ (does not exist).

You know a convergent series from elementary school: the decimal form of
one third. Since you can always extend the decimal expansion with another 3,
the series is

$$0.3 + 0.03 + 0.003 + 0.0003 + 0.00003 + \cdots = \tfrac{1}{3}$$

The sequence is the geometric sequence $3\left(\tfrac{1}{10}\right)^n$, and the sequence of partial
sums is 0.3, 0.33, 0.333, 0.3333, . . . , which converges to $0.\overline{3}$ or $\tfrac{1}{3}$. Thus,

$$\sum_{n=1}^{\infty} 3\left(\tfrac{1}{10}\right)^n = \tfrac{1}{3}.$$

Although the partial sums increase toward one third, the terms of the original
sequence get smaller and smaller. You should see that for a series to have a
finite sum, the infinitely many additions must become negligible. In other
words, unless the terms approach zero, the partial sums will approach infinity.
This idea is expressed in the following theorem.

Theorem 11.3: Divergence Test

If $\lim_{n \to \infty} A_n \neq 0$, then $\sum_{n=1}^{\infty} A_n$ diverges.

EXAMPLE 1   Determine whether the series

$$\sum_{i=1}^{\infty} A_n = 0.51 + 0.501 + 0.5001 + \cdots$$

converges or diverges and justify your conclusion.

Answer   Consider the sequence of terms, A_n. Since the terms
0.51, 0.501, 0.5001, obviously approach 0.5, you can write
$\lim_{n \to \infty} A_n = 0.5$. Since the limit is not zero, the series diverges
by the divergence theorem.

Be sure to distinguish the limit of the sequence from the limit of the series. In
Example 1, the sequence converges to 0.5 but the series diverges. Also, adding
the terms of an arithmetic sequence forms an arithmetic series. Likewise, a
geometric series is the sum of the terms of a geometric sequence. Using the
divergence test above, it is easy to see that every arithmetic series diverges.
However, not all geometric series diverge. Two preliminary results will be
needed in order to determine which ones converge.

Theorem 11.4

$$\lim_{n \to \infty} r^n = \begin{cases} 0 & \text{if } |r| < 1 \\ 1 & \text{if } r = 1 \\ \text{does not exist} & \text{otherwise} \end{cases}$$

With a calculator, you can check these conclusions involving successive powers of a real number. However, you should also be able to see them conceptually. If $r = 1$, the conclusion is obvious, since 1 to any power is still 1 and the resulting constant sequence has the limit 1. If r is between 0 and 1, multiplication is equivalent to finding a fraction of the previous whole and successive products decrease. (The proof is an exercise.) That a similar result holds for bases between -1 and 0 is not hard to check. If $r > 1$, the powers increase without bound and no limit exists. If $r = -1$, the powers form a sequence alternating between -1 and 1, and again the powers do not get arbitrarily close to any single value. Finally, if $r < -1$, the signs again alternate and the absolute values become infinite, so there is no limit.

Because the general term of any geometric sequence can be put into the form $A_n = A_1 r^{n-1}$, the next theorem helps in finding the limit of any infinite geometric sequence that converges.

Theorem 11.5

$$\lim_{n \to \infty} A_1 r^{n-1} = 0 \text{ if } |r| < 1.$$

Proof

For $|r| < 1$ we have $\lim_{n \to \infty} A_1 r^{n-1} = A_1 \lim_{n \to \infty} r^{n-1}$, (by theorem 11.2)

$$= A_1 \cdot 0 \text{ (by theorem 11.4)}$$
$$= 0$$

Therefore, any geometric sequence converges to zero if the common ratio has an absolute value less than 1. For a geometric series we now have the following:

Theorem 11.6

The sum of a geometric series converges if $|r| < 1$ and

$$\sum_{n=1}^{\infty} A_1 r^{n-1} = \frac{A_1}{1 - r}.$$

Proof

The sum of a series is the limit of the partial sums. Since the partial sum of a geometric sequence is given by $S_n = \frac{A_1(1 - r^n)}{1 - r}$ (theorem 10.5), we can find its limit to determine the sum of the series when $|r| < 1$.

$$\lim_{n \to \infty} \frac{A_1(1 - r^n)}{1 - r} = A_1 \lim_{n \to \infty} \frac{(1 - r^n)}{1 - r} \quad \text{(properties 3 and 1)}$$

$$= \frac{A_1 \lim_{n \to \infty} (1 - r^n)}{\lim_{n \to \infty} (1 - r)} \quad \text{(property 4)}$$

$$= \frac{A_1\left(\lim_{n \to \infty} 1 - \lim_{n \to \infty} r^n\right)}{\lim_{n \to \infty} 1 - \lim_{n \to \infty} r} \quad \text{(property 2)}$$

$$= \frac{A_1(1 - 0)}{1 - r} \quad \text{(property 1 and theorem 11.5)}$$

$$= \frac{A_1}{(1 - r)}$$

Therefore, the sum of the series is $\frac{A_1}{1 - r}$.

EXAMPLE 2 Find $\displaystyle\sum_{k=1}^{\infty} 3(0.9)^k$.

Answer Since the series is geometric and $r = 0.9 < 1$, the series converges. Apply the formula to find the sum.

$$\sum_{k=1}^{\infty} 3(0.9)^k = \frac{A_1}{1 - r} = \frac{2.7}{1 - 0.9} = \frac{2.7}{0.1} = 27$$

EXAMPLE 3 Find $\displaystyle\sum_{k=1}^{\infty} \left[3(0.9)^k + 2\left(-\frac{1}{2}\right)^k\right]$.

Answer First, rewrite the series as the limit of a sequence of partial sums.

$$\sum_{k=1}^{\infty} \left[3(0.9)^k + 2\left(-\frac{1}{2}\right)^k\right] = \lim_{n \to \infty} \sum_{k=1}^{n} \left[3(0.9)^k + 2\left(-\frac{1}{2}\right)^k\right]$$

$$= \lim_{n \to \infty} \left[\sum_{k=1}^{n} 3(0.9)^k + \sum_{k=1}^{n} 2\left(\frac{-1}{2}\right)^k\right] \quad \begin{array}{l}\text{(property 1 of}\\ \text{summations)}\end{array}$$

$$= \lim_{n \to \infty} \sum_{k=1}^{n} 3(0.9)^k + \lim_{n \to \infty} \sum_{k=1}^{n} 2\left(\frac{-1}{2}\right)^k \quad \begin{array}{l}\text{(property 2}\\ \text{of limits)}\end{array}$$

$$= 27 + \frac{-1}{1 - \left(\frac{-1}{2}\right)} \quad \begin{array}{l}\text{(Example 2 and}\\ \text{theorem 11.6)}\end{array}$$

$$= 27 - \frac{2}{3} = 26\frac{1}{3}$$

EXAMPLE 4 Suppose you throw a rubber ball 100 feet in the air and it rebounds 60% of its former height on each bounce. How far will the ball travel before it finally appears to come to rest?

Answer Since the height of each bounce is 60% of the previous bounce, the heights of the upward throw and the bounces form a geometric sequence with $A_1 = 100$ and $r = 0.6$. The total distance traveled upward is the sum of the series, and the ball falls the same distance it travels upward each time. Therefore, the total distance traveled is twice the sum of the series, or

$$2 \sum_{n=1}^{\infty} (100)(0.6)^{n-1} = \frac{200}{(1 - 0.6)} = \frac{200}{(0.4)} = 500 \text{ feet.}$$

The divergence test guarantees that if a series $\sum_{n=1}^{\infty} A_n$ converges, then $\lim_{n \to \infty} A_n = 0$. The converse, however, is false. A sequence whose terms approach zero as n approaches infinity does not necessarily have a converging series. For example, consider the harmonic sequence, $A_n = \frac{1}{n}$. Even though $\lim_{n \to \infty} \frac{1}{n} = 0$, the series $\sum_{n=1}^{\infty} \frac{1}{n} = 1 + \frac{1}{2} + \frac{1}{3} + \frac{1}{4} + \cdots$ diverges. To prove that the harmonic series diverges, compare it to the series $\sum_{n=1}^{\infty} B_n$ below.

$$\sum_{n=1}^{\infty} A_n = 1 + \frac{1}{2} + \left(\frac{1}{3} + \frac{1}{4} \right) + \left(\frac{1}{5} + \frac{1}{6} + \frac{1}{7} + \frac{1}{8} \right) + \cdots$$

$$\sum_{n=1}^{\infty} B_n = 1 + \frac{1}{2} + \left(\frac{1}{4} + \frac{1}{4} \right) + \left(\frac{1}{8} + \frac{1}{8} + \frac{1}{8} + \frac{1}{8} \right) + \cdots$$

The terms of the second series are always less than or equal to the corresponding terms of the harmonic terms. Thus, $B_n \leq A_n$ for all n. The groupings show that $\sum_{n=1}^{\infty} B_n = 1 + \frac{1}{2} + \frac{1}{2} + \frac{1}{2} + \frac{1}{2} + \cdots$, which diverges (one more than a constant series). Since the smaller series diverges, the larger, harmonic series must also diverge.

Finally, consider one more type of series that converges.

Telescoping Series
A telescoping series is one in which all but a few terms add up to zero, therefore the sum of the series is the sum of the remaining terms.

EXAMPLE 5 Find $\displaystyle\sum_{n=1}^{\infty} \frac{3}{n^2 + 3n}$.

Answer

$$\sum_{n=1}^{\infty} \frac{3}{n^2 + 3n} = \sum_{n=1}^{\infty} \frac{3}{n(n + 3)}$$

1. Factor the denominator.

$$= \sum_{n=1}^{\infty} \left(\frac{A}{n} + \frac{B}{n + 3} \right)$$

2. Express the fraction as two separate fractions. This process, called partial fractions, reverses the common denominator process. To find the proper values for A and B:

$$\frac{A}{n} + \frac{B}{n + 3} = \frac{A(n + 3)}{n(n + 3)} + \frac{Bn}{n(n + 3)}$$

a. Add the fractions.

$$= \frac{An + 3A + Bn}{n(n + 3)}$$

$$= \frac{(A + B)n + 3A}{n(n + 3)}$$

b. Combine like terms, and compare the result to the original fraction, $\frac{3}{n(n + 3)}$ or $\frac{0n + 3}{n(n + 3)}$.

$$3A = 3 \quad \text{and} \quad A + B = 0$$
$$A = 1 \qquad\qquad 1 + B = 0$$
$$\qquad\qquad\qquad B = -1$$

c. Since the denominators are the same, the corresponding coefficients must be equal.

$$\sum_{n=1}^{\infty} \frac{3}{n^2 + 3n} = \sum_{n=1}^{\infty} \left(\frac{1}{n} + \frac{-1}{n + 3} \right)$$

d. Substitute the values of A and B in the series (step 2).

$$= 1 - \frac{1}{4} + \frac{1}{2} - \frac{1}{5} + \frac{1}{3}$$
$$- \frac{1}{6} + \frac{1}{4} - \frac{1}{7}$$
$$+ \frac{1}{5} - \frac{1}{8} + \frac{1}{6} - \frac{1}{9} + \cdots$$

3. Expand the series as a list. (For $n = 1$, the terms are $\frac{1}{1}$ and $\frac{-1}{4}$ or $1 - \frac{1}{4}$.)

$$= 1 + \frac{1}{2} + \frac{1}{3}$$

4. Look for terms that add up to zero. All the negative terms are the opposite of some positive term. These sums are zero. Write any remaining terms.

$$= \frac{11}{6} \text{ or } 1.8\overline{3}$$

5. Add the remaining terms.

▶ A. Exercises

Show that each series diverges.

1. $\displaystyle\sum_{n=1}^{\infty} \frac{3n}{2n-5}$

2. $\displaystyle\sum_{n=1}^{\infty} \frac{n^2}{7n^2-1}$

3. $\displaystyle\sum_{n=1}^{\infty} \frac{2n^3}{3-5n^3}$

4. $\displaystyle\sum_{n=1}^{\infty} 4$

5. $\displaystyle\sum_{n=1}^{\infty} \frac{1}{n}$

6. $\displaystyle\sum_{n=1}^{\infty} \frac{5}{n}$

Find the sum of each geometric series.

7. $\displaystyle\sum_{n=1}^{\infty} 2\left(\frac{2}{5}\right)^{n-1}$

8. $\displaystyle\sum_{n=1}^{\infty} 6\left(\frac{1}{3}\right)^{n-1}$

9. $\displaystyle\sum_{n=1}^{\infty} \left(\frac{1}{2}\right)^{n}$

10. $\displaystyle\sum_{n=1}^{\infty} 12\left(\frac{5}{6}\right)^{n}$

▶ B. Exercises

Classify each series below, then find the sum or write diverges.

11. $\displaystyle\sum_{n=1}^{\infty} \frac{1}{3}$

12. $\displaystyle\sum_{n=1}^{\infty} \frac{1}{3n}$

13. $\displaystyle\sum_{n=1}^{\infty} \left(\frac{1}{3}\right)^{n}$

14. $\displaystyle\sum_{n=1}^{\infty} 3n$

15. $\displaystyle\sum_{n=1}^{\infty} 4\left(\frac{-1}{2}\right)^{n}$

16. $\displaystyle\sum_{n=1}^{\infty} n!$

17. $\displaystyle\sum_{n=1}^{\infty} 2\left(\frac{9}{7}\right)^{n-1}$

Find the sum of the following telescoping series using the method in Example 5.

18. $\displaystyle\sum_{n=1}^{\infty} \frac{1}{n^2+n}$

19. $\displaystyle\sum_{n=3}^{\infty} \frac{4}{n^2-4}$

20. $\displaystyle\sum_{n=1}^{\infty} \frac{-2}{n^2+4n+3}$

▶ C. Exercises

Find the sum of each series.

21. $\displaystyle\sum_{n=1}^{\infty} \frac{1}{n!}$

22. $\displaystyle\sum_{n=1}^{\infty} (-1)^{n+1}\frac{1}{n!}$

⏦ Dominion Modeling

The first iteration of attaching equilateral triangles on the middle third of each side provides a better approximation to the Koch curve. The resulting shape after this first iteration ($n = 1$) appears below. Explain and simplify each calculation below. Try to identify the pattern developing.

Koch curve construction, iteration 1

23. Calculate the *perimeter*, p_1.

24. Find the area, A_1.

▪ Cumulative Review

25. Specify $f(x) = \sqrt{2x - 3} - 4$, as a translation and specify the domain and range.

26. Graph the function in exercise 25.

27. Simplify $\text{Sin}^{-1} \frac{-\sqrt{3}}{2}$ and $\text{Tan}^{-1} \frac{-\sqrt{3}}{3}$.

28. Simplify $\sin \left(\text{Cos}^{-1} \frac{-2}{5} \right)$ and $\sin (\text{Tan}^{-1} -1)$.

29. Find $\lim\limits_{n \to \infty} \frac{4n + 5}{n^2 - 3}$.

11.3 Limits and Graphs

So far you have considered limits of sequences and series. However, one can apply the same idea to functions. Consider the following limit.

$$\lim_{x \to 3} \frac{x^2 - 9}{x - 3}$$

You can see that for this function $f(x) = \frac{x^2 - 9}{x - 3}$ and $f(3)$ is undefined. Yet, if you calculate $f(x)$ for values of x closer and closer to 3, you will see a pattern.

x	$f(x)$
1	$\frac{-8}{-2} = 4$
2	$\frac{-5}{-1} = 5$
2.5	$\frac{-2.75}{-0.5} = 5.5$
2.9	$\frac{-0.59}{-0.1} = 5.9$

You can also calculate $f(x)$ for x-values larger than 3.

x	$f(x)$
5	$\frac{16}{2} = 8$
4	$\frac{7}{1} = 7$
3.5	$\frac{3.25}{0.5} = 6.5$
3.1	$\frac{0.61}{0.1} = 6.1$

You can see that the function approaches 6 as x approaches 3 from either side. In other words, $\lim_{x \to 3} f(x) = 6$.

This conclusion, that $\lim_{x \to 3} f(x) = 6$, can also be seen on the graph. To graph $f(x)$, factor and cancel, taking specific note of domain restrictions.

$$f(x) = \frac{x^2 - 9}{x - 3}$$
$$f(x) = \frac{(x - 3)(x + 3)}{x - 3}$$
$$f(x) = x + 3 \text{ if } x \neq 3$$

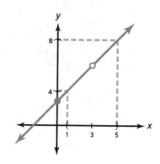

When *x* is less than **2** units from **3** (that is, between **1** and **5**), *f*(*x*) is between **4** and **8**. You should be able to symbolize this using interval notation: if *x* ∈ (1, 5) and *x* ≠ 3, then *f*(*x*) ∈ (4, 8). For a smaller interval, as when *x* ∈ (2, 4) and *x* ≠ 3, then *f*(*x*) ∈ (5, 7) as shown here.

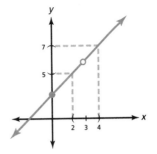

The smaller the *neighborhood* (or interval) centered around *x* = 3, the closer the *y*-values cluster around *y* = 6.

If *x* ∈ (2.5, 3.5), then *f*(*x*) ∈ (5.5, 6.5)

If *x* ∈ (2.9, 3.1), then *f*(*x*) ∈ (5.9, 6.1)

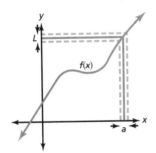

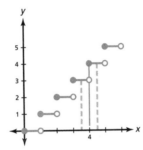

In a smooth curve, if $\lim_{x \to a} f(x) = L$, then *f*(*x*) gets closer and closer to *L* whether you are approaching *a* from the right or from the left. However, not all functions approach the same value from both the positive and negative directions. Consider the greatest-integer function, *y* = [*x*]. As *x* gets closer to 4 from the right-hand side, *f*(*x*) approaches 4. But as *x* approaches 4 from the left-hand side, *f*(*x*) approaches 3. Thus, there are two special limits: the right-hand limit and the left-hand limit. A small superscript is used to distinguish them: − for left (from the negative direction) and + for right (from the positive direction).

Definitions

Right-hand limit   The right-hand limit of *f* as *x* approaches *a*, denoted $\lim_{x \to a^+} f(x)$, is the number to which *f*(*x*) gets closer and closer as *x* gets closer to *a* from the right.

Left-hand limit   The left-hand limit of *f* as *x* approaches *a*, denoted $\lim_{x \to a^-} f(x)$, is the number to which *f*(*x*) gets closer and closer as *x* gets closer to *a* from the left.

Therefore, if $f(x) = [x]$, then $\lim\limits_{x\to 4^+} f(x) = 4$; $\lim\limits_{x\to 4^-} f(x) = 3$. These two limits are called *one-sided limits*. You may wonder which one of these is the real limit.

Definition

$\lim\limits_{x\to a} f(x)$ $\lim\limits_{x\to a} f(x) = L$ if and only if $\lim\limits_{x\to a^+} f(x) = \lim\limits_{x\to a^-} f(x) = L$

You can see from the definition that at each integer value of x in $[x]$, the function has no limit: $\lim\limits_{x\to 4} [x]$ does not exist. In other words, neither of the one-sided limits is the real limit. When the one-sided limits do not match, there is no limit.

Now, you can see how you found the limit for $f(x) = \dfrac{x^2 - 9}{x - 3}$ as x approached 3. The first table of values on p. 554 investigated the limit as x approached 3 from the left: $\lim\limits_{x\to 3^-} f(x) = 6$.

The second table showed that the limit as x approached 3 from the right was also 6: $\lim\limits_{x\to 3^+} f(x) = 6$. Since the two one-sided limits are the same, by the definition above $\lim\limits_{x\to 3} f(x) = 6$.

You can often find limits easily from graphs.

EXAMPLE 1   Find $\lim\limits_{x\to 4} f(x)$ from the graph.

Answer $\lim\limits_{x\to 4^-} f(x) = -3$

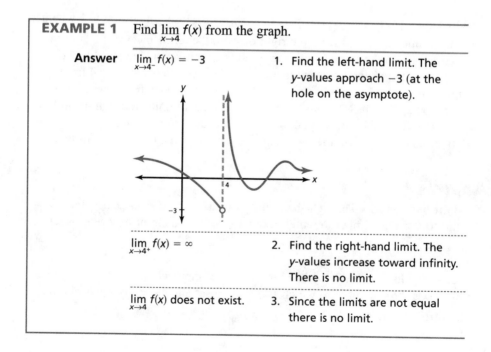

1. Find the left-hand limit. The y-values approach -3 (at the hole on the asymptote).

$\lim\limits_{x\to 4^+} f(x) = \infty$

2. Find the right-hand limit. The y-values increase toward infinity. There is no limit.

$\lim\limits_{x\to 4} f(x)$ does not exist.

3. Since the limits are not equal there is no limit.

It should be emphasized that ∞ is not a real number and therefore is not a limit, but the notation in step 2 above is commonly used. By contrast, a statement such as $\lim\limits_{x \to \infty} f(x) = 2$ indicates the existence of a finite limit of the function as x increases without bound.

▶ A. Exercises

Match each graph to its limit. Use each letter once.

A. $\lim\limits_{x \to 2^+} f(x) = 2$　　　**C.** $\lim\limits_{x \to 2} f(x) = 1$　　　**E.** $\lim\limits_{x \to \infty} f(x) = 1$

B. $\lim\limits_{x \to 2} f(x) = \infty$　　　**D.** $\lim\limits_{x \to 2} f(x) = 3$

1.

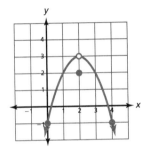

4.

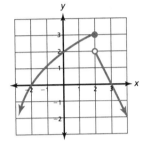

2.

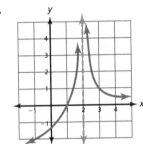

5.

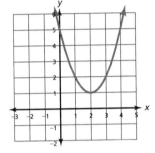

3.

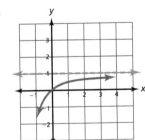

Find $\lim\limits_{x \to 1} f(x)$ for each graph. If there is no limit, explain why.

6.

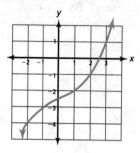

9.

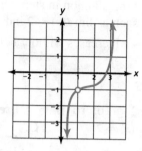

7.

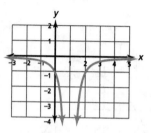

10.

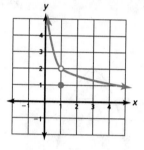

8.

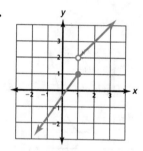

▶ B. Exercises

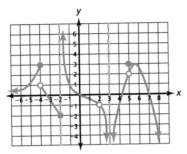

Find the following one-sided limits from the graph of $f(x)$ above.

11. $\lim\limits_{x \to -4^-} f(x)$ 14. $\lim\limits_{x \to -2^+} f(x)$ 17. $\lim\limits_{x \to 5^-} f(x)$

12. $\lim\limits_{x \to -4^+} f(x)$ 15. $\lim\limits_{x \to 2^-} f(x)$ 18. $\lim\limits_{x \to 5^+} f(x)$

13. $\lim\limits_{x \to -2^-} f(x)$ 16. $\lim\limits_{x \to 2^+} f(x)$

Using the same graph, find the following limits and justify your answer.

19. $\lim\limits_{x \to -4} f(x)$ 22. $\lim\limits_{x \to 5} f(x)$

20. $\lim\limits_{x \to -2} f(x)$ 23. $\lim\limits_{x \to 3} f(x)$

21. $\lim\limits_{x \to 2} f(x)$

24. List all the values of x for which no limit exists.

25. For what values of x is the limit not equal to the value of the function?

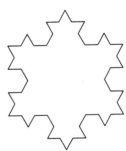 Find the limits by graphing $f(x) = \dfrac{x^3 + 1.5x^2 - 9.7}{2.1x^2 - 7.2x + 5.1}$ on a graphing calculator and examining the graph.

26. $\lim\limits_{x \to 0} f(x)$ 27. $\lim\limits_{x \to 1.73232} f(x)$ 28. $\lim\limits_{x \to 4.5} f(x)$

▶ C. Exercises

29. Find $\lim\limits_{x \to -\infty} f(x)$ from the graph used in the *B Exercises*.

30. Explain what limits such as the one above tells you about a graph.

Dominion Modeling

Consider the second iteration in the construction of the Koch curve to obtain an even better approxima-tion. Explain and simplify your work for each calcula-tion. Try to recognize the pattern developing and express your answer in the form of the pattern.

31. Find the *perimeter*, p_2.

32. Find the *area*, A_2.

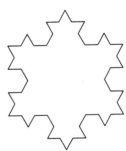

Koch curve construction, iteration 2

33. Graph $y = 2e^{\frac{x}{2}}$.

Solve.

34. $2^{x+3} = 7$

35. $\ln 4x = 0.2$

36. $\dfrac{x + 4}{x^2 + 5x + 6} + \dfrac{5}{x^2 - 9} = \dfrac{1}{x + 3}$

37. Solve the system using Gaussian elimination.

$$x - y + 3z = 5$$
$$x + 2y - z = 3$$
$$2x - 3y + z = 8$$

11.4 Continuous Functions

Earlier you identified a function as continuous if you could draw the graph without lifting your pencil from the paper. You did not learn the technical definition at that time because it involves limits.

You can see that $g(x)$ is not continuous. It has a hole at -2 and a jump at 2. However, it is continuous for restricted domains. In fact $g(x)$ is continuous on $(-\infty, -2)$ $(-2, 2]$, and $(2, \infty)$. But what do "hole" and "jump" mean? To define these terms precisely, let's investigate the following limits.

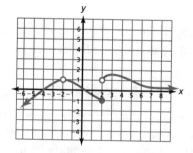

$$\lim_{x \to 2} g(x) \quad \text{and} \quad \lim_{x \to -2} g(x)$$

The first limit is undefined since the right and left-hand limits are not equal. In other words, a *jump* occurs at $x = a$ when $\lim_{x \to a^-} g(x) \neq \lim_{x \to a^+} g(x)$. The second limit exists, but $g(-2)$ is undefined. In other words, a *hole* occurs at $x = a$, when $g(a)$ is undefined.

Furthermore, even if the function is defined, there will be a hole if the value of the function is different from the limit. The jump in this function occurs because $f(3) = 1$, but $\lim_{x \to 3} f(x) = 5$. This shows that in order for a function to be continuous at a given point, the limit must be equal to the value of the function. Since both must exist for them to be equal, three conditions are needed.

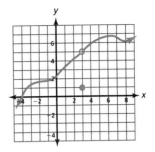

Definitions

Continuous at a point   A function f is continuous at $x = a$ if

1. $f(a)$ is defined,
2. $\lim_{x \to a} f(x)$ exists, and
3. $\lim_{x \to a} f(x) = f(a)$.

Continuous on an interval   A function f is continuous on the interval (a, b) if and only if f is continuous at every point on (a, b).

EXAMPLE 1   Use the definition to prove that $f(x)$ is not continuous.

Answer

$f(1) = -\frac{1}{2}$

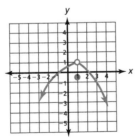

1. Identify $x = 1$ as the point of discontinuity. Find $f(1)$. Since it exists, part 1 of the definition is satisfied.

$\lim_{x \to 1^-} f(x) = 1$ and $\lim_{x \to 1^+} f(x) = 1$
Therefore, $\lim_{x \to 1} f(x) = 1$.

2. Find the one-sided limits. Since they are equal, the limit exists and part 2 of the definition is satisfied.

Since $f(1) \neq \lim_{x \to 1} f(x)$, the function is not continuous at $x = 1$.

3. Part 3 of the definition is not satisfied, which results in a hole.

The intervals of continuity for $f(x)$ in Example 1 are $(-\infty, 1)$ and $(1, \infty)$.

EXAMPLE 2   Prove that $f(x)$ is continuous at $x = -2$.

Answer $f(-2) = 3$

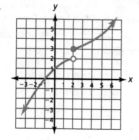

$f(-2) = 3$	1. Part 1 of the definition holds.
$\lim_{x \to -2^-} f(x) = 3 = \lim_{x \to -2^+} f(x)$, so $\lim_{x \to -2} f(x) = 3$	2. Part 2 holds.
$\lim_{x \to -2} f(x) = 3 = f(-2)$, so f is continuous at -2.	3. Part 3 is satisfied.

Remember from Section 2.7 that polynomial curves have no holes, jumps, or gaps. A function of the form $f(x) = a_n x^n + a_{n-1} x^{n-1} + a_{n-2} x^{n-2} + \cdots + a_1 x + a_0$ is always a smooth curve. Any polynomial function is continuous over all real numbers.

EXAMPLE 3   Without graphing, which of the following functions are continuous on $(-\infty, \infty)$?

$$f(x) = x^2, \quad g(x) = \tfrac{1}{x}, \quad h(x) = \begin{cases} x & \text{if } x \neq 0 \\ 5 & \text{if } x = 0 \end{cases}, \quad j(x) = [x]$$

Answer f is continuous for all $x \in \mathbb{R}$ (since it is a polynomial).

g is not continuous when $x = 0$ (function undefined and no limit exists).

h is not continuous when $x = 0$ (jump at $x = 0$ between the linear pieces).

j is not continuous for any $x \in \mathbb{Z}$ (jump at each integer).

▶ A. Exercises

Give the intervals of continuity for each function.

1.

2.

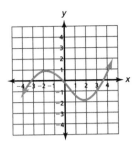

4.

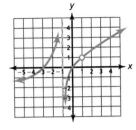

3.

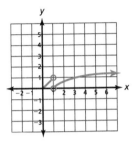

5.

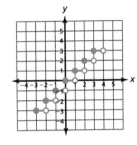

For each discontinuous graph below, identify whether the three parts of the definition of continuity are satisfied at the point of discontinuity.

6.

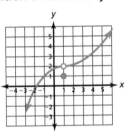

8.

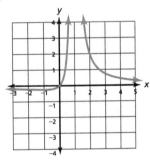

7.

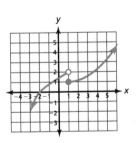

9.

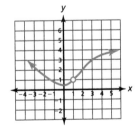

10.

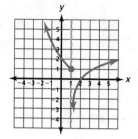

▶ B. Exercises

Use the definition of continuity to prove that $f(x)$ is continuous at $x = 0$.

11.

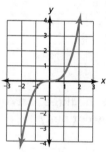

14.

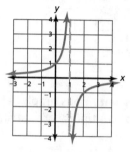

12.

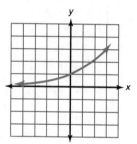

15.

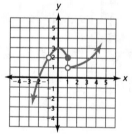

13.

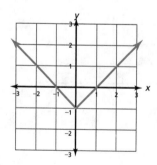

At what value is the function not continuous? Use the definition of
continuity to prove that it is not continuous.

16.

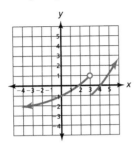

19.

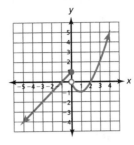

17.

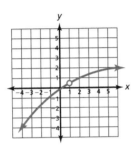

20.

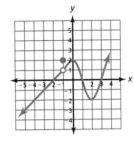

18.

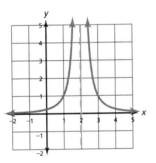

21.

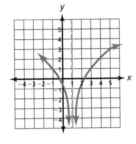

Without graphing, tell whether the function is continuous at the given
point or in the given interval.

22. $f(x) = x^2 + 3x - 6;\ (-\infty, \infty)$

23. $f(x) = \frac{1}{x^2};\ [-3, 2)$

24. $f(x) = |x|;\ x = 0$

25. $f(x) = \frac{x^2 - 4x + 3}{x - 1};\ x = 1$

26. $f(x) = [x];\ (2.5, 2.9)$

27. $f(x) = 0;\ x = \frac{1}{2}$

28. $f(x) = \ln x;\ x = 0$

29. $f(x) = \cos x;\ (-\infty, \infty)$

30. $f(\theta) = \tan \theta;\ (0, \pi)$

▶ C. Exercises

Consider the following four functions:
a. $f(x) = [2x]$ b. $g(x) = 2[x]$ c. $h(x) = [x] - 2$ d. $k(x) = [x - 2]$.

31. Identify the discontinuities for each function.

32. Relate each graph to the graph of $y = [x]$.

▦ Dominion Modeling

Now, consider the third iteration in the construction of the Koch curve. Explain and simplify each calculation. Express your answer according to the pattern.

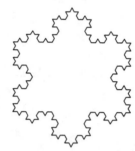

Koch curve construction, iteration 3

33. Find the *perimeter*, p_3.

34. Find the *area*, A_3.

35. Write the area A_3 as a partial sum of a geometric sequence (you may factor $\frac{\sqrt{3}}{4}$ from all the terms). Then simplify it using the appropriate theorem.

▌Cumulative Review

36. Graph $f(x) = 2 \ln (x - 1)$ and find its inverse.

Given mound-shaped data, determine the percentage of data in each interval.

37. more than 2.17 standard deviations above the mean

38. within 1.3 standard deviations of the mean

Solve.

39. $2\sqrt{3x - 2} + 1 = 3x - 2$

40. $\sin 2x + \sin x = 0$

11.5 Infinite Limits and Asymptotes

In the previous section you defined holes and jumps using limits, but what about gaps caused by vertical asymptotes? If the limit of a function as $x \to a$ is $\pm\infty$, then there is a gap for a vertical asymptote.

Definition

Vertical asymptote $f(x)$ has a vertical asymptote at $x = a$, if any of the one-sided limits are infinite: $\lim\limits_{x \to a^-} = \pm\infty$ or $\lim\limits_{x \to a^+} f(x) = \pm\infty$

EXAMPLE 1   Find $\lim\limits_{x \to 0} \frac{1}{x}$ and interpret your answer.

Answer $\lim\limits_{x \to 0^+} \frac{1}{x} = +\infty$ and $\lim\limits_{x \to 0^-} \frac{1}{x} = -\infty$ 1. Note that $\lim\limits_{x \to 0} \frac{1}{x}$ does not exist and the one-sided limits are infinite.

$x = 0$ is a vertical asymptote.   2. Use the definition of vertical asymptote.

3. Graph as a check.

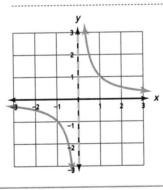

You can also investigate the tails of a graph using limits. By finding the limits as x approaches $\pm\infty$, you can determine what happens to the tails of the graph. You should recall rules for tails from your work with polynomials and rational functions, but you will now be able to verify the rules by using limits.

Horizontal asymptote $f(x)$ has a horizontal asymptote at $y = L$, if $\lim\limits_{x \to \infty} f(x) = L$ or $\lim\limits_{x \to -\infty} f(x) = L$.

EXAMPLE 2   Find $\lim\limits_{x \to \infty} \dfrac{2x + 4}{3x + 1}$ and interpret your answer.

Answer

$\lim\limits_{x \to \infty} \dfrac{2x + 4}{3x + 1} = \lim\limits_{x \to \infty} \dfrac{\frac{2x}{x} + \frac{4}{x}}{\frac{3x}{x} + \frac{1}{x}}$

1. Since the degrees are equal in the denominator and the numerator, the limit is the ratio of the leading coefficients (proved in Section 11.1 exercise 26).

$= \lim\limits_{x \to \infty} \dfrac{2 + \frac{4}{x}}{3 + \frac{1}{x}}$

$= \dfrac{2 + 0}{3 + 0}$

$= \dfrac{2}{3}$

$y = \dfrac{2}{3}$ is a horizontal asymptote.

2. Interpret the answer using the definition of horizontal asymptote.

3. Graph as a check.

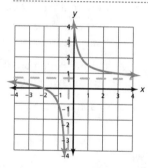

When $\lim\limits_{x \to \infty} f(x) = \infty$, there are no horizontal asymptotes.

EXAMPLE 3   Use limits to find any asymptotes and to discuss the tails of the graph of $y = x^4$.

Answer

no vertical asymptotes

1. x^4 is a polynomial and has a finite limit at each x-value.

Continued ▶

$$\lim_{x \to \infty} x^4 = \infty$$

$$\lim_{x \to -\infty} x^4 = \infty$$

2. As x approaches $\pm\infty$, the function approaches infinity. Since the limits do not exist, there are no horizontal asymptotes. Since both limits approach positive infinity, both tails go up.

3. Graph as a check.

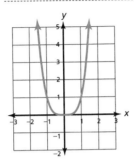

You can now understand the rule of tails for polynomial functions. When the degree is even, both tails go in the same direction. When the degree is odd, the tails go in opposite directions (one limit will be ∞ and the other will be $-\infty$). The rules of tails for rational functions are a bit more complicated, and you will prove them using limits in the exercises.

▶ A. Exercises

Let $f(x) = \frac{25}{x}$, and answer the following:

1. Graph $f(x)$.

2. Find $\lim_{x \to \infty} f(x)$.

3. Find $\lim_{x \to 0^+} f(x)$.

4. Find $\lim_{x \to 0^-} f(x)$.

5. Find $\lim_{x \to 0} f(x)$.

Write limit statements for each vertical and each horizontal asymptote.

6.

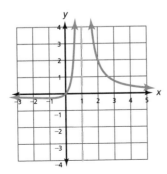

7.

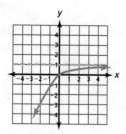

9.

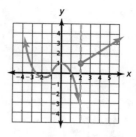

8.

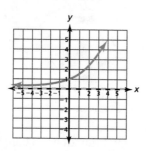

10.

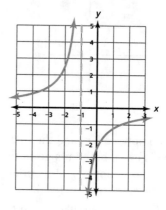

▶ B. Exercises

Find the following limits. Graphing may help.

11. $\lim\limits_{x \to \infty} \left(\dfrac{1}{x - 2} + 3 \right)$

12. $\lim\limits_{\theta \to \frac{\pi}{2}^+} \tan \theta$

13. $\lim\limits_{\theta \to \frac{\pi}{2}^-} \tan \theta$

14. $\lim\limits_{x \to 3} [x]$

15. $\lim\limits_{x \to 2.5} [x]$

16. $\lim\limits_{x \to -\infty} \dfrac{x + 1}{x}$

17. $\lim\limits_{x \to 0} \dfrac{x + 1}{x}$

18. $\lim\limits_{x \to \infty} \dfrac{2x + 1}{x^2 - 3x + 4}$

19. Graph $f(x) = \dfrac{(3x + 5)^2}{(\pi x + 1)(2x - 5)}$ on the graphing calculator and locate the horizontal asymptote.

Let $f(x) = \dfrac{x(x + 1)}{(x + 1)(x - 1)}$; find the following.

20. $\lim\limits_{x \to 3} f(x)$

21. $\lim\limits_{x \to 1^+} f(x)$

22. $\lim\limits_{x \to -1} f(x)$

23. Verify the limits in exercises 20-22 by examining the graph of $f(x)$ on the graphing calculator.

► C. Exercises

24. Discuss the rule of tails if $m > n$ where m is the degree of the numerator and n is the degree of the denominator.

Consider the general rational function

$$f(x) = \frac{a_m x^m + a_{m-1} x^{m-1} + \cdots + a_2 x^2 + a_1 x + a_0}{a_n x^n + a_{n-1} x^{n-1} + \cdots + a_2 x^2 + a_1 x + a_0}.$$

Use limits to prove the rules of tails under the following conditions.

25. If $m < n$

26. If $m = n$

Dominion Modeling

Consider the general term (nth iteration) for the construction of the Koch curve. Explain and simplify each calculation.

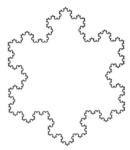

Koch curve construction, several iterations

27. Find the *perimeter*, p_n. Classify the sequence.

28. Find the *area*, A_n.

Cumulative Review

29. Given the following piece function, find all discontinuities; identify which of the three types they are and why.

$$f(x) = \begin{cases} x + 2 & \text{if} \quad x \leq -1 \\ |x^2 - 1| & \text{if} \quad -1 < x < 1 \\ \dfrac{x - 1}{x^2 - 10x + 23} & \text{if} \quad x > 1 \end{cases}$$

Consider the sequence: $\dfrac{1}{2}, \dfrac{3}{4}, \dfrac{5}{8}, \dfrac{7}{16}, \dfrac{9}{32}, \ldots$

30. Give the explicit formula.

31. Find the limit.

Graph the following conic sections. Find the foci, eccentricity, and the equations of any asymptotes.

32. $x^2 + 2y^2 = 100$

33. $3x^2 - 8y^2 = 48$

POLISH MATH

Höené Wronski (1778-1853)

Poland has produced several important mathematicians.

Poland has produced several important mathematicians. The Wronskian, a determinant involving partial derivatives, honors Josef Hoëné de Wronski (1778-1853) of Wolsztyn. Pasch's theorem in geometry is named for Moritz Pasch (1843-91) of Wroclaw (then Breslau). Also born in Wroclaw, Felix Hausdorff (1869-1942) wrote on infinite ordinals in 1907. His book *Grundzuge der Mengenlehre* (1914) served as a founding work on topology. The T_2 spaces in topology are called Hausdorff spaces in his honor. He and his wife, being of Jewish descent, committed suicide to avoid internment by the Nazis.

Born in Warsaw, the leading center of mathematics in Poland, Kazimierz Kuratowski (1896-1980) and Waclaw Sierpinski (1882-1969) both studied and taught at the university there and contributed to the field of topology. When the Nazis took over, the university library and personal libraries of the professors were destroyed. The Nazis also murdered half the math faculty. After the war, however, Kuratowski and Sierpinski returned to the university. Kuratowski's book *Topologie* became a standard work in point set topology, while Sierpinski offered the first course in set theory, and developed the Sierpinski curve, a bizarre closed curve of infinite length containing every interior point of a unit square but less than half the area!

Karol Borsuk (1905-82), also born in Warsaw, studied under Kuratowski and later taught in the university. During the Nazi occupation, Borsuk (and many other faculty members) offered coursework in secret. Imprisoned for this crime and thus separated from his wife and daughters, he eventually escaped and remained in hiding until the war ended. His contributions to topology are numerous; he is best known for the Borsuk-Ulam theorem, which he proved in collaboration with Stanislaw Marcin Ulam (1909-84) of Lemberg, who later moved to Los Alamos (U.S.A.) to work on the atomic bomb.

Stefan Banach (1892-1945) of Kraków was raised by a friend of his father and supported himself by tutoring. His fortune changed, however, when a math professor named Steinhaus, walking through the park during a brief visit to town, overheard him talking to his friend about "Lebesgue measure." This opened a friendship and an opportunity for Steinhaus to explain the current problem he was researching. When Banach figured out the key to the answer, they wrote a paper which launched Banach's mathematical career. In 1920 Banach submitted his dissertation, "On Operations on Abstract Sets and Their Application to Integral Equations." This work defined what are now called Banach spaces and founded the theory of functional analysis. Nazis massacred many of his fellow professors on July 3, 1941, but Banach survived the entire occupation only to die of cancer the following year.

Alfred Tarski (1902-83) of Warsaw taught at the University of Warsaw before going to Harvard and Berkeley. His contributions include work on the foundations of math and logical paradoxes. His most famous paradox was developed with Banach and is called the Banach-Tarski paradox. Using the axiom of choice, they set forth the decomposition of a ball into two balls, each identical to the first.

Even more recently, Benoit Mandelbrot (1924-), developed the theory of fractals. Born in Warsaw, he taught in France, where he wrote his first book on the subject in 1975. In 1982 he wrote a more detailed work entitled *The Fractal Geometry of Nature* while he worked for IBM in New York. Fractals describe the complex geometry of similarity in finer and finer detail. The most famous fractal, the Mandelbrot set, is defined on the complex plane.

Warsaw is the focal point of mathematics in Poland.

Benoit Mandelbrot (1924-), fractal pioneer

11.6 Limit Theorems

The concept of limit can be used to illustrate an important truth. Suppose you lived eighty years and there was no life after death; your life on the earth would be $\frac{80}{80} = 1 = 100\%$ of your existence. Now, let's assume that your life after death was eighty years long: your earthly life would be $\frac{80}{160} = \frac{1}{2} = 50\%$ of your entire existence. If life after death were 720 years, your life here would be only $\frac{80}{80 + 720} = 0.1 = 10\%$. Now extend it to eternity: $\lim_{x \to \infty} \frac{80}{80 + x} = 0$. In other words, this life is very insignificant in light of eternity. It is no wonder that James said that life is "a vapour, that appeareth for a little time, and then vanisheth away" (James 4:14). In light of eternity, the troubles and hardships you suffer for a moment are as nothing. Your selfish achievement is also nothing. Only what you do for the Lord becomes important to the infinite, eternal God whom you serve. So "set your affection on things above, not on things on the earth" (Col. 3:2).

So far, you have learned basic concepts of limits. In this section you will learn several theorems concerning limits, since finding them is a foundational technique in all branches of calculus. Actually, the following theorems concerning limits are rather tedious to prove algebraically. We owe much of this logical and theoretical development to the French mathematician A. L. Cauchy (1789-1857). He proved many theorems and established the theoretical foundation of calculus. In fact, he wrote so much that the periodical *Comptes Rendus*, which published many of his proofs, decided not to accept any article of over four pages—the rule still remains today.

Much of Cauchy's work is presented in the following theorems. Note some similarities to the limit theorems for sequences.

> **Theorem 11.7: Limit of a Constant**
> If $f(x) = c$, where c is a constant, then $\lim_{x \to a} f(x) = c$ for all a.

EXAMPLE 1 Find $\lim\limits_{x \to 700} 5$.

Answer Since $f(x) = 5$ for all x, $f(700) = 5$. By theorem 11.7,

$$\lim\limits_{x \to 700} 5 = 5.$$

Theorem 11.8: Identity
If $f(x) = x$ for all x, then $\lim\limits_{x \to a} f(x) = a$.

Theorem 11.9: Limit of a Sum
If f and g are functions such that $\lim\limits_{x \to a} f(x) = L_1$ and $\lim\limits_{x \to a} g(x) = L_2$, then
$\lim\limits_{x \to a} [f(x) + g(x)] = \lim\limits_{x \to a} f(x) + \lim\limits_{x \to a} g(x) = L_1 + L_2$.

In other words, the limit of a sum is the sum of the limits. This powerful theorem allows you to consider the limit of each term of the function separately.

EXAMPLE 2 Find $\lim\limits_{x \to 5} (x + 3)$.

Answer

$\lim\limits_{x \to 5} (x + 3) = \lim\limits_{x \to 5} x + \lim\limits_{x \to 5} 3$	1. Find the sum of the limits using theorem 11.9.
$= 5 + 3$	2. Apply the identity and constant theorems.
$= 8$	3. Add the limits.

Theorem 11.10: Limit of a Scalar Multiple
If f is a function such that $\lim\limits_{x \to a} f(x) = L$, then $\lim\limits_{x \to a} c \cdot f(x) = c \cdot \lim\limits_{x \to a} f(x) = c \cdot L$, where $c \in \mathbb{R}$.

For a constant times a function, you can move that constant (called a scalar) in front of the limit; the constant becomes a coefficient of the limit.

EXAMPLE 3   Find $\lim\limits_{x \to 3} (2x + 6)$.

Answer $\lim\limits_{x \to 3} (2x + 6) = \lim\limits_{x \to 3} 2x + \lim\limits_{x \to 3} 6$ 1. Find the sum of the limits (theorem 11.9).

$\qquad = 2 \lim\limits_{x \to 3} x + \lim\limits_{x \to 3} 6$ 2. Move the scalar out of the limit (theorem 11.10).

$\qquad = 2 \cdot 3 + 6$ 3. Use the identity and
$\qquad = 12$ constant theorems to find the limits.

Theorem 11.11: Limit of a Product

If f and g are functions such that $\lim\limits_{x \to a} f(x) = L_1$, and $\lim\limits_{x \to a} g(x) = L_2$, then
$\lim\limits_{x \to a} [f(x) \cdot g(x)] = \lim\limits_{x \to a} f(x) \cdot \lim\limits_{x \to a} g(x) = L_1 \cdot L_2$.

Theorem 11.12: Limit of a Quotient

If f and g are functions such that $\lim\limits_{x \to a} f(x) = L_1$, and $\lim\limits_{x \to a} g(x) = L_2 \neq 0$,
then $\lim\limits_{x \to a} \dfrac{f(x)}{g(x)} = \dfrac{\lim\limits_{x \to a} f(x)}{\lim\limits_{x \to a} g(x)} = \dfrac{L_1}{L_2}$.

EXAMPLE 4   Find $\lim\limits_{x \to 1} \left(3x^2 + \frac{x}{4}\right)$.

Answer

$\lim\limits_{x \to 1} \left(3x^2 + \frac{x}{4}\right) = \lim\limits_{x \to 1} 3x^2 + \lim\limits_{x \to 1} \frac{x}{4}$ 1. Use the limit of a sum theorem.

$\qquad = 3 \lim\limits_{x \to 1} (x \cdot x) + \frac{1}{4} \lim\limits_{x \to 1} x$ 2. Use theorem 11.10 and 11.11 to rewrite the products.

$\qquad = 3 \cdot \lim\limits_{x \to 1} x \cdot \lim\limits_{x \to 1} x + \frac{1}{4} \lim\limits_{x \to 1} x$

$\qquad = 3 \cdot 1 \cdot 1 + \frac{1}{4} \cdot 1$ 3. Use theorem 11.8 to find the limits.

$\qquad = 3 + \frac{1}{4}$

$\qquad = \frac{13}{4}$

Theorem 11.13: Limit of a Power

If f is a function such that $\lim\limits_{x \to a} f(x) = L$, then $\lim\limits_{x \to a} [f(x)]^n = [\lim\limits_{x \to a} f(x)]^n = L^n$.

EXAMPLE 5   Find $\lim\limits_{x \to 2} (2x^2 - 3x + 5)$.

Answer

$\lim\limits_{x \to 2} (2x^2 - 3x + 5) = \lim\limits_{x \to 2} 2x^2 - \lim\limits_{x \to 2} 3x + \lim\limits_{x \to 2} 5$	1. Find the sum of limits.
$= 2 \lim\limits_{x \to 2} x^2 - 3 \lim\limits_{x \to 2} x + \lim\limits_{x \to 2} 5$	2. Factor the scalars.
$= 2 \cdot \left[\lim\limits_{x \to 2} x \right]^2 - 3 \lim\limits_{x \to 2} x + \lim\limits_{x \to 2} 5$	3. Use the power, identity, and constant theorems to evaluate.
$= 2 \cdot 2^2 - 3 \cdot 2 + 5$	
$= 7$	

You can see that limits of polynomials can be found by substitution, since polynomials are continuous at every point. Review the definition of continuity.

Whenever a function is continuous at $x = a$, you know that $\lim\limits_{x \to a} f(x) = f(a)$ by definition. This means that whenever a function is continuous at a point, you can find the limit at that point by substitution. When the function is not continuous you can use other methods, which involve canceling as in the next example.

EXAMPLE 6   Find $\lim\limits_{x \to 2} \dfrac{x^2 - x - 2}{x - 2}$.

Answer	$\lim\limits_{x \to 2} \dfrac{x^2 - x - 2}{x - 2} = \lim\limits_{x \to 2} \dfrac{(x - 2)(x + 1)}{x - 2}$	1. Factor and cancel.
	$= \lim\limits_{x \to 2} (x + 1)$	2. Find the limit (substitute $x = 2$).
	$= 3$	

Of course, canceling is allowed only if $x \neq 2$. Since $\lim\limits_{x \to 2} f(x)$ considers only values approaching $x = 2$ without reaching it, canceling is allowed. In the next example, rationalizing the numerator enables you to cancel, which works for the same reason.

EXAMPLE 7 Find $\lim\limits_{x \to 0} \dfrac{\sqrt{x + 3} - \sqrt{3}}{x}$.

Answer

1. Multiply both the numerator and the denominator by the conjugate of the numerator.

$$\lim\limits_{x \to 0} \frac{\sqrt{x + 3} - \sqrt{3}}{x} = \lim\limits_{x \to 0} \frac{(\sqrt{x + 3} - \sqrt{3})(\sqrt{x + 3} + \sqrt{3})}{x(\sqrt{x + 3} + \sqrt{3})}$$

$$= \lim\limits_{x \to 0} \frac{(x + 3) - 3}{x(\sqrt{x + 3} + \sqrt{3})}$$

$$= \lim\limits_{x \to 0} \frac{x}{x(\sqrt{x + 3} + \sqrt{3})}$$ 2. Simplify the numerator and cancel.

$$= \lim\limits_{x \to 0} \frac{1}{\sqrt{x + 3} + \sqrt{3}}$$

$$= \frac{1}{\sqrt{3} + \sqrt{3}}$$ 3. Find the limit. (Substitute $x = 0$.)

$$= \frac{\sqrt{3}}{6}$$

Besides substitution, canceling, and rationalizing the numerator, you may find that trigonometric identities are also helpful in finding limits.

▶ A. Exercises

Find the following limits.

1. $\lim\limits_{x \to 4} (x + 3)^2$

2. $\lim\limits_{x \to 2} \dfrac{3}{x^2}$

3. $\lim\limits_{x \to -1} (x^2 - 3x)$

4. $\lim\limits_{x \to 0} \dfrac{x^2 - x}{x}$

5. $\lim\limits_{x \to 0} 5x$

6. $\lim\limits_{x \to 3} x^3$

7. $\lim\limits_{x \to -1} \dfrac{2x^2 - x - 3}{x + 1}$

8. $\lim\limits_{x \to -1} \dfrac{x^2 - 1}{x + 1}$

9. $\lim\limits_{h \to 0} \dfrac{3h^2 - h}{h}$

10. $\lim\limits_{x \to 0} \dfrac{1}{x - 1}$

▶ B. Exercises

Find the following limits.

11. $\lim\limits_{x \to 1} \dfrac{1}{x - 1}$

12. $\lim\limits_{x \to 2} \dfrac{2 - x}{x^2 - 4}$

13. $\lim\limits_{x \to -3} |x + 3|$

14. $\lim\limits_{t \to 0} \dfrac{\sqrt{t + 1} - 1}{t}$

15. $\lim\limits_{x \to 0} \dfrac{\sqrt{x + 2} - \sqrt{2}}{x}$

16. $\lim\limits_{\theta \to \frac{\pi}{3}} \sin \theta$

17. $\lim\limits_{\theta \to \frac{\pi}{2}} \dfrac{\tan \theta - 1}{\sec \theta}$

18. $\lim\limits_{\theta \to 0} \dfrac{\sin^2 \theta - 1}{\cos \theta}$

19. $\lim\limits_{\theta \to \pi} \sec \theta$

20. $\lim\limits_{x \to 0} [e^x + x^e + \ln(x + e)]$

21. When does $\lim\limits_{x \to a} \dfrac{\sec x}{\sin x} = 0$?

22. When does $\lim\limits_{x \to a} \dfrac{e^{x^2} - e^x}{e^x} = e^{20} - 1$?

⩗ Dominion Modeling

You are now ready to determine the perimeter and area of the Koch curve using the patterns you discovered previously. Explain and simplify your work.

23. Find the *perimeter*, *p*, as *n* goes to infinity.

24. Find the *area*, *A*, as *n* goes to infinity, using the pattern for *n* iterations.

▪ Cumulative Review

Suppose $y = 100$ when $x = 18$.

25. Find *y* when $x = 31$, if *y* varies directly with the square of *x*.

26. Find *y* when $x = 31$, if *y* varies inversely with *x*.

27. Prove the identity $\dfrac{1}{\tan^2 x + 1} - \cos^2 x \tan^2 x = \cos 2x$.

28. If a parabola opens upward with vertex $(2, -3)$ and $p = 4$, write its equation in work form and in general form.

29. Find the principal root of $(3 - 5i)^{\frac{1}{4}}$ using polar coordinates.

Zeno of Elea, a mathematician of ancient Greece, once claimed that you could never go anywhere. He said that to get to a particular place, you must first go halfway there. From that midpoint, you must again go halfway to the desired destination. Consequently, since you always go "halfway there," you can never get there.

Use limits to give an answer to Zeno's paradox. (*Hint:* find the total distance traversed by the 'halves' as a series.)

11 Approximation Methods

Central Difference Formula

Since rate of change is a slope, the rate of change at a certain instant is a limit of a slope.

	Average		Instantaneous
acceleration	$\dfrac{\text{change in velocity}}{\text{change in time}}$	$= \dfrac{v_2 - v_1}{t_2 - t_1}$	$\lim\limits_{t_1 \to t_2} \dfrac{v_2 - v_1}{t_2 - t_1}$
velocity	$\dfrac{\text{change in distance}}{\text{change in time}}$	$= \dfrac{d_2 - d_1}{t_2 - t_1}$	$\lim\limits_{t_1 \to t_2} \dfrac{d_2 - d_1}{t_2 - t_1}$
marginal profit	$\dfrac{\text{change in profit}}{\text{change in production}}$	$= \dfrac{P_2 - P_1}{x_2 - x_1}$	$\lim\limits_{x_1 \to x_2} \dfrac{P_2 - P_1}{x_2 - x_1}$

The rate of change of $f(x)$ with respect to x is symbolized with a superscript or prime mark: $f'(x)$.

EXAMPLE 1 Find the instantaneous rate of change for $f(x) = x^2 - 3$ at $x = 5$.

Answer

$$f'(x) = \lim_{x_1 \to x_2} \frac{f(x_2) - f(x_1)}{x_2 - x_1} = \lim_{x_1 \to x_2} \frac{(x_2^2 - 3) - (x_1^2 - 3)}{x_2 - x_1} = \lim_{x_1 \to x_2} \frac{x_2^2 - x_1^2}{x_2 - x_1}$$

$$= \lim_{x_1 \to x_2} \frac{(x_2 - x_1)(x_2 + x_1)}{x_2 - x_1} = \lim_{x_1 \to x_2} x_2 + x_1 = x_2 + x_2 = 2x_2$$

Since the instantaneous rate of change for any x is $2x$, at $x = 5$ we get $2x = 2 \cdot 5 = 10$.

You will learn more about instantaneous rates in the next chapter. Here is a way to estimate the rate when you don't have a formula for the function.

EXAMPLE 2   Great Stuff, Inc. shows the following profits for the last ten years:

years 1-5 $12,800 $16,000 $20,500 $18,700 $21,400

years 6-10 $22,100 $22,900 $24,600 $25,300 $25,000

Estimate the rate of change (called marginal profit) for the third year.

Answer

$$f'(x) = \frac{f(x + h) - f(x - h)}{2h}$$

1. The central difference formula shown can be used.

$$f'(3) = \frac{f(3 + 1) - f(3 - 1)}{2(1)}$$

$$= \frac{f(4) - f(2)}{2}$$

2. Since we are interested in the third year ($x = 3$), we may use an adjacent value ($h = 1$ year away) to find the rate of change.

$$= \frac{18,700 - 16,000}{2}$$

3. Substitute the profits for the 2nd and 4th years and calculate.

Profits were increasing at a rate of $1350 per year in the third year.

4. The rate of increase of profits is called *marginal profit,* and is important to businesses.

▶ Exercises

For the data in Example 2, estimate the rate of change for
1. the fifth year
2. the eighth year
3. the ninth year
4. What was the largest rate of increase and in which year?
5. For which years was the central difference formula inappropriate?
6. If $f(x) = 3x - 2$, find $f'(x)$.

Math _and_ Scripture

Decay Limits

In Math and Scripture for Chapter 3, an exponential function for the decay of life span was discussed.

1. Give the decay function in standard form.

You will use this function to learn about the problem concerning when Job lived and the limits of life span decay.

Job: Pre-Flood or Post-Flood? Can exponential functions help Bible scholars?

2. How many children did Job have at the start of the narrative (Job 1:2)?

3. Estimate Job's minimum life span from Job 1:2, 13.

4. Estimate Job's minimum life span from Job 42:16-17.

5. How does Job 42:16-17 show that Job probably lived after the flood?

6. Estimate the generation that Job lived in, using your decay function. Which patriarch would have been his contemporary?

Life span Decay Limits

7. In Math and Scripture for Chapter 3, you identified the generation for David. What was it?

8. According to Matthew 1, during what generation would Jesus have lived?

9. Use the chronology and the elapsed generations from David to Jesus (Matt. 1) to estimate the average length of a generation.

10. Estimate your own generation number.

Use the life span decay function to estimate the following life spans in years and months.

11. David
12. Solomon
13. Jesus
14. You
15. What is the limit of the decay function as the generation increases?
16. Give a mathematical reason why the estimates above are so ridiculous.

MAXIMIZING

Give a Bible verse to prove that God stopped the decay of life span around the time of Moses at 70 to 80 years. This is conclusive proof that the function does not apply beyond the time of Moses.

Finally, consider the theme verse. Verse 2 mentions human life span, which we have been studying. However, verse 1 is even more important to the topics of this chapter, which has used the symbols $\forall$ and $\exists$. When both ideas occur in the same sentence, the order of the symbols is important. Both halves of verse 1 require both symbols.

Use H = thing, S = season, T = time, and P = purpose to symbolize each of the following.

17. First half of Ecc. 3:1
18. Second half of Ecc. 3:1

Vital Sines

TO EVERY THING there is a season, and a time to every purpose under the heaven: a time to be born, and a time to die. ✑

ECCLESIASTES 3:1-2A

Chapter 11 Review

Find the limits of the following sequences.

1. $\displaystyle\lim_{n\to\infty} 3 + \frac{4}{n}$

2. $\displaystyle\lim_{n\to\infty} \frac{6n^3 - 4n^2 + 3n - 2}{5n^4 - 1000n^3 + 500n}$

Find the sum of each series or state that it diverges.

3. $\displaystyle\sum_{n=1}^{\infty} 10\left(\frac{4}{5}\right)^n$

4. $\displaystyle\sum_{n=1}^{\infty} \frac{2n - 1}{3n + 4}$

5. $\displaystyle\sum_{n=1}^{\infty} \left(\frac{1}{\sqrt{n}} - \frac{1}{\sqrt{n + 2}}\right)$

6. $\displaystyle\sum_{n=1}^{\infty} \frac{1}{n}$

7. If $\displaystyle\sum_{n=1}^{\infty} A_n = 5$ and $\displaystyle\sum_{n=1}^{\infty} B_n = 6$, find $\displaystyle\sum_{n=1}^{\infty} 2A_n + B_n$.

8. If $\displaystyle\lim_{x\to\infty} A_n = 7$ and $\displaystyle\lim_{x\to\infty} B_n = 4$, find $\displaystyle\lim_{x\to\infty} \frac{A_n{}^2 - 3B_n}{A_nB_n + 2}$

Find the following limits.

9. $\displaystyle\lim_{x\to3} 2x + 1$

10. $\displaystyle\lim_{x\to8} 9$

11. $\displaystyle\lim_{x\to-1} x^3 - 3x^2 + 4x - 1$

12. $\displaystyle\lim_{x\to0} \sin x$

13. $\displaystyle\lim_{x\to0^-} \frac{1}{x^2}$

14. $\displaystyle\lim_{x\to0^-} \frac{1}{x}$

15. $\displaystyle\lim_{x\to0} \frac{5x^2 - 8}{4x^2 - 3x + 1}$

16. $\displaystyle\lim_{x\to7^-} [x]$

17. $\displaystyle\lim_{x\to3} \frac{x^2 - 2x - 3}{4x^2 - 12x}$

18. $\displaystyle\lim_{h\to0} \frac{(4 + h)^2 - 4^2}{h}$

19. $\displaystyle\lim_{a\to0} \frac{\sqrt{a + 4} - 2}{a}$

20. $\displaystyle\lim_{x\to0^+} \sqrt{x + 4}$

Find $\lim\limits_{x \to 2} f(x)$ from each graph.

21.

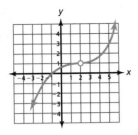

23.

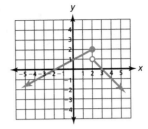

22.

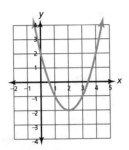

For each function, tell whether it satisfies each requirement for a continuous function at $x = 0$.

24.

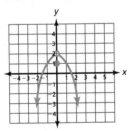

26.

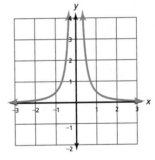

25.

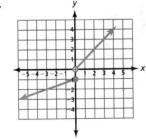

27. The term "counterintuitive" describes things that seem to defy our "common sense." What did you learn about the Koch curve that is counterintuitive?

28. Explain the mathematical significance of Ecc. 3:1-2a.

12 Differential Calculus

Some people get into an aircraft, go up over two miles, and then step out. For a moment they hover, but then gravity takes over and they begin to plummet. Some like to jump in formations, while others like to race. In "vertical speed racing," jumpers try to clock the fastest times in descending a vertical mile, such as from 11,280 feet down to 6000 feet. Some have reached speeds of over 285 miles per hour!

The data from a non-competitive jump on July 11, 1999, appears below. The jumper reached an average speed of 117 mph and a maximum speed of 177 mph. The jumper exited the plane at 10,300 feet and fell over 700 feet before the instruments began recording the time, altitudes, and rates. The parachute opened at 2000 feet.

Time (seconds)	Altitude (feet)	Rate (mph)	Time (seconds)	Altitude (feet)	Rate (mph)	Time (seconds)	Altitude (feet)	Rate (mph)
0	9539	54	17	6758	123	34	3686	100
1	9539	59	18	6554	115	35	3559	104
2	9379	65	19	6419	127	36	3240	82
3	9222	70	20	6215	116	37	3110	86
4	9017	76	21	6011	128	38	2856	104
5	8869	91	22	5873	122	39	2856	112
6	8724	107	23	5738	111	40	2615	133
7	8505	118	24	5534	114	41	2432	122
8	8286	120	25	5399	116	42	2311	107
9	8138	113	26	5261	109	43	2249	88
10	7993	121	27	4991	116	44	2128	97
11	7700	134	28	4853	117	45	2066	76
12	7700	117	29	4389	157	46	2007	59
13	7407	124	30	4389	139	47	2007	43
14	7333	114	31	3878	177	48	1945	41
15	7114	117	32	3751	171	49	1945	25
16	6969	98	33	3686	164			

After this chapter you should be able to

1. use the definition to find derivatives.

2. identify differentiable functions by their graphs.

3. apply theorems to find derivatives.

4. apply derivatives to find velocity and acceleration.

12.1 Definition of Derivative

Pilots who miscalculate their plane's rate of ascent can end up like this plane on Clinch Mountain in Virginia.

One of the classical problems in mathematics was to find the tangent line to a given curve. The solution to the "tangent problem" culminated in the concept of the *derivative*. The derivative is the first of the two major concepts of calculus (the integral is the other).

In the adjacent figure, the curve represents $f(x) = \frac{1}{4}x^2$. The points are $P\left(5, \frac{25}{4}\right)$, $R(4, 4)$, $S\left(3, \frac{9}{4}\right)$, $T(2, 1)$, and $Q\left(1, \frac{1}{4}\right)$. If you draw secant $\overleftrightarrow{PQ}$, its slope is

$$m = \frac{\Delta y}{\Delta x} = \frac{\frac{25}{4} - \frac{1}{4}}{5 - 1} = \frac{6}{4} = \frac{3}{2}.$$

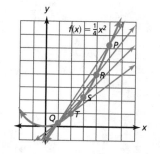

For $\overleftrightarrow{RQ}$, the slope is

$$m = \frac{\Delta y}{\Delta x} = \frac{4 - \frac{1}{4}}{4 - 1} = \frac{\frac{15}{4}}{3} = \frac{5}{4}.$$

Continuing to keep Q fixed and choosing points closer and closer to Q, you will find that the slope of $\overleftrightarrow{SQ}$ is 1, that of $\overleftrightarrow{TQ}$ is $\frac{3}{4}$, and so on. Listing these slopes in order, $\frac{3}{2}, \frac{5}{4}, 1, \frac{3}{4}, \ldots$, notice that the slope gets smaller and smaller. Does it approach some number? Does it continue to decrease? It is obvious from the graph that the tangent line has a positive slope; therefore, the slope does *not* keep decreasing but stops at a point—a limit.

Let $Q(x, f(x))$ represent a point on the graph, and choose another point $Q'(x + h, f(x + h))$, where h represents the difference of the x-values. The slope of $\overline{QQ'}$ is

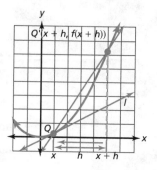

$$m = \frac{\Delta y}{\Delta x} = \frac{f(x + h) - f(x)}{(x + h) - x} = \frac{f(x + h) - f(x)}{h}.$$

The slope of the tangent line (*l*) is then the limit of *m* as *Q'* gets closer and closer to *Q*; that is, as *x* + *h* decreases approaching *x*. This is expressed in terms of *h* approaching 0.

$$m = \lim_{h \to 0} \frac{f(x + h) - f(x)}{h}$$

No matter what curve you are dealing with, the slope of the tangent line at any given point on a curve is obtained in this way. This limit, a real number, is the derivative. The word *derivative* refers to both the slope of the tangent line at a point and to the slope function.

Definitions

Derivative The slope of the line tangent to the function *f* for a given value of *x*, in symbols: $\lim_{h \to 0} \frac{f(x + h) - f(x)}{h}$, if the limit exists.

Derivative The function that represents the derivative for each value of *x*. The derivative function is denoted $f'(x)$ or $\frac{dy}{dx}$:

$$f'(x) = \frac{dy}{dx} = \lim_{h \to 0} \frac{f(x + h) - f(x)}{h}.$$

Hence, $f'(a)$ expresses the slope of the tangent line at *x* = *a*.

Just as the $\triangle$ in $\frac{\triangle y}{\triangle x}$ corresponds to the English letter *d* and stands for *difference* (change in *x* or *y*), so the *d* in $\frac{dy}{dx}$ stands for *differential,* that is the limit of the difference. You know that $\frac{\triangle y}{\triangle x}$ is the ratio of differences. In contrast, although $\frac{dy}{dx}$ sometimes behaves as a fraction, it is not a ratio but rather the limit of a ratio. The derivative may be denoted $f'(x)$, y', $\frac{dy}{dx}$, $\frac{d}{dx}f(x)$, or $\frac{d}{dx}y$.

EXAMPLE 1 Find $f'(x)$ if $f(x) = 3x + 5$.

Answer

$f'(x) = \lim_{h \to 0} \dfrac{f(x + h) - f(x)}{h}$	1. State the definition.
$= \lim_{h \to 0} \dfrac{[3(x + h) + 5] - (3x + 5)}{h}$	2. Substitute for $f(x + h)$ and $f(x)$, then simplify. You can divide by *h* since $h \neq 0$, but is only close to it.
$= \lim_{h \to 0} \dfrac{3x + 3h + 5 - 3x - 5}{h}$	
$= \lim_{h \to 0} \dfrac{3h}{h}$	
$= \lim_{h \to 0} 3$	
$= 3$	3. Find the limit.

EXAMPLE 2   Find $f'(x)$ if $f(x) = \frac{1}{4}x^2$.

Answer

$f'(x) = \lim\limits_{h \to 0} \dfrac{f(x + h) - f(x)}{h}$	1. State the definition.
$= \lim\limits_{h \to 0} \dfrac{\frac{1}{4}(x + h)^2 - \frac{1}{4}x^2}{h}$	2. Substitute for $f(x + h)$ and $f(x)$.
$= \lim\limits_{h \to 0} \dfrac{\frac{1}{4}(x^2 + 2xh + h^2) - \frac{1}{4}x^2}{h}$	3. Simplify the rational expression.
$= \lim\limits_{h \to 0} \dfrac{1}{4} \cdot \dfrac{x^2 + 2xh + h^2 - x^2}{h}$	
$= \lim\limits_{h \to 0} \dfrac{2xh + h^2}{4h}$	
$= \lim\limits_{h \to 0} \dfrac{h(2x + h)}{4h}$	
$= \lim\limits_{h \to 0} \dfrac{1}{4}(2x + h)$	
$= \dfrac{1}{4} \lim\limits_{h \to 0} (2x + h)$	4. Apply the scalar limit theorem 11.10 and substitute for h.
$= \dfrac{1}{4}(2x)$	
$= \dfrac{1}{2}x$	

The slope of the function $f(x) = \frac{1}{4}x^2$ is $\frac{1}{2}x$. In other words, the slope of the tangent line is a variable quantity, but at $x = 1$, it is $\frac{1}{2}(1) = \frac{1}{2}$. You can look back to the graph at the beginning of this section and verify this. Since $f'(x) = \frac{1}{2}x$, it is easily seen algebraically as well as graphically that the slope of the tangent line increases as x increases.

EXAMPLE 3   Find $f'(x)$ if $f(x) = x^{\frac{1}{2}}$, for $x \in [0, +\infty)$.

Answer

$f'(x) = \lim\limits_{h \to 0} \dfrac{f(x + h) - f(x)}{h}$	1. State the definition of the derivative and substitute into it. Recall that $x^{\frac{1}{2}} = \sqrt{x}$.
$= \lim\limits_{h \to 0} \dfrac{\sqrt{x + h} - \sqrt{x}}{h}$	
$= \lim\limits_{h \to 0} \dfrac{(\sqrt{x + h} - \sqrt{x})(\sqrt{x + h} + \sqrt{x})}{h(\sqrt{x + h} + \sqrt{x})}$	2. Rationalize the numerator and simplify to eliminate the h that causes the zero denominator.
$= \lim\limits_{h \to 0} \dfrac{x + h - x}{h(\sqrt{x + h} + \sqrt{x})}$	

Continued ▶

$$= \lim_{h \to 0} \frac{h}{h(\sqrt{x + h} + \sqrt{x})}$$

$$= \lim_{h \to 0} \frac{1}{\sqrt{x + h} + \sqrt{x}}$$

$$= \frac{1}{2\sqrt{x}}$$

$$= \frac{1}{2} x^{\frac{-1}{2}}$$

3. Find the limit by substitution. The answer can also be expressed using rational exponents.

▶ A. Exercises

Find the derivative of each function.

1. $f(x) = 2x$
2. $f(x) = x$
3. $f(x) = 2x + 5$
4. $f(x) = x^2$
5. $f(x) = 2x - 60$
6. $f(x) = 3x^2$
7. $f(x) = x^2 + 2x - 4$
8. $f(x) = 7$
9. $f(x) = 3$

▶ B. Exercises

Find the derivative of each function.

10. $f(x) = 2\sqrt{x}$
11. $f(x) = x^2 - x - 1$
12. $f(x) = x^3$
13. Compare the derivatives of $2x$, $2x + 5$, and $2x - 60$ (exercises 1, 3, 5). What do you find?
14. Compare the derivatives of x, x^2, and x^3 (exercises 2, 4, 12). Can you guess what $\frac{d}{dx} x^4$ may be?
15. Compare the derivatives of 7 and 3 (exercises 8 and 9). What do you find?
16. Find the derivative of the general constant function $f(x) = c$.
17. Find the derivative of the general linear function $f(x) = mx + b$.
18. Find the deriviative of the power function $f(x) = x^n$.
19. Find the derivative of the general quadratic function $f(x) = ax^2 + bx + c$.
20. Let $f(x) = x^2$ and $g(x) = 3x$. Find $\frac{d}{dx}[f(x) + g(x)]$.
21. Find $f'(x)$ and $g'(x)$ in exercise 20. Add $f'(x)$ and $g'(x)$. Is that equal to $\frac{d}{dx}[f(x) + g(x)]$?

▶ C. Exercises

22. What is the derivative of a direct variation function?
23. What is the derivative of an inverse variation function?

⌁ Dominion Modeling

24. Make a scatterplot of altitude as a function of time. Explain this graph in terms of skydiving.
25. Make a linear model of the altitude data. Give the model and graph it over the scatterplot. Find r^2 and *SSE*, plot the residuals, and use them to evaluate the model.
26. Make a quadratic model of the altitude data. Give the model and graph it over the scatterplot. Find r^2 and *SSE*, plot the residuals, and use them to evaluate the model, especially in comparison to the linear model.

■ Cumulative Review

Given: $z_1 = 3 - 5i$ and $z_2 = -4 + 7i$

27. Find z_1z_2 and $\frac{z_1}{z_2}$.
28. Graph $z_1 + z_2$ in the complex plane.
29. If matrix A is 3×3, with $|A| = 7$, find $|A|$ if
    a. one row is multiplied by 5.
    b. all rows are multiplied by 5.
    c. two rows are interchanged.
    d. a multiple of one row is added to another row.

Find the sums.

30. $\displaystyle\sum_{i=1}^{10} 8\left(\frac{1}{3}\right)^i$

31. $\displaystyle\sum_{i=1}^{\infty} 8\left(\frac{1}{3}\right)^i$

12.2 Derivatives and Graphs

Remember that a derivative represents the slope of a tangent line. The process of finding a derivative is called *differentiation,* so functions that have derivatives are *differentiable.*

Albert Einstein (1879-1955), shown at the laying of the cornerstone for Fuld Hall at the Institute for Advanced Studies, used derivatives often in his research.

Definition

Differentiable:
1. $f(x)$ is differentiable at $x = a$ if $f'(a)$ exists.
2. $f(x)$ is differentiable on an interval (a, b) if it is differentiable at every point in (a, b).
3. A function having a derivative at every point of its domain (or on a specified domain such as an open interval) is a differentiable function.

Since a derivative is a limit, no derivative exists if the two one-sided limits are not equal. This means that the tangent lines obtained by limits of secant lines from both sides must be the same. A function is not differentiable at $x = a$ unless a *unique* tangent line exists at $x = a$. None of the graphs in the following figure is differentiable. If there is a hole, gap, jump, or sharp point, the function cannot be differentiated at that point. Also, if the tangent line is vertical at a point, the function is not differentiable at that point.

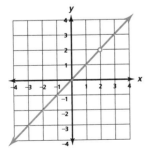
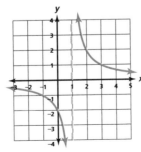
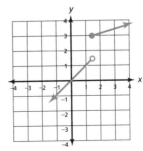
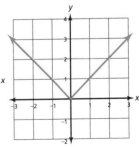

A function that is not continuous at $x = a$ is not differentiable there either. The following theorem states this conclusion, but notice that the converse is not true, as shown in the previous graph with a sharp point.

Theorem 12.1

If f is differentiable at $x = a$, then f is also continuous at $x = a$.

You can find slopes by using derivatives and use slopes to write equations of tangent lines.

EXAMPLE 1 Find the slope of the tangent line for $f(x) = -x^2$ at $x = 3$ and $x = -1$.

Answer

$f'(x) = \lim\limits_{h \to 0} \dfrac{f(x + h) - f(x)}{h}$ | 1. Find $f'(x)$ from the definition as in the previous section.

$= \lim\limits_{h \to 0} \dfrac{-(x + h)^2 - (-x^2)}{h}$

$= \lim\limits_{h \to 0} \dfrac{-(x^2 + 2xh + h^2) + x^2}{h}$

$= \lim\limits_{h \to 0} \dfrac{-2xh - h^2}{h}$

$= \lim\limits_{h \to 0} \dfrac{h(-2x - h)}{h}$

$= \lim\limits_{h \to 0} (-2x - h) = -2x$

$f'(3) = -2(3) = -6$ | 2. Since $f'(x)$ is the slope function, substitute to obtain the desired slopes.
$f'(-1) = -2(-1) = 2$

EXAMPLE 2 Find the equation of the tangent line for $f(x) = -x^2$ at $x = 3$.

Answer

$m = f'(3) = -6$ | 1. Use $f'(3)$ from Example 1.

$f(3) = -(3)^2 = -9$ | 2. Find $f(3)$ to get the coordinates of the point at $x = 3$.

$(3, -9)$ | 3. Write the coordinates of the point.

$y - y_1 = m(x - x_1)$ | 4. Substitute into the point-slope form to find the equation of the line.
$y - (-9) = -6(x - 3)$
$y + 9 = -6x + 18$
$y = -6x + 9$

► A. Exercises

For each graph, is the function differentiable? If not, identify any values of x for which it is not.

1.

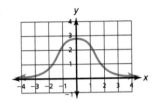

4.

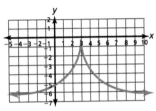

2.

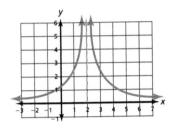

5.

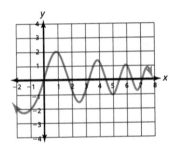

3.

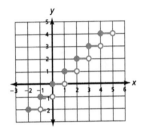

6.

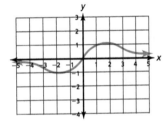

Find the slope of the tangent line for each function at the given values of x.

7. $f(x) = 3x^2$ at $x = 4$ and $x = -2$
8. $f(x) = \sqrt{x}$ at $x = 4$ and $x = 9$
9. $f(x) = x^2 + 3$ at $x = 1$ and $x = -3$
10. $f(x) = x^2 - 3x + 4$ at $x = 1$ and $x = 3$
11. $f(x) = 7.95x^2 + 3.4x - 21$ at $x = 15$ and $x = 23.5$
12. $f(x) = \frac{5}{9}x^3 + \sqrt{14}x^2 - \pi x + \frac{4}{15}$ at $x = -4.5$ and $x = \frac{1}{5}$

► B. Exercises

Is each function differentiable? Identify any point(s) where it is not and tell why. (Graphing may help.)

13. $y = |x|$
14. $y = 5x^2 + 6$
15. $y = 5$

16. $y = |x^2 - 2|$
17. $y = \sin x$
18. $y = \tan x$

Tell whether the function is differentiable. Give the intervals of differentiability.

19. $y = \sqrt{x}$
20. $y = \log x$

Give the equation of the tangent line at $x = 1$ for each function below.

21. $f(x) = 3x^2$
22. $f(x) = \sqrt{x}$
23. $f(x) = x^3$

Graph the function and its tangent line at the given value. Give the equation of the tangent line at that point. Use a graphing calculator.

24. $g(x) = 0.25x^2$; -3
25. $f(x) = (x + 1)^2 - 1$; 4

► C. Exercises

26. Find the derivative of the absolute value function.
27. Find the derivative of the greatest integer function.

Dominion Modeling

28. Make a cubic model of the altitude data. Give the model and graph it with the scatterplot. Find r^2 and *SSE*, plot the residuals, and use them to evaluate the model, especially in comparison to the linear and quadratic models.

29. Make a quartic model of the altitude data. Give the model and graph it with the scatterplot. Find r^2 and *SSE*, plot the residuals, and use them to evaluate the model, especially comparing it to the earlier models.

30. In plotting the residuals for the quartic model, you should notice that the residuals were more tightly clustered about the *x*-axis in the first half, but more widely scattered in the second half. What does this say about the model?

Let $z = 3 + 5i$.

31. Change z to polar form.

32. Find z^5.

33. Find $\sqrt[3]{z}$.

A class of 10 got the following scores on their midterm and final exams.

Student	Joe	Wu	Ann	Al	Pat	Ashley	Shawn	Terry	Brook	Jeff
Midterm	88	92	77	69	82	91	85	67	79	94
Final	82	95	81	77	88	90	81	74	83	87

34. Find the correlation between the two tests.

35. Find the coefficient of determination.

12.3 Properties of Derivatives

In 1642, the year in which Galileo died, a boy was born on Christmas Day in England. His father, a farmer, named him Isaac—Isaac Newton. Little did the world know then that this boy would be one of the greatest mathematicians and physicists of all time. He is responsible for many scientific laws, but it was not until Halley (discoverer of Halley's comet) persuaded him to publish his findings that Newton produced *Principia,* one of the most profound achievements in the field of science.

Newton, along with Leibniz, is credited for many of the theorems concerning derivatives. These theorems provide a faster and easier way of finding derivatives than using the definition.

Theorem 12.2: Derivative of a Constant
For any constant function $f(x) = c$, $f'(x) = 0$.

Proof

$$f'(x) = \lim_{h \to 0} \frac{f(x+h) - f(x)}{h}$$

$$= \lim_{h \to 0} \frac{c - c}{h}$$

$$= \lim_{h \to 0} \frac{0}{h}$$

$$= \lim_{h \to 0} 0$$

$$= 0$$

Theorem 12.3: Derivative of a Linear Function

For the linear function $f(x) = mx + b$, $f'(x) = m$.

Proof

$$f'(x) = \lim_{h \to 0} \frac{f(x+h) - f(x)}{h}$$

$$= \lim_{h \to 0} \frac{[m(x+h) + b] - (mx + b)}{h}$$

$$= \lim_{h \to 0} \frac{mx + mh + b - mx - b}{h}$$

$$= \lim_{h \to 0} \frac{mh}{h}$$

$$= \lim_{h \to 0} m$$

$$= m$$

The two previous theorems reiterate that any constant or linear function has the same slope everywhere. The following theorem is extremely useful in finding derivatives.

Theorem 12.4: Power Rule

If $f(x) = x^n$, then $f'(x) = nx^{n-1}$.

Proof

We will prove the case for $n \in \mathbb{N}$. The theorem also holds when n is a negative, rational, or even an irrational number, but the proofs of these will not be required in this book.

$$f'(x) = \lim_{h \to 0} \frac{f(x + h) - f(x)}{h}$$

$$= \lim_{h \to 0} \frac{(x + h)^n - x^n}{h}$$

$$= \lim_{h \to 0} \frac{\left(x^n + nx^{n-1}h + \frac{n(n-1)}{2}x^{n-2}h^2 + \cdots + h^n\right) - x^n}{h}$$

(by the binomial theorem since $n \in \mathbb{N}$)

$$= \lim_{h \to 0} \frac{h\left(nx^{n-1} + \frac{n(n-1)}{2}x^{n-2}h + \cdots + h^{n-1}\right)}{h}$$

$$= \lim_{h \to 0} \left[nx^{n-1} + \frac{n(n-1)}{2}x^{n-2}h + \cdots + h^{n-1}\right]$$

$$= nx^{n-1} + 0 + \cdots + 0 \quad \text{(Since all } h \text{ approaches 0.)}$$

$$= nx^{n-1}$$

According to this theorem, whenever $f(x) = x^n$, you can find the derivative by using the exponent as the coefficient of x, and then subtracting 1 from the exponent to obtain the new exponent.

EXAMPLE 1   Find $f'(x)$ if $f(x) = x^{21}$

Answer

$f(x) = x^{21}$	1. Recognize the power function, $f(x) = x^n$, with $n = 21$.
$f'(x) = 21x^{20}$	2. Apply the power rule: $f'(x) = nx^{n-1}$

Two additional useful theorems follow.

Theorem 12.5: Derivative of Scalar Times a Function
If $f(x) = cg(x)$, where g is differentiable, then $f'(x) = cg'(x)$.

Proof

Since $g(x)$ is differentiable, $g'(x) = \lim_{h \to 0} \frac{g(x + h) - g(x)}{h}$ exists.

Now, find $f'(x)$.

$$f'(x) = \lim_{h \to 0} \frac{f(x + h) - f(x)}{h}$$

$$= \lim_{h \to 0} \frac{cg(x + h) - cg(x)}{h}$$

Continued ▶

$$= \lim_{h \to 0} \frac{c[g(x + h) - g(x)]}{h} \text{ by factoring } c$$

$$= c \lim_{h \to 0} \frac{g(x + h) - g(x)}{h} \text{ by the limit rule for scalars}$$

$$= cg'(x) \text{ by substitution}$$

EXAMPLE 2   Find $f'(x)$ if $f(x) = 3x^4$.

Answer $f(x) = 3x^4$

Let $g(x) = x^4$

$g'(x) = 4x^3$	1. Power rule
$f(x) = 3g(x)$	2. Substitute
$f'(x) = 3g'(x)$ $= 3\left(4x^3\right)$ $= 12x^3$	3. Derivative of a scalar times a function (theorem 12.5)

We will now prove that the derivative of a sum is the sum of the derivatives.

Theorem 12.6: Derivative of a Sum

If $f(x) = u(x) + v(x)$ when u and v are differentiable, then
$f'(x) = u'(x) + v'(x)$.

Proof

Since $u(x)$ and $v(x)$ are differentiable, the following limits exist:

$$u'(x) = \lim_{h \to 0} \frac{u(x + h) - u(x)}{h} \text{ and } v'(x) = \lim_{h \to 0} \frac{v(x + h) - v(x)}{h}$$

Now, find $f'(x)$.

$$f(x) = u(x) + v(x)$$

$$f'(x) = \lim_{h \to 0} \frac{[u(x + h) + v(x + h)] - [u(x) + v(x)]}{h}$$

$$= \lim_{h \to 0} \frac{u(x + h) - u(x) + v(x + h) - v(x)}{h} \text{ by regrouping}$$

$$= \lim_{h \to 0} \left[\frac{u(x + h) - u(x)}{h} + \frac{v(x + h) - v(x)}{h} \right] \text{ by separating fractions}$$

$$= \lim_{h \to 0} \frac{u(x + h) - u(x)}{h} + \lim_{h \to 0} \frac{v(x + h) - v(x)}{h} \text{ by the limit rule for sums}$$

$$= u'(x) + v'(x) \text{ by substitution}$$

In Example 2, you saw how to find $f'(x)$ step by step to see how each theorem applies. However, once you understand the steps, you can find $f'(x)$ mentally. For each term, multiply the numerical coefficient by the exponent and reduce the power by 1. Examples 3-5 show this shortcut, which combines several steps. You should be able to write the final answer without showing any work.

EXAMPLE 3   Find $f'(x)$ if $f(x) = 2x^8 + 4x^6$.

Answer $f'(x) = \frac{d}{dx}\left(2x^8 + 4x^6\right)$

$\qquad = \frac{d}{dx}\left(2x^8\right) + \frac{d}{dx}\left(4x^6\right)$ 1. Derivative of sum

$\qquad = 2\left(8x^7\right) + 4\left(6x^5\right)$ 2. Power rule with scalar exponents

$\qquad = 16x^7 + 24x^5$

EXAMPLE 4   Differentiate $f(x) = 2x^7 - x^3$.

Answer

$f'(x) = 2 \cdot 7x^{7-1} - 3x^{3-1}$ 1. Power rule

$\qquad = 14x^6 - 3x^2$ 2. Simplify.

EXAMPLE 5   Find the derivative of $f(x) = 3x^3 - 6x^2 + x - 5$.

Answer

$f'(x) = \frac{d}{dx}(3x^3) - \frac{d}{dx}(6x^2) + \frac{d}{dx}x - \frac{d}{dx}5$ 1. Derivative of sum

$\qquad = 9x^2 - 12x + 1 - 0$ 2. Theorems 12.4, 12.5, 12.3,

$\qquad = 9x^2 - 12x + 1$ 12.2

Polynomial functions are easy to differentiate with these formulas. But the product and the quotient (rational function) of two polynomials is more difficult. The next theorem will add some effective tools to your differentiation techniques. Its proof is beyond the scope of this text.

Theorem 12.7: Product Rule
If $f(x) = u(x) \cdot v(x)$, where u and v are differentiable, then
$f'(x) = u(x) \cdot v'(x) + u'(x) \cdot v(x)$.

The product rule states that the derivative of a product is the first term times the derivative of the second, plus the derivative of the first term times the second.

EXAMPLE 6 Find the derivative of $f(x) = (2x^2 - 1)(x^4)$.

Answer

$f'(x) = u(x) \cdot v'(x) + u'(x) \cdot v(x)$

$\quad = (2x^2 - 1)(4x^3) + (4x)(x^4)$

1. Use the product rule. Let $u(x) = 2x^2 - 1$ and $v(x) = x^4$.

- -

$\quad = 8x^5 - 4x^3 + 4x^5$

$\quad = 12x^5 - 4x^3$

2. Simplify the answer.

The derivative in Example 6 could also have been calculated without using the product rule. Using the distributive property allows $f(x)$ to be written as a polynomial function. It then becomes a problem similar to Example 5. Though this may seem simpler in this case, it is not always possible or productive to multiply first and then take the derivative. The value of the product rule will be seen more clearly when you learn to do derivatives such as $f(x) = x^3 \cos x$ or $g(x) = e^x \sqrt{x - 5}$.

▶ A. Exercises

Find the derivatives, justifying each step.

1. $f(x) = 5x^3$
2. $g(x) = x^7 - x^4$
3. $h(x) = 2x^3 + 9x^2$
4. $k(x) = x + 7$
5. $p(x) = x^5 - 2x^4 - x^3 + 3x^2 - 2x + 4$

Find the derivatives. Show work only when necessary.

6. $f(x) = 10$
7. $f(x) = x^{15}$
8. $f(x) = 2x^{12}$
9. $f(x) = 11x^4$
10. $g(x) = x^5 + x^4 + x^3 + x^2 + x + 1$

▶ B. Exercises

Find the derivatives. Show work only when necessary.

11. $g(x) = 6x^4 + 5x^2 + 7$
12. $g(x) = 7x^3 - 2x^2 + 5x - 6$
13. $g(x) = x^4 - 3x^3 + 9$

14. $f(x) = e^5$

15. $g(x) = 10x^{23} - 4x^{17} - 3x^{11} + 2x^5 - x$

16. $f(x) = x^{\frac{1}{3}}$

17. $f(x) = \sqrt{x}$

18. $f(x) = \sqrt[5]{x^{17}}$

Use the product rule to find the derivatives.

19. $h(x) = (x^2 - 5)(2x^6)$

20. $h(x) = (3x^2 + x)\sqrt{x}$

21. $h(x) = 12x(x^3 - 5x)$

22. $h(x) = (x^2 - 9)(3x - 5)$

23. $h(x) = (x^2 + 4x + 2)(x^2 - x - 1)$

▶ C. Exercises

Find the derivative of each of the following.

24. $f(x) = \dfrac{2x + 5}{x}$

25. $g(x) = \dfrac{x^3 - 7x + 2}{x^5}$

◪ Dominion Modeling

26. What is the derivative of the linear model? What is the significance of this number in relation to the line?

27. When is the derivative of the quadratic model equal to -150? From the appropriate units, at what part of the skydiver's descent did this happen?

28. When is the derivative of the quadratic model equal to 150? From the appropriate units, at what part of the skydiver's descent did this happen?

■ Cumulative Review

29. When does matrix A not have an inverse?

Given vectors $\mathbf{u} = \langle 7, 2 \rangle$ and $\mathbf{v} = \langle 1, 9 \rangle$, find the following.

30. $\mathbf{u} \cdot \mathbf{v}$

31. The angle between $\mathbf{u}$ and $\mathbf{v}$

Find the limits.

32. $\displaystyle\lim_{n \to \infty} \dfrac{6n^3 - 5n^2 + 7n - 3}{2n^3 + n^2 - 4n + 3}$

33. $\displaystyle\lim_{x \to -1} \dfrac{x^3 + 1}{x^3 + 6x^2 - 11x + 6}$

12.4 Chain Rule

Recall that composition involves substituting one function into another function. For instance, if

$$u(x) = x^{25} \text{ and } v(x) = x^2 - 9$$
$$\text{then } f(x) = (u \circ v)(x) = u(v(x)) = (x^2 - 9)^{25}.$$

How could you find $f'(x)$? One way would be to use the FOIL method to expand $(x^2 - 9)^{25}$ and then find the derivative of the resulting polynomial. This however, would be a long tedious process. Fortunately, there is an alternative—the chain rule for finding derivatives of compositions.

In the composition $u(v(x))$, $v(x) = x^2 - 9$ is the inside function and the power function x^{25} is the outside function. The chain rule tells you to take the derivative of the outside function (leaving the inside function alone) and multiply by the derivative of the inside function. Since $u'(x) = 25x^{24}$, leaving the inside function intact gives $25(x^2 - 9)^{24}$. Then this is multiplied by the derivative of $v(x)$ which is $2x$. Therefore, $f'(x) = 25(x^2 - 9)^{24}(2x) = 50x(x^2 - 9)^{24}$.

Here is the statement of the chain rule.

Theorem 12.8: Chain Rule
If $f(x) = (u \circ v)(x) = u(v(x))$, where u and v are differentiable, then $f'(x) = u'(v(x)) \cdot v'(x)$.

Sketch of Proof

Since $u'(v(x))$ can be written as $\frac{du}{dv}$ and $v'(x)$ as $\frac{dv}{dx}$, you can see why

$$f'(x) = \frac{du}{dx} = \frac{du}{dv} \cdot \frac{dv}{dx}.$$

Be careful when determining the functions u and v. Remember that u is the "outer" process.

EXAMPLE 1   Find the derivative of $f(x) = (2x^2 - x)^3$.

Answer

Let $v = 2x^2 - x$ and let $u = x^3$ be the outer process (since cubing applies to the entire quantity). Thus, $f(x) = u(v(x))$.	1. Determine u and v.
$f'(x) = u'(v(x)) \cdot v'(x)$ $\quad = 3(v(x))^2 \cdot (4x - 1)$	2. Apply the chain rule. Determine $u'(v(x))$ and $v'(x)$.
$\quad = 3(2x^2 - x)^2 \cdot (4x - 1)$ $\quad = 3(4x^4 - 4x^3 + x^2)(4x - 1)$ $\quad = (4x^4 - 4x^3 + x^2)(12x - 3)$ $\quad = 48x^5 - 60x^4 + 24x^3 - 3x^2$	3. Substitute for $v(x)$ and simplify.

EXAMPLE 2   Find $\frac{dy}{dx}$ if $y = \sqrt[3]{x^2 + 7}$.

Answer

Since $y = (x^2 + 7)^{\frac{1}{3}}$, apply the chain rule, letting $v(x) = x^2 + 7$ and $u(x) = \sqrt[3]{x} = x^{\frac{1}{3}}$.	1. Determine the inner and outer functions.
$y = (x^2 + 7)^{\frac{1}{3}}$	
$y' = \frac{1}{3}(x^2 + 7)^{-\frac{2}{3}} v'(x)$	2. Find the derivative of the outer function times $v'(x)$.
$\quad = \frac{1}{3}(x^2 + 7)^{-\frac{2}{3}}(2x)$	3. Find $v'(x) = 2x$ (the derivative of the inner function).
$\quad = \frac{2x}{3\sqrt[3]{(x^2 + 7)^2}}$	4. Simplify.
$\quad = \frac{2x}{3\sqrt[3]{(x^2 + 7)^2}} \cdot \frac{\sqrt[3]{x^2 + 7}}{\sqrt[3]{x^2 + 7}}$ $\quad = \frac{2x\sqrt[3]{x^2 + 7}}{3x^2 + 21}$	5. Rationalize the denominator if desired.

The denominator in Example 2 is rationalized. Frequently this is not done. In future examples, the denominator will not be rationalized.

Another extremely important derivative is that of $f(x) = e^x$.

Theorem 12.9: Derivative of e^x

If $f(x) = e^x$, then $f'(x) = e^x$.

The number e is important because it is the only exponential function for which the values of the function are always equal to the rate of increase. The base e is therefore the natural base for exponential functions and logarithms.

EXAMPLE 3   Find $f'(x)$ for $f(x) = e^{x^3-4}$.

Answer

Since the exponent is a function of x rather than just x, the chain rule must be used. Let $v(x) = x^3 - 4$ and $u(x) = e^x$.

$f(x) = e^{x^3-4}$

$f'(x) = e^{x^3-4}[v'(x)]$	1. $u'(x) = u(x)$ by theorem 12.9.
$f'(x) = 3x^2 e^{x^3-4}$	2. $v'(x) = 3x^2$ by the power rule, theorem 12.4.

Using theorems 12.8 and 12.9, the following additional derivative formulas can be proved.

Theorem 12.10: Derivative of Exponential Functions
If $f(x) = a^x$, then $f'(x) = (\ln a)a^x$.

Proof

STATEMENTS	REASONS
1. $y = a^x = (e^{\ln a})^x = e^{x \ln a}$	1. Substituting $e^{\ln a}$ for a (these are equivalent since raising e to a power and taking a natural log are inverse operations)
2. $y' = (\ln a)e^{x \ln a}$	2. Chain rule (since the scalar $\ln a$ is the derivative of $x \ln a$)
3. $= (\ln a)a^x$	3. From step 1 ($e^{x \ln a} = a^x$)

Notice that for any exponential function, the derivative is a scalar multiple of the original function: $y' = cy$. That is, the rate of growth is directly proportional to the original function. The function e^x is the natural or basic exponential, because the constant of proportionality is $c = 1$: $y' = y$.

Be careful to classify each function before you differentiate so as not to confuse power functions with exponential functions.

> **EXAMPLE 4** Find the derivatives.
>
> $$f(x) = 2^3 \qquad g(x) = 2^x \qquad h(x) = x^3$$
>
> **Answer**
>
> | | |
> |---|---|
> | $f'(x) = 0$ | 1. No variables; $f(x)$ is a constant. |
> | $g'(x) = (\ln 2)2^x$ | 2. Variable exponent; $g(x)$ is (a general) exponential. |
> | $h'(x) = 3x^2$ | 3. Variable base; $h(x)$ is a power function. |

▶ A. Exercises

Find each derivative.

1. $y = (x^3 - 4)^{12}$
2. $y = (2x + 5)^{100}$
3. $f(x) = (x^2 + 3x - 7)^{21}$
4. $f(x) = (5x^7 - x^4 + 3x)^{17}$
5. $g(x) = 3(x^4 + 2x^2 + 5)^{10}$
6. $g(x) = 5(x - 8)^{50}$
7. $k(x) = x^5 - 8x + 4^x$
8. $k(x) = 7x^3 + 10^9 - 3e^x$
9. $f(x) = 4^{6x}$
10. $f(x) = (3 + e^x)^5$

▶ B. Exercises

Find the derivatives.

11. $h(x) = \sqrt{3x + 5}$
12. $h(x) = \sqrt[4]{(2x + 1)^7}$
13. $k(x) = 5x(x - 8)^{50}$
14. $k(x) = (3x - 1)^{10}(x^2 + 9)^8$
15. $g(x) = 5^{2x}$
16. $f(x) = x \cdot 7^x$
17. $g(x) = x^2 3^x$
18. $k(x) = e^{x^2}$
19. $y = \sqrt{1 + e^x}$

20. $y = \pi^{\sqrt{2}}$

21. $y = (2x + 1)^5$

22. $y = 5^{2x+1}$

23. $y = 5^5$

24. $y = 4^x - x^4 + 4^4$

25. $y = e^{\pi}$

26. Use a graphing calculator to verify that $f(x) = e^x$ and its derivative are the same function. Enter both in the graphing calculator and use the table option to examine the values of the functions at several x-values. They should be equal.

▶ C. Exercises

27. Using successively smaller values of h, find $\lim\limits_{h \to 0} \dfrac{e^h - 1}{h}$.

28. Use the definition of derivative to find the derivative of $f(x) = e^x$.

■ Cumulative Review

Given $A = \begin{bmatrix} 6 & 2 & -1 \\ 5 & 4 & 3 \end{bmatrix}$ $B = \begin{bmatrix} 1 & -1 \\ 2 & 5 \\ 3 & 7 \end{bmatrix}$

$C = \begin{bmatrix} 12 & -6 & -8 \\ 5 & 7 & 4 \end{bmatrix}$ $D = \begin{bmatrix} 2 & 1 & -2 & -5 \\ 5 & 0 & -3 & 4 \\ -7 & 6 & 7 & 11 \\ 8 & -2 & 6 & 2 \end{bmatrix}$

29. Find $2A + 3C$.

30. Find AB.

31. Find $|D|$.

32. What is the significance of a dot product equal to zero?

33. Find the derivative of $f(x) = x^3 - 5x + 4$.

If $g(x) = 1 - x^2$ and $(f \circ g)(x) = \dfrac{1 - x^2}{x^2}$, $x \neq 0$, then find $f(x)$, $f\left(\dfrac{1}{2}\right)$ and $f(2)$.

12.5 Quotient Rule

You are now in a position to prove the quotient rule for derivatives.

The University of Toronto, founded in 1827, has been a leading center for mathematical research in Canada.

Theorem 12.11: Quotient Rule

If $f(x) = \dfrac{u(x)}{v(x)}$, where u and v are differentiable and $v(x) \neq 0$, then

$$f'(x) = \frac{u'(x) \cdot v(x) - u(x) \cdot v'(x)}{[v(x)]^2}.$$

Proof

Rewrite $f(x) = \dfrac{u(x)}{v(x)}$ as a product and apply the product rule.

STATEMENTS	REASONS
1. $f'(x) = u(x) \cdot [v(x)]^{-1}$	**1.** Rewrite $f(x)$.
2. $f'(x) = u'(x)[v(x)]^{-1} + u(x)\dfrac{d}{dx}[v(x)]^{-1}$	**2.** Apply the product rule.
3. $f'(x) = u'(x)[v(x)]^{-1} + u(x) \cdot (-1)[v(x)]^{-2} \cdot v'(x)$	**3.** Apply the chain rule to find the last derivative.
4. $f'(x) = \dfrac{u'(x)}{v(x)} - \dfrac{u(x)v'(x)}{[v(x)]^2}$	**4.** Simplify.
5. $f'(x) = \dfrac{u'(x)v(x) - u(x)v'(x)}{[v(x)]^2}$	**5.** Get a common denominator.

EXAMPLE 1   Find the derivative of $f(x) = \dfrac{5x^3 - 2x^2 - 1}{3x}$.

Answer

$$f'(x) = \frac{u'(x) \cdot v(x) - u(x) \cdot v'(x)}{[v(x)]^2}$$ 1. Use the quotient rule.

$$= \frac{(15x^2 - 4x)(3x) - (5x^3 - 2x^2 - 1)(3)}{(3x)^2}$$

Continued ▶

$$= \frac{45x^3 - 12x^2 - (15x^3 - 6x^2 - 3)}{9x^2}$$

2. Simplify the answer.

$$= \frac{30x^3 - 6x^2 + 3}{9x^2}$$

$$= \frac{10x^3 - 2x^2 + 1}{3x^2}$$

The derivative of the sine is the basic derivative for trig functions. Based on this, along with the quotient rule and chain rule, you can find derivatives for all other trigonometric functions.

Theorem 12.12: Derivative of the Sine Function
If $f(x) = \sin x$, then $f'(x) = \cos x$.

EXAMPLE 2   Find $\frac{d}{dx} \cos x$.

Answer

Let $f(x) = \cos x$

$f(x) = \sin\left(\frac{\pi}{2} - x\right)$ 1. Write $\cos x$ in terms of $\sin x$, using the cofunction identity.

$f'(x) = \cos\left(\frac{\pi}{2} - x\right)(-1)$ 2. Apply theorem 12.12 and the chain rule.

$\quad = -\cos\left(\frac{\pi}{2} - x\right)$

$\quad = -\sin x$ 3. Use the cofunction identity again.

Thus $\frac{d}{dx} \cos x = -\sin x$

EXAMPLE 3   Find $\frac{dy}{dx}$ if $y = \cot x$.

Answer

$y = \cot x$

$y = \frac{\cos x}{\sin x}$ 1. Express the function in terms of sine and cosine.

$\frac{dy}{dx} = \frac{\frac{d}{dx}(\cos x) \sin x - \cos x \frac{d}{dx}(\sin x)}{\sin^2 x}$ 2. Apply theorem 12.11, the quotient rule.

Continued ▶

$$= \frac{-\sin x \cdot \sin x - \cos x \cdot \cos x}{\sin^2 x}$$

3. Substitute the derivatives of the cosine and sine functions and simplify.

$$= \frac{-(\sin^2 x + \cos^2 x)}{\sin^2 x}$$

$$= \frac{-1}{\sin^2 x}$$

4. Pythagorean identity

$$= -\csc^2 x$$

5. Reciprocal identity

EXAMPLE 4 Differentiate $f(x) = 5x^2(\sin x)$.

Answer

Let $u(x) = 5x^2$ and $v(x) = \sin x$.
Then $f(x) = u(x) \cdot v(x)$.

1. Define the factors as $u(x)$ and $v(x)$.

$f'(x) = u'(x) \cdot v(x) + u(x) \cdot v'(x)$
$\quad = 10x \sin x + 5x^2 \cos x$

2. Apply the product rule.

EXAMPLE 5 Differentiate $f(x) = \left(\dfrac{x}{x^2 - 1}\right)^2$.

Answer

Let $u(x) = x^2$ and $v(x) = \dfrac{x}{x^2 - 1}$.

1. Define $u(x)$ and $v(x)$ appropriately for the chain rule.

Then $f(x) = (u \circ v)(x) = u(v(x))$.

$f'(x) = u'(v(x)) \cdot v'(x)$

2. Apply the chain rule.

$$= 2\left(\frac{x}{x^2 - 1}\right) \cdot \frac{1(x^2 - 1) - x(2x)}{(x^2 - 1)^2}$$

3. Sometimes you must apply the quotient rule in the middle of the chain rule. Since $v(x)$ is a quotient, its derivative requires the quotient rule.

$$= \frac{2x[(x^2 - 1) - 2x^2]}{(x^2 - 1)^3}$$

4. Simplify.

$$= \frac{2x(-x^2 - 1)}{(x^2 - 1)^3}$$

$$= \frac{-2x^3 - 2x}{(x^2 - 1)^3}$$

▶ A. Exercises

Find the derivatives.

1. $f(x) = \dfrac{x^2 - 3}{x^2 + 5}$

2. $f(x) = \dfrac{3x}{5x - 6}$

3. $f(x) = \sin (x^2 - 8)$

4. $g(x) = \cos^2 x$

5. $y = \dfrac{x^2 - 5x + 1}{e^x}$

6. $k(x) = \dfrac{\cos x}{x^2 + 3}$

7. $y = \cos x \sin x$

8. $y = \tan x$

9. $y = \sec x$

10. $y = \csc x$

▶ B. Exercises

Find the derivatives.

11. $y = \dfrac{\sin 7x}{5^{2x}}$

12. $g(x) = \csc (e^x + x^e)$

13. $f(x) = e^{\cot x}$

14. $g(x) = \cos (5^{x^2 - 1})$

15. $h(x) = \dfrac{\tan^8 x}{7x^2 - 3x + 1}$

16. $y = \dfrac{e^x \sin x}{2^{\sec x}}$

17. $f(x) = \dfrac{x}{\sqrt{x^2 - 1}}$

18. $h(x) = 4^{\sin (3x^2 + 8)}$

19. $f(x) = \dfrac{\sin x}{\sqrt{x + \cos^2 x}}$

20. $g(x) = \left(\dfrac{\tan x}{5x}\right)^8$

21. Use the graphing calculator to verify if $f(x) = \sin x$, then $f'(x) = \cos x$. Graph the 3 functions $y_1 = f(x)$, $y_2 = f'(x)$ and $y_3 = \cos x$. The y_2 and y_3 graphs will be the same, so use different graph style icons.

▶ C. Exercises

22. Find $f'(x)$ if $f(x) = e^{\left[\frac{4 \tan x}{(x^2 - 1)^2}\right]}$.

23. Prove the power rule $\dfrac{d}{dx}x^n = nx^{n-1}$ is true if n is a negative integer. (*Hint:* Let k be a positive integer such that $n = -k$.)

Solve the following system
$$2x + 5y - 3z = 43$$
$$x - 3y + 12z = -60$$
$$x + 10y + 4z = 37$$

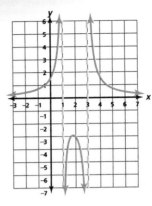

24. by Gaussian elimination.

25. using Cramer's rule.

Use the graph shown for the following exercises.

26. Give intervals for which the function shown is increasing and decreasing.

27. Find $\lim\limits_{x \to 4} f(x)$ and $\lim\limits_{x \to \infty} f(x)$.

28. For what positive value of a is $f'(a) = 0$.

12 Approximation Methods

Cubic Splines

In Chapter 5 you constructed linear splines by splicing linear functions that join each pair of data values. In Chapter 6 you constructed quadratic splines in a similar fashion, but you fitted a parabola to pairs of points so adjacent pieces would connect smoothly. A quadratic spline is differentiable everywhere. In Chapter 8 you learned that you need three points to determine a parabola, but for the quadratic spline only two points were used for each quadratic. The third point was sacrificed so the derivative could be made continuous.

The most valuable spline function is a cubic spline. While four points determine a cubic, we will again sacrifice points to obtain other goals. Thus, a cubic spline fits a cubic polynomial to each pair of points in such a way that the function, the derivative (quadratic), and even the second derivative (linear) are all continuous. This makes cubic splines very useful, and computer software will perform the lengthy computations quickly.

EXAMPLE The cubic spline for 6 data points has been calculated by a computer. The data points were (1, 1), (3, 4), (4, 7), (7, 15), (9, 24), and (10, 34). Evaluate the spline at $x = 6$ and show that the spline has a continuous derivative at $x = 4$.

$$S(x) = \begin{cases} 0.1321(x-1)^3 + 0.9717(x-1) + 1 & \text{if } 1 \le x \le 3 \\ -0.3491(x-3)^3 + 0.7925(x-3)^2 + 2.5566(x-3) + 4 & \text{if } 3 \le x \le 4 \\ 0.0374(x-4)^3 - 0.2548(x-4)^2 + 3.0943(x-4) + 7 & \text{if } 4 \le x \le 7 \\ 0.4401(x-7)^3 + 0.0819(x-7)^2 + 2.5757(x-7) + 15 & \text{if } 7 \le x \le 9 \\ -0.9076(x-9)^3 + 2.7227(x-9)^2 + 8.1849(x-9) + 24 & \text{if } 9 \le x \le 10 \end{cases}$$

Answer $S(6) = 0.0374(2)^3 - 0.2548(2)^2 + 3.0943(2) + 7 = 12.4686$

Next, find the derivatives of the piece function on either side of $x = 4$.

$S'_2(x) = -0.3491(3)(x-3)^2 + 0.7925(2)(x-3) + 2.5566$
$ = -1.0473(x-3)^2 + 1.585(x-3) + 2.5566$

$S'_3(x) = 0.0374(3)(x-4)^2 - 0.2548(2)(x-4) + 3.0943$
$ = 0.1122(x-4)^2 - 0.5096(x-4) + 3.0943$

Evaluate both derivatives at $x = 4$ to see if they agree.

$S'_2(4) = -1.0473(4-3)^2 + 1.585(4-3) + 2.5566 = 3.0943$

$S'_3(4) = 0.1122(4-4)^2 - 0.5096(4-4) + 3.0943 = 3.0943$

Since the spline consists of cubic polynomials that are continuous and have continuous derivatives, the only possible points of discontinuity are at the nodes. If the values agree from both sides, then they are continuous there as well.

Let's review all the approximations you have learned.

Approximation Goal	Method
Constants	Interpolation (trig tables, log tables, etc.) Iteration (for radicals) Series
Solutions of Equations	Irrational solutions Iteration
Functions	Spline (linear, quadratic, cubic) Interpolating polynomial Least squares (best fit line, exponential, other curve)
Derivatives	Central difference formula

▶ Exercises

1. Evaluate the cubic spline in the example at $x = 8$.
2. Determine whether the second derivative is continuous at the knot (7, 15).
3. What is the advantage of a cubic spline over a linear or quadratic spline?

Suppose a company has annual profit figures for 12 years. Suppose further that you calculated the cubic spline, the interpolating polynomial, and the best fit cubic polynomial using the method of least squares.

4. How many piece functions would the cubic spline involve? What degree would the interpolating polynomial be? Why would the spline usually be more useful than the interpolating polynomial?
5. How does a cubic spline differ from a cubic polynomial obtained by the method of least squares?

12.6 Motion Applications

Zeno, who said that a person could not go anywhere, also declared that a flying arrow is really at rest. He argued that the arrow is only in one place at each moment; consequently, according to Zeno, the flying arrow is not moving at any given time and hence is really at rest. Although this paradox of a fly-

This mountain pass in Quebec illustrates a saddle point. From the pass, the road descends to cities on both sides of the ridge; the slope of the tangent line along the road is negative. In contrast, climbers would ascend to summits in either direction along the ridge; the slope of the tangent line as they climb is positive.

ing arrow failed to explain the constant nature of motion, the Greek concept of "at each moment" became the cornerstone of instantaneous velocity, an application of derivatives.

When a car travels at a constant speed in a straight line, the distance traveled is directly proportional to time. The graph of such motion is shown in figure (a). The slope of this graph represents velocity. However, a ball falling from the top of a building does not travel at a constant speed. Due to the effect of gravity, it travels faster and faster as time increases. The graph of this type of motion is shown in figure (b). Because the velocity is changing constantly, the instantaneous velocity at time t_1 is represented by the slope of the line that is tangent to the curve at t_1. Simply stated, the instantaneous velocity is the derivative at t_1.

(a)
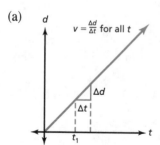

(b)
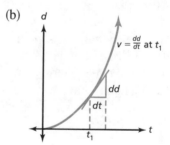

Instantaneous velocity If an object moves along a straight line and the distance traveled is $d = f(t)$, then the *instantaneous velocity* at time t_1 is

$$v(t_1) = \lim_{h \to 0} \frac{f(t_1 + h) - f(t_1)}{h} = f'(t_1).$$

EXAMPLE 1 A car traveling at 55 mph travels the distance $d = 55t$. Find the instantaneous velocity at $t = 4$.

Answer

$f(t) = 55t$	1. State $f(t)$.

$v(t_1) = f'(t_1) = 55 \; \forall t > 0$	2. Differentiate $f(t)$ and find $f'(t_1)$.
$\therefore v(4) = 55$ mph	

EXAMPLE 2 An object falling through the air (assuming no resistance) for t seconds travels $d = -4.9t^2 + v_0 t$ meters where v_0 is the initial velocity (in meters/second). If a man throws a ball downward with an initial velocity of 3 meters/second, what is its velocity in 3 seconds?

Answer

$f(t) = -4.9t^2 - 3t$	1. Find $f(t)$ and $f'(t)$. A down-
$f'(t) = -9.8t - 3$	ward velocity is negative.

$v(3) = f'(3) = (-9.8)(3) - 3$	2. Find $f'(t_1)$.
$\quad = -32.4$ meters/second	

EXAMPLE 3 An object thrown straight up (assuming no resistance) travels a distance (in feet) of $d = -16t^2 + v_0 t$ in t seconds, if v_0 is the initial velocity (in feet/second). For a ball so thrown with an initial velocity of 96 feet/second, find

a. the velocity after 2 seconds.
b. the time it travels upward.
c. the height it reaches before falling back to the earth.

Answer

$f(t) = -16t^2 + 96t$	a. Differentiate $f(t)$, and find $f'(2)$.
$f'(t) = -32t + 96$	
$f'(2) = 32$ feet/second, upward	

$f'(t) = -32t + 96 = 0$	b. Set $f'(t) = 0$, and find t (since
$\quad t = 3$ seconds	$v = 0$ when it stops going up)

Continued ▶

$$f(3) = -16(3)^2 + 96(3)$$
$$= 144 \text{ feet}$$

c. Since the maximum height occurs when $t = 3$ seconds; its height is $f(3)$.

Just as the derivative of the position function represents instantaneous velocity, so the derivative of a velocity function represents instantaneous acceleration.

Instantaneous acceleration   If an object moves along a straight line and the velocity of the object is $v(t)$, then the *instantaneous acceleration* at time t_1 is

$$a(t_1) = \lim_{h \to 0} \frac{v(t_1 + h) - v(t_1)}{h} = v'(t_1).$$

EXAMPLE 4   For the object in Example 3, the velocity function was given by $v(t) = -32t + 96$. Find the acceleration after 3 seconds.

Answer $a(t) = v'(t) = -32$

The negative sign on acceleration implies the velocity is decreasing. Since the acceleration function is constant at 32 ft/sec^2 downward, the acceleration after 3 seconds is the same as at any other time, namely 32 ft/sec^2.

You should become familiar with the key formulas for objects in flight.

Falling Bodies Formula

If an object is dropped or thrown so that gravity is the only other force acting on the object (ignoring air resistance), then its height is given by $h(t) = \frac{1}{2}gt^2 + v_0t + d$, where d is the initial height, v_0 is the initial velocity, and g is acceleration due to gravity. The constant g is -32 ft per sec^2 in traditional units (or -9.8 meters per sec^2 in metric units).

▶ A. Exercises

John throws a ball upward with an initial velocity of 63 feet per second. If he releases the ball when it is 4 feet above ground, answer the following questions (ignoring air resistance).

1. Give the function representing the ball's height above the ground.
2. Find its height after 1 second.
3. Find its height after 2 seconds.
4. Find its height after 3 seconds.
5. How long does it take to hit the ground?
6. Give the function for instantaneous velocity.
7. Find the velocity of the ball after 1 second.
8. Find its velocity when it hits the ground.
9. When does the ball reach its maximum height?
10. What is the acceleration of the ball?

▶ B. Exercises

Suppose Jenna dropped a ball from the roof of a 40-foot building. Ignore air resistance and answer the following questions.

11. What is the initial velocity?
12. Write a function for the height of the ball.
13. Write the velocity function.
14. How long does it take to hit the ground?

An object is launched from ground level with an initial velocity of 176.4 meters per second. Answer the following (ignore air resistance).

15. Give the function for the height of the object.
16. Give the function for the velocity of the object.

17. Find the instantaneous velocity at $t = 4$ sec.
18. Find the instantaneous velocity at $t = 20$ sec.
19. How long does it take to hit the ground?
20. Give the maximum height of the object.
21. Find the acceleration.

Answer the following questions. Assume $d = 1.5$ m in each.
22. Sasha threw a ball, and it hit the ground 7 seconds later. What was the initial velocity in m/s?
23. Blake threw a ball with an initial velocity of 50 m/s. What is its maximum height?
24. Frank wants to throw a ball onto the roof of a building 61 meters high. What must the initial velocity be if he is to succeed?
25. If the velocity of an object thrown upward was -14.7 meters/second at $t = 6$, what was v_0?

▶ C. Exercises

26. Suppose a rocket has a steady linear acceleration for the first few seconds after launching, and its acceleration function is given by $a(t) = 250t$. If the initial height and initial velocity are both zero, then find the velocity function in m/s.

〰 Dominion Modeling

Using the altitude data, find each of the following and give its physical meaning.
27. The derivative of the cubic model
28. The derivative of the velocity function for the cubic model

Given the system $x - 3y = 11$
$$2x + 5y = 0$$

29. find the inverse of the coefficient matrix.

30. use the inverse to solve the system.

Solve.

31. $2x^2 + 67 = -33$

32. $3ix + 5x = 2$

33. $\tan \theta = \cos \theta$ for $0° \leq \theta < 360°$ (to the nearest degree)

Sonya Kovalevsky

Sonya Kovalevski (also called Sophie Kowalewsky and Sonja Kovalevskaya) grew up in a prosperous Russian home. She was born in Moscow on January 15, 1850. She began studying math at age fifteen and later attended the University of Heidelberg.

At the age of 20, Kovalevsky traveled to Berlin for study, her husband staying behind in Russia. When she arrived at Berlin, she sought out Karl Weierstrass, a famous mathematician and teacher. Weierstrass told her to apply for admission to the University of Berlin and to take his classes, but she was refused because she was a woman (women were discouraged from advanced training at that time). Weierstrass, disappointed, decided to tutor her on his own time; they met every week for four years. In 1874 another university, the University of Göttingen, granted her a doctorate on the strength of three of her papers, but no university would permit her to teach.

Dejected, Kovalevsky returned to her husband in St. Petersburg, Russia, where in 1878 their daughter Foufie was born. The new responsibilities occupied her time and drove off the artists and journalists who had involved her in the gossip and flattery of "high society." By 1880, she found new motivation for mathematical research and sought advice from her old teacher Weierstrass. His disappointment at her lack of correspondence vanished, and he gladly helped.

Kovalevsky went to Paris in 1883. While there, she received news of her husband's death. The news came as a shock, and she felt guilt because her role as wife had been crowded out with research. She refused to eat for four days, and passed out on the next. Later that week she returned to mathematics to focus her thoughts and avoid getting morbid. She worked six months before she felt recovered.

Kovalevsky's qualifications eventually overcame the prejudice against females. In 1884 she moved to Sweden when the University of Stockholm offered her a position as lecturer. In 1886 she submitted a paper for the Bordin Prize contest of the French Academy of Sciences. The judges chose the winning paper without knowing the writer's name, and they selected Kovalevsky's "On the Rotation of a Solid Body Around a Fixed Point." The Academy increased the large prize of 3000 francs to 5000 francs because of their esteem for the paper, and the honor of receiving the prize far surpassed the prize money.

Promoted to professor in 1889, Kovalevsky became the only woman to hold a chair of mathematics in all of Europe in her century. She died two years later on February 10, 1891, and is buried in Stockholm. She is remembered in mathematics primarily for advances in differential equations.

The Academy increased the large prize . . . and the honor of receiving the prize far surpassed the prize money.

Math and Scripture

Instantaneous Rates of Life Span Decay

Derivatives can be used to answer several questions related to the life span decay of the patriarchs.

1. Give the equation, $Y = f(x)$, for the log of the life spans.
2. Find Y'. What is this number called? What does it represent?
3. Give the equation $y = f(x)$, the exponential decay function.
4. Find y'.

How fast were the patriarchs' life spans decreasing during each man's generation below?

5. Shem
6. Arphaxad
7. Judah (or Joseph)
8. Find the average decrease in life span per generation from Judah (or Joseph) to Aminadab.
9. Explain the contrast between questions 7 and 8.
10. Give the equation of the tangent line to the curve at the generation of Hezron.
11. Look at your linear spline (Chapter 5 Math and Scripture). Is it continuous?
12. Why would you be unable to answer questions 5-7 using the linear spline?

The theme verse shows the importance of preparation. You can cut wood with a blunt axe but it takes more effort and strength. It is wiser to sharpen the axe first. The same principle applies to the disciplining or sharpening of the mind through disciplined study of mathematics. A wise student will study diligently under the guidance of godly instructors and the Word of God.

MAXIMIZING

Find related verses teaching (1) that fools despise wisdom and instruction and (2) that running with soldiers is only a small step as God prepares you to contend (race) against horses.

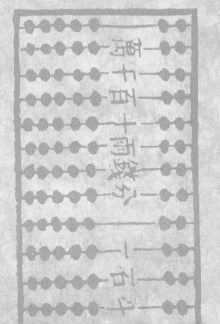

Vital Sines

If THE IRON BE BLUNT, and he do not whet the edge, then must he put to more strength: but wisdom is profitable to direct.

ECCLESIASTES 10:10

Use the definition of the derivative to find $f'(x)$ for:

1. $f(x) = x^2 - 7$

2. $f(x) = x^2 + 2x + 5$

Is each function graphed below differentiable? If not, explain why.

3.

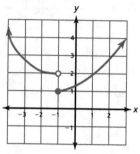

5.

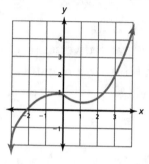

4.

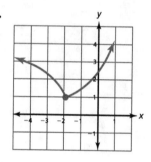

6.

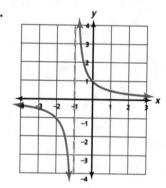

Give these basic derivatives.

7. $y = 10$

8. $y = e^x$

9. $y = x^5$

10. $y = \sin x$

Find $f'(2)$ for each of the following functions.

11. $f(x) = x^5 - 2x^4 + 4x^3 - x^2 - 7x + 9$

12. $f(x) = \sqrt[7]{x^{11}}$

Find the derivative of each.

13. $g(x) = 7^x$

14. $f(x) = x^2 + 3x - 2$

15. $f(x) = x^{\frac{1}{3}}$

16. $y = x(3x^2 + 4)$

17. $y = \dfrac{x^2 + 4x - 1}{3x}$

18. $f(x) = \cos^2 x$

19. $f(x) = \sin(x^2 - 5)$

20. $f(x) = 2 \tan x$

21. $y = \left(\dfrac{e^x - 1}{3}\right)^6$

22. $g(x) = x \cos x$

23. Give the slope of the tangent line to $f(x) = \frac{1}{2}x^2$ at $x = 3$.

24. If $v(x) = 2t^2 + 4t$, find the acceleration at time $t = 3$.

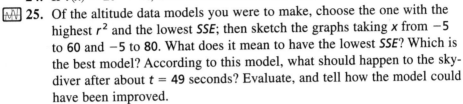 25. Of the altitude data models you were to make, choose the one with the highest r^2 and the lowest *SSE*; then sketch the graphs taking x from -5 to 60 and -5 to 80. What does it mean to have the lowest *SSE*? Which is the best model? According to this model, what should happen to the sky-diver after about $t = 49$ seconds? Evaluate, and tell how the model could have been improved.

26. Give the mathematical significance of Ecclesiastes 10:10.

Table of Common Logarithms

	.0	.1	.2	.3	.4	.5	.6	.7	.8	.9
1	0.0000	0.0414	0.0792	0.1139	0.1461	0.1761	0.2041	0.2304	0.2553	0.2788
2	0.3010	0.3222	0.3424	0.3617	0.3802	0.3979	0.4150	0.4314	0.4472	0.4624
3	0.4771	0.4914	0.5051	0.5185	0.5315	0.5441	0.5563	0.5682	0.5798	0.5911
4	0.6021	0.6128	0.6232	0.6335	0.6435	0.6532	0.6628	0.6721	0.6812	0.6902
5	0.6990	0.7076	0.7160	0.7243	0.7324	0.7404	0.7482	0.7559	0.7634	0.7709
6	0.7782	0.7853	0.7924	0.7993	0.8062	0.8129	0.8195	0.8261	0.8325	0.8388
7	0.8451	0.8513	0.8573	0.8633	0.8692	0.8751	0.8808	0.8865	0.8921	0.8976
8	0.9031	0.9085	0.9138	0.9191	0.9243	0.9294	0.9345	0.9395	0.9445	0.9494
9	0.9542	0.9590	0.9638	0.9685	0.9731	0.9777	0.9823	0.9868	0.9912	0.9956
10	1.0000									

Table of Natural Logarithms

	.0	.1	.2	.3	.4	.5	.6	.7	.8	.9
1	0.0000	0.0953	0.1823	0.2624	0.3365	0.4055	0.4700	0.5306	0.5878	0.6419
2	0.6931	0.7419	0.7885	0.8329	0.8755	0.9163	0.9555	0.9933	1.0296	1.0647
3	1.0986	1.1314	1.1632	1.1939	1.2238	1.2528	1.2809	1.3083	1.3350	1.3610
4	1.3863	1.4110	1.4351	1.4586	1.4816	1.5041	1.5261	1.5476	1.5686	1.5892
5	1.6094	1.6292	1.6487	1.6677	1.6864	1.7047	1.7228	1.7405	1.7579	1.7750
6	1.7918	1.8083	1.8245	1.8405	1.8563	1.8718	1.8871	1.9021	1.9169	1.9315
7	1.9459	1.9601	1.9741	1.9879	2.0015	2.0149	2.0281	2.0412	2.0541	2.0669
8	2.0794	2.0919	2.1041	2.1163	2.1282	2.1401	2.1518	2.1633	2.1748	2.1861
9	2.1972	2.2083	2.2192	2.2300	2.2407	2.2513	2.2618	2.2721	2.2824	2.2925
10	2.3026									

Table of Trigonometric Ratios

Degrees	Radians	sin	cos	tan	cot	sec	csc		
0°00'	0.0000	0.0000	1.0000	0.0000	—	1.000	—	1.5708	90°00'
10'	0.0029	0.0029	1.0000	0.0029	343.8	1.000	343.8	1.5679	50'
20'	0.0058	0.0058	1.0000	0.0058	171.9	1.000	171.9	1.5650	40'
30'	0.0087	0.0087	1.0000	0.0087	114.6	1.000	114.6	1.5621	30'
40'	0.0116	0.0116	0.9999	0.0116	85.94	1.000	85.95	1.5592	20'
50'	0.0145	0.0145	0.9999	0.0145	68.75	1.000	68.76	1.5563	10'
1°00'	0.0175	0.0175	0.9998	0.0175	57.29	1.000	57.30	1.5533	89°00'
10'	0.0204	0.0204	0.9998	0.0204	49.10	1.000	49.11	1.5504	50'
20'	0.0233	0.0233	0.9997	0.0233	42.96	1.000	42.98	1.5475	40'
30'	0.0262	0.0262	0.9997	0.0262	38.19	1.000	38.20	1.5446	30'
40'	0.0291	0.0291	0.9996	0.0291	34.37	1.000	34.38	1.5417	20'
50'	0.0320	0.0320	0.9995	0.0320	31.24	1.001	31.26	1.5388	10'
2°00'	0.0349	0.0349	0.9994	0.0349	28.64	1.001	28.65	1.5359	88°00'
10'	0.0378	0.0378	0.9993	0.0378	26.43	1.001	26.45	1.5330	50'
20'	0.0407	0.0407	0.9992	0.0407	24.54	1.001	24.56	1.5301	40'
30'	0.0436	0.0436	0.9990	0.0437	22.90	1.001	22.93	1.5272	30'
40'	0.0465	0.0465	0.9989	0.0466	21.47	1.001	21.49	1.5243	20'
50'	0.0495	0.0494	0.9988	0.0495	20.21	1.001	20.23	1.5213	10'
3°00'	0.0524	0.0523	0.9986	0.0524	19.08	1.001	19.11	1.5184	87°00'
10'	0.0553	0.0552	0.9985	0.0553	18.07	1.002	18.10	1.5155	50'
20'	0.0582	0.0581	0.9983	0.0582	17.17	1.002	17.20	1.5126	40'
30'	0.0611	0.0610	0.9981	0.0612	16.35	1.002	16.38	1.5097	30'
40'	0.0640	0.0640	0.9980	0.0641	15.60	1.002	15.64	1.5068	20'
50'	0.0669	0.0669	0.9978	0.0670	14.92	1.002	14.96	1.5039	10'
4°00'	0.0698	0.0698	0.9976	0.0699	14.30	1.002	14.34	1.5010	86°00'
10'	0.0727	0.0727	0.9974	0.0729	13.73	1.003	13.76	1.4981	50'
20'	0.0756	0.0756	0.9971	0.0758	13.20	1.003	13.23	1.4952	40'
30'	0.0785	0.0785	0.9969	0.0787	12.71	1.003	12.75	1.4923	30'
40'	0.0814	0.0814	0.9967	0.0816	12.25	1.003	12.29	1.4893	20'
50'	0.0844	0.0843	0.9964	0.0846	11.83	1.004	11.87	1.4864	10'
5°00'	0.0873	0.0872	0.9962	0.0875	11.43	1.004	11.47	1.4835	85°00'
10'	0.0902	0.0901	0.9959	0.0904	11.06	1.004	11.10	1.4806	50'
20'	0.0931	0.0929	0.9957	0.0934	10.71	1.004	10.76	1.4777	40'
30'	0.0960	0.0958	0.9954	0.0963	10.39	1.005	10.43	1.4748	30'
40'	0.0989	0.0987	0.9951	0.0992	10.08	1.005	10.13	1.4719	20'
50'	0.1018	0.1016	0.9948	0.1022	9.788	1.005	9.839	1.4690	10'
6°00'	0.1047	0.1045	0.9945	0.1051	9.514	1.006	9.567	1.4661	84°00'
10'	0.1076	0.1074	0.9942	0.1080	9.255	1.006	9.309	1.4632	50'
20'	0.1105	0.1103	0.9939	0.1110	9.010	1.006	9.065	1.4603	40'
30'	0.1134	0.1132	0.9936	0.1139	8.777	1.006	8.834	1.4573	30'
40'	0.1164	0.1161	0.9932	0.1169	8.556	1.007	8.614	1.4544	20'
50'	0.1193	0.1190	0.9929	0.1198	8.345	1.007	8.405	1.4515	10'
7°00'	0.1222	0.1219	0.9925	0.1228	8.144	1.008	8.206	1.4486	83°00'
10'	0.1251	0.1248	0.9922	0.1257	7.953	1.008	8.016	1.4457	50'
20'	0.1280	0.1276	0.9918	0.1287	7.770	1.008	7.834	1.4428	40'
30'	0.1309	0.1305	0.9914	0.1317	7.596	1.009	7.661	1.4399	30'
40'	0.1338	0.1334	0.9911	0.1346	7.429	1.009	7.496	1.4370	20'
50'	0.1367	0.1363	0.9907	0.1376	7.269	1.009	7.337	1.4341	10'
		cos	sin	cot	tan	csc	sec	Radians	Degrees

Degrees	Radians	sin	cos	tan	cot	sec	csc		
8°00′	0.1396	0.1392	0.9903	0.1405	7.115	1.010	7.185	1.4312	82°00′
10′	0.1425	0.1421	0.9899	0.1435	6.968	1.010	7.040	1.4283	50′
20′	0.1454	0.1449	0.9894	0.1465	6.827	1.011	6.900	1.4254	40′
30′	0.1484	0.1478	0.9890	0.1495	6.691	1.011	6.765	1.4224	30′
40′	0.1513	0.1507	0.9886	0.1524	6.561	1.012	6.636	1.4195	20′
50′	0.1542	0.1536	0.9881	0.1554	6.435	1.012	6.512	1.4166	10′
9°00′	0.1571	0.1564	0.9877	0.1584	6.314	1.012	6.392	1.4137	81°00′
10′	0.1600	0.1593	0.9872	0.1614	6.197	1.013	6.277	1.4108	50′
20′	0.1629	0.1622	0.9868	0.1644	6.084	1.013	6.166	1.4079	40′
30′	0.1658	0.1650	0.9863	0.1673	5.976	1.014	6.059	1.4050	30′
40′	0.1687	0.1679	0.9858	0.1703	5.871	1.014	5.955	1.4021	20′
50′	0.1716	0.1708	0.9853	0.1733	5.769	1.015	5.855	1.3992	10′
10°00′	0.1745	0.1736	0.9848	0.1763	5.671	1.015	5.759	1.3963	80°00′
10′	0.1774	0.1765	0.9843	0.1793	5.576	1.016	5.665	1.3934	50′
20′	0.1804	0.1794	0.9838	0.1823	5.485	1.016	5.575	1.3904	40′
30′	0.1833	0.1822	0.9833	0.1853	5.396	1.017	5.487	1.3875	30′
40′	0.1862	0.1851	0.9827	0.1883	5.309	1.018	5.403	1.3846	20′
50′	0.1891	0.1880	0.9822	0.1914	5.226	1.018	5.320	1.3817	10′
11°00′	0.1920	0.1908	0.9816	0.1944	5.145	1.019	5.241	1.3788	79°00′
10′	0.1949	0.1937	0.9811	0.1974	5.066	1.019	5.164	1.3759	50′
20′	0.1978	0.1965	0.9805	0.2004	4.989	1.020	5.089	1.3730	40′
30′	0.2007	0.1994	0.9799	0.2035	4.915	1.020	5.016	1.3701	30′
40′	0.2036	0.2022	0.9793	0.2065	4.843	1.021	4.945	1.3672	20′
50′	0.2065	0.2051	0.9787	0.2095	4.773	1.022	4.876	1.3643	10′
12°00′	0.2094	0.2079	0.9781	0.2126	4.705	1.022	4.810	1.3614	78°00′
10′	0.2123	0.2108	0.9775	0.2156	4.638	1.023	4.745	1.3584	50′
20′	0.2153	0.2136	0.9769	0.2186	4.574	1.024	4.682	1.3555	40′
30′	0.2182	0.2164	0.9763	0.2217	4.511	1.024	4.620	1.3526	30′
40′	0.2211	0.2193	0.9757	0.2247	4.449	1.025	4.560	1.3497	20′
50′	0.2240	0.2221	0.9750	0.2278	4.390	1.026	4.502	1.3468	10′
13°00′	0.2269	0.2250	0.9744	0.2309	4.331	1.026	4.445	1.3439	77°00′
10′	0.2298	0.2278	0.9737	0.2339	4.275	1.027	4.390	1.3410	50′
20′	0.2327	0.2306	0.9730	0.2370	4.219	1.028	4.336	1.3381	40′
30′	0.2356	0.2334	0.9724	0.2401	4.165	1.028	4.284	1.3352	30′
40′	0.2385	0.2363	0.9717	0.2432	4.113	1.029	4.232	1.3323	20′
50′	0.2414	0.2391	0.9710	0.2462	4.061	1.030	4.182	1.3294	10′
14°00′	0.2443	0.2419	0.9703	0.2493	4.011	1.031	4.134	1.3265	76°00′
10′	0.2473	0.2447	0.9696	0.2524	3.962	1.031	4.086	1.3235	50′
20′	0.2502	0.2476	0.9689	0.2555	3.914	1.032	4.039	1.3206	40′
30′	0.2531	0.2504	0.9681	0.2586	3.867	1.033	3.994	1.3177	30′
40′	0.2560	0.2532	0.9674	0.2617	3.821	1.034	3.950	1.3148	20′
50′	0.2589	0.2560	0.9667	0.2648	3.776	1.034	3.906	1.3119	10′
15°00′	0.2618	0.2588	0.9659	0.2679	3.732	1.035	3.864	1.3090	75°00′
10′	0.2647	0.2616	0.9652	0.2711	3.689	1.036	3.822	1.3061	50′
20′	0.2676	0.2644	0.9644	0.2742	3.647	1.037	3.782	1.3032	40′
30′	0.2705	0.2672	0.9636	0.2773	3.606	1.038	3.742	1.3003	30′
40′	0.2734	0.2700	0.9628	0.2805	3.566	1.039	3.703	1.2974	20′
50′	0.2763	0.2728	0.9621	0.2836	3.526	1.039	3.665	1.2945	10′
16°00′	0.2793	0.2756	0.9613	0.2867	3.487	1.040	3.628	1.2915	74°00′
10′	0.2822	0.2784	0.9605	0.2899	3.450	1.041	3.592	1.2886	50′
20′	0.2851	0.2812	0.9596	0.2931	3.412	1.042	3.556	1.2857	40′
30′	0.2880	0.2840	0.9588	0.2962	3.376	1.043	3.521	1.2828	30′
40′	0.2909	0.2868	0.9580	0.2994	3.340	1.044	3.487	1.2799	20′
50′	0.2938	0.2896	0.9572	0.3026	3.305	1.045	3.453	1.2770	10′
		cos	sin	cot	tan	csc	sec	Radians	Degrees

Degrees	Radians	sin	cos	tan	cot	sec	csc		
17°00′	0.2967	0.2924	0.9563	0.3057	3.271	1.046	3.420	1.2741	73°00′
10′	0.2996	0.2952	0.9555	0.3089	3.237	1.047	3.388	1.2712	50′
20′	0.3025	0.2979	0.9546	0.3121	3.204	1.048	3.356	1.2683	40′
30′	0.3054	0.3007	0.9537	0.3153	3.172	1.049	3.326	1.2654	30′
40′	0.3083	0.3035	0.9528	0.3185	3.140	1.049	3.295	1.2625	20′
50′	0.3113	0.3062	0.9520	0.3217	3.108	1.050	3.265	1.2595	10′
18°00′	0.3142	0.3090	0.9511	0.3249	3.078	1.051	3.236	1.2566	72°00′
10′	0.3171	0.3118	0.9502	0.3281	3.047	1.052	3.207	1.2537	50′
20′	0.3200	0.3145	0.9492	0.3314	3.018	1.053	3.179	1.2508	40′
30′	0.3229	0.3173	0.9483	0.3346	2.989	1.054	3.152	1.2479	30′
40′	0.3258	0.3201	0.9474	0.3378	2.960	1.056	3.124	1.2450	20′
50′	0.3287	0.3228	0.9465	0.3411	2.932	1.057	3.098	1.2421	10′
19°00′	0.3316	0.3256	0.9455	0.3443	2.904	1.058	3.072	1.2392	71°00′
10′	0.3345	0.3283	0.9446	0.3476	2.877	1.059	3.046	1.2363	50′
20′	0.3374	0.3311	0.9436	0.3508	2.850	1.060	3.021	1.2334	40′
30′	0.3403	0.3338	0.9426	0.3541	2.824	1.061	2.996	1.2305	30′
40′	0.3432	0.3365	0.9417	0.3574	2.798	1.062	2.971	1.2275	20′
50′	0.3462	0.3393	0.9407	0.3607	2.773	1.063	2.947	1.2246	10′
20°00′	0.3491	0.3420	0.9397	0.3640	2.747	1.064	2.924	1.2217	70°00′
10′	0.3520	0.3448	0.9387	0.3673	2.723	1.065	2.901	1.2188	50′
20′	0.3549	0.3475	0.9377	0.3706	2.699	1.066	2.878	1.2159	40′
30′	0.3578	0.3502	0.9367	0.3739	2.675	1.068	2.855	1.2130	30′
40′	0.3607	0.3529	0.9356	0.3772	2.651	1.069	2.833	1.2101	20′
50′	0.3636	0.3557	0.9346	0.3805	2.628	1.070	2.812	1.2072	10′
21°00′	0.3665	0.3584	0.9336	0.3839	2.605	1.071	2.790	1.2043	69°00′
10′	0.3694	0.3611	0.9325	0.3872	2.583	1.072	2.769	1.2014	50′
20′	0.3723	0.3638	0.9315	0.3906	2.560	1.074	2.749	1.1985	40′
30′	0.3752	0.3665	0.9304	0.3939	2.539	1.075	2.729	1.1956	30′
40′	0.3782	0.3692	0.9293	0.3973	2.517	1.076	2.709	1.1926	20′
50′	0.3811	0.3719	0.9283	0.4006	2.496	1.077	2.689	1.1897	10′
22°00′	0.3840	0.3746	0.9272	0.4040	2.475	1.079	2.669	1.1868	68°00′
10′	0.3869	0.3773	0.9261	0.4074	2.455	1.080	2.650	1.1839	50′
20′	0.3898	0.3800	0.9250	0.4108	2.434	1.081	2.632	1.1810	40′
30′	0.3927	0.3827	0.9239	0.4142	2.414	1.082	2.613	1.1781	30′
40′	0.3956	0.3854	0.9228	0.4176	2.394	1.084	2.595	1.1752	20′
50′	0.3985	0.3881	0.9216	0.4210	2.375	1.085	2.577	1.1723	10′
23°00′	0.4014	0.3907	0.9205	0.4245	2.356	1.086	2.559	1.1694	67°00′
10′	0.4043	0.3934	0.9194	0.4279	2.337	1.088	2.542	1.1665	50′
20′	0.4072	0.3961	0.9182	0.4314	2.318	1.089	2.525	1.1636	40′
30′	0.4102	0.3987	0.9171	0.4348	2.300	1.090	2.508	1.1606	30′
40′	0.4131	0.4014	0.9159	0.4383	2.282	1.092	2.491	1.1577	20′
50′	0.4160	0.4041	0.9147	0.4417	2.264	1.093	2.475	1.1548	10′
24°00′	0.4189	0.4067	0.9135	0.4452	2.246	1.095	2.459	1.1519	66°00′
10′	0.4218	0.4094	0.9124	0.4487	2.229	1.096	2.443	1.1490	50′
20′	0.4247	0.4120	0.9112	0.4522	2.211	1.097	2.427	1.1461	40′
30′	0.4276	0.4147	0.9100	0.4557	2.194	1.099	2.411	1.1432	30′
40′	0.4305	0.4173	0.9088	0.4592	2.177	1.100	2.396	1.1403	20′
50′	0.4334	0.4200	0.9075	0.4628	2.161	1.102	2.381	1.1374	10′
25°00′	0.4363	0.4226	0.9063	0.4663	2.145	1.103	2.366	1.1345	65°00′
10′	0.4392	0.4253	0.9051	0.4699	2.128	1.105	2.352	1.1316	50′
20′	0.4422	0.4279	0.9038	0.4734	2.112	1.106	2.337	1.1286	40′
30′	0.4451	0.4305	0.9026	0.4770	2.097	1.108	2.323	1.1257	30′
40′	0.4480	0.4331	0.9013	0.4806	2.081	1.109	2.309	1.1228	20′
50′	0.4509	0.4358	0.9001	0.4841	2.066	1.111	2.295	1.1199	10′
		cos	sin	cot	tan	csc	sec	Radians	Degrees

Degrees	Radians	sin	cos	tan	cot	sec	csc		
26°00'	0.4538	0.4384	0.8988	0.4877	2.050	1.113	2.281	1.1170	64°00'
10'	0.4567	0.4410	0.8975	0.4913	2.035	1.114	2.268	1.1141	50'
20'	0.4596	0.4436	0.8962	0.4950	2.020	1.116	2.254	1.1112	40'
30'	0.4625	0.4462	0.8949	0.4986	2.006	1.117	2.241	1.1083	30'
40'	0.4654	0.4488	0.8936	0.5022	1.991	1.119	2.228	1.1054	20'
50'	0.4683	0.4514	0.8923	0.5059	1.977	1.121	2.215	1.1025	10'
27°00'	0.4712	0.4540	0.8910	0.5095	1.963	1.122	2.203	1.0996	63°00'
10'	0.4741	0.4566	0.8897	0.5132	1.949	1.124	2.190	1.0966	50'
20'	0.4771	0.4592	0.8884	0.5169	1.935	1.126	2.178	1.0937	40'
30'	0.4800	0.4617	0.8870	0.5206	1.921	1.127	2.166	1.0908	30'
40'	0.4829	0.4643	0.8857	0.5243	1.907	1.129	2.154	1.0879	20'
50'	0.4858	0.4669	0.8843	0.5280	1.894	1.131	2.142	1.0850	10'
28°00'	0.4887	0.4695	0.8829	0.5317	1.881	1.133	2.130	1.0821	62°00'
10'	0.4916	0.4720	0.8816	0.5354	1.868	1.134	2.118	1.0792	50'
20'	0.4945	0.4746	0.8802	0.5392	1.855	1.136	2.107	1.0763	40'
30'	0.4974	0.4772	0.8788	0.5430	1.842	1.138	2.096	1.0734	30'
40'	0.5003	0.4797	0.8774	0.5467	1.829	1.140	2.085	1.0705	20'
50'	0.5032	0.4823	0.8760	0.5505	1.816	1.142	2.074	1.0676	10'
29°00'	0.5061	0.4848	0.8746	0.5543	1.804	1.143	2.063	1.0647	61°00'
10'	0.5091	0.4874	0.8732	0.5581	1.792	1.145	2.052	1.0617	50'
20'	0.5120	0.4899	0.8718	0.5619	1.780	1.147	2.041	1.0588	40'
30'	0.5149	0.4924	0.8704	0.5658	1.767	1.149	2.031	1.0559	30'
40'	0.5178	0.4950	0.8689	0.5696	1.756	1.151	2.020	1.0530	20'
50'	0.5207	0.4975	0.8675	0.5735	1.744	1.153	2.010	1.0501	10'
30°00'	0.5236	0.5000	0.8660	0.5774	1.732	1.155	2.000	1.0472	60°00'
10'	0.5265	0.5025	0.8646	0.5812	1.720	1.157	1.990	1.0443	50'
20'	0.5294	0.5050	0.8631	0.5851	1.709	1.159	1.980	1.0414	40'
30'	0.5323	0.5075	0.8616	0.5890	1.698	1.161	1.970	1.0385	30'
40'	0.5352	0.5100	0.8601	0.5930	1.686	1.163	1.961	1.0356	20'
50'	0.5381	0.5125	0.8587	0.5969	1.675	1.165	1.951	1.0327	10'
31°00'	0.5411	0.5150	0.8572	0.6009	1.664	1.167	1.942	1.0297	59°00'
10'	0.5440	0.5175	0.8557	0.6048	1.653	1.169	1.932	1.0268	50'
20'	0.5469	0.5200	0.8542	0.6088	1.643	1.171	1.923	1.0239	40'
30'	0.5498	0.5225	0.8526	0.6128	1.632	1.173	1.914	1.0210	30'
40'	0.5527	0.5250	0.8511	0.6168	1.621	1.175	1.905	1.0181	20'
50'	0.5556	0.5275	0.8496	0.6208	1.611	1.177	1.896	1.0152	10'
32°00'	0.5585	0.5299	0.8480	0.6249	1.600	1.179	1.887	1.0123	58°00'
10'	0.5614	0.5324	0.8465	0.6289	1.590	1.181	1.878	1.0094	50'
20'	0.5643	0.5348	0.8450	0.6330	1.580	1.184	1.870	1.0065	40'
30'	0.5672	0.5373	0.8434	0.6371	1.570	1.186	1.861	1.0036	30'
40'	0.5701	0.5398	0.8418	0.6412	1.560	1.188	1.853	1.0007	20'
50'	0.5730	0.5422	0.8403	0.6453	1.550	1.190	1.844	0.9977	10'
33°00'	0.5760	0.5446	0.8387	0.6494	1.540	1.192	1.836	0.9948	57°00'
10'	0.5789	0.5471	0.8371	0.6536	1.530	1.195	1.828	0.9919	50'
20'	0.5818	0.5495	0.8355	0.6577	1.520	1.197	1.820	0.9890	40'
30'	0.5847	0.5519	0.8339	0.6619	1.511	1.199	1.812	0.9861	30'
40'	0.5876	0.5544	0.8323	0.6661	1.501	1.202	1.804	0.9832	20'
50'	0.5905	0.5568	0.8307	0.6703	1.492	1.204	1.796	0.9803	10'
34°00'	0.5934	0.5592	0.8290	0.6745	1.483	1.206	1.788	0.9774	56°00'
10'	0.5963	0.5616	0.8274	0.6787	1.473	1.209	1.781	0.9745	50'
20'	0.5992	0.5640	0.8258	0.6830	1.464	1.211	1.773	0.9716	40'
30'	0.6021	0.5664	0.8241	0.6873	1.455	1.213	1.766	0.9687	30'
40'	0.6050	0.5688	0.8225	0.6916	1.446	1.216	1.758	0.9657	20'
50'	0.6080	0.5712	0.8208	0.6959	1.437	1.218	1.751	0.9628	10'
		cos	sin	cot	tan	csc	sec	Radians	Degrees

Degrees	Radians	sin	cos	tan	cot	sec	csc		
35°00'	0.6109	0.5736	0.8192	0.7002	1.428	1.221	1.743	0.9599	55°00'
10'	0.6138	0.5760	0.8175	0.7046	1.419	1.223	1.736	0.9570	50'
20'	0.6167	0.5783	0.8158	0.7089	1.411	1.226	1.729	0.9541	40'
30'	0.6196	0.5807	0.8141	0.7133	1.402	1.228	1.722	0.9512	30'
40'	0.6225	0.5831	0.8124	0.7177	1.393	1.231	1.715	0.9483	20'
50'	0.6254	0.5854	0.8107	0.7221	1.385	1.233	1.708	0.9454	10'
36°00'	0.6283	0.5878	0.8090	0.7265	1.376	1.236	1.701	0.9425	54°00'
10'	0.6312	0.5901	0.8073	0.7310	1.368	1.239	1.695	0.9396	50'
20'	0.6341	0.5925	0.8056	0.7355	1.360	1.241	1.688	0.9367	40'
30'	0.6370	0.5948	0.8039	0.7400	1.351	1.244	1.681	0.9338	30'
40'	0.6400	0.5972	0.8021	0.7445	1.343	1.247	1.675	0.9308	20'
50'	0.6429	0.5995	0.8004	0.7490	1.335	1.249	1.668	0.9279	10'
37°00'	0.6458	0.6018	0.7986	0.7536	1.327	1.252	1.662	0.9250	53°00'
10'	0.6487	0.6041	0.7969	0.7581	1.319	1.255	1.655	0.9221	50'
20'	0.6516	0.6065	0.7951	0.7627	1.311	1.258	1.649	0.9192	40'
30'	0.6545	0.6088	0.7934	0.7673	1.303	1.260	1.643	0.9163	30'
40'	0.6574	0.6111	0.7916	0.7720	1.295	1.263	1.636	0.9134	20'
50'	0.6603	0.6134	0.7898	0.7766	1.288	1.266	1.630	0.9105	10'
38°00'	0.6632	0.6157	0.7880	0.7813	1.280	1.269	1.624	0.9076	52°00'
10'	0.6661	0.6180	0.7862	0.7860	1.272	1.272	1.618	0.9047	50'
20'	0.6690	0.6202	0.7844	0.7907	1.265	1.275	1.612	0.9018	40'
30'	0.6720	0.6225	0.7826	0.7954	1.257	1.278	1.606	0.8988	30'
40'	0.6749	0.6248	0.7808	0.8002	1.250	1.281	1.601	0.8959	20'
50'	0.6778	0.6271	0.7790	0.8050	1.242	1.284	1.595	0.8930	10'
39°00'	0.6807	0.6293	0.7771	0.8098	1.235	1.287	1.589	0.8901	51°00'
10'	0.6836	0.6316	0.7753	0.8146	1.228	1.290	1.583	0.8872	50'
20'	0.6865	0.6338	0.7735	0.8195	1.220	1.293	1.578	0.8843	40'
30'	0.6894	0.6361	0.7716	0.8243	1.213	1.296	1.572	0.8814	30'
40'	0.6923	0.6383	0.7698	0.8292	1.206	1.299	1.567	0.8785	20'
50'	0.6952	0.6406	0.7679	0.8342	1.199	1.302	1.561	0.8756	10'
40°00'	0.6981	0.6428	0.7660	0.8391	1.192	1.305	1.556	0.8727	50°00'
10'	0.7010	0.6450	0.7642	0.8441	1.185	1.309	1.550	0.8698	50'
20'	0.7039	0.6472	0.7623	0.8491	1.178	1.312	1.545	0.8668	40'
30'	0.7069	0.6494	0.7604	0.8541	1.171	1.315	1.540	0.8639	30'
40'	0.7098	0.6517	0.7585	0.8591	1.164	1.318	1.535	0.8610	20'
50'	0.7127	0.6539	0.7566	0.8642	1.157	1.322	1.529	0.8581	10'
41°00'	0.7156	0.6561	0.7547	0.8693	1.150	1.325	1.524	0.8552	49°00'
10'	0.7185	0.6583	0.7528	0.8744	1.144	1.328	1.519	0.8523	50'
20'	0.7214	0.6604	0.7509	0.8796	1.137	1.332	1.514	0.8494	40'
30'	0.7243	0.6626	0.7490	0.8847	1.130	1.335	1.509	0.8465	30'
40'	0.7272	0.6648	0.7470	0.8899	1.124	1.339	1.504	0.8436	20'
50'	0.7301	0.6670	0.7451	0.8952	1.117	1.342	1.499	0.8407	10'
42°00'	0.7330	0.6691	0.7431	0.9004	1.111	1.346	1.494	0.8378	48°00'
10'	0.7359	0.6713	0.7412	0.9057	1.104	1.349	1.490	0.8348	50'
20'	0.7389	0.6734	0.7392	0.9110	1.098	1.353	1.485	0.8319	40'
30'	0.7418	0.6756	0.7373	0.9163	1.091	1.356	1.480	0.8290	30'
40'	0.7447	0.6777	0.7353	0.9217	1.085	1.360	1.476	0.8261	20'
50'	0.7476	0.6799	0.7333	0.9271	1.079	1.364	1.471	0.8232	10'
43°00'	0.7505	0.6820	0.7314	0.9325	1.072	1.367	1.466	0.8203	47°00'
10'	0.7534	0.6841	0.7294	0.9380	1.066	1.371	1.462	0.8174	50'
20'	0.7563	0.6862	0.7274	0.9435	1.060	1.375	1.457	0.8145	40'
30'	0.7592	0.6884	0.7254	0.9490	1.054	1.379	1.453	0.8116	30'
40'	0.7621	0.6905	0.7234	0.9545	1.048	1.382	1.448	0.8087	20'
50'	0.7650	0.6926	0.7214	0.9601	1.042	1.386	1.444	0.8058	10'
		cos	sin	cot	tan	csc	sec	Radians	Degrees

Degrees	Radians	sin	cos	tan	cot	sec	csc		
44°00′	0.7679	0.6947	0.7193	0.9657	1.036	1.390	1.440	0.8029	46°00′
10′	0.7709	0.6967	0.7173	0.9713	1.030	1.394	1.435	0.7999	50′
20′	0.7738	0.6988	0.7153	0.9770	1.024	1.398	1.431	0.7970	40′
30′	0.7767	0.7009	0.7133	0.9827	1.018	1.402	1.427	0.7941	30′
40′	0.7796	0.7030	0.7112	0.9884	1.012	1.406	1.423	0.7912	20′
50′	0.7825	0.7050	0.7092	0.9942	1.006	1.410	1.418	0.7883	10′
45°00′	0.7854	0.7071	0.7071	1.000	1.000	1.414	1.414	0.7854	45°00′
		cos	sin	cot	tan	csc	sec	Radians	Degrees

Normal Curve Table

AREAS UNDER THE STANDARD NORMAL CURVE

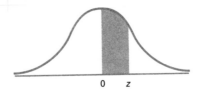

Percent of area under the curve between 0 and z.

	.00	.01	.02	.03	.04	.05	.06	.07	.08	.09
.0	.0000	.0040	.0080	.0120	.0160	.0199	.0239	.0279	.0319	.0359
.1	.0398	.0438	.0478	.0517	.0557	.0596	.0636	.0675	.0714	.0753
.2	.0793	.0832	.0871	.0910	.0948	.0987	.1026	.1064	.1103	.1141
.3	.1179	.1217	.1255	.1293	.1331	.1368	.1406	.1443	.1480	.1517
.4	.1554	.1591	.1628	.1664	.1700	.1736	.1772	.1808	.1844	.1879
.5	.1915	.1950	.1985	.2019	.2054	.2088	.2123	.2157	.2190	.2224
.6	.2257	.2291	.2324	.2357	.2389	.2422	.2454	.2486	.2517	.2549
.7	.2580	.2611	.2642	.2673	.2704	.2734	.2764	.2794	.2823	.2852
.8	.2881	.2910	.2939	.2967	.2995	.3023	.3051	.3078	.3106	.3133
.9	.3159	.3186	.3212	.3238	.3264	.3289	.3315	.3340	.3365	.3389
1.0	.3413	.3438	.3461	.3485	.3508	.3531	.3554	.3577	.3599	.3621
1.1	.3643	.3665	.3686	.3708	.3729	.3749	.3770	.3790	.3810	.3830
1.2	.3849	.3869	.3888	.3907	.3925	.3944	.3962	.3980	.3997	.4015
1.3	.4032	.4049	.4066	.4082	.4099	.4115	.4131	.4147	.4162	.4177
1.4	.4192	.4207	.4222	.4236	.4251	.4265	.4279	.4292	.4306	.4319
1.5	.4332	.4345	.4357	.4370	.4382	.4394	.4406	.4418	.4429	.4441
1.6	.4452	.4463	.4474	.4484	.4495	.4505	.4515	.4525	.4535	.4545
1.7	.4554	.4564	.4573	.4582	.4591	.4599	.4608	.4616	.4625	.4633
1.8	.4641	.4649	.4656	.4664	.4671	.4678	.4686	.4693	.4699	.4706
1.9	.4713	.4719	.4726	.4732	.4738	.4744	.4750	.4756	.4761	.4767
2.0	.4772	.4778	.4783	.4788	.4793	.4798	.4803	.4808	.4812	.4817
2.1	.4821	.4826	.4830	.4834	.4838	.4842	.4846	.4850	.4854	.4857
2.2	.4861	.4864	.4868	.4871	.4875	.4878	.4881	.4884	.4887	.4890
2.3	.4893	.4896	.4898	.4901	.4904	.4906	.4909	.4911	.4913	.4916
2.4	.4918	.4920	.4922	.4925	.4927	.4929	.4931	.4932	.4934	.4936
2.5	.4938	.4940	.4941	.4943	.4945	.4946	.4948	.4949	.4951	.4952
2.6	.4953	.4955	.4956	.4957	.4959	.4960	.4961	.4962	.4963	.4964
2.7	.4965	.4966	.4967	.4968	.4969	.4970	.4971	.4972	.4973	.4974
2.8	.4974	.4975	.4976	.4977	.4977	.4978	.4979	.4979	.4980	.4981
2.9	.4981	.4982	.4982	.4983	.4984	.4984	.4985	.4985	.4986	.4986
3.0	.4987	.4987	.4987	.4988	.4988	.4989	.4989	.4989	.4990	.4990
3.1	.4990	.4991	.4991	.4991	.4992	.4992	.4992	.4992	.4993	.4993
3.2	.4993	.4993	.4994	.4994	.4994	.4994	.4994	.4995	.4995	.4995
3.3	.4995	.4995	.4995	.4996	.4996	.4996	.4996	.4996	.4996	.4997
3.4	.4997	.4997	.4997	.4997	.4997	.4997	.4997	.4997	.4997	.4998
3.5	.4998									
4.0	.49997									
4.5	.499997									
5.0	.4999997									

Symbols

$\mathbb{N}$	natural numbers		π	pi
$\mathbb{Z}$	integers		θ	theta (angle variable)
$\mathbb{Q}$	rational numbers		$\alpha, \beta, \gamma, \phi$	alpha, beta, gamma, phi (angles)
$\mathbb{R}$	real numbers		δ, ε	delta, epsilon (arbitrarily small values)
$\mathbb{C}$	complex numbers		μ	population mean (mu)
$\approx$	approximately equal		σ	population standard deviation (sigma)
$<, \leq$	less than (or equal to)		$\bar{x}, \bar{y}$	sample means (x-bar, y-bar)
$>, \geq$	greater than (or equal to)		s	sample standard deviation
$\subseteq, \subset$	subset (proper)		$\hat{y}$	predicted value of y (y-hat)
$\in$	is an element of		∞	infinity
$\varnothing$	empty set		$\lim\limits_{n \to \infty} A_n$	limit of a sequence
$\{\}$	set			
$\forall$	for all, for every		$\lim\limits_{x \to a} f(x)$	limit of a function
$\exists$	there exists, there is		$\lim\limits_{x \to a^+} f(x)$	right-hand limit
$\therefore$	therefore			
$\ni$	such that		$\lim\limits_{x \to a^-} f(x)$	left-hand limit
(a, b)	ordered pair		$\sum\limits_{i=1}^{n} A_i$	nth partial sum of a sequence
(a, b)	open interval			
$[a, b]$	closed interval		$\sum\limits_{i=1}^{\infty} A_i$	infinite series
$\vec{v}$	vector			
$\mathbf{v}$	vector		Δ	change in (capital delta)
$<a, b>$	vector		$\dfrac{\Delta y}{\Delta x}$	change in y over change in x
$f(x)$	function of x			
$f^{-1}(x)$	inverse function		y'	first derivative
$\lvert x \rvert$	absolute value function		$f'(x)$	first derivative
$[x]$	greatest integer function		$f''(x), f'''(x)$	second, third derivative
$\sqrt{}$	square root		$f^{(n)}(x)$	nth derivative
$\sqrt[3]{}$	cube root		$\dfrac{dy}{dx}$	derivative
$\sqrt[n]{}$	nth root			
$n!$	n factorial		$\dfrac{d^2 y}{dx^2}, \dfrac{d^3 y}{dx^3}$	second, third derivative
e	natural log base (exponentials and logs)			

Selected Answers

Chapter 1—Trigonometry

1.1

1.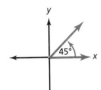

3.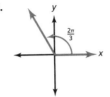

5.

7. α and θ are positive; β is negative.   **9.** $\frac{\pi}{12}$

11. $210°$ **13.** $\frac{3\pi}{2}$ **15.** about $309°$ **17.** 0.5

19. 0.9 **21.** $-\frac{7\pi}{4}, \frac{9\pi}{4}, \frac{17\pi}{4}$ (Answers may vary.)

23. $\frac{\pi}{180} \approx 0.0175$ **25.** $s = 2\pi$ **27.** $r = 3$

29. $s = \frac{10\pi}{3}$ **31.** $10, (1, 4)$ **33.** $\sqrt{170}, \left(\frac{1}{2}, -\frac{1}{2}\right)$

35. $B(15, -9); AM + MB = \sqrt{85} + \sqrt{85} = 2\sqrt{85} = AB$

1.2

1. $\sin A = \frac{\sqrt{21}}{5}$; $\cos A = \frac{2}{5}$; $\tan A = \frac{\sqrt{21}}{2}$

$\csc A = \frac{5\sqrt{21}}{21}$; $\sec A = \frac{5}{2}$; $\cot A = \frac{2\sqrt{21}}{21}$

$\sin C = \frac{2}{5}$; $\cos C = \frac{\sqrt{21}}{5}$; $\tan C = \frac{2\sqrt{21}}{21}$

$\csc C = \frac{5}{2}$; $\sec C = \frac{5\sqrt{21}}{21}$; $\cot C = \frac{\sqrt{21}}{2}$

3. $\sin N = \frac{\sqrt{35}}{6}$; $\cos N = \frac{1}{6}$; $\tan N = \sqrt{35}$

$\csc N = \frac{6\sqrt{35}}{35}$; $\sec N = 6$; $\cot N = \frac{\sqrt{35}}{35}$

$\sin L = \frac{1}{6}$; $\cos L = \frac{\sqrt{35}}{6}$; $\tan L = \frac{\sqrt{35}}{35}$

$\csc L = 6$; $\sec L = \frac{6\sqrt{35}}{35}$; $\cot L = \sqrt{35}$

	sine	cosine	tangent	cotangent	secant	cosecant
5.	$\frac{4\sqrt{17}}{17}$	$\frac{\sqrt{17}}{17}$	4	$\frac{1}{4}$	$\sqrt{17}$	$\frac{\sqrt{17}}{4}$
7.	$\frac{-\sqrt{37}}{37}$	$\frac{-6\sqrt{37}}{37}$	$\frac{1}{6}$	6	$\frac{-\sqrt{37}}{6}$	$-\sqrt{37}$
9.	$\frac{3\sqrt{10}}{10}$	$\frac{\sqrt{10}}{10}$	3	$\frac{1}{3}$	$\sqrt{10}$	$\frac{\sqrt{10}}{3}$
11.	$\frac{\sqrt{2}}{2}$	$\frac{\sqrt{2}}{2}$	1	1	$\sqrt{2}$	$\sqrt{2}$
13.	0.6691	0.7431	0.9004	1.111	1.346	1.494
15.	0	-1	0	undefined	-1	undefined
17.	0	1	0	undefined	1	undefined

	sin	cos	tan	cot	sec	csc
19.	$+$	$-$	$-$	$-$	$-$	$+$
21.	$-$	$+$	$-$	$-$	$+$	$-$

23. $\frac{2\sqrt{3}}{3}$ **31.** $\left(-\frac{1}{2}, 3\right)$ [1.1]   **33.** $\frac{22\pi}{45}$ or 1.54 [1.1]

1.3

1. $75°$ **3.** $40°$

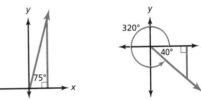

5. $68°$ **7.** $\frac{\pi}{4}$

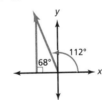

9. 0.4436 **11.** 0.0553 **13.** 4.694 **15.** -1.082

17. $180°, 210°, 225°, 240°, 270°$ **19.** $-\sqrt{2}$

21. $\frac{1}{2}$ **23.** $-\sqrt{3}$ **25.** $-\frac{1}{2}$ **27.** $\frac{1}{2}$

29. $64°20', 244°20'$ **31.** $84°20', 264°20'$

33. $213°, 327°$ **37.** 0.47 [1.1]

39. $\frac{2\sqrt{53}}{53} \approx 0.2747$ [1.2]

1.4

1. $\angle A = 33°45', \angle B = 56°15', b = 7.5$

3. $\angle A = 77°20', b = 4.5, c = 20.5$

5. $\angle B = 25°50', a = 14.4, b = 7.0$

7. $\angle A = 8°, a = 3.3, b = 23.8$

9. $\angle A = 38.5°$, $a = 2.4$, $c = 3.8$
11. 6445.5 feet or 1.2 miles   **13.** 64.0 feet
15. 460.2 feet or 0.1 mile
17. 80.6 nautical miles   **23.** $\frac{x}{2}$ [1.2]
25. -0.7660 [1.3]

1.5

1. SAA, one   **3.** ASA, one   **5.** SAS, one
7. SSA, one   **9.** SSS, one
11. $\angle C = 79°$, $a = 12.8$, $b = 12.3$
13. $\angle C = 29°41'$ or 29.7°; $\angle A = 68°19'$ or 68.3°;
$a = 11.3$
15. $\angle A = 17°35'$ or 17.6°, $\angle B = 147°25'$ or 147.4°,
$b = 25.0$; $\angle A = 162°25'$ or 162.4°, $\angle B = 2°35'$
or 2.6°, $b = 2.1$ **17.** no solution
19. $\angle A = 47°37'$ or 47.6°, $\angle B = 32°23'$ or 32.4°,
$b = 4.4$ **25.** 1.3352 radians [1.4]
27. III and IV; same as its reciprocal ratio, sine. [1.2]
29. 0.6428 [1.4]

1.6

1. $\angle A = 48.5°$, $\angle B = 38.6°$, $\angle C = 92.9°$
3. $\angle B = 74.2°$, $\angle C = 41.8°$, $a = 24.3$
5. $\angle A = 35.9°$, $\angle C = 66.1°$, $b = 26.7$
7. law of sines; $\angle C = 68.5°$, $a = 10.0$, $b = 30.1$
9. basic trig ratios; $\angle C = 30°$, $a = 8.7$, $c = 5.0$
11. 235 feet   **13.** 2 miles   **15.** 303 feet
21. about 286.5° [1.1]
23. $\sec \theta = \frac{1}{\cos \theta}$, $\csc \theta = \frac{1}{\sin \theta}$, $\cot \theta = \frac{1}{\tan \theta}$ [1.2]
25. 10.6 [1.5]

1.7

1. -11 **3.** $\frac{8}{9}$ **5.** $\frac{5}{11}$ **7.** 23°12'   **9.** 40°36'
11. 49°24'   **13.** 50.3   **15.** 6.9   **17.** 109.3 or 80.9
19. 0.5774   **21.** -0.5774 **23.** -0.4245
25.

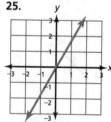

27.

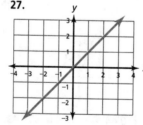

33. SSA [1.5]   **35.** 8.9 ft [1.1]

Chapter 1 Review

1. 135°   **3.** 90°   **5.** $\frac{\pi}{4}$ **7.** $\frac{89\pi}{18}$ **9.** $\sqrt{65}$, $\left(\frac{7}{2}, 3\right)$
11. $\sin A = \frac{7\sqrt{58}}{58}$, $\cos A = \frac{3\sqrt{58}}{58}$, $\tan A = \frac{7}{3}$
$\csc A = \frac{\sqrt{58}}{7}$, $\sec A = \frac{\sqrt{58}}{3}$, $\cot A = \frac{3}{7}$
$\sin B = \frac{3\sqrt{58}}{58}$, $\cos B = \frac{7\sqrt{58}}{58}$, $\tan B = \frac{3}{7}$
$\csc B = \frac{\sqrt{58}}{3}$, $\sec B = \frac{\sqrt{58}}{7}$, $\cot B = \frac{7}{3}$

13.

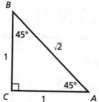

15. 0.7808   **17.** -1.7251
19. $\angle B = 17°$; $b = 5.2$, $c = 17.8$ **21.** 80.2 feet
23. $\angle C = 55°$, $b = 7.4$, $c = 7.7$ **25.** 57.8
27. $\frac{-1}{5}$ **29.** 73.3° or 73°18'

Chapter 2—Polynomials

2.1

1. {(0, 2), (−1, 4), (3, 6)}; Answers will vary.
3. {(4, 5), (4, −2), (3, 9)}; Answers will vary.
5. {2, 3, 4}; {−3, 3, 4}   **7.** $y = x + 5$
9. $y = 2x - 3$ **11.** function   **13.** function
15. not a function   **17.** −14, 1, 7, −2
19. 10, 5, 3, 6
21. {(−3, −14), (2, 1), (4, 7), (1, −2)}

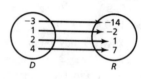

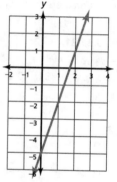

23. {(−3, 10), (2, 5), (4, 3), (1, 6)}

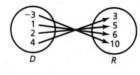

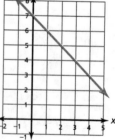

25. a. $\frac{9}{8}$;
b. $\frac{-b}{2} + 1$ or $\frac{2 - b}{2}$;
c. $2x + 1$; d. $3x - 2$

27. {(−5, 19.047), (0.36, 2.9166), (14.53, 6.3967),
(234.1, 8614)}   **33.** II and III; II and IV [1.2]
35. 11.7 [1.4]   **37.** $b = 442$ ft, $\angle C = 41°$ [1.5]

2.2

1. $4x - y = 19$ **3.** $f(x) = -\frac{1}{2}x + \frac{3}{4}$

5. $m = \frac{-2}{3}$, $b = 1$ **7.** no slope, no y-intercept

9. $-\frac{1}{4}$

11. $D = \mathbb{R}$; $R = \mathbb{R}$; function

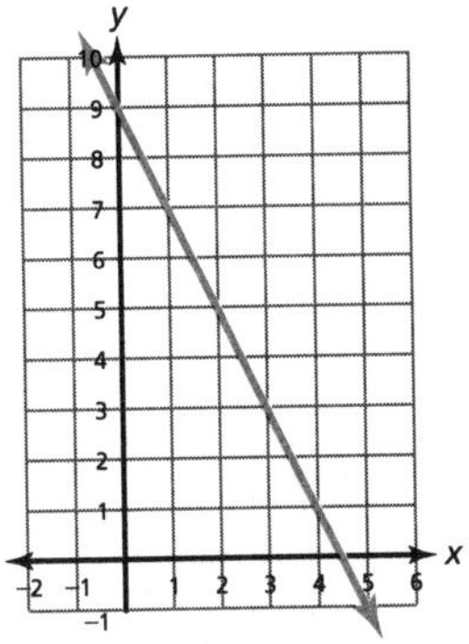

13. $D = \mathbb{R}$; $R = \mathbb{R}$, function

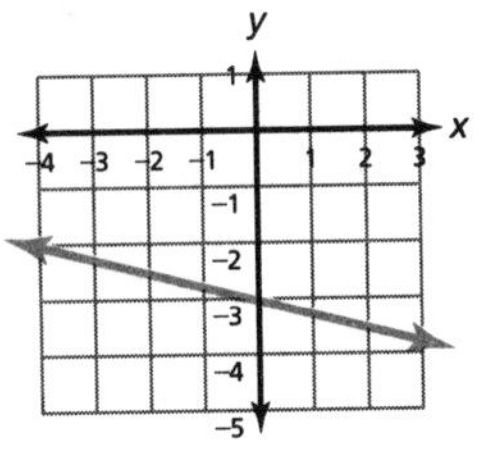

15. $D = \mathbb{R}$; $R = \mathbb{R}$, function

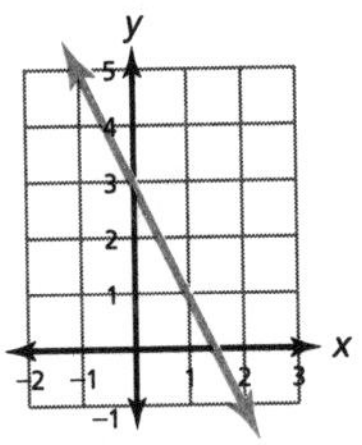

17. $D = \mathbb{R}$; $R = \mathbb{R}$, function

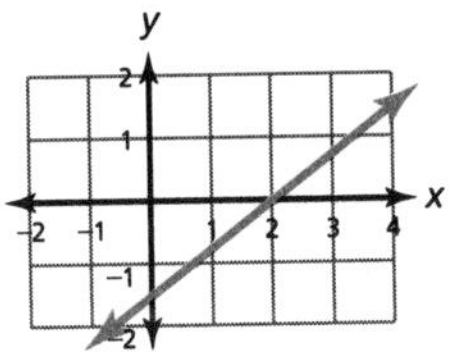

19. $D = \mathbb{R}$; $R = \{3\}$, function

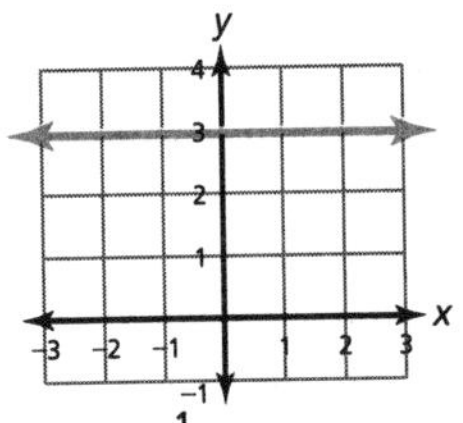

21. $D = \mathbb{R}$; $R = \mathbb{R}$, function

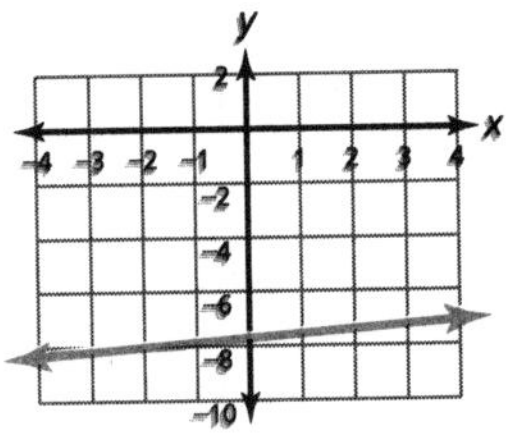

23. $y = \frac{1}{2}x + 4$ **25.** $y = \frac{2}{3}x + 2$

27. $y = -\frac{16}{7}x + 5$

29.

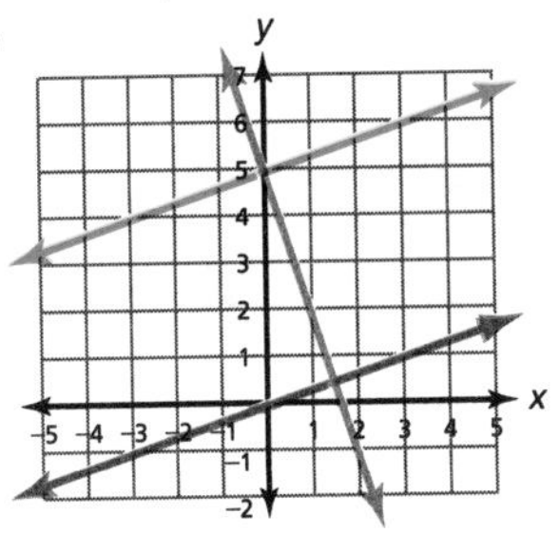

The -3 changes the slope but not the y-intercept. The implied constant of 0 translates the graph down 5 units.

31. Vertical lines fail the vertical line test. Notice that they have no function form.

37. -1 [2.1] **39.** IV, 80° [1.3]

41. 29°, 47°, 104° [1.6]

2.3

1. $-24, -9$ **3.** opens up, has minimum value

5. $D = \mathbb{R}$, $R = \{y \mid y \geq -25\}$

7. $h(x) = -5(x + 3)^2 + 47$, $(-3, 47)$, max

9. $h(x) = 3\left(x - \frac{3}{2}\right)^2 - \frac{87}{4}$, $\left(\frac{3}{2}, \frac{-87}{4}\right)$, min

11. $y = (x + 1)^2 - 6$

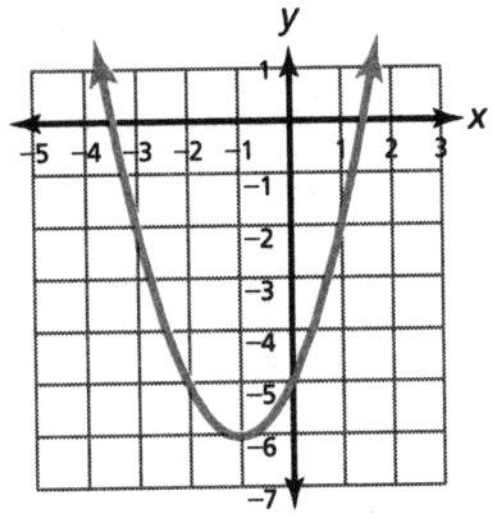

13. $y = 2(x + 2)^2 - 15$

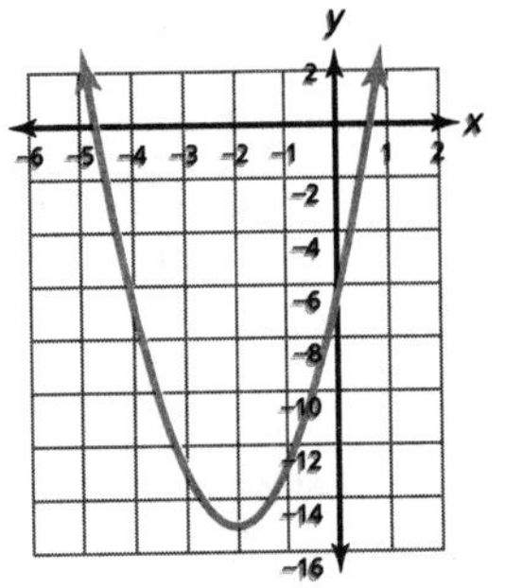

15. $y = \left(x + \frac{3}{2}\right)^2 - \frac{37}{4}$

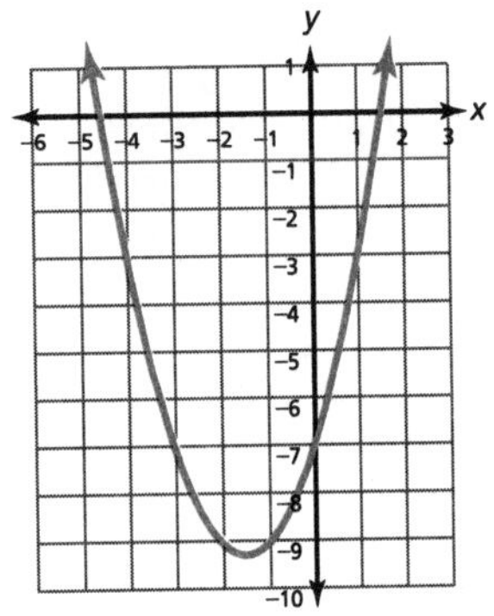

17. $y = -\left(x + \frac{5}{2}\right)^2 + \frac{33}{4}$

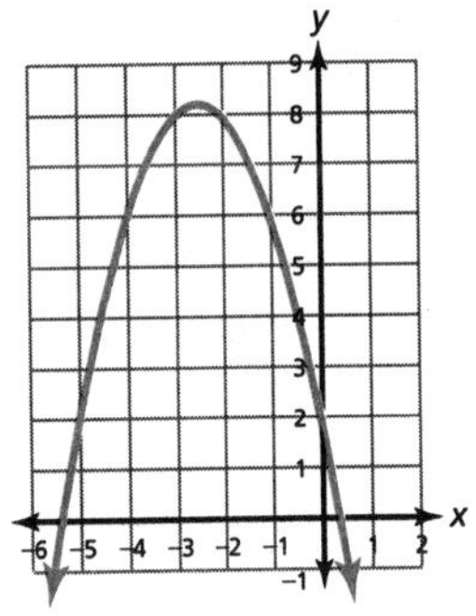

19.

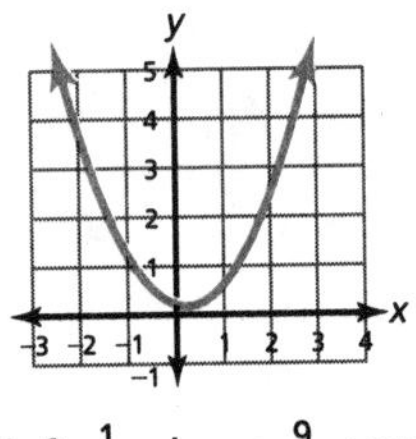

21. left $\frac{1}{2}$, down $\frac{9}{4}$, upward, $x = \frac{-1}{2}$

23. right $\frac{1}{2}$, up $\frac{29}{4}$, downward, $x = \frac{1}{2}$ **25.** $-4, 5$

27. $\frac{-2 + \sqrt{19}}{3}$, $\frac{-2 - \sqrt{19}}{3}$

33. $\sin x = \frac{-10\sqrt{149}}{149}$; $\cos x = \frac{-7\sqrt{149}}{149}$; $\tan x = \frac{10}{7}$; 235° [1.2]

35. $\tan x = \pm \frac{3\sqrt{10}}{20} \approx \pm 0.4743$ [1.2]

37. $\sqrt{29} \approx 5.4$; midpoint $(0.5, -6)$ [1.1]

2.4

1. $-6x^4 + 5x^3 + 3x - 8$; degree 4, -6, -8

3. $x^2 + 9$; degree 2, 1, 9 **5.** 28; degree 0, 28, 28

7. no **9.** yes, no degree **11.** -14 **13.** 34

15. $2 + i$ **17.** $4x^2 + 4x - 3$; $2x^2 + 4x + 1$

19. $x^2 - 2x + 4$; $x^2 - 4x + 6$ **21.** -27 **23.** 4, 7

25. $\pm 2, \pm 2i$

27. No zeros if $a \neq 0$. If $a = 0$ all real numbers are zeros.

33.

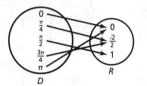

[2.1]

35. 40,860 square feet ≈ 0.938 acres [1.7]

37. min: $\left(\frac{5}{6}, -\frac{1}{12}\right)$ [2.3]

2.5

1. $10x^3 + 48x^2 + 198x + 796$; R. 3186

3. $-6x^3 + 12x^2 - 20x + 40$ R. -80

5. $5x^3 + 9x^2 + 12x + 14$ R. 14 **7.** 3 **9.** 0

11. $(x + 4)(x^2 - 4x + 16)$; when the remainder is zero, the divisor is a factor of the dividend.

13. 114 **15.** -31

17. $Q(x) = (2x - 1)(x + 1)(x + 3)$

19. $P(x) = (x - 1)(x - 3)(x + 4)^2$

21. $P(x) = (x - 1)(x + 1)(x - i)^2(x + i)^2$

23. $x^3 - 6x^2 + 12x - 8$

25. $4x^3 - 24x^2 + 21x - 5$ **29.** $4x - 6y = 5$ [2.2]

31. $3x^5 - 6x^4 + x^3 + 3$ [2.4]

33. 7.4 square miles [1.7]

2.6

1. $\pm 1, \pm 2, \pm 4$ **3.** $\pm 1, \pm 2, \pm 4, \pm 8, \pm 16$

5. $\pm 1, \pm \frac{1}{2}, \pm 2$ **7.** 6; multiplicity 4

9. 0; multiplicity 32 **11.** $-i, -3$ **13.** $0, -1, -2i$

15. $-\sqrt{3}, 6$ **17.** -3 **19.** $\frac{1}{5}, 3, \sqrt{3}i, -\sqrt{3}i$

21. $1, -\frac{1}{4}$ **23.** $-6, \frac{1}{2}, 2$ **25.** 0

27. 6; $P(x) = x^6 - 8x^5 + 5x^4 + 48x^3 + 19x^2 - 40x - 25$

29. 3; $P(x) = x^3 - 5x^2 - 2x + 10$

33. $59°2'$ [1.7] **35.** 4 [2.4]

2.7

1. $D = \mathbb{R}$; $R = \{y \mid y \leq 2\}$; polynomial; even degree

3. $D = \{x \mid x \neq -1\}$; $R = \{y \mid y \geq -2\}$; not polynomial; hole (not continuous)

5. $D = \mathbb{R}$; $R = \{y \mid y \leq 3\}$; not polynomial; asymptote (tail doesn't approach $\pm\infty$)

7. $D = \mathbb{R}$; $R = \{y \mid y \geq -3\}$; polynomial; even degree

9. left tail down, right tail up; symmetric about the origin

11. both tails up; symmetry across y-axis

13. tails irrelevant to constant function; symmetry across the y-axis and the origin

15. the degree of $P(x)$ is 5

17. -1, 1 (multiplicity 2), two complex roots

19. $P(-4) = -12$, $P(-2) = 2$, $P\left(-\frac{1}{2}\right) = -0.625$, $P(1) = 8$, $P(2) = 30$

21.

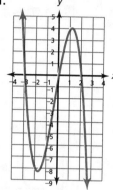

23.

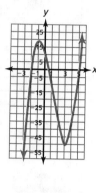

25.

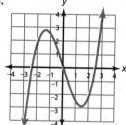

27.

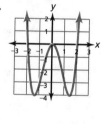

29.

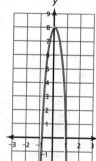

35. 20.5 ft [1.7]

37. 6.28 [1.1]

39. $x = 0, 5, \pm\frac{\sqrt{6}}{2}$ [2.6]

Chapter 2 Review

1. $D = \{1, 2, 5\}$,
$R = \{2, 3, 4\}$, function

3. $D = \{2\}$, $R = \mathbb{R}$,
not a function

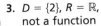

5.

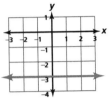

$D = \mathbb{R}$, $R = \{-3\}$,
function

7. $\{(-2, -1), (0, -1), (1, 2), (4, 23)\}$, 2, quadratic

9. $\{(-2, -28), (0, -10), (1, -10), (4, 26)\}$, 3,
polynomial

11. $m = \frac{3}{5}$, $b = -\frac{2}{5}$ **13.** $y = -x + 3$

15. $V(3, -2)$, axis: $x = 3$

17. $x^4 + 2x^3 - 5x^2 - 9x + 2$; $x^2 - 2x - 1$ R. 3

19. left tail down, right tail up

21. 3(mult. 2), $\frac{1}{2}$(mult. 1), -4(mult. 5)

23. $R(x) = x^3 - 8x^2 + 22x - 20$

25. $D = \mathbb{R}$, $R = \mathbb{R}$

27. $D = \mathbb{R}$, $R = \{-6\}$

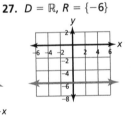

29.

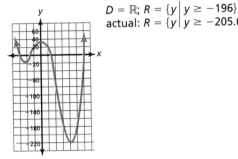

$D = \mathbb{R}$; $R = \{y \mid y \geq -196\}$
actual: $R = \{y \mid y \geq -205.6\}$

Chapter 3—Functions

3.1

1. $D = \mathbb{R}$, $R = \mathbb{R}$; odd

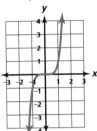

3. $D = \mathbb{R}$, $R = \mathbb{R}$; odd

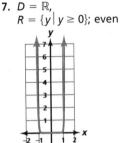

5. $D = \mathbb{R}$,
$R = \{y \mid y \leq 0\}$; even

7. $D = \mathbb{R}$,
$R = \{y \mid y \geq 0\}$; even

9. C   **11.** B   **13.** 54

15. -2.9×10^{20} **17.** 3C

19. n **21.** $\mathbb{R}$

23. $\{y \mid y \geq 0\}$ for $C > 0$; $\{y \mid y \leq 0\}$ for $C < 0$

29. yes [2.1]   **31.** $x = 3 \pm \sqrt{2}$ [2.4]

3.2

1. $D = \mathbb{R}$, $R = \{y \mid y > 0\}$; exponential growth

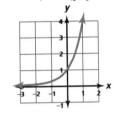

x	y
2	16
1	4
0	1
-1	$\frac{1}{4}$
-2	$\frac{1}{16}$
-3	$\frac{1}{64}$

3. $D = \mathbb{R}$, $R = \{y \mid y > 0\}$; exponential growth

x	$g(x)$
2	50
1	10
0	2
-1	$\frac{2}{5}$
-2	$\frac{2}{25}$
-3	$\frac{2}{125}$

5. $D = \mathbb{R}$, $R = \{y \mid y > 0\}$; exponential decay

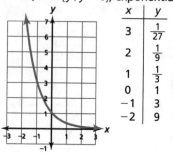

x	y
3	$\frac{1}{27}$
2	$\frac{1}{9}$
1	$\frac{1}{3}$
0	1
−1	3
−2	9

7. $\frac{1}{9}$, 1, $\sqrt{3}$, 3   **9.** power function of degree 7
11. exponential decay function
13. exponential decay function   **15.** Bank A
17. \$4622.81   **19.** \$4940.32   **21.** \$4970.41
23. 2.2974   **25.** 2.4
31. $f(x) = ax^2 + bx + c$ is a power function of
degree 2 if $b = 0$ and $c = 0$ [3.1]
33. a constant function [2.2]
35. 185° and −535° [1.1]

3.3
1. $\left\{(-4, 0), \left(\frac{-1}{2}, 3\frac{1}{2}\right), (0, 4), \left(\frac{3}{4}, 4\frac{3}{4}\right), (2, 6)\right\}$
3. $\left\{(-4, -4), \left(\frac{-1}{2}, -1\right), (0, 0), \left(\frac{3}{4}, 0\right), (2, 2)\right\}$
5. $\left\{(-4, \frac{1}{256}), \left(-\frac{1}{2}, \frac{1}{2}\right), (0, 1), \left(\frac{3}{4}, 2\sqrt{2}\right), (2, 32)\right\}$
7. $\left\{(-4, -3), \left(\frac{-1}{2}, \frac{-1}{2}\right), (0, 0), \left(\frac{3}{4}, \frac{3}{4}\right), (2, 1)\right\}$
9. $\left\{(-4, 4), \left(\frac{-1}{2}, 4\right), (0, 4), \left(\frac{3}{4}, 4\right), (2, 4)\right\}$
11. down 7   **13.** left 4   **15.** left 1, up 6
17. All x such that $0 \le x < 1$ **19.** −2, 1, 2
21. $D = \mathbb{R}$;   **23.** $D = \mathbb{R}$;
$R = \{y \mid y \ge 0\}$; $R = \mathbb{Z}$;
continuous   discontinuous

   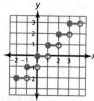

25. $D = \mathbb{R}$;   **27.** $D = \mathbb{R}$;
$R = \{0, 1, 3\}$; $R = \mathbb{R}$;
discontinuous   discontinuous

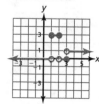   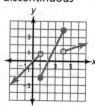

29. $D = \mathbb{R}$;
$R = \{y \mid 0 \le y \le 4\}$;
continuous

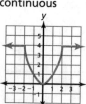

31. $D = \mathbb{R}$;
$R = \{y \mid y \ge 1\}$;
continuous

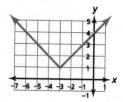

33. $D = \mathbb{R}$; $R = \mathbb{R}$; discontinuous

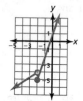

37. 63°, 21°, 65°, 47° [1.3]
39. decay [3.2]
41. −1, −3, [2.3]

3.4
1. 7 days (1 week)   **3.** $f(x + 7) = f(x)$
5.

θ	$\sin \theta$	$\tan \theta$
0	0	0
$\frac{\pi}{6}$	$\frac{1}{2}$	$\frac{\sqrt{3}}{3}$
$\frac{\pi}{4}$	$\frac{\sqrt{2}}{2}$	1
$\frac{\pi}{3}$	$\frac{\sqrt{3}}{2}$	$\sqrt{3}$
$\frac{\pi}{2}$	1	undefined
$\frac{2\pi}{3}$	$\frac{\sqrt{3}}{2}$	$-\sqrt{3}$
$\frac{3\pi}{4}$	$\frac{\sqrt{2}}{2}$	−1
$\frac{5\pi}{6}$	$\frac{1}{2}$	$-\frac{\sqrt{3}}{3}$
π	0	0
$\frac{7\pi}{6}$	$-\frac{1}{2}$	$\frac{\sqrt{3}}{3}$
$\frac{5\pi}{4}$	$-\frac{\sqrt{2}}{2}$	1
$\frac{4\pi}{3}$	$-\frac{\sqrt{3}}{2}$	$\sqrt{3}$
$\frac{3\pi}{2}$	−1	undefined
$\frac{5\pi}{3}$	$-\frac{\sqrt{3}}{2}$	$-\sqrt{3}$
$\frac{7\pi}{4}$	$-\frac{\sqrt{2}}{2}$	−1
$\frac{11\pi}{6}$	$-\frac{1}{2}$	$-\frac{\sqrt{3}}{3}$

7. π **9.** $-\sqrt{3}$ **11.** 0.1045   **13.** 0.7771
15. 4.331

17. $\tan B = \frac{b}{a} = \cot A$; $\tan\left(\frac{\pi}{2} - \theta\right) = \cot \theta$

19. $D = \mathbb{R}$, $R = \{0, 1, 2\}$, period = 5

21. Let $n \in \mathbb{Z}$. After 2 periods, $5n = 10$.
$$g = \begin{cases} 0 & \text{if } 5n - 5 < x \le 5n - 3 \\ 1 & \text{if } 5n - 3 < x \le 5n - 1 \\ 2 & \text{if } 5n - 1 < x \le 5n \end{cases}$$

23. $g(x + 5) = g(x)$ **29.** 331 [2.5]

31.   [2.7]

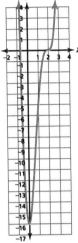

3.5

1. $\{(0.1745, 0.9848), (0.3840, 0.9272), (1.239, 0.3257), (0.7854, 0.7071), (1.396, 0.1739)\}$

3. $A = 3$, period = 2π, phase shift = 0

5. $A = 3$, period = 2π, phase shift = $\frac{-\pi}{2}$

7. $A = 2$, period = $\frac{2\pi}{5}$, phase shift = 0

9. $A = 2$, period = π, phase shift = $\frac{-\pi}{2}$

11. $y = \pm 2 \sin \frac{1}{2}\left(\theta - \frac{\pi}{2}\right)$ or $y = \pm 2 \sin\left(\frac{1}{2}\theta - \frac{\pi}{4}\right)$

13. $y = \pm 4 \cos \frac{2}{5}\theta$

15. $\tan(-x) = -\tan x$, not continuous

17. $x = \frac{\pi}{2} + k\pi$, $k \in \mathbb{Z}$

19. $D = \mathbb{R}$, $R = \{y \mid -A \le y \le A\}$

21.

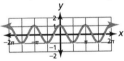

23.

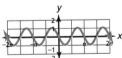

25.

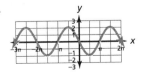

27.

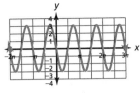

37. 3 [3.2]
39. 1 [3.2]

29.

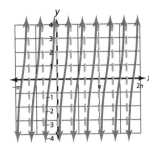

3.6

1.

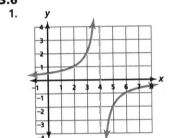

3.

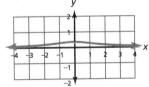

5. $x = -3$ **7.** no vertical asymptote

9. $f(2) = -\frac{1}{21}$, $f(-6) = \frac{1}{11}$

11. $D = \{x \mid x \ne -3\}$,   **13.** $D = \mathbb{R}$,
$R = \{y \mid y \ne 0\}$ $R = \{y \mid 0 < y \le 1\}$

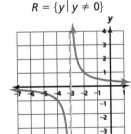

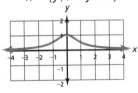

15.

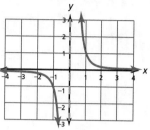

$D = \{x \mid x \neq 0\},$
$R = \{y \mid y > 0\}$

17.

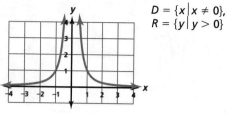

19.

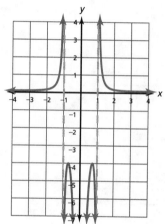

21.

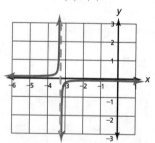

23.

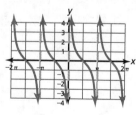

$D = \{x \mid x \neq k\pi,$
$k \in \mathbb{Z}\}, R = \mathbb{R};$

zeros:
$\left\{x \mid x = \frac{\pi}{2} + k\pi\right\},$
$k \in \mathbb{Z};$ period $\pi;$

odd; not
continuous

25. period $= 2\pi$; $\csc(\theta + 2\pi) = \dfrac{1}{\sin(\theta + 2\pi)} = \dfrac{1}{\sin \theta} = \csc \theta$

27. even; $\sec(-\theta) = \dfrac{1}{\cos(-\theta)} = \dfrac{1}{\cos \theta} = \sec \theta$

29. odd; $\cot(-\theta) = \dfrac{1}{\tan(-\theta)} = \dfrac{1}{-\tan(\theta)} = -\cot \theta$

31.

33.

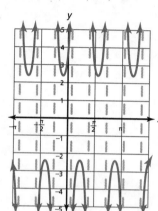

41. $C = 83°,$
$b = 7.8,$
$c = 12.3$
[1.5]

43. 15 [3.3]

45.

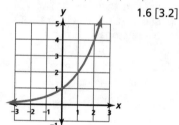

1.6 [3.2]

3.7

1. y-intercept: $(0, -1)$; x-intercepts: $(1, 0)$, $(3, 0)$; horizontal: $y = 0$; vertical: $x = 2$; $D = \{x \mid x \neq 2\}$; $R = \mathbb{R}$

3. y-intercept: $(0, 1)$; no x-intercepts; horizontal: $y = 0$; vertical: $x = -2$, $x = 3$; $D = \{x \mid x \neq -2, x \neq 3\}$; $R = \{y \mid y \geq 1 \text{ or } y < 0\}$

5. y-intercept: $(0, 3)$; $D = \{x \mid x \neq -2\}$; vertical: $x = -2$

7. y-intercept: $\left(0, \frac{1}{3}\right)$; $D = \{x \mid x \neq -6, x \neq 2\}$; vertical: $x = -6$, $x = 2$

9. y-intercept: $(0, 0)$; $D = \mathbb{R}$; no vertical asymptote

11. 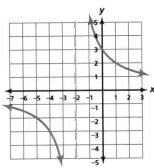 reduced and proper; *x*-intercept: none; horizontal: $y = 0$

13. 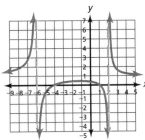 improper (degrees same)

15. reduced and proper; *x*-intercept: 0; horizontal: $y = 0$; continuous, odd

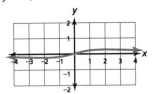

17.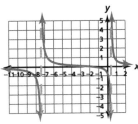

19.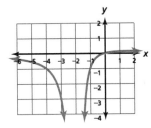

21.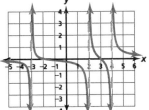

23.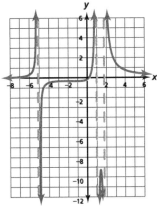

31. *g, j, q, r* [3.1]

33. $\pm 1, \pm 2, \pm 3, \pm 4, \pm 6, \pm 12$ [2.5]

3.8

1. *x*-intercepts: $(-5, 0)$, $(0, 0)$, $(3, 0)$; *y*-intercept: $(0, 0)$ **3.** $y = x + 7$

5. improper, reduced; $D = \{x \mid x \neq -5\}$; horizontal: $y = 3$; vertical: $x = -5$

7. improper, unreduced; $D = \{x \mid x \neq -2, 0, 4\}$; horizontal: $y = \frac{3}{5}$; vertical: $x = 4$

9. improper, unreduced; $D = \{x \mid x \neq \pm 2, 5\}$; horizontal: $y = 1$; vertical: $x = -2, x = 5$

11. vertical: $x = -3, x = 4$; horizontal: $y = 1$; *x*-intercepts: $(-2, 0)$, $(2, 0)$; *y*-intercept: $\left(0, \frac{1}{3}\right)$

13. vertical: $x = 0$; oblique: $y = x - 2$; *x*-intercept: $(1, 0)$; no *y*-intercept

15. vertical: none; horizontal: $y = \frac{1}{2}$; *x*-intercepts: $(1, 0)$, $(-2, 0)$; *y*-intercept: $(0, -2)$

17. vertical: $x = 5, x = -1$; horizontal: $y = 1$; *x*-intercepts: $(0, 0)$, $(-2, 0)$; *y*-intercept: $(0, 0)$

19. vertical: $x = 1, x = -1$; oblique: $y = x - 2$; *x*-intercept: $(2, 0)$; *y*-intercept: $(0, 2)$

21.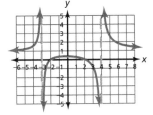

23.

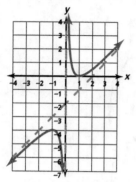

25.

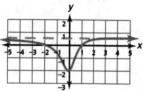

27.

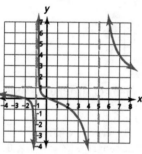

29.

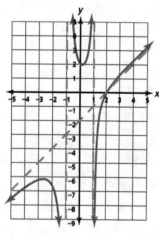

31.

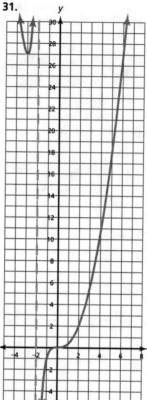

35. $a = 66$ [1.6]

37. The slope is the tangent of the angle of inclination, therefore $\tan^{-1} -2$ is the angle of inclination. The calculator will give the principal value of $-63.4°$. Since the angle of inclination is given as a positive angle, and $\tan(x + \pi) = \tan x$, we get $-63.4° + 180° = 116.6°$ [1.7]

39. $D = \left\{ x \mid x \neq -1, x \neq \frac{1}{6} \right\}$ [3.7]

Chapter 3 Review

1. $\{(-5, -750), (-2, -48), (0, 0), (2, 48), (3, 162)\}$, power function
3. $\left\{ \left(-5, \frac{1}{243}\right), \left(-2, \frac{1}{9}\right), (0, 1), (2, 9), (3, 27) \right\}$, exponential function
5. $\{(-5, -5), (-2, -2), (0, 0), (2, 2), (3, 3)\}$, identity function
7. $\{(-5, 1069), (-2, 58), (0, 4), (2, -2), (3, 13)\}$, polynomial function
9. $\left\{ \left(-5, -\frac{1}{2}\right), \left(-2, -\frac{\sqrt{3}}{2}\right), (0, 0), \left(2, \frac{\sqrt{3}}{2}\right), (3, 1) \right\}$, trigonometric function
11. amplitude: 2; period: 2π; phase shift: $-\pi$
13. y-intercept: $(0, 1)$; horizontal: $y = 0$; $D = \mathbb{R}$
15. y-intercept: $(0, -5)$; x-intercept: $(5, 0)$; no asymptotes (hole at $x = -9$); $D = \{x \mid x \neq -9\}$
17. x-intercept: $(-1, 0), (-5, 0), (4, 0)$; y-intercept: $\left(0, \frac{20}{3}\right)$; oblique: $y = x + 2$; vertical: $x = \pm\sqrt{3}$; $D = \{x \mid x \neq \pm\sqrt{3}\}$
19. even, symmetric across the y-axis

21. $D = \mathbb{R}$;
$R = \{y \mid y \geq -3\}$

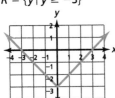

23. $D = \mathbb{R}$;
$R = \{y \mid y > 0\}$

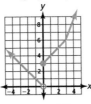

25. amplitude: 1; period: π; phase shift: $\dfrac{-\pi}{4}$

27.

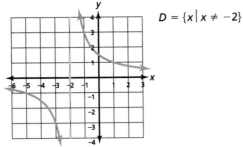

$D = \{x \mid x \neq -2\}$

29.

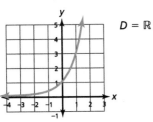

$D = \mathbb{R}$

31.

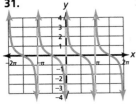

33.

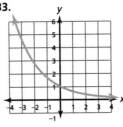

35.

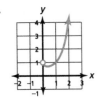

Chapter 4—Inverse Functions

4.1

1. $(-1, 2]$ **3.** $[-3, 3)$ **5.** $[4, \infty)$
7. increasing on $(-\infty, \infty)$, one-to-one
9. constant for $x \in (-5, -3] \cup [3, 5)$, increasing on $[-3, 0]$, decreasing on $[0, 3]$, not one-to-one

11. none; not
one-to-one

13. decreasing;
one-to-one

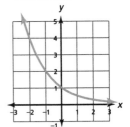

15. none; not
one-to-one

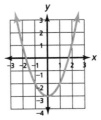

17. increasing;
one-to-one

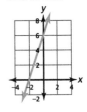

19. increasing;
one-to-one

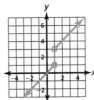

21. decreasing;
one-to-one

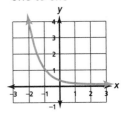

27. trig function, -1 [3.5]
29. exponential function, 40 [3.2]
31. rational function, 1 [3.7]

4.2

1. -3 **3.** $-2x^2 + 7$ **5.** $45a^2 + 30ab + 5b^2$
7. $-2a^2 - 8a + 25$ **9.** -3145; 12,418,880; 1567
11. $-2x^2 + 25x - 63$ **13.** $\dfrac{-2x + 7}{5x^2}, x \neq 0$
15. $5x^3 - 45x^2$ **17.** $\dfrac{5x^2}{x - 9}, x \neq 9$ **19.** $x^2 + 1$
21. $25x^3 - 40x + 24$ **23.** $\dfrac{5x}{9} - 4$ **25.** $\dfrac{5x - 4}{9}$
27.

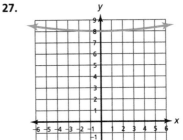

29. $k \circ h = k(h(x)) = 5x^2 + 36$

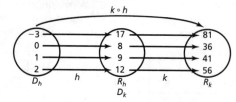

31. $fg(x) = f(x)\,g(x)$
$= (-2x + 7)(5x^2)$
$= (5x^2)(-2x + 7)$
$= g(x)f(x)$
$= (gf)(x)$
Thus, multiplication of functions is commutative.
$[(fg)h](x) = [f(x)g(x)]h(x)$
$= [(-2x + 7)(5x^2)](x - 9)$
$= (-10x^3 + 35x^2)(x - 9)$
$= -10x^4 + 125x^3 - 315x^2$
$[f(gh)](x) = f(x)[g(x)h(x)]$
$= (-2x + 7)[(5x^2)(x - 9)]$
$= (-2x + 7)(5x^3 - 45x^2)$
$= -10x^4 + 125x^3 - 315x^2$
$\therefore [(fg)h](x) = [f(gh)](x)$
Thus, multiplication of functions is associative.

33. 63,495   **37.** 5120 [3.2]   **39.** $\frac{5}{3}$ [2.2]

4.3

1. $f^{-1} = \{(7, 4), (-3, 2), (7, 5), (8, 1)\}$; not a function.

3. $f^{-1}(x) = -\frac{1}{4}x + \frac{3}{2}$

5. $x = |y|$ or $y = \pm x$ is not a function; $g(x)$ is not one-to-one since $g(1) = 1$ and $g(-1) = 1$.

7. $y = 4 \pm \sqrt{x}$ is not a function; original function is not one-to-one since $f(3) = 1$ and $f(5) = 1$.

9. $f^{-1}(x) = \frac{1}{2x - 1}$, $x \neq \frac{1}{2}$

11. inverses   **13.** not inverses   **15.** not inverses

17.

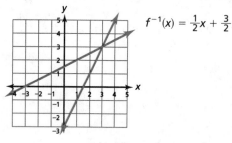

$f^{-1}(x) = \frac{1}{2}x + \frac{3}{2}$

19.

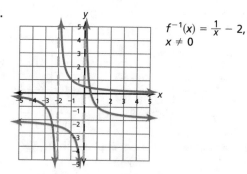

$f^{-1}(x) = \frac{1}{x} - 2$, $x \neq 0$

21.

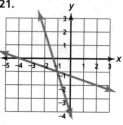

23.

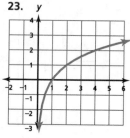

25.

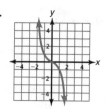

33. $\frac{2\pi}{3}$ [3.5]
35. $\frac{\pi}{6}$ to the right [3.5]

37.

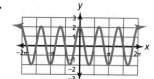

[3.5]

4.4

1. 2   **3.** -2

5. $D = \{x \mid x \geq 2\}$; x-intercept: $(2, 0)$; no y-intercept

7. $D = \{x \mid x \geq 0\}$; no x-intercept; y-intercept: $(0, 1)$

9. $D = \mathbb{R}$; x-intercept: $(-2, 0)$; y-intercept: $(0, \sqrt[3]{2})$

11. $D = \mathbb{R}$; x-intercept: $(-13{,}977.08, 0)$; y-intercept: $(0, 6.43)$

13. $D = \{x \mid x \leq 0\}$, $R = \{y \mid y \geq 0\}$

15. $D = \{x \mid x \geq -4\}$, $R = \{y \mid y \geq -3\}$

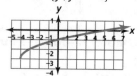

17.

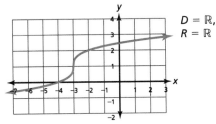

$D = \mathbb{R},$
$R = \mathbb{R}$

19.

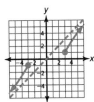

$f: [0, \infty);$
$f^{-1}: (-\infty, 1]$

21.

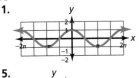

$f: (-\infty, -1] \cup [1, \infty);$
$f^{-1}: (-\infty, -3] \cup [3, \infty)$

27. $A \approx 63.9\ [1.7]$ **29.** tangent and cotangent [3.4]

4.5

1.

3.

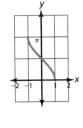

5.

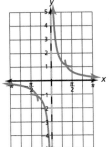

7. $\frac{\pi}{3}$ **9.** $\frac{\pi}{6}$ **11.** $\frac{\pi}{4}$ **13.** $\frac{\sqrt{3}}{3}$ **15.** $\frac{2}{3}$
17. 0.349   **19.** 0.7759

21.

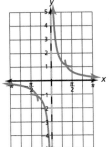

restricted domain:
$x \in \left[-\frac{\pi}{2}, \frac{\pi}{2}\right]$

23. 0.9709   **25.** 1.4022
27. 0.9033
29. 1.0472 $\left(\text{or } \frac{\pi}{3}\right)$
35. 143° [1.7]
37. $f(x) = \frac{1}{2}x + 7\ [2.2]$
39. $f(x) = \frac{3}{2}x + \frac{15}{2}\ [4.2]$

4.6

1. $2^y = x$ **3.** $4^{-2} = \frac{1}{16}$ **5.** $10^3 = 1000$
7. $e^0 = 1$ **9.** $a^1 = a \Rightarrow \log_a a = 1$
11. $\log_5 125 = 3$ **13.** $\log_8 64 = 2$
15. $\log_7 343 = 3$
17. $D = \{x \mid x > 0\};$ **19.** $D = \{x \mid x > 0\};$
    $R = \mathbb{R}$ $R = \mathbb{R}$

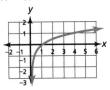   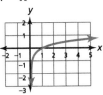

21. 9   **23.** -3 **25.** -4 **29.** $(-\infty, 0), (0, \infty)$ [3.3]
31. $[3, \infty)$ [3.3]   **33.** no, it is continuous [3.3]

4.7

1. $\log x + \log y$ **3.** $4 \log a - 2 \log b$
5. $3 \log x + 2 \log y + 5 \log z$ **7.** 1.2104
9. 4.3018   **11.** 138.33   **13.** 4.64   **15.** 1.91
17. $P + Q$ **19.** $\frac{1}{2}Q$ **21.** $Q + 7$
25. $f(x) = \ln(x + 2) - 3; g(x) = e^{x+2} - 3$ [4.6]
27. neither [3.1]

4.8

1. 6   **3.** 8.7   **5.** 75.8   **7.** 60.5   **9.** 3.1
11. 1.6×10^{-9} **13.** \$2718.28   **15.** \$2316.37
17. \$14,288.26   **19.** \$11,500
21. \$2733.20, \$3917.50, \$5288.10, \$9074.50
23. 5192 feet   **31.** $\mathbb{R}$ [2.4]
33. $\{x \mid x \neq 3\}$ [3.8]   **35.** $\{x \mid x \geq -2\}$ [4.4]

Chapter 4 Review

1. decreasing;   **3.** none; not one-to-one
    one-to-one

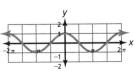

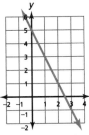

5. even   **7.** $f^{-1}(x) = \sqrt[3]{x + 7}$, function
9. $f^{-1}(x) = x^2 - 1, x \geq 0$, function
11. not inverses   **13.** $\frac{\pi}{6}$ **15.** $\frac{\pi}{6}$ **17.** 0.5716
19.

$D = \{x \mid -1 \leq x \leq 1\},$
$R = \left\{y \mid \frac{-\pi}{2} \leq y \leq \frac{\pi}{2}\right\}$

21. $x^2 + 3x + 1; 11$ 23. $\frac{3x+2}{x^2-1}$ if $x \neq \pm 1; \frac{8}{3}$
25. $9x^2 + 12x + 3; 63$ 27. $25^2 = 625$
29. -5 31. $\frac{3\sqrt{34}}{34}$ 33. 3.12199   35. 19 minutes

Chapter 5—Equations

5.1
1. yes 3. yes 5. yes; $x^3 - 2x^2 + 6x$
7. $-4, \frac{-3 \pm \sqrt{5}}{2}$ 9. $0, 1 \pm \frac{\sqrt{2}}{2}i$
11. $x = \pm 1, \pm\sqrt{2}$ 13. $x = -\frac{1}{2}, 1, -6$
15. $x = -1, 3, \pm 2\sqrt{2}$ 17. $x = \frac{2}{3}, \pm\frac{\sqrt{2}}{2}i$
19. $x = 1, -2, \frac{3}{2}$ 21. $x = -3.162$
29.   [2.7]

31. amplitude: $\frac{1}{2}$; period: 3π; phase shift: $\frac{\pi}{4}$ right [3.5]

5.2
1. $10x$ 3. $x^2 - 2x + 1$ 5. $3r^2 + 9r - 12$
7. $3n^2 - 5n + 2$ 9. $x^2 - 1$ 11. $x = \pm 5$
13. $x = 0$ 15. $r = -2, -\frac{4}{3}$ 17. $n = \frac{5}{3}$
19. $x = 2, -\frac{2}{3}$ 21. 8   23. 60 mph   25. $x = 0.885$
29. quadrant II: $(-4, 5), (-8, 10), (-12, 15)$; quadrant IV: $(4, -5), (8, -10), (12, -15)$ [4.5]
31. 30-60-90 triangle; hypotenuse: 14, sides: 7, $7\sqrt{3}$ [1.4]
33. $x^5 + 7x^4 + 10x^3 - 18x^2 - 27x + 27 = 0$ [3.1]

5.3
1. $x = 25$ 3. $x = 32$ 5. $x = 162$ 7. $x = 7$
9. $x = 5$ 11. $x = 4$ 13. $x = 4$ 15. $r = -2$
17. $p = 3$ 19. $t = \pm\frac{4\sqrt{5}}{9}$ 21. $x = \frac{81}{25}$
29. $b = 29, c = 29$ and $\angle C = 72°$; acute isosceles triangle [1.5]   31. 180° [1.1]

5.4
1. $x = 4$ 3. $x = 3$ 5. $x = \pm\frac{1}{2}$ 7. $x = 6$
9. $x \approx 1.303$ 11. $\frac{3}{2}$ 13. $x = -1$ 15. $x = 0$
17. $x = 400$ 19. $x = 81$ 21. $x \approx 0.24$
23. $x \approx -1.77$ 25. $x \approx 0.13$ 27. $x \approx 5.58$
29. $x = 2$ 31. $x = \pm 2$
37. cofunction identity [3.4]
39. odd-even identity [3.4]
41. Pythagorean theorem [1.6]

5.5
1. $\frac{1}{\sin\theta} = \frac{1}{\frac{y}{r}} = \frac{r}{y} = \csc\theta$

3. $x^2 + y^2 = r^2$
$$\frac{x^2}{x^2} + \frac{y^2}{x^2} = \frac{r^2}{x^2}$$
$$1 + \left(\frac{y}{x}\right)^2 = \left(\frac{r}{x}\right)^2$$
$$1 + \tan^2\theta = \sec^2\theta$$
$$\tan^2\theta + 1 = \sec^2\theta$$

5. $\sin\theta + \cos\theta\cot\theta = \sin\theta + \cos\theta\cot\theta$
$$= \sin\theta + \cos\theta \cdot \frac{\cos\theta}{\sin\theta}$$
$$= \frac{\sin^2\theta}{\sin\theta} + \frac{\cos^2\theta}{\sin\theta}$$
$$= \frac{\sin^2\theta + \cos^2\theta}{\sin\theta}$$
$$= \frac{1}{\sin\theta}$$
$$= \csc\theta$$

7. $\frac{\tan\theta\cos\theta}{\sin\theta} = \frac{\tan\theta\cos\theta}{\sin\theta}$
$$= \frac{\frac{\sin\theta}{\cos\theta}\cdot\cos\theta}{\sin\theta}$$
$$= \frac{\sin\theta}{\sin\theta}$$
$$= 1$$

9. $\sin\theta\sec\theta - \sin\theta\csc\theta = \sin\theta\sec\theta - \sin\theta\csc\theta$
$$= \sin\theta\left(\frac{1}{\cos\theta}\right) - \sin\theta\left(\frac{1}{\sin\theta}\right)$$
$$= \frac{\sin\theta}{\cos\theta} - \frac{\sin\theta}{\sin\theta}$$
$$= \tan\theta - 1$$

11. $\sec^4\theta + \sec^2\theta\tan^2\theta - 2\tan^4\theta$
$$= \sec^4\theta + \sec^2\theta\tan^2\theta - 2\tan^4\theta$$
$$= (\sec^2\theta + 2\tan^2\theta)(\sec^2\theta - \tan^2\theta)$$
$$= [\sec^2\theta + 2(\sec^2\theta - 1)][\sec^2\theta - (\sec^2\theta - 1)]$$
$$= (\sec^2\theta + 2\sec^2\theta - 2)(\sec^2\theta - \sec^2\theta + 1)$$
$$= (3\sec^2\theta - 2)(1)$$
$$= 3\sec^2\theta - 2$$

13. $\frac{1 + \cos\theta}{\sin\theta} + \frac{\sin\theta}{1 + \cos\theta}$
$$= \frac{1 + \cos\theta}{\sin\theta}\left(\frac{1 + \cos\theta}{1 + \cos\theta}\right) + \frac{\sin\theta}{1 + \cos\theta}\left(\frac{\sin\theta}{\sin\theta}\right)$$
$$= \frac{1 + 2\cos\theta + \cos^2\theta + \sin^2\theta}{\sin\theta(1 + \cos\theta)}$$
$$= \frac{1 + 2\cos\theta + 1}{\sin\theta(1 + \cos\theta)}$$
$$= \frac{2 + 2\cos\theta}{\sin\theta(1 + \cos\theta)}$$
$$= \frac{2(1 + \cos\theta)}{\sin\theta(1 + \cos\theta)}$$
$$= \frac{2}{\sin\theta}$$
$$= 2\csc\theta$$

15. 0.9232   17. 0.5495   19. 0.5877
27. $3e^2 \approx 22.2$ [5.4]   29. $f^{-1}(x) = \frac{3x}{1-x}$ [4.3]

5.6
1. $\frac{\sqrt{2} - \sqrt{6}}{4}$ 3. $\frac{-\sqrt{2} + \sqrt{6}}{4}$ 5. $\frac{\sqrt{2} - \sqrt{6}}{4}$
7. $2 - \sqrt{3}$ 9. $\sqrt{6} - \sqrt{2}$ 11. $\frac{24}{25}$ 13. $\frac{7}{24}$
15. $\frac{1517}{156}$

17. $\sin(-x) = \sin(0 - x)$
$= \sin 0 \cos x - \cos 0 \sin x$
$= (0)\cos x - (1)\sin x$
$= -\sin x$

19. $\sin\left(\frac{\pi}{2} - x\right) = \sin\frac{\pi}{2}\cos x - \cos\frac{\pi}{2}\sin x$
$= (1)\cos x - (0)\sin x$
$= \cos x$

21. $\sec\left(\frac{\pi}{2} - x\right) = \dfrac{1}{\cos\left(\frac{\pi}{2} - x\right)}$
$= \dfrac{1}{\sin x}$
$= \csc x$

23. $[\cos(x - y)][\cos(x + y)]$
$= (\cos x \cos y + \sin x \sin y)$
$\cdot (\cos x \cos y - \sin x \sin y)$
$= \cos^2 x \cos^2 y - \sin^2 x \sin^2 y$
$= \cos^2 x(1 - \sin^2 y) - (1 - \cos^2 x)\sin^2 y$
$= \cos^2 x - \sin^2 y \cos^2 x - \sin^2 y + \sin^2 y \cos^2 x$
$= \cos^2 x - \sin^2 y$

25. $\sin(x + y) = \sin[x - (-y)]$
$= \sin x \cos(-y) - \cos x \sin(-y)$
$= \sin x \cos y - \cos x (-\sin y)$
$= \sin x \cos y + \cos x \sin y$

27. $\tan(x + \pi) = \dfrac{\tan x + \tan \pi}{1 - \tan x \tan \pi}$
$= \dfrac{\tan x + 0}{1 - \tan x (0)}$
$= \dfrac{\tan x}{1}$
$= \tan x$

29. $\dfrac{\cos(x - y)}{\cos(x + y)} = \dfrac{\cos x \cos y + \sin x \sin y}{\cos x \cos y - \sin x \sin y}$

$= \dfrac{\frac{\cos x \cos y}{\sin x \cos y} + \frac{\sin x \sin y}{\sin x \cos y}}{\frac{\cos x \cos y}{\sin x \cos y} - \frac{\sin x \sin y}{\sin x \cos y}}$

$= \dfrac{\frac{\cos x}{\sin x} + \frac{\sin y}{\cos y}}{\frac{\cos x}{\sin x} - \frac{\sin y}{\cos y}}$

$= \dfrac{\cot x + \tan y}{\cot x - \tan y}$

33. $4x^3 + 8x^2 - 3x - 9$ [4.2]

35. $4x^2 + 2x - 3;\ 8x^2 + 26x + 18$ [4.2]

5.7

Quadrant II	Quadrant III	Quadrant IV
1. I	II	II

3. $\dfrac{\sqrt{2 + \sqrt{2}}}{2}$ **5.** $\dfrac{\sqrt{2 - \sqrt{3}}}{2}$

7. $\dfrac{\sqrt{8 + 2\sqrt{6} + 2\sqrt{2}}}{4}$ or $\dfrac{\sqrt{2 + \sqrt{2} + \sqrt{3}}}{2}$

9. $\cos 2x = \cos^2 x - \sin^2 x$
$= (1 - \sin^2 x) - \sin^2 x$
$= 1 - 2\sin^2 x$

11. $\cos x = \cos 2\left(\frac{x}{2}\right)$
$\cos x = 1 - 2\sin^2\frac{x}{2}$
$2\sin^2\frac{x}{2} = 1 - \cos x$
$\sin^2\frac{x}{2} = \frac{1}{2}(1 - \cos x)$
$\sin\frac{x}{2} = \pm\sqrt{\frac{1}{2}(1 - \cos x)}$

13. $\dfrac{1 + \tan^2 x}{2 \tan x} = \dfrac{1 + \frac{\sin^2 x}{\cos^2 x}}{\frac{2 \sin x}{\cos x}}$

$= \dfrac{\frac{\cos^2 x + \sin^2 x}{\cos^2 x}}{\frac{2 \sin x \cos x}{\cos^2 x}}$

$= \dfrac{1}{2 \sin x \cos x}$
$= \dfrac{1}{\sin 2x}$
$= \csc 2x$

15. $\sqrt{\dfrac{1 - \cos x}{1 + \cos x}} = \sqrt{\dfrac{(1 - \cos x)(1 + \cos x)}{(1 + \cos x)(1 + \cos x)}}$

$= \dfrac{\sqrt{1 - \cos^2 x}}{1 + \cos x}$

$= \dfrac{\sqrt{\sin^2 x}}{1 + \cos x}$

$= \dfrac{\sin x}{1 + \cos x}$

17. $\dfrac{2\sin^2\frac{x}{2} + \cos x}{\sec x} = \dfrac{(2)\left(\frac{1}{2}\right)(1 - \cos x) + \cos x}{\frac{1}{\cos x}}$

$= \dfrac{1 - \cos x + \cos x}{\frac{1}{\cos x}}$

$= \dfrac{1}{\frac{1}{\cos x}}$

$= \cos x$

19. $\sin^4 x - \cos^4 x = (\sin^2 x - \cos^2 x)(\sin^2 x + \cos^2 x)$
$= -(\cos^2 x - \sin^2 x)(1)$
$= -(1 - \sin^2 x - \sin^2 x)$
$= -(1 - 2\sin^2 x)$
$= 2\sin^2 x - 1$

21. $\sec 2x + \tan 2x = \dfrac{1}{\cos 2x} + \dfrac{\sin 2x}{\cos 2x}$
$= \dfrac{1 + \sin 2x}{\cos 2x}$
$= \dfrac{1 + 2\sin x \cos x}{\cos^2 x - \sin^2 x}$
$= \dfrac{\cos^2 x + 2\sin x \cos x + \sin^2 x}{\cos^2 x - \sin^2 x}$
$= \dfrac{(\cos x + \sin x)(\cos x + \sin x)}{(\cos x + \sin x)(\cos x - \sin x)}$
$= \dfrac{\cos x + \sin x}{\cos x - \sin x}$

23. $\sin 3x + \sin x$
$$= \sin (2x + x) + \sin x$$
$$= \sin 2x \cos x + \cos 2x \sin x + \sin x$$
$$= (2 \sin x \cos x) \cos x + (2 \cos^2 x - 1) \sin x$$
$$\quad + \sin x$$
$$= 2 \sin x \cos^2 x + 2 \sin x \cos^2 x - \sin x + \sin x$$
$$= 4 \sin x \cos^2 x$$
$$= 2(2 \sin x \cos x) \cos x$$
$$= 2 \sin 2x \cos x$$

27. $\cos (-x) = \cos x, \sin (-x) = \sin x$ [3.4]

29. $\sec x = \frac{1}{\cos x}, \csc x = \frac{1}{\sin x}$, reciprocal identities [1.2, 5.5]

31. $\dfrac{\cos \theta}{\sin \theta} = \dfrac{\cos \theta}{\sin \theta}$
$$= \dfrac{\frac{x}{r}}{\frac{y}{r}}$$
$$= \frac{x}{r} \cdot \frac{r}{y}$$
$$= \frac{x}{y}$$
$$= \cot \theta \text{ [5.5]}$$

5.8
1. $x = \frac{3\pi}{2}$ **3.** $x = \frac{\pi}{6}, \frac{11\pi}{6}$ **5.** $x = \frac{\pi}{3}, \frac{2\pi}{3}, \frac{4\pi}{3}, \frac{5\pi}{3}$
7. $x = \frac{\pi}{4}, \frac{3\pi}{4}, \frac{5\pi}{4}, \frac{7\pi}{4}$ **9.** $x = \frac{\pi}{2}, \frac{3\pi}{2}, \frac{\pi}{6}, \frac{7\pi}{6}$
11. $x = \frac{\pi}{3}, \frac{5\pi}{3}, \pi$ **13.** $x = 0, \pi, \frac{\pi}{3}, \frac{5\pi}{3}$
15. $x = \frac{\pi}{3}, \frac{2\pi}{3}, \frac{4\pi}{3}, \frac{5\pi}{3}$ **17.** $\mathbb{R}$ **19.** $x = \frac{\pi}{4}$ **21.** $\varnothing$
23. $x = 0, \frac{\pi}{3}, \frac{2\pi}{3}, \pi, \frac{4\pi}{3}, \frac{5\pi}{3}$
25. $x = \frac{\pi}{8}, \frac{3\pi}{8}, \frac{\pi}{4}, \frac{5\pi}{8}, \frac{7\pi}{8}, \frac{9\pi}{8}, \frac{11\pi}{8}, \frac{13\pi}{8}, \frac{15\pi}{8}, \frac{3\pi}{4},$
$\frac{5\pi}{4}, \frac{7\pi}{4}$ **27.** $x = 0.8411, 5.4421$
29. $x = 0.5880, 3.7296, 2.3562, 5.4978$
33. $x = -\frac{\ln 3}{2} \approx -0.55$ [4.6] **35.** $x = 2$ [3.1]
37. $x = \frac{1 \pm \sqrt{11}}{2}$ [5.2]

Chapter 5 Review
1. $x = 1, -3$ **3.** $x = \frac{-9 \pm \sqrt{57}}{4}$
5. $x = -6, 2, -1$ **7.** $x = 5$ **9.** $x = 8$
11. $x = \pm 5$ **13.** $x = \frac{1}{9}$ **15.** $x = 243$
17. $x = \frac{\pi}{4}, \frac{5\pi}{4}, 0, \pi$ **19.** $x = -3, -2, -1, 5$
21. $x = -0.7253$
23. $\sin (x + 2\pi) = \sin x \cos 2\pi + \cos x \sin 2\pi$
$$= \sin x(1) + \cos x(0)$$
$$= \sin x$$
25. $\tan \left(\frac{\pi}{2} - \theta\right) = \dfrac{\sin \left(\frac{\pi}{2} - \theta\right)}{\cos \left(\frac{\pi}{2} - \theta\right)}$
$$= \dfrac{\cos \theta}{\sin \theta}$$
$$= \cot \theta$$

27. $1 - \sin x \cos x \tan x = 1 - \sin x \cos x \left(\dfrac{\sin x}{\cos x}\right)$
$$= 1 - \sin^2 x$$
$$= \cos^2 x$$
29. 1.254 **31.** 0.4339

Chapter 6—Conic Sections and Polar Graphs

6.1
1. $(3, 0); r = 7; D = \{x \mid -4 \leq x \leq 10\};$
$R = \{y \mid -7 \leq y \leq 7\}$
3. $(5, -1); r = 2\sqrt{2}; D = \{x \mid 5 - 2\sqrt{2} \leq x \leq 5 + 2\sqrt{2}\}; R = \{y \mid -1 - 2\sqrt{2} \leq y \leq -1 + 2\sqrt{2}\}$
5. $(-3, -2); r = 3; D = \{x \mid -6 \leq x \leq 0\};$
$R = \{y \mid -5 \leq y \leq 1\}$
7. $(-1, 0); r = \sqrt{5}; D = \{x \mid -1 - \sqrt{5} \leq x \leq -1 + \sqrt{5}\}; R = \{y \mid -\sqrt{5} \leq y \leq \sqrt{5}\}$
9. **11.**

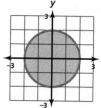 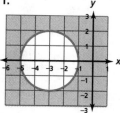

13. $x^2 + (y + 4)^2 = 4$
15.

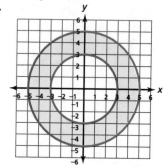

17. $(x - 3)^2 + (y + 3)^2 = 169$
19. $(x + 6)^2 + (y + 5)^2 = 18$
21. $(x - 1)^2 + (y - 1)^2 = 1$
23. $(x - 2)^2 + (y - 5)^2 = 121$ **25.** $3x + y = 9$
27.

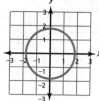

31. 3003 ft, approximately 0.57 mi [1.4]
33. 7 is 10^2 or 100 times greater [4.8]
35. \$7764.85 [4.8]

6.2

1. 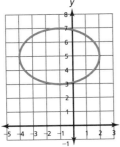 $D = \{x \mid -4 \le x \le 2\};$
$R = \{y \mid 3 \le y \le 7\}$

3. 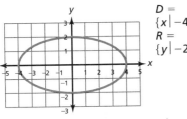 $D = \{x \mid -4 \le x \le 4\};$
$R = \{y \mid -2 \le y \le 2\}$

5. $D = \{x \mid -3 \le x \le 3\};$ **7.** $D = \{x \mid -3 \le x \le 3\};$
$R = \{y \mid -2 \le y \le 8\}$ $R = \{y \mid -2 \le y \le 2\}$

 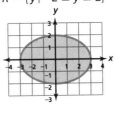

9. 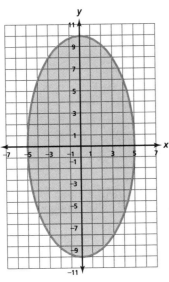 $D = \{x \mid -5 \le x \le 5\};$
$R = \{y \mid -10 \le y \le 10\}$

11.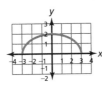

13.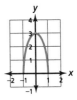

15.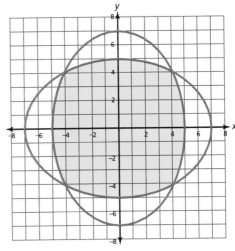

17.

19. $\dfrac{(x-2)^2}{25} + \dfrac{(y-3)^2}{4} = 1$ **21.** $\dfrac{x^2}{289} + \dfrac{y^2}{225} = 1$

23. $\dfrac{x^2}{9} + \dfrac{y^2}{25} = 1$ **25.** $\dfrac{x^2}{25} + \dfrac{y^2}{16} = 1$

27. $(-3, -1 + 3\sqrt{5})(-3, -1 - 3\sqrt{5})$

31. $85.9°$ [1.1]   **33.** $\sqrt{3}$ [1.2]

6.3

1. $F(0, 5.25)$; D: $y = 4.75$ **3.** $F(2, 4.25)$; D: $y = 3.75$

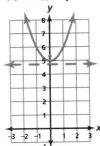

5.

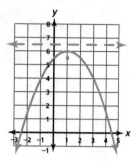

$F(1, 5.5); D: y = 6.5$

7.

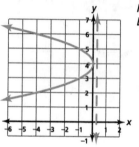

$F(-4.75, 0);$
$D: x = -5.25$

9.

$F(-0.25, 4);$
$D: x = 0.25$

11. $F(-8, 2); D: y = 0$

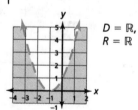

13. $F(0, 5.979);$
$D: y = 5.821$

15. 1

17.

$D = \mathbb{R},$
$R = \mathbb{R}$

19.

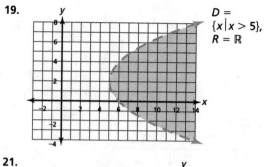

$D =$
$\{x \mid x > 5\},$
$R = \mathbb{R}$

21.

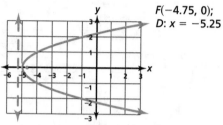

23.

25. The parabola grows wider.

27.

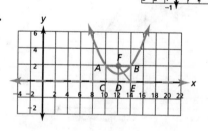

29.

1. $\overline{AB} \parallel \overline{CD}$ (Given)
2. $FA = AC, FB = BE$ (Definition of parabola)
3. $AC = BE = FD$ (Parallel lines are equidistant at all points)
4. $FA + FB = AB$ (Betweenness of points)
5. $FA + FB = AC + BE$ (Addition property of equality: step 2)

6. $AB = 2FD$ (Substitution: step 3 and 4 into step 5)
7. $AB = 2(2p)$ (p is the distance from the vertex to the focus and vertex to the directrix)
8. $AB = 4p$ (Simplify)

9. $\frac{AB}{p} = \frac{4}{1}$ (Multiplication property of equality) yes, it will be the same for all parabolas since the reasons above hold for all parabolas.

33. sin and cos: $[-1,1]$, tan and cot: $(-\infty, \infty)$, sec and csc: $(-\infty, -1] \cup [1, \infty)$ [3.5]

35. $x = 82.22°$ [5.8]   37. $x = 13°$ [5.8]

6.4

1. $(0, 0)$; $y = 0$; $(\pm 5, 0)$; $y = \pm\frac{4}{3}x$

3. $(2, 0)$; $y = 0$; $(2 \pm 7.2, 0)$; $y = \pm\frac{2}{3}(x - 2)$

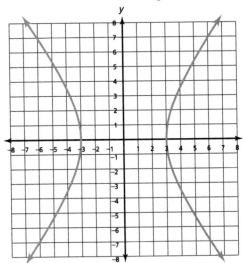

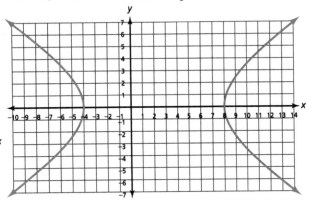

5. $(-1, 0)$; $y = 0$; $(-1 \pm 5.8, 0)$;
$y = \pm\frac{5}{3}(x + 1)$

7. $(-1, -2)$; $x = -1$;
$(-1, -2 \pm 3.2)$;
$y = \pm 3(x + 1) - 2$

9. $(5, 2)$; $y = 2$; $(5 \pm 2.2, 2)$;
$y = \pm 2(x - 5) + 2$

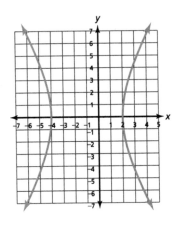

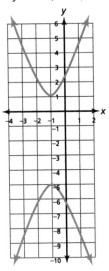

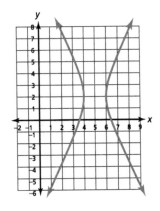

11. $D = \{x \mid x \le -3 \text{ or } x \ge 3\}$; $R = \mathbb{R}$

13. $D = \mathbb{R}$; $R = \{y \mid y \le -3 \text{ or } y \ge 1\}$

15. $D = \mathbb{R}$; $R = \mathbb{R}$ **17.** $\frac{y^2}{64} - \frac{x^2}{16} = 1$

19. $\frac{y^2}{225} - \frac{x^2}{64} = 1$ **21.** No equation exists.

23. $\frac{(y + 3)^2}{16} - \frac{(x + 3)^2}{9} = 1$

25. $y \ge 1$; $f(x) = \frac{2}{3}\sqrt{9 + (x + 3)^2} - 1$

29. $f(x) = 1 + a^x$ where $a > 1$ [4.6]

31. $y = 3 \sin 2(x - \pi)$ [3.5] **33.** 7 [4.2]

6.5

1. $k = 5$ **3.** $k = 6$ **5.** $k = 4$

7.

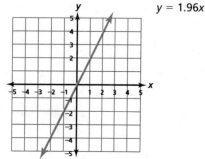

$A = \frac{6}{B}$

9.

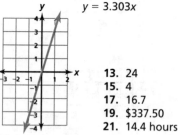

$y = 1.96x$

11.

$y = 3.303x$

13. 24
15. 4
17. 16.7
19. \$337.50
21. 14.4 hours

27. $\frac{(x - 2)^2}{4} + \frac{(y - 1)^2}{9} = 1$ [6.2]

29. $\frac{(y - 3)^2}{9} - \frac{(x + 1)^2}{16} = 1$ [6.4]

6.6

1. $(1.7, 1)$ **3.** $(1, 0)$ **5.** $(-1.5, 2.6)$ **7.** $(2\sqrt{2}, 45°)$
9. $(17, 28°)$

11. $r \cos \theta = 6$; vertical line through $(6, 0°)$

13. $r \cos \theta + r \sin \theta = 3$; oblique line through $(3, 90°)$, $(3, 0°)$

15. $r = 5$; circle with radius 5 centered at the pole

17. $x = 5$; vertical line through $(5, 0)$

19. $x^2 + y^2 = 25$; circle with center $(0, 0)$ and radius 5

21. $x^2 + (y - 3)^2 = 9$; circle with center $(0, 3)$ and radius 3

23. B **25.** A **27.** F **29.** C **31.** H
37.

$\sin^2 x + \cos^2 x = 1$	$\sin^2 x + \cos^2 x = 1$
$\dfrac{\sin^2 x}{\sin^2 x} + \dfrac{\cos^2 x}{\sin^2 x} = \dfrac{1}{\sin^2 x}$	$\dfrac{\sin^2 x}{\cos^2 x} + \dfrac{\cos^2 x}{\cos^2 x} = \dfrac{1}{\cos^2 x}$
$1 + \cot^2 x = \csc^2 x$	$\tan^2 x + 1 = \sec^2 x$ [5.5]

39. 30° 34' [1.6] **41.** $f(x) = \frac{4}{x}$ [6.5]

6.7

1.

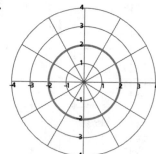

3.

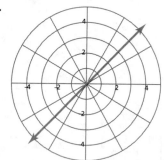

5.

7.

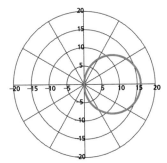

9.

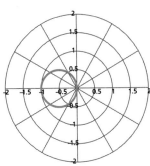

11. circle; $r = \frac{k}{2}$;
center $\left(\frac{k}{2}, 0\right)$
or $\left(\frac{k}{2}, \pi\right)$

13. 9 petals; 7
15. 16 petals; 5

17.

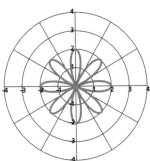

19.

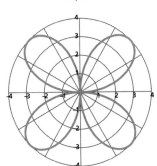

21.

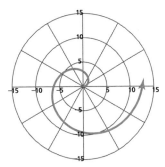

23.

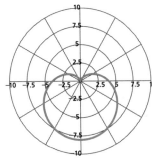

25.

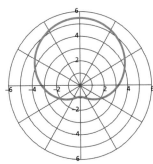

31. $f(x) = \dfrac{\sqrt{32 - 6x^2}}{2}$, $x > 0$ [4.4]

33. sin: III, IV; cos: II, III; tan: II, IV [1.2]

6.8

1. F   **3.** B   **5.** C
7. limaçon with loop

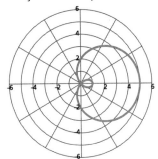

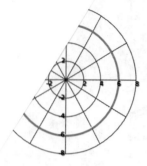

lemniscate

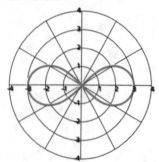

13. lemniscate

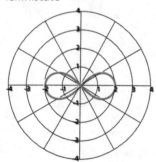

15. circle

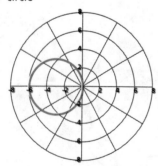

17. cardioid

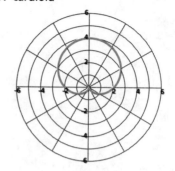

19. rose

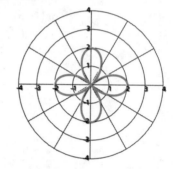

21. limaçon without loop

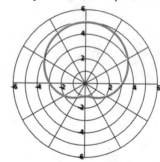

23. $\left(\frac{3}{2}, \frac{\pi}{3}\right), \left(\frac{3}{2}, \frac{5\pi}{3}\right)$ **25.** $\left(\frac{1}{2}, \frac{\pi}{6}\right), \left(\frac{1}{2}, \frac{5\pi}{6}\right)$

33.

2	−7	16	−33
2	−5	7	−8
2	−1	1	0
2	1	4	7

$f(-2) = -33; f(-1) = -8; f(1) = 0; f(2) = 7$ [2.5]

35. f is translated one unit left and g is translated one unit up. [3.2]

37. no, f has a hole at $x = -4$ [3.8]

Chapter 6 Review

1.

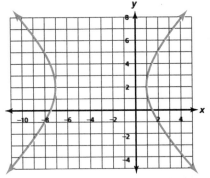

3.

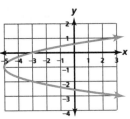

5.

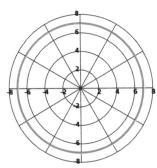

7.

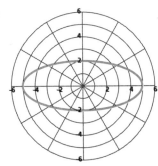

9.

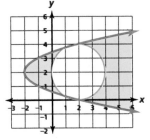

11. $(x + 2)^2 + (y + 5)^2 = 16$; $e = 0$

13. $x = \frac{1}{16}y^2 + 5$; $e = 1$ **15.** $r = 3$; $e = 0$

17. $(x - 4)^2 + y^2 = 16$ **19.** $(4.2, 315°)$

21.

23. polar: $\left(-5, \frac{5\pi}{3}\right)$, $\left(5, \frac{8\pi}{3}\right)$;

rectangular: $\left(-\frac{5}{2}, \frac{5\sqrt{3}}{2}\right)$

25.

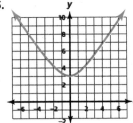

27.

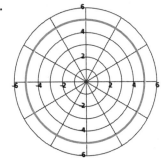

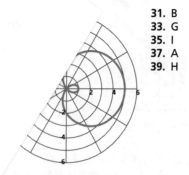

31. B
33. G
35. I
37. A
39. H

...er 7—Complex Numbers

1. $7 - i$ 3. $6 + 3i$ 5. $\frac{11}{13} + \frac{23}{13}i$ 7. $11 - 6i$

9. $-2 - 23i$ 11. $\frac{50}{41} - \frac{1}{41}i$

13. $2.88 + 13.55i$ 15. -1 17. $-i$ 19. $x = \pm 2i$

21. $x = \frac{45}{34} - \frac{27}{34}i$ 23. $x = \frac{-3 \pm \sqrt{21}}{3}$

25. $x = \frac{-79}{1105} - \frac{333}{1105}i$ 27. $(x + 3i)(x - 3i)$

29. $(x + 2i)(x + 6i)$ 31. $(x - 3i)(x - 6i)$

33.

Let $z \in \mathbb{C}$	1. Given
$z = a + bi$, where a, $b \in \mathbb{R}$	2. Definition of complex number
$\bar{z} = a - bi$	3. Definition of conjugate
$z \cdot \bar{z} = (a + bi)(a - bi)$	4. Mult. property of equality
$z \cdot \bar{z} = a^2 - abi + abi - b^2i^2$	5. Definition of mult. for complex numbers
$z \cdot \bar{z} = a^2 + b^2$	6. Substitute for i^2
$a^2 + b^2 \in \mathbb{R}$	7. Closure property of mult. and addition over $\mathbb{R}$
$\therefore z \cdot \bar{z} \in \mathbb{R}$ for every $z \in \mathbb{C}$	8. Substitution

35.

$z \in \mathbb{R}$	1. Given
Let $z = a + 0i$	2. Definition of complex number
$\bar{z} = a - 0i$	3. Definition of conjugate
$z = a + 0i = a$	4. Zero property for multiplication; identity property for addition
$\bar{z} = a - 0i = a$	
$\therefore z = \bar{z} \; \forall z \in \mathbb{R}$	5. Transitive property of equality

39. hyperbola [6.4] 41. 51.8°, 308.2° [5.8]

7.2

1.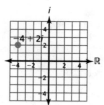

3.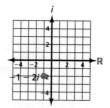

5. <7, 3> 7. <0, 6>

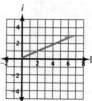

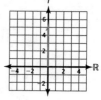

9. $2\sqrt{17}$ 11. $2\sqrt{41}$ 13. 9 15. $-2 + 2i$

17. $4\sqrt{3} - 4i$ 19. $\sqrt{85}$ 21. $\sqrt{10}$ 23. $\theta \approx 40°36'$

25. $\frac{15\pi}{7}, \frac{29\pi}{7}, \frac{43\pi}{7}$

27. :Prompt A
:Prompt B
:Prompt C
:Prompt D
:Disp $\sqrt{((A + C)^2 + (B + D)^2)}$

35. $f(x) = \tan \frac{1}{3}\left(x - \frac{\pi}{8}\right)$ [3.5] 37. b [6.8]

7.3

1. $\sqrt{2}$ cis $\frac{3\pi}{4}$ 3. 9 cis 0 5. 2 cis $\frac{5\pi}{4}$ 7. 6 cis $\frac{3\pi}{2}$

9. 5 cis 5.64 11. $3i$ 13. $6 - 6\sqrt{3}i$

15. $-2.08 + 4.55i$

17. $(2 + 2\sqrt{3}) + (2 - 2\sqrt{3})i$; $4\sqrt{2}$ cis $\frac{23\pi}{12}$

19. $-6 - 6\sqrt{3}i$; 12 cis $\frac{4\pi}{3}$ 27. $x = \frac{\pi}{2}$ [5.8]

29. $x = 1.159, 5.124$ [5.8]

31. $f \circ g = f, g \circ f = g$ [4.2]

7.4

1. $-2 + 2i$ 3. $128 + 128i$ 5. $-239 - 28,560i$

7. $\sqrt[3]{4}$ cis $\frac{\pi}{2}$ 9. $\sqrt[6]{2}$ cis $\frac{\pi}{12}$

11. 7 cis 25°, 7 cis 205°

13. 3 cis $\frac{\pi}{8}$, 3 cis $\frac{5\pi}{8}$, 3 cis $\frac{9\pi}{8}$, 3 cis $\frac{13\pi}{8}$

15. 2 cis 7°, 2 cis 67°, 2 cis 127°, 2 cis 187°, 2 cis 247°, 2 cis 307°

17. $\pm 2, \pm 2i$ 19. $1 + i, -1 - i$

21. $-1.9 + 0.79i, 1.9 - 0.79i$ 23. $-239 - 28,560i$

27. $x = \frac{4489}{256} \approx 17.5$ [5.3] 29. $3 \le x \le 64$ [5.3]

7.5

1. <1, 5>

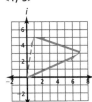

3. <0, 1>

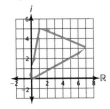

5. <−14, −5>

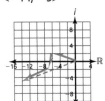

7. <2, 8>

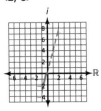

9.

<8, 7>

11. <10, 8>   **13.** <2, −1>   **15.** <6, −4>
17. $-4\vec{i} - 9\vec{j}$ **19.** $-4\vec{i} + 10\vec{j}$
25.

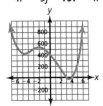

27. zeros: $x = \pm\sqrt{3}$; vertical: $x = 1$, $x = -\frac{1}{2}$;
horizontal: $y = \frac{3}{2}$ [3.8]

7.6

1. 31   **3.** 0, orthogonal   **5.** 6   **7.** 0, orthogonal
9. $\frac{21}{5} + 4\pi\sqrt{2}$ **11.** −69   **13.** 18   **15.** 14.7
17. 8.3   **19.** <−7, 1>   **21.** <8, 14>
23. a.

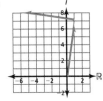

b.

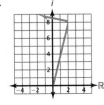

c.

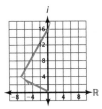

d.

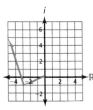

25. 36°52′   **29.** $x \approx 0.6025$ [5.4]
31. [6.4]

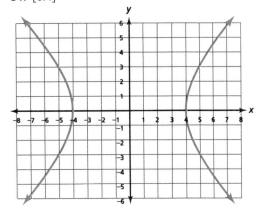

33. 20°, 70° [1.4]

7.7

1. 107°   **3.** a force equal to the force of gravity
5. 5 mph at a bearing of 143°
7. 141 mi at a bearing of 270°
9. 168 mph at a bearing of 237°
17. A varies directly with r^2. [6.5]
19. <11,5> [7.5]

Chapter 7 Review

1. $-3 + 5i$ **3.** $(7x + i)(7x - i)$ **5.** $\alpha = \frac{2}{5}$, $\beta = \frac{11}{5}$
7. $2\sqrt{3}$ **9.** $\sqrt{58} \approx 7.6$ **11.** $4 - 4\sqrt{3}i$
13. $-\sqrt{2} + \sqrt{2}i$ **15.** -4
17. $\frac{\sqrt{2}}{2} + \frac{\sqrt{2}}{2}i$, $\frac{-\sqrt{2}}{2} + \frac{\sqrt{2}}{2}i$, $\frac{-\sqrt{2}}{2} - \frac{\sqrt{2}}{2}i$,
$\frac{\sqrt{2}}{2} - \frac{\sqrt{2}}{2}i$ **19.** 64 cis 0
21. a. $\sqrt{2}$ cis $\frac{7\pi}{4}$; b. 30 cis $\frac{\pi}{3}$; c. 3 cis $\frac{3\pi}{2}$
23. 92°44′

Chapter 8—Matrix Algebra

8.1

1. $(8, -3)$ **3.** $\left(5, \frac{-1}{2}\right)$ **5.** $\varnothing$ **7.** $(2.1, 1.2)$
9. $(1, -2)$ **11.** $(1, -7, -1)$; $(10, -4, 2)$
13. $(13, -3, 3)$ **15.** $\left(12 - \frac{4}{3}s - 8t, s, t\right)$, $(0, 3, 1)$
17. $(s - 3t + 5, s, t)$ **23.** 40°, 45°, 95° [1.6]
25. $f(x) = 3 \cos 4\left(x - \frac{\pi}{3}\right)$ [3.5]
27. $2\sqrt{2}$ cis $\frac{7\pi}{4}$ [7.3]

3. $\begin{bmatrix} -5 & -8 & 4 \\ 3 & 7 & 4 \end{bmatrix}$

$\begin{bmatrix} 7.92 & 15.076 & 28.92 \\ 87.48 & -169.9 & 9.77 \end{bmatrix}$

$\text{, } g = -2, h = -55$

$\begin{bmatrix} 26 \\ 46 \end{bmatrix}$ **13.** $\begin{bmatrix} 4 \\ -2 \end{bmatrix}$

$\begin{bmatrix} -2 \\ 4 & 11 \end{bmatrix} + \begin{bmatrix} 8 & 3 \\ -6 & 9 \end{bmatrix} + \begin{bmatrix} -9 & 7 \\ 12 & 3 \end{bmatrix} =$

$\begin{bmatrix} 13 & 1 \\ -10 & 20 \end{bmatrix} + \begin{bmatrix} -9 & 7 \\ 12 & 3 \end{bmatrix} = \begin{bmatrix} 4 & 8 \\ 2 & 23 \end{bmatrix}$

$\begin{bmatrix} 5 & -2 \\ -4 & 11 \end{bmatrix} + \left[\begin{bmatrix} 8 & 3 \\ -6 & 9 \end{bmatrix} + \begin{bmatrix} -9 & 7 \\ 12 & 3 \end{bmatrix} \right] =$

$\begin{bmatrix} 5 & -2 \\ -4 & 11 \end{bmatrix} + \begin{bmatrix} -1 & 10 \\ 6 & 12 \end{bmatrix} = \begin{bmatrix} 4 & 8 \\ 2 & 23 \end{bmatrix}$

17. $(5+6)\begin{bmatrix} 4 & -2 & 3 \\ 2 & 3 & 1 \end{bmatrix} = 11\begin{bmatrix} 4 & -2 & 3 \\ 2 & 3 & 1 \end{bmatrix} = \begin{bmatrix} 44 & -22 & 33 \\ 22 & 33 & 11 \end{bmatrix}$

$5\begin{bmatrix} 4 & -2 & 3 \\ 2 & 3 & 1 \end{bmatrix} + 6\begin{bmatrix} 4 & -2 & 3 \\ 2 & 3 & 1 \end{bmatrix} =$

$\begin{bmatrix} 20 & -10 & 15 \\ 10 & 15 & 5 \end{bmatrix} + \begin{bmatrix} 24 & -12 & 18 \\ 12 & 18 & 6 \end{bmatrix} = \begin{bmatrix} 44 & -22 & 33 \\ 22 & 33 & 11 \end{bmatrix}$

19. $\begin{bmatrix} 4 & -2 \\ -6 & 2 \end{bmatrix}\begin{bmatrix} 3 \\ 5 \end{bmatrix} = \begin{bmatrix} 2 \\ -8 \end{bmatrix} = \begin{bmatrix} -6 & 4 \\ -1 & -1 \end{bmatrix}\begin{bmatrix} 3 \\ 5 \end{bmatrix}$ but

$\begin{bmatrix} 4 & -2 \\ -6 & 2 \end{bmatrix} \ne \begin{bmatrix} -6 & 4 \\ -1 & -1 \end{bmatrix}$

21. $\begin{bmatrix} 3 & 1 & 4 \\ 2 & 1 & 6 \end{bmatrix}\begin{bmatrix} 6 \\ -3 \\ -2 \end{bmatrix} = \begin{bmatrix} 7 \\ -3 \end{bmatrix}$

25. $3, -4$ (multiplicity 2), $\pm i$ [2.6]

27. $h \approx 646$ ft [1.7]   **29.** increasing [4.5]

8.3

1. $(-2, 4)$ **3.** $\left(\frac{11}{7}, -9, 4\right)$

5. $\left(\frac{9}{2} - 5t, 2 - 3t, t\right)$; dependent   **7.** $(-2, 3)$

9. $\varnothing$ **11.** $\left(\frac{13 - t}{14}, \frac{2 - 12t}{7}, t\right)$; $(1, 2, -1)$

13. $\left(\frac{8t - 12}{5}, \frac{7t + 17}{5}, t\right)$; $(-4, 2, -1)$ **15.** $\left(\frac{-1}{2}, 3, 2\right)$

17. $\left(\frac{1}{2}, -2, 0, 3\right)$ **19.** $\left(\frac{49}{120}, \frac{259}{48}\right)$

25. $2ab; b^2 - a^2$ [5.7]   **27.** $\frac{d}{c}; -\frac{c}{d}$ [5.5]

29. $\pm\sqrt{\frac{1+b}{2}}; \pm\sqrt{\frac{1}{2}\left(1 \pm \sqrt{\frac{1+b}{2}}\right)}$ [5.7]

8.4

1. 87   **3.** -8 **5.** 15   **7.** $\begin{bmatrix} 2 & 7 & 8 \\ -3 & 5 & 2 \\ 4 & -5 & 6 \end{bmatrix}$ **9.** -126

11. 28   **13.** -88

15. $|A| = 0$; each entry times its cofactor is zero.

17. $|A| = a_{11} \cdot a_{22} \cdot a_{33} \cdots \cdot a_{nn}$ **19.** -24 **21.** 0

29. $\frac{x^2 + 4x + 3}{x + 1}; \frac{x^2 + x}{3x^2 + 4x + 1}$ [4.2]

31. [3.2]

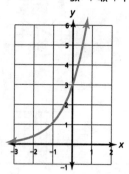

8.5

1. 64   **3.** -6 **5.** 6   **7.** 2   **9.** 442   **11.** 0   **13.** 0

15. 810

23. [3.7]

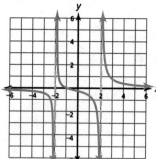

25. [4.5]

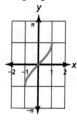

8.6

1. $(2, -3)$ **3.** $\varnothing$ **5.** $(2, 7)$ **7.** $y = \frac{13}{19}$

9. $y = \frac{20}{11}$ **11.** $(5, -2, 0)$ **13.** $\left(\frac{1}{3}, 5, 1\right)$

15. $(-0.119, -3.495, -3.585)$ **17.** $v = \frac{-1}{3}$

19. 1   **25.** $x \approx 1.5098$ [5.4]   **27.** $\frac{160}{9}$ [6.5]

8.7

1. 46   **3.** 420   **5.** 0, not invertible

7. 0, not invertible   **9.** $\frac{1}{6}$ **11.** 6

13. $\begin{bmatrix} \frac{1}{2} & \frac{-3}{4} \\ -1 & 2 \end{bmatrix}$ **15.** $\begin{bmatrix} 2 & -3 \\ -3 & 6 \end{bmatrix}$

17. $\begin{bmatrix} \frac{11}{3} & \frac{-4}{3} & -2 \\ \frac{-4}{3} & \frac{2}{3} & 1 \\ 2 & -1 & -1 \end{bmatrix}$ **19.** $\begin{bmatrix} 1 & 2 & \frac{9}{2} \\ 0 & -1 & -3 \\ \frac{1}{2} & 0 & -1 \end{bmatrix}$

21. $\begin{bmatrix} 7 & 2 & 4 & -3 \\ -1 & 1 & 0 & 0 \\ -4 & -2 & -3 & 2 \\ 3 & 1 & 2 & -1 \end{bmatrix}$

23. $\begin{bmatrix} -\dfrac{68}{699} & -\dfrac{161}{699} & \dfrac{71}{699} \\ -\dfrac{45}{233} & -\dfrac{62}{233} & \dfrac{23}{233} \\ -\dfrac{125}{699} & -\dfrac{224}{699} & \dfrac{38}{699} \end{bmatrix}$ **25.** $(-2, 7)$

27. $(9, 8, -2)$ **31.** $x = 4$ [5.3]

33. $x = \dfrac{-21 + 15\sqrt{2} + 28\sqrt{3} - 20\sqrt{6}}{39}$ [5.1]

35. 97 [8.4]

Chapter 8 Review

1. $(3, -2)$ **3.** $\begin{bmatrix} -22 & 21 \\ -31 & 18 \end{bmatrix}$ **5.** 162

7. $\begin{bmatrix} \dfrac{4}{5} & \dfrac{1}{10} & \dfrac{3}{10} \\ \dfrac{-3}{2} & \dfrac{1}{2} & 0 \\ \dfrac{-7}{10} & \dfrac{1}{10} & \dfrac{-1}{5} \end{bmatrix}$ **9.** $\begin{bmatrix} -2 & -2 \\ 4 & -7 \\ 4 & -6 \end{bmatrix}$

11. $(0, 4, 9)$ **13.** 8   **15.** $\dfrac{1}{128}$ **17.** $\dfrac{1}{256}$ **19.** 32

21. $\begin{bmatrix} 2 & 0 & 0 & 0 \\ 0 & 2 & 0 & 0 \\ 0 & 0 & 2 & 0 \\ 0 & 0 & 0 & 2 \end{bmatrix}$

Chapter 9—Statistics

9.1
1. 13   **3.** 39   **5.** 43   **7.** 41.4   **9.** 33 and 46
11. 89.2   **13.** 89.5
15. $\dfrac{h + l}{2}$, h: highest score, l: lowest score
17. a parameter   **19.** 172.72   **21.** 20.655
23. (Answers may vary.) ignores people who never pass the intersection and those who work other shifts or at home
27. $A = 70°29'$, $B = 67°31'$, $a = 29.6$ or $A = 25°31'$, $B = 112°29'$, $a = 13.5$ [1.5]
29. interchange two rows [8.5]
31. $\dfrac{(x - 5)^2}{25} + \dfrac{(y + 2)^2}{10.9375} = 1$ [6.2]

9.2
1. 120   **3.** 0.9   **5.** 15.1   **7.** 46.87   **9.** 2.8
11. 41   **13.** 1619.67   **15.** 12.1   **17.** 144   **19.** 850
21. 306.274   **23.** 43.75   **29.** $2x - 7y = 39$ [2.2]
31. vertical asymptote [3.6]

9.3
1. 0.71   **3.** -0.57 **5.** -1.43 **7.** $\bar{y} = 80$, $s_y = 10$
9. $\bar{y} = 5$, $s_y = 2$ **11.** 43.3   **13.** -1.78

15. $z(39) = -1.21$, $z(42) = -0.37$, $z(44) = 0.20$, $z(45) = 0.48$, $z(47) = 1.05$ **17.** 100
19. 0.63 standard deviation above the mean
21. 0.96   **23.** 0.10
27. $\sin^2 x + \cos^2 x = 1$, $1 + \cot^2 x = \csc^2 x$, $\tan^2 x + 1 = \sec^2 x$ [5.5]

29. [6.7]

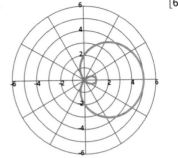

9.4
1. 0   **3.** 89%   **5.** 6   **7.** [107, 113]
9. [101, 119] or [102.15, 117.5]
11. No, because of the mounds at both 11 and 15
13. [5.45, 22.55]   **15.** 100%; yes, it exceeds 88.9%
17. data in [40.7, 45.1] is 71% > 68%
19. data in [36.3 , 49.5] is 100% > 99.5%
25. 402°, 762°, 1122°, $-318°$, $-678°$, $-1038°$ [1.1]
27. $y = 4$ [3.2]   **29.** $y = \dfrac{8}{9}$ [3.8]

9.5
1. 45.5%   **3.** 38.7%   **5.** 54.1%   **7.** 14.5%
9. 5.9%   **11.** 91.9%   **13.** 97.7%   **15.** 23.6%
17. $-0.51 \le z \le 0.51$ **19.** $-1.34 \le z \le 1.34$
21. 90.9%   **23.** 86.4%
25. 39.7, about 40th percentile
27. 2.9%, about the 3rd percentile
33. 22°, 40°, 118° [1.6]
35. [6.7]

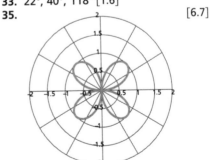

9.6
1. $m = -\dfrac{1}{2}$ **3.** $y = -\dfrac{1}{2}x + 7$ **5.** 0   **7.** 8
9. best-fit line improves on average by 45%, slope of line is positive   **11.** $\bar{x} = 4.6$, $\bar{y} = 6$
13. 46   **15.** $m = -1.38$ **17.** $y = -1.38x + 12.35$

19. best-fit line improves on average by 96%, slope is negative. **21.** $m = 0.1762$

23. $y = 0.1762x - 2.852$ **25.** $r^2 = 0.9933$

31. $-6, -3, 2, 5$ [2.6]

33.

[2.7]

35. $\left(\frac{36}{23}, -\frac{8}{23}\right)$ [8.6]

9.7

1. $H_0: \mu_1 = \mu_2$ **3.** $z = \pm3.08$

5. Mrs.Yiuchi's class gets the pizza. **7.** 2.24

9. Do not reject H_0. **11.** $H_0: \mu = 500$ **13.** 2.54

15. They surpassed the national average.

17. 2.33 **19.** Reject H_0.

21. $z = 2.704$; $p = 0.0069 < \alpha$, therefore reject H_0.

27. vertical: $x = -1$, $x = 3$; horizontal: $y = 1$; x-intercepts: $(-3, 0)$, $(4, 0)$; y-intercept: $(0, 4)$ [3.8] **29.** $A \approx 109$ units^2 [1.7] **31.** 79% [9.5]

Chapter 9 Review

1. 45 **3.** 43.5 **5.** 11 **7.** 3.69 **9.** $\bar{x} = 46$, $s = 16$

11. 19.5% **13.** 77.0% **15.** $-0.77 \leq z \leq 0.77$

17. $z \geq 1.04$ **19.** [4, 16] **21.** $H_0: \mu = 11$

23. $z = 1.89$ **25.** $y = 1.84x + 5.9$

27. 93.75% by Chebyshev's rule

29. 81.98%; by the central limit theorem

Chapter 10—Sequences

10.1

1. $2, \frac{1}{2}, 2, \frac{1}{2}, 2, \frac{1}{2}, \ldots$

3. $11, 7, 3, -1, -5, -9, \ldots$; arithmetic

5. $3, 4, 7, 11, 18, 29, \ldots$; Fibonacci

7. $27, 18, 12, 8, \frac{16}{3}, \frac{32}{9}, \ldots$; geometric

9. $\frac{1}{2}, \frac{1}{4}, \frac{1}{6}, \frac{1}{8}, \frac{1}{10}, \frac{1}{12}, \ldots$; harmonic

11. $A_n = A_{n-1}$; $A_1 = 6$

13. $A_n = 2A_{n-1}$; $A_1 = 3$; geometric

15. $A_n = A_{n-1} + n$; $A_1 = 3$

17. $A_n = \frac{1}{10}A_{n-1} + 1$; $A_1 = 8$

19. $A_n = \dfrac{1}{\frac{1}{A_{n-1}} + 1}$; $A_1 = 1$; harmonic

21. 2, 13, 68, 343, 1718, 8593, 42,968

25. $\sin A = \frac{3\sqrt{34}}{34}$, $\cos A = \frac{5\sqrt{34}}{34}$, $\tan A = \frac{3}{5}$ [1.4]

27. $m = \frac{13}{4}$ [2.2] **29.** no slope [2.2]

10.2

1. $-3, -1, 1, 3, 5, \ldots$ **3.** $0, 1, 3, 6, 10, \ldots$

5. $2, \frac{3}{2}, \frac{4}{3}, \frac{5}{4}, \frac{6}{5}, \ldots$ **7.** $-2, 1, 4, 7, 10, \ldots$

9. $x + y, 2(x + y), 6(x + y), 24(x + y), 120(x + y), \ldots$

11. $-11.77, -15.07, -18.37, -21.67, -24.97, \ldots$

13. $A_n = 3(2)^{n-1}$; geometric **15.** $A_n = \sqrt{n}$

17. $A_n = \frac{1}{-2 + 7n}$; harmonic **19.** $A_n = \frac{n-1}{n}$

21. $A_n = \frac{1}{\sqrt{5}}\left[\left(\frac{1 + \sqrt{5}}{2}\right)^n - \left(\frac{1 - \sqrt{5}}{2}\right)^n\right]$, Fibonacci

23. $\frac{1}{47}$; $\frac{1}{138}$ **25.** $\frac{6}{7}$; $\frac{19}{20}$ **27.** $1, \frac{1}{4}, \frac{1}{7}, \frac{1}{10}, \frac{1}{13}, \ldots$

31. $3 + i, 5 - 2i$; no x-intercept [6.6]

33. bearing of 83.3° [7.7]

10.3

1. $5, 11, 17, 23, 29$ **3.** $9, -3, 1, -\frac{1}{3}, \frac{1}{9}$

5. log 64, log 128, log 256, log 512, log 1024

7. $-17, -11, -5, 1, 7$ **9.** $-2, 1, -\frac{1}{2}, \frac{1}{4}, -\frac{1}{8}$

11. geometric, $r = 2$; $A_n = \frac{1}{6}(2)^n$

13. arithmetic, $d = 3$; $A_n = 3n - 2$

15. neither **17.** neither **19.** neither **21.** $\frac{x^{20}}{y^{17}}$

23. $A_n = 100(0.6)^n$, n = number of bounces; 6

25. $A_n - A_{n-1} = d$ where d is a constant, since A_n is arithmetic.

Thus, $kA_n - kA_{n-1} = k(A_n - A_{n-1}) = kd$.

$\therefore kA_n$ is arithmetic with common difference kd.

27. $\dfrac{A_n{}^k}{A_{n-1}{}^k} = \left[\dfrac{A_n}{A_{n-1}}\right]^k = r^k$

$\therefore A_n{}^k$ is geometric with ratio r^k.

35. $\pm1, \pm3, \pm\frac{1}{2}, \pm\frac{3}{2}, \pm\frac{1}{4}, \pm\frac{3}{4}$ [5.1]

37. variable in the exponent [3.2] **39.** 18 [8.4]

10.4

1. $1 - 1 = 0$ is divisible by 6; true

3. $27 - 3 = 24$ is divisible by 6; true

5. $343 - 7 = 336$ is divisible by 6; true

7. $P(k) = k^3 - k$

9.
$$k^3 - k = 6c$$
$$k^3 + 3k^2 + 3k + 1 - k - 1 = 6c + 3k^2 + 3k$$
$$(k + 1)^3 - (k + 1) = 6k + 3k(k + 1)$$
$P(k + 1)$ is divisible by 6 since $6k$ and $3k(k + 1)$ are both divisible by 6.

11. Let $P(n): (1 + n)^2 \geq 1 + n^2$.

1. $P(1)$ is true, since
$$P(1): (1 + 1)^2 \geq 1 + 1^2$$
$$4 \geq 2$$

2. Show $P(k) \rightarrow P(k + 1)$
Suppose $P(k)$ is true, then
$(k + 1)^2 \geq 1 + k^2$
$k^2 + 2k + 1 \geq 1 + k^2$
$k^2 + 4k + 1 \geq k^2 + 2k + 1$ (add $2k$ to both sides)
$k^2 + 4k + 4 \geq 1 + k^2 + 2k + 1$ (add 3 to the larger side and 1 to the smaller)
$(k + 2)^2 \geq 1 + (k + 1)^2$ (factor)
$[1 + (k + 1)]^2 \geq 1 + (k + 1)^2$
then $P(k + 1)$ is true.

$\therefore$ $P(n)$ is true for all $n \in \mathbb{N}$ by mathematical induction

13. Let $P(n)$: $2^n > n$.
  1. $P(1)$ is true, since
     $P(1)$: $2^1 > 1$
     $2 > 1$
  2. Show $P(k) \rightarrow P(k + 1)$
     Suppose $P(k)$ is true, then
     $2^k > k$
     Since $2^k > 1$, you add the larger number to the larger side
     $2^k + 2^k > k + 1$
     $2^k(1 + 1) > k + 1$
     $2^k \cdot 2 > k + 1$
     $2^{k+1} > k + 1$;
     then $P(k + 1)$ is true;
     $\therefore$ $P(n)$ is true for all $n \in \mathbb{N}$.

15. Let $P(n)$: $a(b_1 + b_2 + b_3 + \cdots + b_n) = ab_1 + ab_2 + ab_3 + \cdots + ab_n$ for $n \geq 2$.
  1. $P(2)$ is true, since
     $a(b_1 + b_2) = ab_1 + ab_2$ by the distributive property.
  2. $P(k) \rightarrow P(k + 1)$.
     Suppose $P(k)$ is true, then
     $a(b_1 + b_2 + b_3 + \cdots + b_k) = ab_1 + ab_2 + ab_3 + \cdots + ab_k$
     $a(b_1 + b_2 + b_3 + \cdots + b_k) + ab_{k+1} = ab_1 + ab_2 + ab_3 + \cdots + ab_k + ab_{k+1}$
     $a(b_1 + b_2 + b_3 + \cdots + b_k + b_{k+1}) = ab_1 + ab_2 + ab_3 + \cdots + ab_k + ab_{k+1}$ by factoring
     then $P(k + 1)$ is true;
     $\therefore$ $P(n)$ is true for all $n \in \mathbb{N}$, $n \neq 1$.

19. $f(x)$ [2.6]   **21.** $(-\infty, 1), (1, \infty)$ [3.6]

10.5

1. 3, 3.3, 3.33, 3.333, 3.3333   **3.** 1, 4, 9, 16, 25

5. $1, 1 + \frac{x}{2}, 1 + \frac{x}{2} + \frac{x^2}{6}, 1 + \frac{x}{2} + \frac{x^2}{6} + \frac{x^3}{24},$
   $1 + \frac{x}{2} + \frac{x^2}{6} + \frac{x^3}{24} + \frac{x^4}{120}$ **7.** $-1, 0, -1, 0, -1$

9. 35   **11.** $1 + i$ **13.** 1062   **15.** 438.75

17. 868   **19.** 20,100

21. Let $P(n)$: $1^2 + 2^2 + 3^2 + \cdots + n^2 = \frac{n(n + 1)(2n + 1)}{6}$

  1. $P(1)$ is true; since
     $$P(1): 1^2 = \frac{1(1 + 1)[2(1) + 1]}{6} = \frac{1 \cdot 2 \cdot 3}{6} = 1$$
  2. Show $P(k) \rightarrow P(k + 1)$.
     Suppose $P(k)$ is true, then
     $$1^2 + 2^2 + 3^2 + \cdots + k^2 = \frac{k(k + 1)(2k + 1)}{6}$$
     $$1^2 + 2^2 + 3^2 + \cdots + k^2 + (k + 1)^2$$
     $$= \frac{k(k + 1)(2k + 1)}{6} + (k + 1)^2$$
     $$= \frac{2k^3 + 3k^2 + k}{6} + \frac{6k^2 + 12k + 6}{6}$$

$$= \frac{2k^3 + 9k^2 + 13k + 6}{6}$$

$$= \frac{(k + 1)(k + 2)(2k + 3)}{6}$$

$$= \frac{(k + 1)[(k + 1) + 1][2(k + 1) + 1]}{6}$$

$\therefore$ $P(n)$ is true for all $n \in \mathbb{N}$.

23. Let $P(n)$: $1^4 + 2^4 + \cdots + n^4 = \frac{n(n + 1)(2n + 1)(3n^2 + 3n - 1)}{30}$

  1. $P(1)$ is true, since
     $$P(1): 1^4 = \frac{1(1 + 1)[2(1) + 1][3(1)^2 + 3(1) - 1]}{30}$$
     $$= \frac{1 \cdot 2 \cdot 3 \cdot 5}{30} = 1$$
  2. Show $P(k) \rightarrow P(k + 1)$.
     Suppose $P(k)$ is true, then
     $$1^4 + 2^4 + \cdots + k^4$$
     $$= \frac{k(k + 1)(2k + 1)(3k^2 + 3k - 1)}{30}$$
     $$1^4 + 2^4 + \cdots + k^4 + (k + 1)^4$$
     $$= \frac{k(k + 1)(2k + 1)(3k^2 + 3k - 1)}{30} + (k + 1)^4$$
     $$= \frac{k(k + 1)(2k + 1)(3k^2 + 3k - 1) + 30(k + 1)^4}{30}$$
     $$= \frac{(k + 1)[k(2k + 1)(3k^2 + 3k - 1) + 30(k + 1)^3]}{30}$$
     $$= \frac{(k + 1)(6k^4 + 9k^3 + k^2 - k + 30k^3 + 90k^2 + 90k + 30)}{30}$$
     $$= \frac{(k + 1)(6k^4 + 39k^3 + 91k^2 + 89k + 30)}{30}$$
     $$= \frac{(k + 1)(k + 2)(2k + 3)(3k^2 + 9k + 5)}{30}$$
     $$= \frac{(k + 1)[(k + 1) + 1][2(k + 1) + 1][3(k + 1)^2 + 3(k + 1) - 1]}{30}$$
     $\therefore$ $P(n)$ is true for all $n \in \mathbb{N}$

31. $8666.27 [4.8]   **33.**

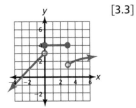

[3.3]

35. Answers will vary. If a test is extremely easy and most students do well. [9.5]

10.6

1. $S_n = \frac{n(3n - 1)}{2}$; 145   **3.** $S_n = n(2n + 5)$; 250

5. $S_n = 3^n - 1$; 59,048

7. $S_n = 2(2^n - 1) + \frac{3n^2 + 3n}{2}$; 2211   **9.** -60

11. $2^{201} - 2$ **13.** 190 **15.** 730 **17.** 21,523,599
19. $\frac{11}{7}$
27. a. decreasing; b. neither; c. increasing;
d. neither [4.1]
29. $f^{-1}(x) = -\ln 2x$; $p^{-1}(x) = \sqrt[3]{x - 1}$ [4.3]
31. 28 [10.5]

Chapter 10 Review
1. 4620.866; 10,305.707 **3.** $A_n = -2n + 14$; -2
5. $A_n = \frac{-1}{5}n + \frac{37}{5}$; $\frac{29}{5}$
7. $A_n = 8_5(3)^{n-5}$; 1944 or $A_n = 8_5(-3)^{n-5}$; -1944
9. $\frac{1}{198}$ **11.** 39,916,800 **13.** 5.25 **15.** 8.99999
17. Write the sum of the first n terms of the
sequence.
$S_n = A_1 + A_2 + A_3 + A_4 + A_5 + \cdots + A_n$
Since A is an arithmetic sequence, each term
can be expressed using the explicit formula
and common difference: $A_2 = A_1 + d$,
$A_3 = A_1 + 2d$, etc. Use these to express S_n.
$S_n = A_1 + (A_1 + d) + (A_1 + 2d) + (A_1 + 3d)$
$\quad + (A_1 + 4d) + \cdots + [A_1 + (n - 1)d]$
Now use the commutative property to reverse
the order of the original terms in S_n.
$S_n = A_n + A_{n-1} + A_{n-2} + A_{n-3} + \cdots + A_1$
Each term can be expressed using the common
difference by subtracting from the last term.
For example, $A_{n-1} = A_n - d$, $A_{n-2} = A_n - 2d$,
etc. Substitute these quantities.
$S_n = A_n + (A_n - d) + (A_n - 2d) + (A_n - 3d)$
$\quad + (A_n - 4d) + \cdots + [A_n - (n - 1)d]$
Add the two equations for S_n, then divide
both sides by 2.
$S_n = A_n + (A_n - d) + (A_n - 2d) + \cdots$
$\qquad + [A_n - (n - 1)d]$
$S_n = A_1 + (A_1 + d) + (A_1 + 2d) + \cdots$
$\qquad + [A_1 + (n - 1)d]$
$\overline{2S_n = (A_1 + A_n) + (A_1 + A_n) + (A_1 + A_n)}$
$\qquad + \cdots + (A_1 + A_n) = n(A_1 + A_n)$
$S_n = \frac{n(A_1 + A_n)}{2}$
19. Let $P(n)$: $1 + 3 + 5 + \cdots + (2n - 1) = n^2$.
1. $P(1)$ is true, since
$P(1)$: $(2 \cdot 1 - 1) = 1 = 1^2$
2. Show $P(k) \rightarrow P(k + 1)$
Suppose $P(k)$ is true, then
$1 + 3 + 5 + \cdots + (2k - 1) = k^2$
$1 + 3 + 5 + \cdots + (2k - 1) + [2(k + 1) - 1]$
$= k^2 + 2(k + 1) - 1$
$= k^2 + 2k + 1$
$= (k + 1)^2$
then $P(k + 1)$ is true;
$\therefore$ $P(n)$ is true for all $n \in \mathbb{N}$
21. 91,578,912

Chapter 11—Limits and Calculus

11.1
1. 5 **3.** $\frac{5}{7}$ **5.** 8 **7.** 4 **9.** no limit **11.** 0.25
13. 8 **15.** 46 **17.** $\frac{1}{12}$ **19.** $\frac{6}{5}$ **21.** 0 **23.** 10; 1
25. 0; 5
31. [3.8]

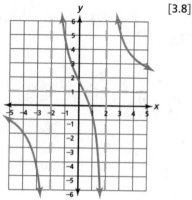

33. $\tan(\theta + \pi) = \tan \theta$; $\tan \theta = \frac{1}{\cot \theta}$;
$\cot\left(\frac{\pi}{2} - \theta\right) = \tan \theta$ [5.6]

11.2
1. $\lim A_n = \frac{3}{2} \neq 0$ **3.** $\lim A_n = \frac{-2}{5} \neq 0$
5. harmonic **7.** $\frac{10}{3}$ **9.** 1 **11.** constant, diverges
13. geometric, $\frac{1}{2}$ **15.** geometric, $-\frac{4}{3}$
17. geometric with $r > 1$, diverges **19.** $\frac{25}{12}$
25. $y = \sqrt{2x}$ translated right $\frac{3}{2}$ and down 4.
D: $\left\{x \mid x \geq \frac{3}{2}\right\}$, R: $\{y \mid y \geq -4\}$ [4.4]
27. $-\frac{\pi}{3}$; $-\frac{\pi}{6}$ [4.5] **29.** 0 [11.1]

11.3
1. D **3.** E **5.** C **7.** no limit; $\lim\limits_{x \to 1} f(x) = -\infty$
9. -1 **11.** 3 **13.** -2 **15.** -1 **17.** 2
19. no limit; one-sided limits differ
21. -1; one-sided limits agree
23. $-\infty$; neither one-sided limit exists
25. 5 **27.** 0
33. [3.2]

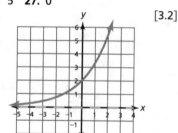

35. $x \approx 0.3054$ [5.4] **37.** $\left(\frac{69}{19}, \frac{-2}{19}, \frac{8}{19}\right)$ [8.3]

11.4

1. $(-\infty, 2), [2, \infty)$ **3.** $(0, 1), (1, \infty)$

5. $\{[n, n + 1) \mid n \in \mathbb{Z}\}$

7. (1) yes, (2) no, (3) no **9.** (1) no, (2) yes, (3) no

11. (1) $f(0) = 0$; (2) $\lim_{x \to 0^-} f(x) = 0 = \lim_{x \to 0^+} f(x)$;

(3) $\therefore \lim_{x \to 0} f(x) = f(0)$

13. (1) $f(0) = -1$; (2) $\lim_{x \to 0^-} f(x) = -1 = \lim_{x \to 0^+} f(x)$;

(3) $\therefore \lim_{x \to 0} f(x) = f(0)$

15. (1) $f(0) = 3$; (2) $\lim_{x \to 0^-} f(x) = 3 = \lim_{x \to 0^+} f(x)$;

(3) $\therefore \lim_{x \to 0} f(x) = f(0)$

17. $x = 1$; $f(1)$ is undefined.

19. $x = 0$; $\lim_{x \to 0} f(x)$ does not exist.

21. $x = 1$; $\lim_{x \to 1} f(x) = -\infty$ and therefore does not exist.

23. no **25.** no **27.** yes **29.** yes **37.** 1.5% [9.5]

39. $x = \dfrac{5 \pm 2\sqrt{2}}{3}$ [4.4]

11.5

1.

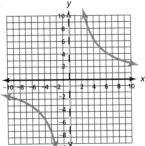

3. ∞

5. no limit

7. $\lim_{x \to \infty} f(x) = 1$

9. $\lim_{x \to 2^-} f(x) = -\infty$

11. 3 **13.** ∞

15. 2

17. no limit

19. $y = 1.4323$

21. ∞

23.

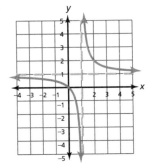

29. jump at $x = -1$ $\left(\lim_{x \to -1^-} f(x) = 1 \text{ but} \right.$

$\left. \lim_{x \to -1^+} f(x) = 0 \right)$; hole at $x = 1$ ($f(x)$ is undefined); gaps at $x = 5 \pm \sqrt{2}$ (vertical asymptotes) [3.3] **31.** 0 [11.1]

33. foci: $(\pm\sqrt{22}, 0)$, $e = \dfrac{\sqrt{22}}{4} \approx 1.17$, asymptotes:

$y = \pm\dfrac{\sqrt{6}}{4}$

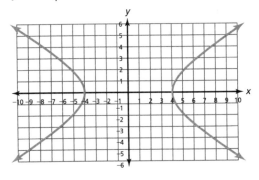

11.6

1. 49 **3.** 4 **5.** 0 **7.** -5 **9.** -1 **11.** no limit

13. 0 **15.** $\dfrac{\sqrt{2}}{4}$ **17.** 1 **19.** -1

25. $y \approx 296.6$ [6.5]

27. $\dfrac{1}{\tan^2 x + 1} - \cos^2 x \tan^2 x$

$= \dfrac{1}{\sec^2 x} - \cos^2 x \left(\dfrac{\sin^2 x}{\cos^2 x} \right)$

$= \cos^2 x - \sin^2 x$

$= \cos 2x$ [5.6]

29. $0.4 + 1.5i$ [7.4]

Chapter 11 Review

1. 3 **3.** 40 **5.** $1 + \dfrac{1}{\sqrt{2}}$ **7.** 16 **9.** 7 **11.** -9

13. ∞ **15.** -8 **17.** $\dfrac{1}{3}$ **19.** $\dfrac{1}{4}$ **21.** 1

23. no limit

25. defined at $f(0)$, no limit, limit not equal to $f(0)$

Chapter 12—Differential Calculus

12.1

1. 2 **3.** 2 **5.** 2 **7.** $2x + 2$ **9.** 0 **11.** $2x - 1$

13. They are all 2. **15.** The derivatives are 0.

17. $f'(x) = m$ **19.** $f'(x) = 2ax + b$

21. $f'(x) = 2x$, $g'(x) = 3$, $f'(x) + g'(x) = 2x + 3 = \dfrac{d}{dx}[f(x) + g(x)]$; yes

27. $23 + 41i$; $-\dfrac{47}{65} - \dfrac{1}{65}i$ [7.1]

29. a. 35; b. 875; c. -7; d. 7 [8.5] **31.** 4 [11.2]

12.2

1. yes **3.** yes **5.** no, $x \in \mathbb{Z}$

7. $f'(4) = 24$, $f'(-2) = -12$

9. $f'(1) = 2$, $f'(-3) = -6$

11. $f'(15) = 241.9$, $f'(23.5) = 377.05$

13. no; $x = 0$; sharp point **15.** yes **17.** yes

19. no, a vertical tangent exists at $x = 0$; $(0, \infty)$

21. $y = 6x - 3$ **23.** $y = 3x - 2$

25. $y = 10x - 16$ **31.** $\sqrt{34}$ cis 59.04° [7.3]

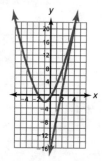

33. $1.7 + 0.6i$; $-1.4 + 1.2i$; $-0.3 - 1.8i$ [7.4]
35. 0.684 [9.6]

12.3
1. $15x^2$ **3.** $6x^2 + 18x$
5. $5x^4 - 8x^3 - 3x^2 + 6x - 2$ **7.** $15x^{14}$ **9.** $44x^3$
11. $24x^3 + 10x$ **13.** $4x^3 - 9x^2$
15. $230x^{22} - 68x^{16} - 33x^{10} + 10x^4 - 1$
17. $\frac{1}{2}x^{-\frac{1}{2}} = \frac{1}{2\sqrt{x}}$ **19.** $16x^7 - 60x^5$
21. $48x^3 - 120x$ **23.** $4x^3 + 9x^2 - 6x - 6$
29. $|A| = 0$ [8.7]   **31.** $\theta \approx 67.7°$ [7.7]   **33.** 0 [11.4]

12.4
1. $36x^2(x^3 - 4)^{11}$ **3.** $(42x + 63)(x^2 + 3x - 7)^{20}$
5. $(120x^3 + 120x)(x^4 + 2x^2 + 5)^9$
7. $5x^4 - 8 + (\ln 4)4^x$ **9.** $(6 \ln 4)4^{6x}$
11. $\frac{3}{2\sqrt{3x + 5}}$ **13.** $5(x - 8)^{49}(51x - 8)$
15. $(2 \ln 5)5^{2x}$ **17.** $x\,3^x(2 + x \ln 3)$
19. $\frac{e^x}{2\sqrt{1 + e^x}}$ **21.** $10(2x + 1)^4$ **23.** 0 **25.** 0
29. $\begin{bmatrix} 48 & -14 & -26 \\ 25 & 29 & 18 \end{bmatrix}$ [8.2]   **31.** 3254 [8.4]
33. $3x^2 - 5$ [12.3]

12.5
1. $\frac{16x}{(x^2 + 5)^2}$ **3.** $2x \cos(x^2 - 8)$ **5.** $\frac{-x^2 + 7x - 6}{e^x}$
7. $\cos 2x$ **9.** $\sec x \tan x$
11. $\frac{7 \cos 7x - (2 \ln 5) \sin 7x}{5^{2x}}$ **13.** $-e^{\cot x} \csc^2 x$
15. $\frac{\tan^7 x[(56x^2 - 24x + 8)\sec^2 x - (14x - 3)\tan x]}{(7x^2 - 3x + 1)^2}$
17. $\frac{-1}{(x^2 - 1)^{\frac{3}{2}}}$
19. $\frac{2 \cos x(x + \cos^2 x) - \sin x(1 - 2 \sin x \cos x)}{2(x + \cos^2 x)^{\frac{3}{2}}}$
25. $(3, 5, -4)$ [8.6]
27. about 2; 0 [11.3, 11.5]

12.6
1. $f(t) = -16t^2 + 63t + 4$ **3.** 66 ft   **5.** 4 seconds
7. 31 ft/s (upward)   **9.** after 1.97 seconds
11. 0 ft/s   **13.** $f'(t) = -32t$
15. $f(t) = -4.9t^2 + 176.4t$
17. $f'(4) = 137.2$ m/s upward   **19.** 36 seconds
21. -9.8 m/s² (decreasing)   **23.** 129.05 m
25. 44.1 m/s   **29.** $\begin{bmatrix} \frac{5}{11} & \frac{3}{11} \\ \frac{-2}{11} & \frac{1}{11} \end{bmatrix}$ [8.7]
31. $x = \pm 5\sqrt{2}i$ [7.1]   **33.** 38°, 142° [5.8]

Chapter 12 Review
1. $2x$ **3.** no, jump at $x = -1$ **5.** yes   **7.** 0
9. $5x^4$ **11.** 53   **13.** $(\ln 7)7^x$ **15.** $\frac{1}{3}x^{\frac{-2}{3}} = \frac{1}{3\sqrt[3]{x^2}}$
17. $\frac{x^2 + 1}{3x^2}$ **19.** $2x \cos(x^2 - 5)$
21. $\frac{2}{243}e^x(e^x - 1)^5$ **23.** $m = 3$

Glossary

abscissa The first coordinate of an ordered pair.

absolute value The distance of a point from the origin (on a number line or in the complex plane).

absolute value function A function that uses absolute values in its rule.

ambiguous case A triangle in which two sides and an angle opposite one of them are known; more than one solution of the triangle is possible.

amplitude Half the distance between the maximum and minimum values of a periodic function.

angle of depression The angle formed by a horizontal line and the line of sight as the observer looks at an object that is below the horizontal.

angle of elevation The angle formed by a horizontal line and the line of sight as the observer looks at an object that is above the horizontal.

argument The angle formed by the positive real axis with the terminal ray passing through the graph of a complex number.

arithmetic sequence A sequence in which any two consecutive terms differ by a constant, called the common difference.

asymptote A line which a graph approaches either as x approaches a specific value or as x increases or decreases without bound.

augmented matrix A matrix for a system of equations which includes a column for the constants.

bell curve The standard normal distribution.

best-fit line A linear model for data obtained by minimizing the squared errors (least squares method).

central angle An angle that has its vertex at the center of a circle.

circle The intersection of a right circular conical surface and a plane that is perpendicular to the axis; the locus of points in a plane at a fixed distance (radius) from a fixed point (center) of the plane.

closed interval An interval that includes its endpoints, denoted $[a, b]$.

coefficient matrix A rectangular array of numbers representing the coefficients of a system of equations.

coefficient of determination The square of the correlation, denoted r^2; the reduction in error obtained by using a regression model instead of the mean.

cofunction identity A trig identity expressing the relationship between a trig function and its cofunction (sine to cosine, etc.).

common logarithm Base ten logarithm.

complex number The sum of a real number and a pure imaginary number, $a + bi$ (where $a, b \in \mathbb{R}$ and $i = \sqrt{-1}$).

composition of functions The function obtained by mapping domain elements of f to range elements of g: $f(g(x))$.

concavity The direction that a curve bends on an interval (up or down).

conditional equation An equation that has a limited number of solutions.

conical surface The union of all lines that connect the points of a simple curve in a given plane to a given point not in the plane.

conic section The intersection of a conical surface and a plane.

conjugate axis The axis perpendicular to the transverse axis at the center of a hyperbola.

conjugate of a complex number A complex number obtained by changing the sign of the imaginary part of a given complex number.

consistent system A system of equations that has at least one solution.

constant function A function of the form $f(x) = k$, where $k \in \mathbb{R}$.

continuous function A function with no breaks in its graph (no gaps, holes, jumps, etc.).

convergent series A series with a finite sum.

correlation A measure of the relationship between two variables; ranges from -1 to 1.

cosine function The set of ordered pairs in which the first coordinate is the measure of an angle and the corresponding second coordinate is the cosine of the angle.

coterminal angles Angles in standard position with the same terminal rays.

decreasing function A function such that $f(x_1) > f(x_2)$ whenever $x_1 < x_2$.

dependent system A consistent system of equations with an infinite number of solutions.

derivative The instantaneous rate of change of a variable; the slope of a tangent line to a curve.

determinant A real number calculated from a square matrix by using minors.

differentiable function A function that has a derivative at every point of its domain.

directrix The fixed line in the definition of a parabola.

direct variation A function of the form $f(x) = kx$, where $k \in \mathbb{R}, k > 0$.

divergent series A series that does not converge.

domain The set of first coordinates of the ordered pairs of a relation.

dot product of vectors A scalar obtained by adding the products of corresponding coordinates.

eccentricity Deviation of a conic section from a circular path.

echelon form A matrix in which the entries below the main diagonal are zero.

ellipse The intersection of a right circular conical surface and a plane that intersects only one nappe of the surface, is not parallel to an element of the surface, and is not perpendicular to the axis of the surface; the locus of points in a plane such that the sum of the distances from two fixed points (foci) to a point is a constant.

equal matrices Matrices with the same dimensions and equal corresponding entries.

even function A function such that $f(-x) = f(x)$ for all x; the graph is symmetric across the y-axis.

explicit formula A formula for the nth term of a sequence based only on n.

exponential function A function of the form $f(x) = Ca^x$, where $c > 0$, $a > 0$, $a \neq 1$, and $x \in \mathbb{R}$.

extrapolation Using a model to predict values outside the range of the data.

extremum A maximum or minimum value of a function as well as local maximum and minimum values.

factorial A sequential product; $n! = n(n-1)(n-2) \cdots (3)(2)(1)$, where $n \in \mathbb{N}$ and $0! = 1$.

Fibonacci sequence The sequence in which $A_{n+1} = A_n + A_{n-1}$ for each $n = 2, 3, 4, \ldots$.

focus(pl, foci) The fixed point(s) described in the definitions of a parabola, ellipse, and hyperbola.

function A relation in which every first coordinate has one and only one second coordinate associated with it.

Gaussian elimination A method of solving a system by adding equations in matrix form.

geometric sequence A sequence in which the ratio of every two consecutive terms is a constant, r, called the common ratio.

greatest integer function The greatest integer less than or equal to x, denoted $[x]$, where $x \in \mathbb{R}$.

harmonic sequence A sequence A_n such that the reciprocals form an arithmetic sequence.

hyperbola The intersection of a right circular conical surface and a plane that intersects both nappes of the conical surface; the locus of points in a plane having a constant difference of distances from the two foci.

hypothesis A proposition advanced as possibly true.

hypothesis testing Testing one hypothesis concerning parameters against another hypothesis.

identity An equation that is true for all values of the variable.

identity function The function $f(x) = x$, having equal first and second coordinates.

identity matrix A square matrix having ones down the main diagonal and zeros elsewhere.

imaginary number Any complex number $a + bi$ such that $b \neq 0$.

imaginary part The coefficient b of the imaginary unit of a complex number in standard form.

imaginary unit The number i, equal to $\sqrt{-1}$, which is the basis of the complex number system.

inclination of a line The angle that a line makes with the positive x-axis.

inconsistent system A system of equations that has no solution.

increasing function A function such that $f(x_1) < f(x_2)$ whenever $x_1 < x_2$.

independent system A consistent system of equations that has a finite number of solutions.

inflection point A point at which a graph reverses concavity.

initial ray The initial position of an angle viewed as a sweeping ray, usually the x-axis.

interpolation The estimation of a function value between two known function values.

inverse of a function The function (or relation) obtained by interchanging the first and second coordinates of each ordered pair of a function, denoted $f^{-1}(x)$ if a function.

inverse variation A function of the form $y = \frac{k}{x}$, where k is a non-zero constant.

level of significance The probability of incorrectly rejecting the null hypothesis.

limit of a function The value approached by a function $f(x)$ as x approaches a given value.

limit of a sequence The value approached by the terms of a sequence A_n as n approaches ∞.

linear function A function having a line as its graph

linear regression A method of finding the best-fit line to data points using the method of least squares.

logarithm The exponent of a base required to obtain a given value, denoted $\log_a x$.

logarithmic function The inverse of the exponential function, $x = a^y$, denoted by $y = \log_a x$, where $a \neq 1$, $a > 0$, and $x > 0$.

magnitude of a vector The length of the vector (or modulus of associated complex number).

major axis The axis on which the foci of an ellipse are located.

mathematical induction A method of proving formulas or statements for each natural number by checking that the statement holds for $n = 1$ and then showing that each statement guarantees the next.

mean The sum of a set of values divided by the number of values.

mean deviation The mean of the absolute values of the deviations in a set of data.

median The middle value in a set of data when ordered by magnitude (or average of two middle values when there are an even number of values).

method of least squares Minimizing the sum of squared errors to obtain an optimal model.

midrange The mean of the highest and lowest values in a set of data; the midpoint of the range.

minor The determinant obtained by crossing out the row and column of a given entry of a square matrix.

minor axis The axis of an ellipse perpendicular to the major axis through the center.

mode The most frequently occurring value in a set of data.

model A function used for approximation based on data values at selected points.

modulus The absolute value of a complex number (distance from the complex origin).

monotonic function A function that is either nondecreasing or nonincreasing.

mound shaped data A set of data that can be approximated by the bell curve.

multiplicity The number of factors of a polynomial having a given factor as a zero.

nappe One of the two parts of a conical surface that join at the vertex.

natural logarithm A logarithm whose base is e.

neighborhood of a point An open interval centered at the given point.

nondecreasing function A function such that $f(x_1) \le f(x_2)$ whenever $x_1 < x_2$.

nonincreasing function A function such that $f(x_1) \ge f(x_2)$ whenever $x_1 < x_2$.

odd function A function for which $f(-x) = -f(x)$ for all x; the graph of an odd function is symmetric across the origin.

one-sided limit The limit as x approaches a given number from the right (right-hand limit) or from the left (left-hand limit).

one-to-one correspondence A pairing of the elements of two sets A and B so that each element of A corresponds to exactly one element of B, and every element of B corresponds to some domain element.

one-to-one function A function such that $f(a) = f(b)$ implies $a = b$ for all domain elements a, b (passes horizontal line test).

open interval An interval in which the endpoints are not included; notation is (a, b).

ordinate The second coordinate of an ordered pair.

parabola The intersection of a right circular conical surface and a plane that is parallel to an element of the conical surface; the locus of points in a plane that are equidistant from a fixed point (focus) and a fixed line (directrix) in the plane.

parameter The true value of a quantity for a population, usually estimated by a statistic (or any symbolic constant in a formula).

partial derivative The derivative of a function of more than one variable with respect to just one of the variables.

partial sum The sum of a finite number of terms of a sequence.

percentile rank The percentage of values less than or equal to a given value in a set of data.

period The length of a cycle for the values of a periodic function.

periodic function A function such that $f(x + c) = f(x)$ for all x, where c is a constant (called the period).

phase shift A horizontal translation of a trigonometric function affected by replacing x with $x \pm c$ in the function.

piece function A function with a multi-part rule; usually defined on various intervals.

polar axis A ray from the origin that coincides with the positive x-axis.

polar coordinates The set of points (r, θ) where r is a radius from the pole and θ is the angle with the polar axis.

pole The origin for polar coordinates.

polynomial function A function with a polynomial as its rule.

power function A function with a monomial as its rule.

proper rational function A reduced rational function such that the degree in the numerator is less than that of the denominator.

pure imaginary number A number of the form ai, where $a \in \mathbb{R}$ and $a \ne 0$.

quadratic function A polynomial function of degree 2.

quadrantal angle An angle whose terminal ray lies on one of the axes.

radian The measure of an angle formed by two radii of a circle so that the intercepted arc has a length equal to the radius of the circle.

radical equation An equation having a variable under a radical.

radical function A function having a radical containing a variable in its rule.

range The set of second coordinates of the ordered pairs of a function.

range of data The difference between the largest and smallest values in a set of data.

rational equation An equation having terms with variables in their denominators.

rational function A function that is a ratio of two polynomial functions (denominator not zero).

real part The real constant (*a*) of a complex number in standard form (*a* + *bi*).

reciprocal function A function obtained by finding the multiplicative inverse of another function; especially the reciprocal trigonometric functions secant, cosecant, and cotangent.

recursive formula A formula for the *n*th term of a sequence based on previous terms.

reference angle An acute angle of a reference triangle that has its vertex at the origin.

reference triangle A right triangle formed by drawing a perpendicular from the terminal ray of an angle to the *x*-axis.

relation Any set of ordered pairs.

residual The difference between a known value and the corresponding predicted value from a model.

resultant vector The vector that represents the sum of two or more vectors.

root of an equation A solution to an equation.

secant line A line joining two points on a curve.

sector of a circle The region bounded by two radii of a circle and the intercepted arc.

segment of a circle The region bounded by a chord of a circle and the subtended arc.

sequence An infinite list of numbers (terms); a function having the natural numbers as its domain.

series The sum of the terms of a sequence.

sine function The set of ordered pairs in which the first coordinate is the measure of an angle and the corresponding second coordinate is the sine of the angle.

slope of a line The ratio of vertical change to horizontal change for any two points on a line.

spline A continuous piece function that passes through given data points.

standard deviation A measure of variability of data, the square root of the variance.

standard form of a complex number The form *a* + *bi*; $a, b \in \mathbb{R}$.

standard normal distribution The function

$$f(x) = \frac{1}{\sqrt{2\pi}} e^{-\frac{1}{2}x^2}.$$

standard position of an angle An angle with its initial ray along the positive *x*-axis and the vertex at the origin.

standard position of a vector A vector having the origin as its initial point.

statistic An estimate of a population characteristic based on a sample.

strictly monotonic function A function that is either increasing or decreasing over its entire domain.

sum of squared deviations The total of the squared differences from the mean for a set of values.

tangent function The set of ordered pairs in which the first coordinate is the measure of an angle and the corresponding coordinate is the tangent of the angle.

tangent line at a point The limit of secants of a graph as the second point approaches the first.

telescoping series A series in which all but a few initial terms add up to zero.

terminal ray The final position of an angle considered as a sweeping ray.

test of hypothesis A statistical test to determine whether apparent differences are significant.

transverse axis The axis containing the center and the foci of a hyperbola.

unit circle A circle whose center is at the origin and whose radius is one unit.

variance The average of squared deviations; a measure of variability in a set of data.

vector A directed line segment.

vertex A point where a conic section intersects an axis of symmetry.

y-intercept The point(s) where a relation intersects the *y*-axis.

zero matrix A matrix with zeros for all of its entries.

zero of a function An *x*-intercept; point(s) where a function intersects the *x*-axis.

zero polynomial The constant term 0.

z-score The number of standard deviations of a score above or below the mean.

Index

Acknowledgments

Chapter 1. Alligator data from *Probability and Statistics for Engineers, 4th edition*, by R.L. Scheaffer and J.T. McClave © 1995. Reprinted with permission of Brooks/Cole, an imprint of the Wadsworth Group, a division of Thomson Learning. Fax 800 700-2214.

Chapter 2. Braking reaction data reprinted with permission by Dr. Ian Murray, the Department of Optometry and Neurosciences, Manchester, United Kingdom.

Chapter 3. Sunspot data reprinted with permission by Solar Influences Data Analysis Center, Brussels, Belgium. Data available at http://www.astro.oma.be/SIDC/DATA/ in monssnns.dat. Available May 28, 2001.

Chapter 5. Permission granted by P.C. Hoffman, D.A. Funk, and T.D. Syverud to use the Table 6A, "Heifer weight and height measurements for field survey herds," in "Growth Rates of Holstein Replacement Heifers in Selected Wisconsin Dairy Herds" at http://www.inform.umd.edu/EdRes/Topic/AgrEnv/ndd/youngsto/ GROWTH_RATES_OF_HOLSTEIN_REPLACEMENT_HEIFERS.html (available as of May 28, 2001).

Chapter 9. SAT data reprinted by permission of the College Entrance Examination Board, the copyright owner. For 1972-1986, a formula was applied to the original mean and standard deviation to convert the mean to the recentered scale. For 1987-1995, individual student scores were converted to the recentered scale and then the mean was recomputed. For 1996-1999 most students received scores on the recentered score. (Any score on the original scale was converted to the recentered scale prior to recomputing the mean.)

Chapter 12. Skydiving data provided by a SkyCorder ® skydive recorder, courtesy of Geoff Werbin.

Photograph Credits

The following agencies and individuals have furnished materials to meet the photographic needs of this textbook. We wish to express our gratitude to them for their important contribution.

AKG-London
Architect of the Capital
Berndt, Prof. Bruce
 (Courtesy of)
Bob Jones Academy
Bob Jones University
 Collection, The
Chicago Stock Exchange
CORBIS
COREL Corporation
Cordon Art B.V.
DigitalSTOCK
Dover Publications
Giffin, Noel, TRIUMF Research
 Lab
Göttingen University
 Observatory
Isaac Newton Institute for
 Mathematical Sciences
Japan National Tourist
 Organization
Joanne Williams Photography
Krämer, Stefan
Los Alamos National
 Laboratories
Matsushita Electric Industrial
 Co., Ltd.
McCloskey, William
NASA
New Millenium Experience
 Company, The
O. Væring Aftf. AS
Paramount's Carowinds
PhotoDisc, Inc.
Russel, J.G.
Samfoto AS
The Masters and Fellows of
 Trinity College, Cambridge
Thomas Stieltjes Institute for
 Mathematics
Thyssen Aufzuege
Timken Corporation, The
University of Oklahoma, History
 of Sciences Collections
University of Toronto
Unusual Films
U.S. Army Parachute Team:
 Golden Knights
USDA
U.S. Geological Survey

(Special thanks to *Elevator World Magazine* for supplying the image (which appeared on their June 1998 cover) of Thyssen Aufzuege's glass elevator located in the atrium in the SI Centre in Stuttgart, Germany.)

Cover
Noel Giffin: TRIUMF Research Lab; digitalSTOCK; PhotoDisc, Inc.; The Timken Corporation

Title Page
The Timken Corporation (left); PhotoDisc, Inc.; digitalSTOCK; Noel Giffin: TRIUMF Research Lab

Introduction
CORBIS viii; *The Ascension* by Benjamin West, from the Bob Jones University Collection ix

Chapter 1
© Joanne Williams 1; NASA 8; John Paul Clough 19; Unusual Films 34

Chapter 2
J.G. Russell 44-45; Paramount's Carowinds 65; AKG-London 86; © photo: O.Væring Aftf. AS 87 (top); Ole Daniel Enersen / NN / Samfoto 87 (bottom)

Chapter 3
NASA 104-105; DigitalSTOCK 107, 111; NPS Photo by M. Woodbridge Williams 128

Chapter 4
CORBIS 170-171; Ron Tagliapietra 172; Courtesy of Matsushita Electrical Industrial Co., Ltd. 198; PhotoDisc, Inc. 199 (top); JNTO 199 (bottom); LANL/ PAO8600K12 200; Photograph 48ct, Alaska Earthquake set, USGS 210

Chapter 5
USDA 94-CS-3990 220-221; NMEC/QA Photos 230; CORBIS 240; digitalSTOCK 246

Chapter 6
Unusual Films 272-273; PhotoDisc, Inc. 274; Architect of the Capital 282; Thyssen Aufzuege 307; Courtesy of Professor Bruce Berndt 312; PhotoDisc, Inc. 313 (top); William McCloskey 313 (bottom); PhotoDisc, Inc. 316

Chapter 7
Noell Giffin, TRIUMF Research Lab 338-339, 352, 358; NASA 368 (both); Unusual Films 379

Chapter 8
NASA 390-391; digitalSTOCK 399; Dover Publications 410 (left), The Master and Fellows of Trinity College, Cambridge 410 (right); Stefan Krämer, Göttingen 411; digitalSTOCK 431 (top); ©1999-2001 www.arttoday.com 431 (bottom); History of Science Collections, University of Oklahoma 442

Chapter 9
Unusual Films 446-447; © 1999-2001 www.arttoday. com 449; Courtesy of Gauss-Gesellschaft, University of Göttingen 462; Public Domain 466; digitalSTOCK 467 (top); Dover Publications 467 (bottom); © 1999-2001 www.arttoday.com 482

Chapter 10
Chicago Stock Exchange, Inc. 492-493; PhotoDisc, Inc. 494, 501; Unusual Films 511; Dover Publications 533

Chapter 11
Phil Larson 538-539; M.C. Escher's "Snakes" © 2000 Cordon Art B.V.-Baarn-Holland. All Rights Reserved 540; Dover Publications 572; PhotoDisc, Inc. 573 (top), 579; Photograph reproduced with kind permission from the Isaac Newton Institute for Mathematical Sciences, Cambridge, UK 573 (bottom)

Chapter 12
Sgt. 1st Class Ken Kassens, U.S. Army Parachute Team 586-587; Ron Tagliapietra 588; Courtesy of the Archives of the Institute For Advanced Study 593; University of Toronto 609; COREL Corporation 616